# The Great Ideas

Man
Mathematics
Matter
Mechanics
Medicine
Memory and Imagination
Metaphysics
Mind
Monarchy
Nature
Necessity and Contingency
Oligarchy
One and Many
Opinion
Opposition
Philosophy
Physics
Pleasure and Pain
Poetry
Principle
Progress
Prophecy
Prudence
Punishment
Quality
Quantity

Reasoning
Relation
Religion
Revolution
Rhetoric
Same and Other
Science
Sense
Sign and Symbol
Sin
Slavery
Soul
Space
State
Temperance
Theology
Time
Truth
Tyranny
Universal and Particular
Virtue and Vice
War and Peace
Wealth
Will
Wisdom
World

Images of Marx, Engels, and Lenin stare off uncomprehendingly above crowds who gathered at the May Day parade in Moscow, 1990, with banners decrying the failures of Soviet communism, the popular discontent.

# The
# Great Ideas
# Today

# 1990

*Encyclopædia Britannica, Inc.*

CHICAGO
AUCKLAND • GENEVA • LONDON • MADRID • MANILA • PARIS
ROME • SEOUL • SYDNEY • TOKYO • TORONTO

Figure 1 in "Mental Images in Cognitive Psychology" is reproduced from
"Mental Rotation of Three-Dimensional Objects," by R. N. Shepard and J. Metzler,
in *Science*, vol. 171, Feb. 19, 1971, pp. 701–3.
Copyright © 1971 by the American Association for the Advancement of Science.
Reprinted with permission from the AAAS and R. N. Shepard.

Figures 2–4 in "Mental Images in Cognitive Psychology" are reproduced from
*Ghosts in the Mind's Machine*, by Stephen Michael Kosslyn, pp. 46, 64, 97,
by permission of W. W. Norton & Company, Inc.
Copyright © 1983 by Stephen M. Kosslyn.

Figure 5 in "The New Pythagoreans III" is reproduced from
*Eye Movements and Vision*, by Alfred L. Yarbus, p. 174.
Copyright © 1967 by Plenum Press.
Reprinted with permission from Plenum Publishing Corporation.

Figure 7a in "The New Pythagoreans III" is reproduced from
"Brain Mechanisms of Vision," by David H. Hubel and Torsten N. Wiesel,
in *Scientific American*, September 1979, p. 159.
Copyright © 1979 by David H. Hubel and Torsten N. Wiesel.
Reprinted with permission from the authors.

Figure 8 in "The New Pythagoreans III" is reproduced from
*Programs of the Brain*, by J. Z. Young, p. 127.
Copyright © 1976 by Oxford University Press.
Reprinted with permission from the publisher.

Figures 10a–b, 11a, and 12 in "The New Pythagoreans III" are reproduced from
*Listening*, by Stephen Handel, pp. 18, 20, 148, 260.
Copyright © 1989 by Massachusetts Institute of Technology.
Reprinted with permission from the publisher.

Figure 11b in "The New Pythagoreans III" is reproduced from
"Perception of Spectral Modifications on Orchestral Instrument Tones,"
by J. W. Gordon and J. M. Grey, in *Computer Music Journal*, vol. 2, no. 1, 1978,
by permission of The MIT Press, Cambridge, Massachusetts.
Copyright © 1978 Computer Music Journal.

*The Nature of the Physical World* (Introduction), by Sir Arthur S. Eddington,
was originally published by The Macmillan Company and Cambridge University Press.
Copyright © 1928 by The Macmillan Company.
Reprinted with permission of Cambridge University Press.

"Reality and Appearances," by Mortimer J. Adler, is reprinted from
*Ten Philosophical Mistakes*, by Mortimer J. Adler, pp. 181–90,
with permission of Macmillan Publishing Company.
Copyright © 1985 by Mortimer J. Adler.

"The Invincible Ignorance of Science," by A. Brian Pippard, is reprinted from
*Contemporary Physics*, vol. 29, no. 4, 1988, pp. 393–405.
Reprinted with permission from Taylor & Francis Ltd. © 1988.

Library of Congress Number: 61-65561
International Standard Book Number: 0-85229-526-X
International Standard Serial Number: 0072-7288

## A NOTE ON REFERENCE STYLE

In the following pages, passages in *Great Books of the Western World* are referred to by the initials '*GBWW*,' followed by volume, page number, and page section. Thus, '*GBWW*, Vol. 39, p. 210b' refers to page 210 in Adam Smith's *The Wealth of Nations*, which is Volume 39 in *Great Books of the Western World*. The small letter 'b' indicates the page section. In books printed in single column, 'a' and 'b' refer to the upper and lower halves of the page. In books printed in double column, 'a' and 'b' refer to the upper and lower halves of the left column, 'c' and 'd' to the upper and lower halves of the right column. For example, 'Vol. 53, p. 210b' refers to the lower half of page 210, since Volume 53, James's *Principles of Psychology*, is printed in single column. On the other hand, 'Vol. 7, p. 210b' refers to the lower left quarter of the page, since Volume 7, Plato's *Dialogues*, is printed in double column.

*Gateway to the Great Books* is referred to by the initials '*GGB*,' followed by volume and page number. Thus, '*GGB*, Vol. 10, pp. 39–57' refers to pages 39 through 57 of Volume 10 of *Gateway to the Great Books*, which is James's essay, "The Will to Believe."

*The Great Ideas Today* is referred to by the initials '*GIT*,' followed by the year and page number. Thus '*GIT* 1968, p. 210' refers to page 210 of the 1968 edition of *The Great Ideas Today*.

# Contents

# Preface

Anyone who looks at the contents of this issue of *The Great Ideas Today* will realize that it contains much talk of science, and those who think science is not something they care greatly about may be tempted to wait till next year, as they say in baseball, hoping for better luck. But of course the science discussed in these pages is not, this year or ever, of the specialist sort that nonscientists find forbidding—or at any rate it is no more than what is found in the *Great Books* themselves, none of which are addressed to specialists. And in fact the questions discussed here are not so much scientific as philosophical. They are, first, what is real in our perception of things, and second, what is the nature of perception itself—how do our minds really work? These are matters of moment to everyone, whether they regard themselves as scientific or not.

The questions are taken up pretty much in that order. Thus in Part One of the volume we find Eva T. H. Brann, dean at St. John's College, Annapolis, Maryland, who has completed a large book of her own on the subject of the imagination, addressing herself, in what is substantially a chapter from that book, to the subject of mental images. This is of interest because, while most people believe they have such images, they are not verifiable by anyone else—you can't "see" what I "see"—so they are difficult to analyze scientifically; indeed cognitive psychologists, frustrated in the effort, tend to deny that they really exist. But if they do not, then what is it that we *think* we "see"?

We have also, in Part One, a discussion by Evelyn Fox Keller of the role of gender in science, and how it affects both our sense of reality and our way of defining it. Dr. Keller, who has written widely on this subject, points out that science has been essentially masculine in its way of seeing the world, and she argues that it has therefore been blind to some things that feminist insight, long ignored in research, has been able to discover. Her presentation is that of a social scientist, but her earlier field was biology and she came to that after study in physics, so she can see the problems she considers as it were from both sides.

If we go on to Part Two and take up the essay by Thomas K. Simpson called "The New Pythagoreans III: The Scientists of the Mind (Part One)," we discover that the question we have been considering as to the nature of reality is dealt with again in a fundamental way, and that the effort leads in Mr. Simpson's view necessarily to the second question of how we know the nature of things, so far as we do—how the mind works, in short. This is seen as intelligible only if our understanding of it is consistent with what is really "out there" to be seen. In the first of two essays on this problem, and carrying on his fascinating discussion of what he regards as the revolution in science of our time, Mr. Simpson begins once again with a Platonic dialogue, this time the *Theaetetus,* where reason in the sense of *logos* is seen to defeat itself in its quest for knowledge save as it learns, in the manner of the eye, to *create* the world it observes. How this can be done without falling into mere solipsism is the trick that science only now—so Mr. Simpson contends—is beginning to see.

Next skip if you will to the first item among the "Additions to the Great Books Library," in Part Four. There will be found three short writings on the difference between reality and appearances. One might begin with the selection from Sir Arthur S. Eddington's *The Nature of the Physical World,* and then read the comments by Brian Pippard and Mortimer J. Adler; one sees that the issue is whether science or our senses, which are not in agreement, give us the true picture of the world. After that, readers might look in Part Three at the essay by Stanley L. Jaki called "Determinism and Reality," where the claim of quantum theory that there is a fundamental indeterminacy in the nature of things is questioned; and *then* would perhaps be the time to consult Professor Pippard's lecture on "The Invincible Ignorance of Science," again in Part Four, in which, disagreeing with what Mr. Simpson says on the same matter, Mr. Pippard argues that consciousness, considered as the awareness of ourselves, is inherently beyond the reach of science to know.

Other subjects are dealt with also, of course, in this year's volume. One of them is architecture, on which we have never had any comment beyond what seemed appropriate for the Pompidou Centre in Paris when it was constructed in 1977 (see *GIT* 1977). But it is architecture in more general terms which is now discussed, in Part One, by Kenneth Frampton, former chairman of the Division of Architecture at Columbia University and author of *Modern Architecture: A Critical History,* among other books. Professor Frampton limits himself to the building, both private and public, which has been done in the developed world since the Second World War, and draws attention to work in Italy, Spain, and Japan, of which most Americans know little if anything. He is interested in possible alternatives to the Post-Modernism we now see in urban high-rise buildings, which are elaborated in various ways from the desire to avoid monotony, but which are inconsistent structurally and make little if any aesthetic sense.

Relevant to this essay are the portions of John Ruskin's classic work *The Stones of Venice,* which appear in Part Four. What is reprinted from that very long and formless book, which is always abridged, are not the sections devoted to Venice itself, but those in which Ruskin sets forth the principles, as they seem to him to be, of good architecture anywhere. These principles are found exemplified in the Gothic, whose revival in Victorian times Ruskin did so much—by no means altogether willingly or happily—to inspire; but it is what inheres in Gothic design rather than what is superficial or merely decorative to it that interests him, and his treatment of the subject remains worth reading even after we have lost our interest in that example.

We publish also this year an essay by Harvey D. Goldstein on "Tragedy and Comedy," two ideas which are discussed and exemplified often in the *Great Books,* and which are of profound importance in the mind and art of the West. Mr. Goldstein's focus is chiefly on the Bible, on the two Homeric poems, and on *Hamlet,* but he speaks passingly of other works, too, and readers have many recognitions as they contemplate what after all are not merely two literary forms but two ways of looking at human life—*the* two ways, one may argue, since between them they seem to encompass everything, though it is difficult to reconcile their points of view.

In that connection, readers may want to read the story by Gustave Flaubert, called "A Simple Heart," which appears among this year's reprints. One of the best tales Flaubert ever wrote—indeed a perfect thing in its way, such as he tried always, with immense strain, to produce—it has long since established itself as a permanent piece of short fiction, and it deserves the anthologizing, as it does the academic study, which it commonly gets. Here illustrated by Ron Villani, who has done much good work for *The Great Ideas Today,* it handles its great theme without sentiment and without Flaubert's indicating (as he would have been proud to think) any determination as to the nature of the life he recounts.

Finally, we take note of the long essay among the "Special Features" in Part Three by Mortimer J. Adler, editor of *The Great Ideas Today,* which is in some way our pièce de résistance for the year. In it Dr. Adler takes it upon himself to rescue Marxism from the error into which it seems to have fallen, without rejecting its basic insight—this as a kind of gift to President Mikhail Gorbachev of the Soviet Union, should he maintain his position (the essay was written in the winter of this year), and from a desire, too, that the capitalist world not forget what it owes to socialism, and needs from it. Actually an account of one of his Aspen seminars, as the members made their way through relevant readings, the piece offers what Dr. Adler conceives as a vision of the end of the conflict between capitalism and communism, and as such it may have some claim to stand even when its details are outdated by developments, as they are certain before long to be.

# Current Developments in the Arts and Sciences

# Developments in Contemporary Architecture 1945–1990

## Kenneth Frampton

Professor Kenneth Frampton is an architect and architectural historian. He was educated at the Architectural Association in London and has worked as an architect in England, Israel, and the United States. He has designed award-winning apartments in London (1964), and before emigrating to the United States in 1965 he served for three years as technical editor of the magazine *Architectural Design*.

From 1965 to 1972 he was a member of the faculty at the School of Architecture of Princeton University. Since then, with the exception of three years at the Royal College of Art in London (1974–77), Professor Frampton has taught continuously at Columbia University, serving as chairman of the Division of Architecture (1986–89). Professor Frampton has been a frequent lecturer here and abroad, as well as a visiting professor and jury member at various architectural competitions. Most recently he was president of the EEC Jury Award, a prize given to a building built in the European Economic Community (1988). He has received numerous awards and fellowships, among them the AIA National Honors Award (1985) and the Gold Medal from L'Académie d'Architecture in Paris (1987).

Professor Frampton is also a frequent contributor to architectural journals here and abroad. His books include *Modern Architecture: A Critical History* (1980), which has been translated into nine languages, and *Modern Architecture 1851 to 1945* (1981). Forthcoming books include an anthology of essays under the title *Labor, Work, and Architecture* (Rizzoli) and *Studies in Tectonic Culture* (MIT Press).

## Introduction*

Any account of the last twenty years of contemporary architecture is compelled to take into consideration three seemingly extraneous factors. The first of these stems from the erosion of any clear socio-cultural program in relation to architectural production, beginning in the late 1940s with the dismantling of the public welfare programs of the American New Deal. The conscious reprivatization of the environment is most evident perhaps in the liquidation of the publicly owned Greenbelt New Towns of the Roosevelt era. While Continental Europe has continued to maintain a more publicly responsible approach to the maintenance of social welfare, the fact is that even in social democratic strongholds such as Sweden or The Netherlands, the private sector has recently been given a larger role in civic development.

The second disturbing factor arises from the mass ownership of the automobile and the concomitant proliferation of consumer society. These two techno-economic transformations have been furthered by the emergence of the universal megalopolis, as this appears in Los Angeles, the Ruhrgebiet, the Tokyo–Osaka corridor, and in the continuous urbanized region stretching from Boston to Washington, D.C. Here as elsewhere, the car has led to the extensive proliferation of suburban development, to the general decline of the public realm and the erosion of the traditional city. The so-called pedestrianization movement is symptomatic in this regard, for by trying to compensate for the loss of the traditional city, it invariably ends by transforming the traditional urban core into a Disneyland of conspicuous consumption.

---

*I am indebted to the following for their kind permission to include protions of my writings under copyright by them in this essay: Academy Editions for extracts from *Modern Architecture and the Critical Present,* published by *Architectural Design* magazine, London, in 1982; Thames & Hudson for extracts from *Modern Architecture: A Critical History,* first published by Thames & Hudson in 1980 and issued as an augmented second edition in 1985; and the Walker Art Center, Minneapolis, Minnesota, for extracts from "Twilight Gloom to Self-Enclosed Modernity: Five Japanese Articles," as this appeared in the catalogue *Tokyo, Form and Spirit,* published by the Walker Art Center in 1986.

The third transforming factor is the ever-increased architectural pluralism of the present epoch, which seems to have come into being as an almost unconscious stylistic response to the radical and often negative global changes brought about by modernization. This plurality of expression runs a wide gamut, from the neo-modernism of the recent so-called Deconstruction movement to the reactionary anti-modernism of contemporary Classical Revival.

In order to afford some sort of synoptic view, I have elected to approach such a heterogeneous body of cultural expression in two ways. In the first place, I have adopted a series of generic isms or classes of production with which I have tried to assemble and evaluate the main evolving trends of the last twenty years. It cannot be emphasized enough that these isms are not to be understood as polemical groupings in the old avant-gardist sense of the term. While these isms may occasionally be used as slogans by certain of the protagonists involved, each is in the main a convenient critical rubric under which to group a specific ideological and operational approach.

In the second place, I have tried to frame this general taxonomy by a prologue and an epilogue. While the first of these texts deals with two important transitional architects of the so-called second generation, the last affords a more detailed account of late modern developments, as these have manifested themselves in Japan, Spain, and Portugal.

While the so-called battle of styles of the last quarter of the nineteenth century and the first quarter of the twentieth has passed into history, the echo of a similar conflict of values and genres seems to reappear in many of these isms—so much so that Rationalism may be seen as a reinterpretation of Neoclassicism, and Productivism may be seen as a fulfillment of the selfsame technological approach as was first witnessed in the Crystal Palace, England, built to designs by Joseph Paxton in 1851. By a similar token, American Formalism and Populism can be compared, if not to precise historical genres, then certainly to particular concerns. That is to say, just as American Formalism may be seen as a self-conscious reinterpretation of the forms of the heroic avant-garde of the interwar period, so can American Populism be regarded as capitalizing on rather loosely conceived notions of the vernacular as this was once generally available to the society at large.

Three further isms may be usefully isolated in order to identify three distinct revisionist positions within the current architectural debate. These are Structuralism, Regionalism, and Revivalism. Since Structuralism is an exclusively Dutch "anthropological" approach to modern form, it may arguably be regarded as a special case of a more general "regional" phenomenon, as this has manifested itself over the past three decades in various so-called marginal but nonetheless developing countries. Revivalism, on the other hand, may also be seen as a subset of Rationalism in that it is largely an Anglo-American phenomenon favoring copybook revival of the Western Classical syntax; although today this line varies widely from Giorgio Grassi's "rational-classical" but nonetheless still modern approach, to Léon Krier's anti-modern, Biedermeier attitude.

## Part 1: Prologue, the second generation: Louis Kahn and Carlo Scarpa

Louis Kahn, an American, and Carlo Scarpa, an Italian, may both be considered as belonging to the "second generation," inasmuch as Kahn (born in 1901) and Scarpa (born in 1906) may both be seen as members of a generation caught between the post-1918 avant-garde and those whom the Swiss historian Sigfried Giedion was later to identify as the "Third Generation," of whom the most prominent member is the Danish architect Jørn Utzon (born in 1918).

The year 1945 appears as an ideological watershed between the socially committed ethos of the New Deal and an incipient, post-Second World War impulse toward monumentality. This last comes into being partly as a result of America's status as a world power and partly out of the general cultural anxiety that attended the end of the war. Two texts published in 1945 establish the climate of the period with some precision: *Built in U.S.A.—Since 1932,* edited by Elizabeth Mock, which derived from an exhibition of that title staged at the Museum of Modern Art, New York City—in which over half of the illustrations were devoted to the works of the New Deal—and *The New Architecture and City Planning,* edited by Paul Zucker, recording the proceedings of a symposium held in Columbia University in 1944. This last was devoted to the growing need for monumental expression, a theme elaborated by Giedion in his paper of 1944, *The Need for a New Monumentality.* Five years after the symposium, the theme resurfaced in the first issue of *Perspecta—The Yale Architectural Journal,* founded by George Howe. In this inaugural number Henry Hope Reed advanced the case that the New Deal had dealt a severe blow to the culture of affluence, and that the provisions arising out of the Depression had effectively inhibited the capacity of architects to create monumental form. Despite Reed's pessimistic conclusion that our capacity to create monuments had been lost, he was soon to be proven wrong, for America was about to enter on a period of almost unprecedented monumental building.

While the Graduate School of Design at Harvard, under the direction of Walter Gropius, helped to consolidate the Functionalist approach of the New Deal, the School of Architecture at Yale under Howe's leadership played a formative role in the development of American postwar monumentality. Howe championed the cause of the New Monumentality not only through the founding of *Perspecta* but also through his influence on the selection of architects for Yale's expansion program which began in the early 1950s. Indeed, when Reed's article appeared in *Perspecta* in 1950, Kahn had already been selected to design the Yale Art Gallery.

With the completion of this building in 1954, Kahn helped to establish American postwar monumentality as a cultural force in its own right. He did so with a work that was hardly to be compared to the rhetoric generally attained by American official architecture throughout the 1950s, for his art gallery was based on a subtle fusion of certain tectonic precepts that he had found to different degrees in the work of Buckminster Fuller (1895–1983) and Ludwig Mies van der Rohe (1886–1969). Kahn took from Fuller the principle of space-frame construction that he then deployed as the twentieth-century equivalent of Gothic form while from Mies he assumed a certain expressive "silence" as the only appropriate response to the spiritual emptiness produced by the techno-scientific processes of modernization. Kahn's concept of a geodesic skyscraper with tetrahedronal space-frame floors—a vertical truss against the wind—enabled him to return to an architectural intention that would have been appreciated by Eugène-Emmanuel Viollet-le-Duc, the nineteenth-century champion of Gothic building. This much is evident from one of the clearest statements of intent that Kahn ever produced:

> In Gothic times, architects built in solid stones. Now we can build with hollow stones. The spaces defined by the members of a structure are as important as the members. These spaces range in scale from the voids of an insulating panel, voids for air, lighting and heat to circulate, to spaces big enough to walk through and live in. The desire to express voids positively in the design of a structure is evidenced by the growing interest and work in the development of space-frames. . . . Design habits leading to the concealment of structure had no place in this implied order. Such habits retard the development of an art. I believe that in architecture, as in all art, the artist instinctively keeps the marks which reveal how a thing was done. The feeling that our present-day architecture needs embellishment stems in part from our tendency to fair joints out of sight, to conceal how parts are put together. Structures should be devised which can harbour the mechanical needs of rooms and spaces. [1]

The fundamental themes of Kahn's subsequent career are all outlined in this remarkable passage, from the notion of conceptually transposing solid and void—see the reference to hollow stones—to the idea of explicitly integrating mechanical systems with the structure. Kahn was to conceive of this integration at two different levels: first, as the "representative" integration of service runs that would allow mechanical equipment to become as expressively significant in a building as the load-bearing structure itself; and second, as the so-called *servant* spaces comprising stair and elevator shafts and ventilation ducts as these appear, say, in Kahn's Richards Medical Research Building in Philadelphia of 1957–64. In this way, Kahn's generic, generalized, typological functionalism superseded, as it were, the organic, ergonomic functionalism of the prewar Modern Movement.

The tension between modernization and monumentality in Kahn's work was to assume a particularly dramatic form in his preoccupation with urban development, and above all in the various plans that he made for Philadelphia between 1952 and 1962. Kahn was to remain preoccupied with the myth and reality of Philadelphia throughout his life. For him, this city could not be entered, let alone experienced, through the high-speed osmosis of the airport and the freeway. As far as Kahn was concerned, Philadelphia had to be approached through that which had graced all cities since time immemorial, namely, through an honorific gateway, which in the case of Philadelphia could be conceived as the monumental Beaux-Arts concourse and peristyle of 30th Street Station.

Something of Kahn's sense for the institutional and political continuity that is to be found in cities may be gleaned from a text which he wrote in the early sixties:

> The City, from a simple settlement, became the place of assembled institutions. Before the institution was the natural agreement—the sense of commonality. . . . The measure of the greatness of a place to live must come from the character of its institutions, sanctioned through how sensitive they are to renewed agreement and desire for new agreement. [2]

Kahn's concern for the continuity of the city as an assembly of institutions is paralleled by his efforts to reconcile the contrary demands being made upon the traditional city by the ever-changing dynamic of modernization. This much is clear from the way he thought of the automobile in relation to the city. We find him stating:

> The circumstantial demands of the car, of parking and so forth, will eat away all the spaces that exist now and pretty soon you have no identifying traces of what I call loyalties—the landmarks. Remember, when you think of your city, you think immediately of certain places which identify the city, as you enter it. If they're gone, your feeling for the city is lost and gone. . . . If, because of the demands of the motorcar, we stiffen and harden the city—omitting water, omitting the green world—the city will be destroyed. Therefore the car, because of its destructive value, must start us rethinking the city in terms of the green world, in terms of the world of water, and of air, and of locomotion. . . . [3]

From the scale of the tectonic element to the scale of mega-urban form, Kahn constantly attempted to reintegrate the most advanced technology with a more timeless sense of both structure and place in order to neutralize the destructive aspects of technology. This explains equally his efforts to interpret space-frame construction in tectonic terms and his attempt to transform the technical given of the elevated freeway into a new form of civic architecture. Such a preoccupation lay behind Kahn's paradoxical thesis that "the streets want to become a building" and his projection of what he called "viaduct architecture," that was to be the primary impulse behind his 1957 plan for the Midtown City Center Forum in Philadelphia.

The oscillation in Kahn's work between modernization and monumentality is perhaps never more evident than in Kahn's projected cylindrical parking towers by which the City Center Forum was to have been surrounded.

If at one level the monumental for Kahn was contingent upon the institution and the city, at another level it turned upon the structure and the joint. These two poles were related to each other by light, that is to say, by the way in which light, as revealed through structure, may impart a specific character to a given institution or civic element. Thus, of rooms Kahn was to write: "Architecture comes from the making of a Room. . . . The Room is the place of the mind. In a small room one does not say what one would in a large room. In a room with only one other person . . . the vectors of each meet. A room is not a room without natural light. Natural light gives the time of day and (allows) the mood of the seasons to enter." [4]

But Kahn wrote equally of the penetration of light into the multi-leveled freeway viaducts he proposed for the enclosure of midtown Philadelphia in the early sixties, and of the necessity of allowing a sliver of light to enter the darkest room, to penetrate even into a cinema, to reveal how dark it is. The optimized, windowless climate-controlled box was anathema to Kahn. So by the same token was the jointless, underdetailed building so often to be found in commercial modern architecture. Thus, as far as Kahn was concerned, the joint was the touchstone of the tectonic, just as it had been for Viollet-le-Duc and Gottfried Semper (1803–79) before him. It made no difference whether the building was of a domestic scale or a civic mega-structure. Here, of course, one finds a certain common ground with Mies—most dramatically displayed, perhaps, when one compares Mies's Promontory Apartments in Chicago (1949) with Kahn's projected parking tower for the Midtown Philadelphia plan. An exposed trabeated reinforced concrete frame is the primary expressive element in both works. Moreover, the structure is similarly articulated in each case; that is to say, the perimeter concrete columns, carrying spandrels, diminish in section as they rise upward due to a decrease in compressive stress. But a fundamentally anthropomorphic conception of the joint comes with the intricate system of assembly adopted for the prefabricated concrete diagrid floors employed in Kahn's Richards Medical Research Building.

It is uncanny how the two most significant architects of the "second generation" were both to mature relatively late, for just as Kahn did not realize a building of significance until 1952 when he was fifty-one, so Scarpa did not achieve work of decisive consequence until his conversion of Abbatellis Palace, Palermo, in 1953, by which time he was forty-seven.

Prior to emerging as an architect in the full sense of the term, there are two preparatory periods in Scarpa's life when he is alternatively engaged either in craft design or with exhibitions. The first of these periods follows his graduation in 1926 and lasts for twenty years, during which time he works on the design of glassware and various interiors for the Venetian glass industry. During the second period, lasting from the early forties to the mid-fifties, he is primarily occupied with the design of exhibitions and pavilions for the Venice Biennale. The brilliance of the gallery sequences he designed during this period serves to establish his reputation as an exceptional exhibition designer, and thereafter follows a spate of quite remarkable exhibition designs, as distinguished for the sensitivity and understanding of the exhibits themselves as for the distinct quality of the sequential settings contrived for their display. Prominent among Scarpa's achievements during this period were the topographical/historical exhibits that he designed for the cities of Messina and Venice and his totally fresh approach to the display of modern art that reached a decisive point with his memorable Piet Mondrian retrospective exhibition staged in Rome in 1956.

Two shop interiors of the late 1950s—one for Olivetti in the Piazza San Marco, Venice (1958), and one for Gavina, in Bologna (1961)—crystallized Scarpa's mature architectural manner, along with the refurbishing of the Querini Stampalia Gallery, Venice, in 1963. The salient aspects of Scarpa's mature style are fully represented in all of these works. His intensely tectonic approach to the detailing of architectural form may be broken down into the following three aspects.

In the first place, the space is organized as though it were a mythic narrative with one referential or symbolic incident following after another. Indeed, threshold, entry, forecourt, aperture, bridge, and stairway play a more fundamental orchestrated role in Scarpa's architecture than in the work of any other comparable twentieth-century designer. Second, the architectural promenade that serves slowly to unite all these episodes is given precise definition by Scarpa's habit of developing articulate foci throughout. These intense microcosmic points of interest are invariably brought into being by resolving in a particularly effective but poetic way each specific intersection, joint, or hinge. In this regard, no less a figure than Kahn himself was to appreciate Scarpa's architecture as being predicated on the "adoration of the joint."

Last but not least, Scarpa's sequential architecture invariably depends upon drawing precise but delicate contrasts between subtly different materials. He is particularly fond of displaying traditional plaster rendering techniques, such as *stucco lucido,* polished plaster, or *marmarine,* that is a form of plaster made from marble dust. These subtly different tactile surfaces are first brought into telling contrast with wood, metal, and concrete in the Gavina store, although equally tactile sequences are evident in the Olivetti showroom, above all perhaps in the paving, where Murano glass tesserae are arranged in four different colors, each distinguishing separate zones in the store. These distinct mosaic sequences are set into a light cement ground so as to create precise but deliberately irregular alignments, reminiscent of the pictorial schemes of Paul Klee. Scarpa's capacity for evoking simultaneous metaphors in his work is evident here in the way in which this Klee-like mosaic floor simulates the familiar effect of shallow water playing over flooded stone paving at the time of the infamous Venetian *aigua alta,* or "highwater," when the center of the city periodically floods.

Similar local metaphoric references reappear in the Querini Stampalia design, not only in the existing twin-arched portico that remains perennially open to invasion by floodwater, commemorated by Scarpa in a spiral stairway descending into the canal, but also in the delicate entry bridge that, in its gentle rise, boarded deck, and teak and tubular steel handrail, does much to remind one of marine detailing in general, and perhaps of gondola construction in particular.

There is an evident "orientalism" in all of Scarpa's work, ranging from the fretted wooden *fusuma* lattice screens that first appear in the Olivetti and Gavina showrooms to the almost Islāmic layout of certain episodes in Scarpa's garden design, as in the fountain watercourse which and enlivens the garden court to the rear of the Querini Stampalia.

In the Museo Civici (originally Castelvecchio) at Verona, on which Scarpa worked at various times between 1957 and 1964, the garden court is the beginning rather than the end of the spatial sequence, and it leads almost at once to what may surely be regarded as the largest single "joint" of Scarpa's career: the tectonic setting of the Cangrande fourteenth-century equestrian statue that is placed, high up on a pedestal, in the ultimate fulcrum of the entire complex, at a suspended bridge point not only between the ground and the roof but also between the original fourteenth-century foundation and the Napoleonic addition. Of this multiple architectural "moment" Maria Antonietta Crippa has written:

> Scarpa gradually arrived at a design for a large corbel as a simple
> exhibition plane, making the gesture of a hand offering the statue of
> the knight to the spectator's gaze. . . . [In this way] Scarpa conceives of
> a museum as akin to a theatrical staging involving the spectator. In the
> Castelvecchio Museum he expresses a variety of moods; using space,
> he plays with different linguistic associations and articulations. The
> public is presented with art not as a static-contemplative experience but

as a dramatic-contemplative one mediated by the architect's sensitive interpretation. [5]

A double homage, made toward the end of his life, points to the somewhat contradictory character of Scarpa's architecture. In a 1976 address entitled "Can architecture be poetry?" [6] he was to give virtually equal weight, in terms of his own development, to the profound ontology of Shintō architecture and to the highly mannered, elegant, almost exclusively graphic effects practiced by the Viennese *Jugendstil* architect Josef Hoffmann. These two antecedents, so to speak, are evident in the last major works of Scarpa's career, the Brion Cemetery at San Vito d'Altivole near Treviso in 1972 and the Banco Popolare di Verona, started in 1973 and completed in 1975.

More than any other single work of Scarpa's career, the Brion Cemetery (fig. 1) testifies to his lifelong admiration for the work of the American architect Frank Lloyd Wright. This influence is patently evident in the design of the cemetery chapel and in the arcuated, flat form of the Brion tomb itself that reminds one of similar arcuated forms in Paolo Soleri's Neo-Wrightian Arcosanti Settlement under construction near Phoenix, Arizona, from 1955 to the present.

As to the multiple meanings latent in Scarpa's use of the arcuated form in this particular instance, the Italian architect Paolo Portoghesi has perceptively written: "It could be said that Scarpa reflected at length, with a structuralist approach on the word *arca* (in Italian, *arca* means both ark and sarcophagus—translator's note) and its historical meanings, on the Latin origin which defines its sense, close to that of coffin or monumental sarcophagus. . . . Scarpa explores the connotations of the term, its diachronic and synchronic value, and perhaps doesn't reject even the suggestive reference to that most sacred of arks: that of Noah. The tomb of the Brion family is thus contemporaneously "arch", "bridge", "roof", "overturned boat"; it is pushed towards land so as not to move the tombs away from . . . the earth to which the body returns as to the maternal breast. . . ." [7]

In many ways the Banco Popolare di Verona was Scarpa's ultimate statement about the full expressive potential of any given tectonic syntax in all its ramifications. From the design of the surrogate entablature, formed after Scarpa's microtectonic "ziggurat" molding, to the elaborate thin column support of this loggia form, fashioned out of riveted and welded tubular steel, the entire body of the Banco Popolare is permeated by repetitive themes of this order. The result is that just as the entablature molding reappears in the heavy stepped window surrounds of the rusticated base, so the lightweight thin column motif of the loggia finds itself thematically reiterated in the heavyweight, freestanding, coupled columns that help to support the floors above the mezzanine level of the bank.

Unlike Kahn, who left such a mark on civic design and urban development, the importance of Scarpa's legacy does not reside in an attempt to devise appropriate monumental forms for unprecedented public institutions, nor was Scarpa to tackle any of the heroic urban themes broached by Kahn. Instead, to a greater extent than Kahn and, in this regard, somewhat closer to Wright, Scarpa demonstrated the full potential of the elaborated joint together with the tactile surface as two primary agents with which to enrich the modern culture of built-form without regressing into the aporias of historicism. We may say that memory and invention are equally present in Scarpa, without either one being unduly dominant.

Figure 1. Brion Cemetery, San Vito d'Altivole, Italy, by Carlo Scarpa.

## Part 2: The isms of contemporary architecture

### (1) Rationalism: Europe 1965–1985

Italian Neo-Rationalism, the so-called *Tendenza,* was an attempt to redeem architecture from its total co-option by megalopolitan development. This return to rational form was initiated by the publication of two complementary texts, Aldo Rossi's *The Architecture of the City* of 1966, and Giorgio Grassi's *The Logical Construction of Architecture* of 1967.

Aware of the tendency of modern commercial development to absorb every significant cultural gesture, Rossi structured his theoretical

13

position about the idea of a historical typology that through reference to vernacular forms could enrich the rational paradigms of the Enlightenment. Returning to the Neoplatonic forms projected at the end of the eighteenth century by Étienne Boullée (1728–99) and C.-N. Ledoux (1736–1806), and to the typological order elaborated in the nineteenth century by J.-N.-L. Durand (1760–1834), Rossi and Grassi sought to achieve a kind of *architecture degree zero* that would not only relate to the earlier rigor of the prewar Italian Modern Movement but would also counter the reductive tendencies of late modern Functionalism. To posit the monument as an urban generator was to return to the cultural strategies of the Quattrocento [fifteenth century]—to that moment when the monument first became the means by which to project new values into the Gothic fabric of the medieval town. Rossi not only saw the monument as a repository of collective memory but also as the one architectural strategy with which to reassert the continuity of the public realm. It was a commitment to that which Hannah Arendt has called "the space of public appearance." [8] At the same time, the *Tendenza* was affected by a skeptical stoicism which enabled it to endow its work with a kind of Brechtian critical distance. A similar air of poetic detachment can be found in the pioneering works of Adolf Loos (1870–1933) and Heinrich Tessenow (1876–1950), two architects who were equally preoccupied with transcending the sterile cultural legacy of the modern state.

The canonical monuments projected by the *Tendenza* are to be distinguished from the large-scale urban interventions made by such latter-day Neo-Rationalists as the Belgian Maurice Culot or the Luxembourg architects Rob and Léon Krier. The Krier-Culot circle has recently moved toward an anti-modern more or less Classical Revivalist position, which over the years has become increasingly dogmatic and thus more detached from the material conditions of current reality. After Tessenow's book *Kleinstadt und Handwerk* (*The Provincial City and Craftsmanship,* 1918), the Krier-Culot circle insisted on returning to a craft-based culture and on the need to rebuild the "ruined" contemporary city from scratch. Its almost Messianic rejection of contemporary reality has served to distance this movement from the more critical "negativity" of the Italian Neo-Rationalists. Like the Italians, however, the Krier-Culot group remains opposed to zoning the city according to land use. Thus, Krier and Culot have attempted to resist the bureaucratic dissection and dismantling of the traditional city. In so doing they have condemned zoning as a physical parallel to the capitalist division of labor. Krier first demonstrated this "anti-zoning" thesis in his Echternach proposal of 1970, where he envisioned revitalizing the center of an old provincial city by inserting a mixed-use arcade into its core.

Within Italian Neo-Rationalism, subtle differences obtain between the picturesque metaphysics of Rossi and the tectonic stoicism of Grassi.

This difference was never more pronounced than in their respective projects for a students' dormitory at Chieti in 1976. Where Rossi's proposal remains possessed by a nostalgic recall of nineteenth-century bathing huts, Grassi reasserts his commitment to an analogical architecture—that is to say, to an architecture which resynthesizes rather than merely replicates the forms of collective memory. Grassi's student dormitory complex at Chieti posits an urban enclave which embodies the full range of an appropriately inflected typological form from the public status of the arcaded street to the private status of the dormitory wings. It acknowledges that not all parts of a given work are equally monumental, just as it accepts the fact that an urban intervention must of necessity be limited from both a physical and a temporal point of view.

Among the Italians who have contributed to the *Tendenza,* mention must be made of Carlo Aymonino, Bruno Minardi, Vittorio Gregotti, Franco Purini, and Laura Thermes. Seminal roles have also been played by Massimo Scolari, Enzo Bonfanti, and Manfredo Tafuri, all of whom have been major critical influences. Outside Italy the *Tendenza*'s greatest impact has been in the Ticino, Switzerland, where a regional Neo-Rationalist school has been active since the early 1960s. However, this school, based in Lugano, has been as much influenced by Le Corbusier (1887–1965), Kahn, and German Functionalists as by the Italians. It came into being under the leadership of Tita Carloni, and today it comprises a number of architects of exceptional caliber, including Luigi Snozzi, Aurelio Galfetti, Livio Vacchini, Flora Ruchat, and above all Mario Botta.

Botta's contribution to the evolution of Neo-Rationalism has been of particular import, for he has been able to distance himself from the so-called negative thought of the Italians without succumbing to sentimental aestheticism. Botta's creative resistance has manifested itself on a number of interrelated levels at once, running from urbanism to technology. At the beginning of his career he collaborated with Snozzi on the design of two important urban projects. The first of these was a proposal for a new administrative center in Perugia (1971); the second was a project for the development of "air rights" over the Zürich railway terminus, designed in 1978. In both instances what was projected was an urban mega-form: a "viaduct-arcade" in the first instance and a "bridge-arcade" in the second. The advantage of this kind of approach seems to be threefold. First, it posits an urban fragment which can be realized by a single authority in a relatively short period of time; second, it is a rational matrix which is able to provide for the current and future needs of the institution; and third, it is a horizontal form that, while large enough to harmonize with the overall fabric of the city, also serves as a micro-urban metaphor.

Botta's achievement has also been remarkable for the private houses that he built during the first fifteen years of his career. Aside from

15

displaying a sensitive approach to the history and topography of the site and using concrete block as a way of evoking the local agrarian vernacular, Botta also frames views from his houses in such a way as to secure the remaining unspoiled vistas of the region. These largely introspective houses, while excluding the development by which they are surrounded and of which they are part, also suggest the agricultural structures that were once the only buildings in this landscape.

Throughout the seventies, Neo-Rationalism enjoyed a wide following in Continental Europe. In France its influence was apparent in the work of architects as different as Bernard Huet and H. E. Ciriani; in Germany the movement found its principal adherents in J. P. Kleihues and Oswald Mathias Ungers. An important achievement of this school is Kleihues's Vinetaplatz block in Berlin-Wedding, which is significant for its reinterpretation of the perimeter-block, a residential type of the late 1920s. In the interim, following his return from the United States in 1975, Ungers has continually attempted to refine his essentially Rationalist approach to urban form. His conviction that in the future we shall often find ourselves confronted with the problems of planned shrinkage, rather than expansion or renewal, has given a particular cast to his contextual approach. For Ungers, a fragmentary urban strategy means either framing limited forms of present urban patterns in accordance with the existing topographical and institutional constraints, as in his 1978 proposal for Hildesheim, or, where confronted with urban retrenchment, it has meant opting for self-contained "cities in miniature," as in his 1977 unbuilt project for the Hotel Berlin, sited adjacent to the historic Lutzowplatz in Berlin.

## (2) *Formalism and Populism: America 1965–1990*

The origin of American Formalism lies in the emergence of the so-called New York Five—Peter Eisenman, Charles Gwathmey, Michael Graves, John Hejduk, and Richard Meier. Around 1965, all of these architects began to produce Formalist works which attempted in varying degrees to elaborate the prewar syntax of the European avant-garde architect. Where Eisenman attempted to reinterpret Theo van Doesburg (1883–1931) and Giuseppe Terragni (1904–41), Gwathmey, Graves, and Meier chose to follow the precepts of Le Corbusier, while Hejduk, for his part, paid greater attention, at least at the beginning of his career, to certain didactic aspects latent in Mies van der Rohe's American work.

For the New York Five, Formalism initially meant rejecting the more pragmatic socially conscious traditions of the Modern Movement, as exemplified above all in the late American Bauhaus work of Marcel Breuer and Gropius. Instead, they favored building on the formal legacy of Purism and Neo-Plasticism. Typical early examples of the Five's Formalism are to be found in Eisenman's House VI (the Frank

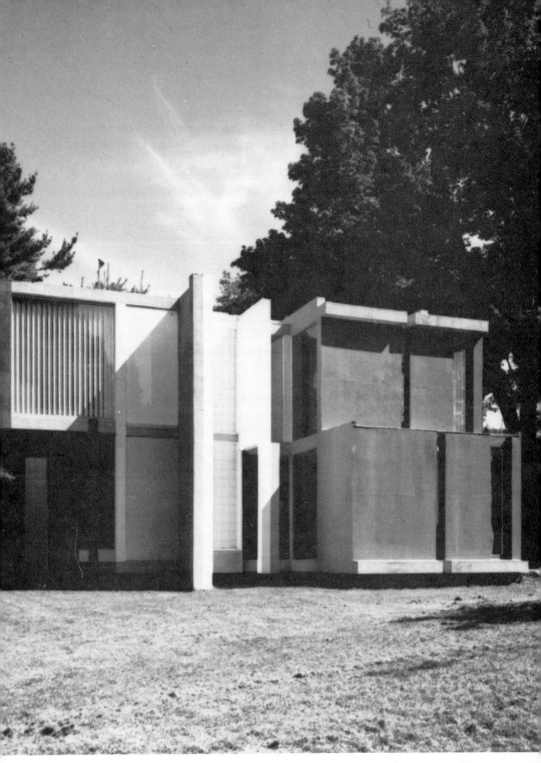

Figure 2. House VI, West Cornwall, Connecticut, by Peter Eisenman.

Residence; fig. 2), built in West Cornwall, Connecticut, in 1972, and in Meier's Smith House built in Darien, Connecticut, in 1967. Around the same time, Gwathmey and Meier began to build housing for New York State's Urban Development Corporation, and this large public undertaking meant that they had to modify to a large degree many of the Formalist principles they had employed in their private houses. At the beginning, the Formalists tended to ignore the urban implications of architectural form, a stance that was all the more surprising given the degree to which they were all initially influenced by the urban theories of Colin Rowe.

Since the mid-seventies, the New York Five have evolved in quite distinct ways. Thus, where Graves has gone on to indulge in pseudo Art Deco work enriched with Classical features, as exemplified in his Portland Civic Center (fig. 3), built in Portland, Oregon, in 1979–84, or in his much more recent Convention Hotel completed in Orlando for Walt Disney in 1988–90, Hejduk has largely confined himself to a series of highly speculative projects bordering on pure art. Similarly, where Eisenman has moved away from his early Neo-Plastic houses, Meier has gone on to develop his own idiosyncratic, highly elaborated Neo-Purist manner. It is clear that Meier's brilliant, filigree-like approach, wherein his buildings are invariably faced throughout in white enameled metal, has led to a series of works of unsurpassed elegance and public appeal, ranging from the Applied Art Museum in Frankfurt, West Germany (fig. 4), completed in 1984, to the High Museum of Art, realized in Atlanta, Georgia, in 1983 (fig. 5).

Eisenman is the only one of the original New York Five architects who has developed an elaborate theoretical position. A perennial theme in this regard has been his affinity for Structuralist and post-Structuralist thought. In lieu of the prewar utopia, he has pursued the ideal of a scientifically based, autonomous language for architecture, comparable in its ambitions to Arnold Schoenberg's twelve-tone invention in the field of music. Eisenman sees the precedent for this new language as residing in the pioneering work of the Italian Rationalists, and above all in Terragni's pioneering Rationalist work, the Casa del Fascio, erected at Como in 1932–36. It is indicative of a paradoxically conservative streak in Eisenman's development that he grounds his self-referential syntactic architecture in Italian abstraction derived, in the last analysis, from Classical precedents. This is all the more surprising given that, since the late sixties, Eisenman has sought a formal architecture which would categorically repudiate all traditional references.

Obsessed with orthogonally derived, syntactical transformations and permutations, Eisenman has shifted the ground of his intellectual legitimation. He has passed from an appeal to Noam Chomsky's generative grammar in the second half of the sixties to a dependence on the deconstructing philosophical processes set forth in Jacques Derrida's *Of*

Figure 3. Portland Civic Center, Portland, Oregon, by Michael Graves.

Figure 4. (Right and opposite) Two views of the Applied Art Museum, Frankfurt, West Germany, by Richard Meier.

*Grammatology,* first published in English in 1967. This shift, evident in House VI, announces Eisenman's abandonment of abstract structural form in favor of a Structuralist play with "differences." All in all, Eisenman has been consistently more interested in demonstrating fugal-formal processes than in evolving a single systematic methodology, and from this point of view, Derrida's insistence on the shifting, unstable referent in language affords a convenient paradigm.

Most recently, Eisenman has added a topographical, site-specific, approach to his method, and this promises to be spatially more accommodating than the orthogonal permutations he has hitherto employed. Once again he has felt the need to adduce an extra-architectural discourse as a point of departure, invoking fractal geometry, in this instance, as the generative technique.

Among the New York Five, Eisenman is the only American Formalist whose work has become increasingly elaborate over the years. He is, moreover, the only architect of his generation whose work remains as an active bridge between the New York Five and the formal concerns of the emerging generation—in particular the so-called European Deconstructionists as represented by such works as Bernard Tschumi's Parc de la Villette, Paris (1982), Zahar Hadid's Hong Kong Peak Competition

winner (1983), Coop Himmelblau's Hamburg Media Tower (1985), and Rem Koolhaas's National Dance Theatre for The Hague, realized in The Netherlands in 1987. Eisenman's haptic inventiveness has certainly kept abreast of these developments as his recent "fractured" projects amply testify—from his Wexner Center for Visual Arts (fig. 6), built in Columbus, Ohio, in 1989, to his project for a hotel in Barcelona, dating from 1990.

As the critic Charles Jencks has pointed out, Eisenman is not the only one of his generation to have gravitated toward the so-called Deconstructionist approach. [9] This is evident in the work of certain Southern Californian architects who have moved in a similar direction, above all Frank Gehry in his Aerospace Museum, completed at Santa Monica in 1982. Unlike Eisenman, however, Gehry's work displays certain figurative tendencies that seem to lie closer to the Populist line in current American architecture.

In his highly influential book of 1966, entitled *Complexity and Contradiction in Architecture,* Robert Venturi was to argue for an informal approach that would permit buildings to be designed in such a way that they would immediately relate to the context in which they were situated. As far as America was concerned, this context was more often

Figure 5. High Museum of Art, Atlanta, Georgia, by Richard Meier.

than not the highway commercial "strip" or the suburban subdivision, rather than any kind of traditional urban form. Venturi also advocated what he termed an inclusive manner of expression, wherein an open-ended and undemanding style would assure popular acceptance—that is to say, its accessibility to the man in the street. With the publication of *Learning from Las Vegas* in 1972, written in collaboration with Denise Scott Brown and Steven Izenour, Venturi assessed the need, as he put it, to set order against disorder, and vice versa. With this publication, Venturi shifted his ground. He moved from an ironic advocacy of Main Street as being "almost all right" to a perception of it as a kind of instant consumerist "utopia."

This slightly ironic Populist thesis was initially well received in both America and Europe, a following that gained impetus, as it were, by the support it received from the historian and critic Vincent Scully. Scully rallied to the Populist cause, first with his laudatory introduction to Venturi's *Complexity and Contradiction in Architecture* (1966) and then with his own book, *The Shingle Style Revisited* (1974). Venturi went on

Figure 6. Wexner Center for Visual Arts, Columbus, Ohio, by Peter Eisenman.

to receive the acclaim of such architects as Charles Moore and Robert Stern who, while adopting a somewhat different set of ad hoc attitudes toward modern form, were nonetheless equally open to exploiting the seemingly ready-made imagery of popular culture and the laissez-faire capacity of the American balloon frame.

The overall effect of appropriating ready-made imagery was to stimulate a rather indiscriminate reaction against all forms of modern expression in architecture, a situation which Jencks, to whom I have already referred, was prompt to identify as Post-Modern. In his book, *The Language of Post-Modern Architecture* (1977), Jencks effectively characterized Post-Modernism as being a populist, pluralist art of immediate communicability. Although it has its serious defenders, in retrospect, this broad populist Post-Modern position seems to lie uneasily suspended between an expression that pretends to derive from some lost or ersatz vernacular form and a never-ending series of gratuitously fashionable stylistic displays bordering at worst on pure kitsch and at best on a kind of pseudo avant-gardism.

Each year American Populism grows increasingly diffuse in its eclectic parodies, ranging from Art Deco conceits on the one hand to pseudo-vernacular and Neoclassical pastiche on the other. The original Venturi polemic of the "dumb and ordinary" has long since been left behind; a critical moment that was perhaps best epitomized in the elegant banality of Venturi's Trubek and Wislocki houses built on Cape Cod in 1973 (designed in collaboration with John Rauch). The fact is that a middle-class Populism that expresses itself in terms of individually competitive images and very little else has the effect of inhibiting the collective evolution of an architectural culture for the society as a whole. This much is all too painfully evident in the work of Moore and his followers, and even in the work of ostensibly more subversive figures such as Gehry. In the last analysis, Populism is a form of architectural creativity that, paradoxically, depends upon a somewhat gratuitous devaluation of traditional symbols. It is an "avant-gardism" that deals in a kind of tawdry pathos, to quote Jencks's assessment of Moore and William Turnbull's Kresge College, completed at the University of California at Santa Cruz (1973). [10]

### (3) Structuralism: Europe 1955–1975

The insistence of the European Rationalist movement on the critical importance of the block and the street, as manifested in the writings and works of Rossi, Grassi, and the Krier brothers, finds a certain parallel in the work of the Dutch Structuralists, a small group of architects revolving about the figure of Aldo van Eyck. Van Eyck began his critique of the prewar architectural avant-garde soon after 1945, and the long duration of his influence makes him comparable to Buckminster Fuller. Among the surviving members of the Team X faction, formed at the last CIAM (Congrès Internationaux d'Architecture Moderne) meeting (Dubrovnik, 1956), van Eyck's antireductive position is the only one that still appears relevant today. His categorical attack on the "functionalist city" served to distance him from the critical but still somewhat functionalist stance assumed by other prominent Team X members, such as the British architects Alison and Peter Smithson, and the American Shadrach Woods. Van Eyck's anti-functionalist critique stemmed from anthropological interests that commenced with the journeys that he made to Africa in the early 1950s. In 1959 he made a study of the Dogon civilization, and the village communities of this culture thereafter served as the model for his theory of "labyrinthine clarity."

Van Eyck demonstrated this concept in practice in his Amsterdam Municipal Orphanage, completed in 1960, in which a series of orthogonally cellular classroom units were grouped around a series of domed spaces that served as the center-points of the five individual "homes." In the theory of van Eyck, "place" and "occasion" are conceived of as cultural occurrences that ought to be stimulated and allowed in the structure of architectural form. His orphanage was thus ordered about "places" in an almost Heideggerian sense, with such elements as thresholds, sunken circles, and storytelling rings that were designed both to inform daily ritual and to stimulate play. This concept of a place that provides for, or rather provokes, an occasion without determining its specific nature, has done much to ensure van Eyck's continued influence on his main followers, Jan Van Stigt, Piet Blom, and Herman Hertzberger.

While van Eyck's concept of the city in miniature has probably found its most literal interpretation in Blom's Kasbah Housing built at Hengelo, The Netherlands, in 1973, his notion of spontaneous spatial appropriation has attained its most subtle realization in Hertzberger's Centraal Beheer Insurance Company Building, which was completed in Apeldoorn, The Netherlands, in 1972. Appropriation by the user is fully explored here in the way the available spaces may be rearranged so as to accommodate quite different patterns of assembly and work. Following van Eyck, Hertzberger holds to the anarchic view that this open rendering of built-form as a socially catalytic agent will assist contemporary architecture in overcoming the seeming cultural inaccessibility of its form.

However, Dutch Structuralism has architectural dimensions that go beyond the cultural-anthropological considerations outlined above. The explicitly tectonic elaboration of its component parts and the manner of its assembly bring it remarkably close to the structurally rationalist precepts propounded by Viollet-le-Duc in the second half of the nineteenth century. Like the works of Kahn, by whom Hertzberger has been influenced, a rationalism of construction and structure is posited, in addition to the logic of geometrically ordered "anthropological" form. As in Kahn's late masterworks (such as his Kimbell Art Museum at Fort Worth, Texas, 1966–72 (fig. 7), or his Mellon Center for British Art at Yale, New Haven, Connecticut, 1969–74), the Dutch Structuralists articulate their constructional procedure in order to arrive at a "phenomenology" of built-form. On the other hand, their position is to be distinguished from Kahn's on two basic counts: first, they eschew the use of honorific material, such as travertine, and second, they permit their repetitive cellular units to inflect or erode the mass image of the composition in an informal and haptic way, a random expression totally antipathetic to the monumental expression pursued by Kahn.

*(4) Productivism: America and Europe 1950*

The recent Productivist movement, more commonly known as High-Tech, has its main origins after 1945 in the work of three men: Mies van der Rohe, with his minimalist cult of "almost nothing," Buckminster Fuller with his Dymaxion (dynamism plus efficiency) principle of design,

Figure 7. Kimbell Art Museum, Fort Worth, Texas, by Louis Kahn.

and Konrad Wachsmann, whose concern for the actual processes of machine tool production (see his prefabricated, wooden General Panel System House, 1945, designed with Gropius) made him a pioneer of the Productivist approach. Another early advocate of Productivism was the Swiss architect Max Bill, whose demountable exhibition pavilion for the Swiss National Exhibition in Lausanne (1964) corresponded to his own notion of *Produktform,* wherein all structural and architectonic order is seen to derive directly from the processes of production and assembly (cf. Paxton's Crystal Palace, 1851). The priority accorded to production at the Hochschule für Gestaltung [College of Design], founded by Bill at Ulm, West Germany, in 1955, led to the creation of a Department of Industrialized Building in which prefabricated built-form was largely reduced to production and assembly, as we may judge from projects designed by the faculty and students of whom Herbert Ohl and Willi Ramstein are the most well known.

Since the mid-1950s, Productivism has ranged over a wide area, assuming quite different forms, from Frei Otto's first tented structures, which made their debut between 1955 and 1963 in a series of German garden exhibitions, to Buckminster Fuller's 250-foot diameter geodesic sphere (fig. 8), built as the official American pavilion for the world exhibition staged in Montreal in 1967. Expo 67 also saw the most ambitious attempt yet made at realizing a high-rise residential labyrinth out of prefabricated, heavyweight reinforced concrete modules. This was Moshe Safdie's Habitat '67 complex that consisted of stacked living units and roof terraces stepping back in the form of a series of inter-locking dwellings.

The so-called Groupe d'Étude d'Architecture Mobile (GEAM), founded in 1958, was also to favor a Productive approach to architec-tural form, as is evident in the work of Yona Friedman and Eckhard Schulze-Fielitz. Friedman had already adopted Wachsmann's space-frame approach by 1956 as a basis for open-ended urban infrastructure elevated on open latticework columns well above the surface of the earth. While Friedman's urban proposals were hardly realizable, the idea of a series of superimposed platforms upon which people would be at liberty to rearrange their accommodation at will, through deploy-ment of standard components such as kitchens, bathrooms, etc., became the fundamental precept of Nicolaas Habraken's Stichting Architecten Research (SAR) team that was active in Eindhoven, The Netherlands, from 1960 to 1964.

Aside from the contributions of Fuller and Wachsmann, Productivism in the United States has been largely conceived in terms of skeleton-and-skin construction with the strongest emphasis falling on the latter. The Miesian cult of "almost nothing," evident in the undulating curtain walls of his famous glass skyscraper projects of the twenties, came to be adopted as general practice in America, first in the pioneering work of the Skidmore, Owings & Merrill firm (SOM), as is evident in their Heinz Vinegar Plant, in Pittsburgh, of 1952, and then in the work of Eero Saarinen and Associates which began with Saarinen's General Motors Technical Center built at Warren, Michigan (1948–56).

In retrospect, it is possible to observe two distinct Productivist "schools" in the United States. The first is a latter-day post-Miesian movement in which the skeleton and skin are equally stressed. Orig-inating in Chicago, this approach is to be found in the work of such architects as George Schipporeit, Jacques Brownson, Bruce Graham, Gene Summers, Dirk Lohan, Myron Goldsmith, and the early Helmut Jahn. The second school came into being with the independent work of Saarinen's former assistants. This school has since moved toward stressing the curtain wall at the expense of the structure, as is evident in the recent work of Gunnar Birkerts, Anthony Lumsden, Cesar Pelli, Kevin Roche, and John Dinkeloo. Where the post-Miesian school has to its credit such Chicago monuments as the Chicago Civic Center, the Lake Point Tower (fig. 9), McCormick Place, and the 1,450-foot-high Sears Tower designed by Graham and Fazlur Khan of SOM, the Saarinen school has not only built over a wider typological range but also achieved more sensational results. This much is suggested by Pelli's Pacific Design Center, completed in Los Angeles in 1971, and by his tour de force in minimalist curtain-wall construction, the San Bernardino City Hall of 1969.

Figure 8. The 250-foot diameter geodesic sphere, Montreal, by Buckminster Fuller.

A somewhat more brutal approach characterized the early work of Roche and Dinkeloo, particularly the assembly plant they built for Cummins Engine Company at Darlington, England, in 1965, or their Ford Foundation Building, New York City (fig. 10), of 1968, where, following Saarinen's John Deere and Company headquarters at Moline, Illinois, they placed a greater expressive burden on the frame. In their recent work, however, such as the United Nations Plaza Hotel in New York City (1979), they have opted for the skin alone and more recently still they have moved away from minimalism altogether to favor instead a kind of pseudoclassical pastiche, as evident, say, in their new zoo complex for Central Park, New York City, completed in 1988. This rather regressive development has since turned out to be the fate of the Saarinen school as a whole, and little is left of the pristine, product-oriented minimalism that was the characteristic feature, indeed the touchstone of its early approach.

Figure 9. Lake Point Tower, Chicago, by Schipporeit-Heinrich Associates.

Apart from the influence of Buckminster Fuller on Louis Kahn, Fuller's main influence has been outside the United States and above all in England, where his work took hold with the publication of Reyner Banham's *Theory and Design in the First Machine Age* (1960). The last chapter of this historical retrospective proposed Fuller as the true prophet of the future. The main theoreticians to propagate Fuller in England were John McHale and James Meller and then, at the level of polemical design, the "neo-futurist" Archigram Group, comprising Peter Cook, Dennis Crompton, Warren Chalk, David Greene, Ron Herron, and Michael Webb. Fuller also exerted an influence on Cedric Price, whose Fun Palace project of 1961 was projected as an open multistory infrastructure. Like the polemical work of Friedman, this structure could, in theory, be manipulated and rearranged by its users.

Until recently, the English Productivist school remained largely theoretical, so much so that Archigram was more involved with the image of industrialized building than with the mastery of it. Only with the emergence of a slightly younger generation has the influence of Buckminster Fuller finally made itself fully felt. This influence initially manifested itself in the Neo-Wrightian, Neo-Miesian practice of Team 4 in 1963, and then more decisively with the splitting up of this team into the separate practices by Norman Foster and Richard Rogers in 1970. European Productivism came into its own with the Centre Pompidou, Paris, realized in 1971–77 to the designs of Renzo Piano and Rogers. While Foster and Rogers have each since established a considerable body of independent work, their mutual debt to Piano is evident, above all for their combination of synthetic skins with lightweight metal construction. Among the many remarkable buildings that Foster and Rogers have each since achieved, particular notice has to be taken of Rogers's Lloyds Building, London (1984), and Foster's Hongkong and Shanghai Banking Corporation Headquarters, completed in Hong Kong in 1985.

In many respects the achievements of Foster Associates represents the apotheosis of Productivism, since their work seems to be situated in an intelligent middle ground that eschews to an equal degree both the reductive minimalism of the American Neo-Miesian school and the excessively technological rhetoric that is evident in the later work of Rogers, particularly in the Lloyds Building, where it becomes difficult to perceive the building due to the elegant high-tech service elements that seem to overwhelm its surface—the bathroom cores, elevators, exposed framework, and stair towers with which it is festooned.

Aside from the recent Hongkong and Shanghai Bank, which is a structurally expressive high-rise slab, the work of Foster Associates has been characterized by pursuit of the elegant, high-tech enclosure, such as we find in their Willis Faber & Dumas insurance offices built in Ipswich, England, in 1975. Faced entirely in large suspended sheets of tinted plate glass that are hung like a crystallized necklace about the undulating perimeter of the building, the Willis Faber offices are so lacking in rhetoric as to make even the main entrance hard to find.

On balance, however, what Foster has been able to achieve with his high-tech approach is an elegantly articulated architecture conceived in the main as though each commission was nothing more than an occasion for a gigantic piece of industrial design. That this was, and still is, the primary cultural aim of the work is borne out by a revealing text that Foster himself wrote in 1977.

> Design can be many things to many people. To us, as an office, it is
> a means of integrating and resolving conflicts, to avoid an either/or
> situation, to recognise needs which might be spiritual as well as material,
> and to recognise that beautiful things can and should be reconciled
> with moving through the maze of cost, time and quality control. We
> really do not see why "art" and "business" have to be put into separate

Figure 10. Ford Foundation Building, New York City, by Kevin Roche and John Dinkeloo.

pigeonholes. If you break down the conflict between private and public, the individual and the community, and between short- and long-term requirements, this raises the whole issue of multi-use and flexible building—flexibility for choice, change, and growth, and the problems of flexibility as well as the bonuses. In the end, it means resolving and integrating many conflicting requirements.

High technology is not an end in itself, but rather a means to social goals and wider possibilities. High-technology buildings are hand-crafted with the same care as bricks and mortar or timber. Hand-crafted care is the factor that makes a building loved by its users and by those who look at it. However, materials have changed, quality control no longer comes from site-based crafts. [11]

This is the same credo that underlies the well-serviced technological anonymity we will no doubt encounter again in 1991, when the third London airport, at Stanstead, will open, built to the designs of Foster Associates.

The basic precepts of Productivism may be summarized as follows. The building is invariably conceived as a well-serviced shelter in which the space is subdivided as flexibly and openly as possible. The adaptability of this space is usually assured by the provision of an integrated network of services. Wherever possible, a clear separation is maintained between *servant spaces* such as lavatories, elevators, ventilation ducts, etc., and the *served areas* such as open planned offices. Finally, the overall structure is usually rendered as nothing more than the *produktform* of its components; that is to say, the total assembly is determined as much by production as by function.

No current program lends itself better to Productivism than the modern airport, whose quintessentially dynamic nature means that it tends to be a processal assembly rather than a finished object. And yet, with the exceptions of Frankfurt and Stanstead, the giant airports of the last decades, such as we find in Seattle, Fort Worth, and Atlanta, each with its own internal transit system, are hardly examples of high-quality *produktformen*.

Unlike either Populism or Structuralism, Productivism is a development of the functionalist-oriented attitudes initiated by the prewar architectural avant-garde. It is also a continuation of the quasi-industrialized approach to building first developed by Paxton. This line of historical development may be seen as culminating in the work of such designers as Jean Prouvé who, while they are not architects in the strict sense, have devoted their entire careers to the rationalization and refinement of modular, lightweight form. Prouvé's career has been exemplary in this respect—first with his pioneering of the neoprene joint and the press-formed panel wall, and then at the level of modular construction. His long career extends from the pressed-metal modules of his Maison du Peuple, built at Clichy, Paris, in 1939, to the modular pre-rusted, rustproof steel window wall that he devised for the Free University of Berlin, designed by Shadrach Woods and Manfred Schiedhelm and completed in 1973.

## (5) Critical Regionalism 1960–1980

The term Critical Regionalism is not intended to denote the vernacular, as this was once spontaneously produced by the interaction of climate, culture, and craft. The intention is to identify those regional "schools" whose aim has been to represent and serve particular constituencies. Such a regional expression depends on a rapport between a local political constituency and the architectural profession. One could say that one of the mainsprings of Critical Regionalism is a discernible aspiration for some degree of cultural, economic, and political independence. In his seminal essay "Universal Civilization and National Cultures" (1961), [12] the French philosopher Paul Ricoeur insists that in the last analysis everything will depend on the capacity of rooted culture to recreate its own tradition, while appropriating foreign influences at the level of both culture and civilization. Such a process of assimilation and transformation is impure by definition.

If a single Regionalist principle can be identified as taking priority over any other, it is surely the commitment to *place* rather than *space*. The universal megalopolis is patently indifferent to such a differentiation. It intends, in fact, the reduction of the environment to little more than a vast field of ever-changing, fungible, commodity values. As an abacus for development, the megalopolis provides for an illusory landscape in which natural form is mixed up at random with man-made instruments, and vice versa. Regionalism would seem to offer the sole possibility of resisting the rapacity of this mix. Its salient cultural precept is "place creation," and its general model is the enclave, that is to say, the bounded domain as a foil to the placelessness of the modern motorized environment. Among other factors contributing to the emergence of a regionalism of this order is not only a certain prosperity but also some kind of anti-centrist consensus—an aspiration at least to some form of cultural, economic, and political independence from the otherwise uncontainable megalopolis.

The concept of a local or national culture is a paradoxical proposition, not only because of the present obvious antithesis between rooted culture and universal civilization, but also because all cultures, both ancient and modern, seem to have depended for their intrinsic development on a certain cross-fertilization with other cultures. As Ricoeur seems to imply, regional or national cultures must today, more than ever, be ultimately constituted as locally inflected manifestations of "world culture." It is surely no accident that this paradoxical proposition arises at a time when global modernization continues to undermine, with ever-increasing force, all forms of traditional culture.

It is necessary nonetheless to identify the factors which distinguish Regionalism from the demagogic tendencies of Populism. In contradistinction to Regionalism, the primary goal of Populism is to function as an instrumental sign. More often than not, such a sign seeks not a critical perception of reality but the sublimation of desire through metaphoric allusion. Its fundamental aim is to attain some reflexive gratification as efficiently as possible.

Critical Regionalism is a dialectical proposition, for it consciously seeks to counter the reductive tendency of universal Modernism with values and images that are essentially rooted. At the same time, after the ethical attitudes assumed by the Viennese circle around the Austrian critical writer Karl Kraus—the circle of Ludwig Wittgenstein and Adolf Loos—Critical Regionalism recognizes that modernization has long since precluded the continuation of any authentic vernacular culture. There is no way to incorporate this into modern building without losing it. The "regionalism" in question, then, has to be invented as a form of self-conscious resistance; it cannot be merely assumed as a received vernacular form.

It is my contention that Critical Regionalism flourishes as a marginal discourse within the cultural fissures that articulate advanced industrialized societies in unexpected ways. These borderline manifestations may be characterized as the interstices of freedom. Their existence is proof that the model of a hegemonic center surrounded by dependent provinces is hardly an adequate characterization of our cultural potential. A regionally inflected modernism began to appear in Los Angeles in the 1920s in the work of the so-called Southern California school, and in Rio de Janeiro, in the 1930s and 1940s, in the early work of Gregori Warchavchick, Oscar Niemeyer, Lúcio Costa, and Alfonso Reidy. A similar manifestation occurred at around the same time in Caracas, Venezuela, in the work of Carlos Raúl Villanueva, and again in Argentina, in the pioneering work of Amancio Williams, above all perhaps in Williams's canonical "House Over the Brook" built in Mar del Plata in 1945. Influenced by Mies van der Rohe and the pioneer of reinforced concrete engineering, Robert Maillart, this bridge house celebrated in equal degree both advanced technology and the environment in which it was situated.

The work of the Italian architect Gino Valle may be seen as belonging to a similar critically regionalist genre, inasmuch as his entire career has been centered in the city of Udine. From his Udine studio, Valle was to make one of the earliest postwar reinterpretations of the Lombardy farmhouse, as in his Casa Quaglia built at Sutrio in 1956. Thereafter, Valle was to be largely engaged throughout the late fifties in the evolution of a new industrial format for the Lombardy region. This particular architectural activity reached its zenith in his Zanussi Factory Offices built at Pordenone in 1961.

The critical potential of provincial culture resides in its ability to cultivate the artistic capacity of a region, while reinterpreting influences coming from the outside. Switzerland, with its intricate linguistic and cultural boundaries and its cosmopolitan tradition, has always been exemplary in this regard, for where the cantonal system has served to sustain local culture, the federation has facilitated the ready assimilation of foreign influences.

The work of Mario Botta, with its dedication to the topography and its feeling for rationalized local production, typifies the essence of the Swiss regional approach. Apprenticed to the Ticinese architect Carloni and later trained under Scarpa in Venice, Botta was also fortunate in being able to work, however briefly, for both Kahn and Le Corbusier. Two particular factors may be seen as being key to Botta's regionalism: on the one hand, his preoccupation with "building the site," on the other, his conviction that the loss of the historical city can only be compensated for on a fragmentary basis. With regard to this last, his school at Morbio Inferiore, Switzerland, of 1977 asserts itself as a micro-urban realm, that is to say, as some kind of civic compensation for the progressive loss of truly public space in the nearby urban center of Chiasso, where banks, brokerage houses, and tourism have jointly overtaken all the more traditional forms of civic use.

Between 1960 and 1980 the Ticino school produced a number of remarkable buildings, many of which were collectively designed. Credit is due in this instance to the leadership of the older generation—such figures as Carloni, Galfetti, and Dolf Schnebli, who frequently collaborated with younger architects.

From the point of view of critical theory we have to regard regional culture not as something given and immutable but rather as something which has to be self-consciously cultivated. Such a process of conscious assimilation and reinterpretation seems to be evident in the work of the Danish architect Jørn Utzon, above all in his Bagsûaerd Church (fig. 11), completed in a suburb outside Copenhagen in 1976. Here, precast concrete infill elements of standardized dimensions are combined, in a particularly articulate way, with in situ reinforced concrete shell vaults that span the principal public volumes. And while this combination of modular assembly and in situ casting may appear at first to be nothing more than an appropriate integration of the full range of concrete techniques that are now at our disposal, the case can be made that the way in which these techniques are combined incorporates a number of dialogically opposed values.

At one level, we may claim that this prefabricated modular assembly not only accords with the technical value of universal civilization but also represents its capacity for normative application, whereas a cast in situ vault is a singular structural invention applied to a unique site. It may be argued, in the light of Ricoeur, that where the first technique

35

Figure 11. Bagsůaerd Church (interior), suburb outside Copenhagen, by Jørn Utzon.

affirms the norms of universal civilization, the other proclaims the values of idiosyncratic culture.

Yet another dialogue is evoked as soon as one passes from the optimum modular cladding of the exterior of Utzon's church to the far from optimum shell vault spanning the nave. This last is uneconomic in the sense that such a span could have been economically achieved with steel trusswork. Here, a particular form has been deliberately selected for its symbolic capacity to signify the sacred. And yet, this highly configurated section can hardly be regarded as traditionally Western. Indeed, the only precedent for such a peculiar section is a Chinese pagoda roof, a paradigm that is cited by Utzon in his seminal essay of 1962, "Platforms and Plateaus: Ideas of a Danish Architect." [13]

The subtle and contrary allusions incorporated into this folded concrete shell roof are of far greater import than the mere reinterpretation of an Oriental timber form in Occidental concrete technology; while the main vault over the nave suggests the presence of a religious space, it does so in such a way as to preclude an exclusively Western reading. A similar Occidental/Oriental interpenetration also occurs in the wooden fenestration and slatted partitions which seem to allude both to the Nordic vernacular of the stave church and to the fretted traditional timberwork of China. The intention behind these complex procedures of synthesis seems to be as follows: first, to revitalize certain devalued Western forms through a recasting of their essential nature, and second, in so doing to realize a certain paradoxical secularization of religious form. This is arguably a more appropriate way to render a church in a secular age, where traditional ecclesiastical iconography runs the risk of degenerating into kitsch.

This revitalization of Occidental cultural forms with Oriental elements by no means exhausts the ways in which the Bagsůaerd Church is inflected. Utzon has also exploited the agricultural metaphor implicit in its barnlike form as a way of giving public expression to a spiritual, preindustrial institution.

An equally complex, cross-cultural attitude may be found in the work of the veteran Mexican architect Luis Barragán, whose finest houses invariably assume a markedly topographical form. That is to say, they cannot be really perceived, experienced, or photographed, as freestanding aesthetic objects. They have the nature of being compounds, or rather domains, inscribed into the landscape. As much a landscape designer as an architect, Barragán has always sought a sensual and earthbound architecture, an architecture compounded of enclosures, stelae, fountains, and watercourses; an architecture laid into volcanic rock and lush vegetation; an architecture that refers indirectly to the Mexican *estancia*. Of Barragán's feeling for mythical and rooted beginnings, it is sufficient to cite his memories of the almost apocryphal pueblo of his childhood.

My earliest childhood memories are related to a ranch my family owned
near the village of Mazamitla. It was a *pueblo* with hills, formed by
houses with tile roofs and immense eaves to shield passers-by from the
heavy rains which fall in that area. Even the earth's color was interesting
because it was red earth. In this village, the water distribution system
consisted of great gutted logs, in the form of troughs, which ran on a
support structure of tree forks, 5 meters high, above the roofs. This
aqueduct crossed over the town, reaching the patios, where there were
great stone fountains to receive the water. The patios housed the stables,
with cows and chickens, all together. Outside, in the street, there
were iron rings to tie the horses. The channeled logs, covered with
moss, dripped water all over town, of course. It gave this village
the ambience of a fairy tale. No, there are no photographs. I have
only its memory. [14]

This preoccupation with an "irrigated architecture" shows the extent
to which Barragán has been influenced by Islāmic culture. The same
may be said of his preoccupation with the privacy of the courtyard
house. These concerns are evident in his opposition to the techno-
scientific ravages imposed on the modern world, and in his criticism of
the erosion of nature which modernization has brought about.

Everyday life is becoming much too public. Radio, TV, telephone all
invade privacy. Gardens should therefore be enclosed and not open to
public gaze. . . . Architects are forgetting the need of human beings
for half-light, the sort of light that imposes a tranquility, in their living
rooms as well as in their bedrooms. About half the glass that is used in
so many buildings—homes as well as offices—would have to be removed
in order to obtain the quality of light that enables one to live and work
in a more concentrated manner. . . .

   Before the machine age, even in the middle of cities, Nature was
everybody's trusted companion. . . . Nowadays, the situation is reversed.
Man does not meet with Nature, even when he leaves the city to
commune with her. Enclosed in his shiny automobile, his spirit stamped
with the mark of the world whence the automobile emerged, he is,
within Nature, a foreign body. A billboard is sufficient to stifle the
voice of Nature. Nature becomes a scrap of Nature and man a scrap
of man. [15]

By the time of his first house and studio built around an enclosed
court in Tacubaya, Mexico D.F., in 1947, Barragán had already moved
away from the syntax of the International Style. And yet his work has
always remained committed to the abstract forms which have characterized the art of our era. Barragán's penchant for large, abstract planes
set into discretely planted courtyards is perhaps at its most intense in
his gardens for the residential districts of Las Arboleadas (1958–61)
and Los Clubes (1961–64), and in his freeway monument, Satellite City
Towers, designed with Mathias Goeritz in 1957.

No one has perhaps expressed the idea of a Critical Regionalism more forcefully than the American Harwell Hamilton Harris, in his address "Regionalism and Nationalism," given at the North West Regional Council of the American Institute of Architects in Eugene, Oregon, in 1954. This was the occasion when he first advanced his felicitous distinction between restricted and liberated Regionalism.

Opposed to the Regionalism of Restriction is another type of regionalism, the Regionalism of Liberation. This is the manifestation of a region that is *especially in tune with the emerging thought of the time.* We call such a manifestation 'regional' *only because it has not yet emerged elsewhere.* It is the genius of this region to be more than ordinarily aware and more than ordinarily free. Its virtue is that its manifestation has *significance for the world outside itself.* To express this regionalism architecturally it is necessary that there be building—preferably a lot of building—at one time. Only so can the expression be sufficiently general, sufficiently varied, sufficiently forceful to capture people's imaginations and provide a friendly climate long enough for a new school of design to develop.

San Francisco was made for Maybeck. Pasadena was made for Greene and Greene. Neither could have accomplished what he did in any other place or time. Each used the materials of the place; but it is not the materials that distinguish the work. . . . A region may develop ideas. A region may accept ideas. Imaginations and intelligence are necessary for both. In California in the late Twenties and Thirties modern European ideas met a still developing regionalism. In New England, on the other hand, European Modernism met a rigid and restrictive regionalism that at first resisted and then surrendered. New England accepted European Modernism whole because its own regionalism had been reduced to a collection of restrictions. [16]

Despite an apparent freedom of expression, such a level of liberative regionalism seems to be difficult to achieve in North America today. Such are the inroads made by the media, big business, and consumerism. Despite highly individualistic forms of expression, only a few firms today display any commitment to the cultivation of a rooted American culture. An atypical example of current "regional" work in North America is the sensitively sited series of houses designed by Andrew Batey and Mark Mack for the Napa Valley area in California; another is the public work of the architect Harry Wolf, whose practice, until recently, was largely restricted to North Carolina. Wolf's metaphoric approach to place-making was polemically demonstrated in his 1982 competition entry for the Fort Lauderdale, Florida, Riverfront Plaza. There he projected a giant sundial, alluding to the fact that Fort Lauderdale not only has the same latitude as the eighteenth-century astronomical observatory built at Jaipur, India, but that it also possesses something of cultural significance, both the plaza and the observatory depending in different ways on the worship of the sun.

## Epilogue

One should perhaps note that the following two "case studies," located in Japan and in the Iberian Peninsula, could well be regarded as being part of the general regional dispersal and articulation that I have outlined above. I have elected to characterize both as "late modern" largely because they can also be seen as continuations of impulses that have their origins in the period prior to the Second World War.

*Late Modernism 1: The Japanese Modern Movement, 1960–1985*

The first Japanese Modern Movement in architecture began in 1926 with the formation of the so-called Japanese Secession Group, which included among its early members Tetsuro Yoshida, who designed the canonical reinforced-concrete-framed Tokyo General Post Office in 1931. At the same time, those of a slightly younger generation, such as Kunio Maekawa and Junzō Sakakura began to work for internationally known modern architects such as Le Corbusier. Others were already studying at the Bauhaus by the late 1920s. Sakakura completed his European experience by designing a work of international importance, the Japanese pavilion at the World Exhibition in Paris of 1937, in which the architectonic order of the traditional teahouse was reinterpreted in modern, neo-Corbusian, terms. Sakakura's open-space planning, together with the clear articulation of interior space, bore a distant but distinct resemblance to the spatial order of traditional Japanese architecture.

A more restrained modern interpretation of tradition informed the domestic practice of Isoya Yoshida, while in contrast to this conservatism stood the conceptual boldness of men such as Rentchitchiro Kawakita, whose entry for the Soviet Kharkov Theatre competition of 1931 went well beyond the received paradigms of his day. Indeed, its mega-structural engineering postulated form of the kind that Kenzō Tange achieved only later in his twin stadia, known as the National Gymnasium (fig. 12), built for the 1964 Olympic Games in Tokyo. While Tange was not so concerned as Kawakita with mechanical movement, the parabolic volumes of these stadia were covered by a catenary metal roof hung from prowlike concrete "horns" issuing out of the ends of the elliptical concrete ring beams supporting the seating.

Just prior to his now famous Hiroshima Peace Center of 1955, Tange began his extensive career with a whole series of governmental commissions, starting with his city hall designs for Shimizu and Tokyo (1952–57) and culminating both in his Kagawa Prefectural Office, Takamatsu, of 1958 and in his masterly Kurashiki City Hall, Okayama, of 1960. Where Tokyo City Hall was a tour de force in a trabeated reinforced concrete frame, Kagawa's Prefecture attained a balance in its synthesis of trabeated "timber" frames, drawn from the Heian era, with elements discreetly abstracted from the received vocabulary of the International Style. By making a discrete reference to both Buddhist and Shintō prototypes, this work established Tange as the most important figure to emerge in Japan after the Second World War.

Following the mega-structural lead established by Tange in his mega-lomaniacal Tokyo Bay proposal of 1960, a younger group of Japanese architects, known as the Metabolists, began to react against this official monumentality. Instead they proposed a series of "plug-in" mega-structures wherein, as in the work of Noriaki Kurokawa, the living cells would be reduced to prefabricated pods randomly attached to the surface of vast helicoid skyscrapers. Alternatively, as in the projects of Kiyonori Kikutake, similar pods would cling like limpets to the inner and outer surfaces of large cylinders floating in the sea. Kikutake's floating cities are surely among the most poetic visions of the Metabolist movement, and yet, despite the prevalence of the offshore oil drilling rig, such marine cities are patently inappropriate to the accommodation of everyday life.

The so-called Japanese New Wave of the late sixties emerged as an anti-Metabolist reaction under the leadership of the architect Arata Isozaki, whose stature became evident with his Fukuoka Mutual Bank of 1966 in Kyushu and his Central Library of Kitakyusu City, completed in 1975. Unlike the Metabolists, the Japanese New Wave believed that one could no longer sustain a meaningful relationship between the one-shot building and the urban whole. This realistic and ironic position was to find itself variously expressed in introverted houses designed by an even younger generation of architects, such as Tadao Ando, Toyo Ito, and Hiroshi Hara.

Unlike Kurokawa, who launched himself into a commercial practice on the basis of his role in the Metabolist movement, Isozaki and Fumihiko Maki emerged at a much slower pace, each taking a more considered course of development. Thus, while Isozaki remained in Tange's office for nearly a decade after his graduation in 1954, Maki moved to the United States in 1953, studying first at the Cranbrook Academy of Art, Michigan, and then at the Graduate School of Design, Harvard University. Later, when Maki returned from the States to assume the professorship at Tokyo University, Isozaki elected to become the unofficial leader of the so-called New Wave architects.

Isozaki's seminal "Space of Darkness" essay of 1964, written a year after he founded his own independent practice, formulates the critical stance that his work would adopt during the next decade. Taking as his point of departure the novelist Jun'ichirō Tanizaki's ironic, anti-Western, anti-technocratic essay of 1933, entitled "In Praise of Shadows," Isozaki employed Tanizaki's critical nostalgia as a way of

(Overleaf) Figure 12. National Gymnasium, Tokyo, by Kenzō Tange.

renouncing the simpleminded trabeated reinforced concrete style of the Tange generation that had become the received manner of Japanese modern architecture in the postwar years. Isozaki's counter concept of the "space of darkness" lay suspended between two poles. While it confronted the chaotic technocratic reality of the megalopolis, it also recognized the critical pressure, so to speak, of Tanazaki's ghosts, the Japanese spirit lying latent in the surrounding technological "gloom." From such reflections, Isozaki evolved a highly illusory superficial style which he called "twilight gloom" and which is first evident in his branch bank buildings of the 1970s. The Gunma Prefectural Museum of Fine Arts (fig. 13), constructed in the town of Takasaki from 1971 to 1974, expands the syntactic potential of Isozaki's "twilight" metal skin construction through a set of cubic forms that serve to stabilize the overall mass of the building, somewhat after the manner of the American minimalist artist Sol LeWitt.

Between 1972 and 1975, Isozaki moved away from his preoccupation with dematerialized gridded forms toward an architecture predicated on the revelation of tectonic form. This first appears in the shell vaults that roof the main volumes in the Kita-Kyūshū Municipal Library of 1975 and in the Fujimi Country Clubhouse in Ōita of 1974. Like the Gunma Museum, the Kita-Kyūshū Library and the Fujimi Country Clubhouse were representative works, comparable in their civic deportment to the finest public buildings of Tange. This technocratic-tectonic line comes to an abrupt end in Isozaki's career with the highly eclectic and atectonic Tsukuba Civic Center, completed in 1983, wherein rusticated fragments find themselves mixed up with the silver remains of Isozaki's abandoned "twilight-gloom" manner.

Nothing could be further from Isozaki's aestheticized nihilism than Maki's faith in tectonic reason. In his commitment to the possibility of evolving rational urban forms, Maki is unique among the Japanese architects of his generation. From his earliest ideas of "collective form" to the staged realization of his Hillside Terrace Housing Complex, built in Tokyo in three phases over an eleven-year period, Maki's position stands in strong contrast to the negative thought of the Japanese New Wave. His work is all the more challenging for its refusal to become enslaved either by the master-planning illusions of the West or by the aestheticized nihilism of the East.

Maki's urbanism is linked to the traditional concept of *oku*, wherein the conceptual space field is seen as receding toward a distant sacred object such as a shrine or a temple situated in the mountains. As Maki concedes, it is unclear to what degree *oku* may be consciously cultivated in the present; nonetheless, he goes on to state: "The history of Japanese cities eloquently teaches us that the desirable qualities of space are to be found not only in its expanse but also in the creation of depth." [17]

Maki's personal maturity as an architect comes with two related works of exceptional refinement dating from the late 1970s. These are his own house, built in Tokyo in 1978, and the Iwasaki Art Museum (fig. 14), completed at Ibusenki, Kyushu, in the following year. Both of these structures display, more decisively than other buildings by Maki, the underlying tension in his work between a drive toward monumental symbolic form and a penchant for informal expressiveness. Apart from the Fujisawa Municipal Gymnasium (1984), few works from Maki's career can compare with the diminutive lightness and elegance of his own house, a work in which subtle symmetries are introduced into an otherwise unsymmetrical plan. In these instances, a dynamic informality is redressed by the form of a centering device that in the Iwasaki assumes the form of a symbolic cruciform in welded steel. On the other hand, like Isozaki's Sports Hall for the 1992 Olympics, Maki's Fujisawa Gymnasium represents something of a return to the high tectonic manner of Tange in his prime: that is, to the structurally expressive style of his buildings for the Tokyo Olympics.

Born in 1936 and educated at Tokyo University, Hiroshi Hara is the eldest of the Japanese New Wave architects and the one who has been perhaps the least influenced by the Isozaki generation. While he has been just as committed as Ito and Ando to an architecture of resistance, the singularity of his approach is indicative of his independence. Indeed, if there are any discernible influences on Hara's work and thought, they seem to lie outside of Japan in the Structuralist approach advanced by van Eyck and his followers. Even then, the influence is on the level of thought rather than style, as is clear from Hara's statement of 1978, "Anti-Traditional Architectural Contrivance":

Modernization has made it difficult to maintain architectural openness firstly because population increase, urban migration, and the centralization of cities have resulted in higher densities and an acute shortage of land. Given that the existence of a common environment is a prerequisite for the condition of 'openness,' architectural extension has become virtually impossible. Secondly, modernization has also brought about a change in human relationships themselves. The traditional neighborhood atmosphere has been destroyed.

To design an open architectural environment today, it would necessarily have unsatisfactory qualities because it would be too 'interactive.' Aspects such as 'noise' necessarily increase the degree of control which has to be exercised in such an environment. . . .

Scope for cultural reconstruction, therefore, lies in countering the openness of traditional architecture. The image of a closed architecture is favored by the discontinuous layouts, as opposed to the continuous ones of open-architecture. [18]

(Overleaf) Figure 13. Gunma Prefectural Museum of Fine Arts, Takasaki, Japan, by Arata Isozaki.

Figure 14. Iwasaki Art Museum,
Ibusenki, Kyushu, Japan, by
Fumihiko Maki.

While Hara's trans-historical analysis of the sociocultural connotations of "open" versus "closed" architecture serves to justify his own
introspective preferences, particularly with regard to the design of domestic environments, it also supports his conception of the dwelling as
having a reciprocal, almost compensatory, relationship with the chaotic
vastness of the modern city. And while his earliest works—the Itoh
house of 1967 in Tokyo and the Keisho Kindergarten in Machida City
of 1968—are quasi-expressionistic exercises displaying close affinities
with a self-consciously evoked "universal" vernacular, his Awazu House
of 1972 and his own Hara House of 1974 were each treated as Lil-
liputian micro-urban realms.

Like Hara, Toyo Ito takes an introverted approach to the modern
megalopolis, regarding it as though it were delirious nature, devoid of
sense. Within this context, he sees the sole chance for signification as
the insertion of a poetic domain within the randomness of the "non-
place urban realm." Ito's PMT Building, Nagoya, of 1978, consists of
structural intervention conceived as an artificial high-tech membrane.
This critically aesthetic intention is evident from Ito's essay "Collage
and Superficiality in Architecture" (1978), in which he wrote:

48

. . . Most Japanese cities are not structured according to clear physical patterns such as grids or radiating networks. Therefore, we do not comprehend urban space through pattern but rather through collage or the empirical composition of symbols discontinuously scattered about. The architectural *mélange* of the typical Japanese city consists of traditional wooden architecture, stylistic architecture imported from Europe and modern architecture brought from the United States. Big cities such as Tokyo have been growing as a complex of architectural symbols derived from various periods and places. When we walk about these bustling streets, we are wrapped in a membrane consisting of these icons. The incessant change and rapid development through which Japanese cities have passed have favored lightness, superficiality and disorder. The heavy and ordered harmony to be found in European cities is entirely absent. Surface richness in a Japanese city does not consist of a historical accumulation of buildings but rather arises out of a nostalgia for our lost architectural past which is indiscriminately mixed with the superficial icons of the present. Behind an endless desire for nostalgic satisfaction there resides a void without any substance. What I wish to attain in my architecture is not another nostalgic object, but rather a certain superficiality of expression in order to reveal the nature of the void hidden beneath. [19]

The climax of Ito's work to date is unquestionably his own residence (fig. 15), the so-called Silver Hut, completed in 1984 in the Nakano sub-urb of Tokyo. This house exploits standard materials and techniques—perforated metal sheet and space-frame construction—in order to project itself as a kind of found object. Influenced by Kazuo Shinohara's appraisal of the U.S. moon-landing vehicle, as a new unaesthetic Func-tionalist paradigm, Ito has returned to the anarchic attitudes of his own generation. Thus, his Silver Hut is predicated on a highly economical procedure of assembling off-the-peg standard components. This is ap-parent in the roof vault made of prefabricated diamond sections and suspended canvas sun blinds. The Silver Hut aspires to being a general proposition combining experience of the Japanese vernacular with the techniques of the late twentieth century. Through similar lightweight ad hoc assemblies, he has attempted to explore the potential of a kind of expedient, technologically oriented "nomadism."

Tadao Ando's architecture is critical in a quite different sense, in that it resists being absorbed into the consumerist landscape of the modern city. Ando employs walls in order to establish "a human zone where the individual will can develop in the midst of the standardiza-tion of the surrounding society." [20]  In his hands the wall not only excludes the surrounding urban chaos, it also serves to symbolize the relationship between man and nature, as this may be mediated by the interaction of the structure with light, wind, and water. In his "The Wall as Territorial Delineation," [21] Ando argues that the fundamen-tal ropes of architecture in both the East and the West have been effectively nullified by the advent of the universal rigid frame. He cites the salient role played by the symbolic, nonstructural post in traditional Japanese architecture, and he goes on to point out how the rhythm of the Western colonnade has been rendered equally obsolete and hence culturally inaccessible by the infinitely greater spanning capacity of the reinforced concrete frame. As far as Ando is concerned, architecture must accommodate daily life while remaining symbolic. To this end his work has always been structured about absolutes: wall versus columns, square versus circle, concrete versus glass, dark versus light, materiality versus immateriality. The essential character of his work resides finally in the interaction between these last three pairs. This is evident from the way that he uses light to transform both volume and mass, and from the way in which it changes the volume of the building, according to the hour, transforming dark into light and ponderous mass into scintillating surface.

It is no accident that Ando, who is one of the most regionally con-scious architects in Japan, should be based at Ōsaka rather than Tokyo, and that his theoretical writings should formulate more clearly than any other architect of his generation a set of precepts which comes close to the idea of Critical Regionalism. This is most evident in the tension he perceives between universal modernization and the idiosyncrasy of rooted culture. Thus, we find him writing an essay entitled "From Self-Enclosed Modern Architecture toward Universality":

> Born and bred in Japan, I do my architectural work here. And I suppose it would be possible to say that the method I have selected is to apply the vocabulary and techniques developed by an open, universalist Modernism in an enclosed realm of individual life styles and regional differentiation. But it seems difficult to me to attempt to express the sensibilities, customs, aesthetic awareness, distinctive culture, and social traditions of a given race by means of the open internationalist vocabulary of Modernism. [22]

By "enclosed Modern Architecture" Ando intends the literal creation of walled enclaves by virtue of which man is able to recover and sustain some vestige of his former intimacy with both nature and culture. Thus he writes:

> After World War II, when Japan launched on a course of rapid economic growth, the people's value criteria changed. The old, fundamentally feudal family system collapsed. Such social alterations as concentration of information and places of work in cities led to overpopulation of agricultural and fishing villages and towns (as was probably true in other parts of the world as well). Overly dense urban and suburban populations made it impossible to preserve a feature that was formerly most characteristic of Japanese residential architecture: intimate connection with nature and openness to the natural world. What I refer to as enclosed Modern Architecture is a restoration of the unity between house and nature that Japanese houses have lost in the process of modernization. [23]

In his small courtyard houses, often set within dense urban fabric, Ando employs concrete in such a way as to stress the taut homogeneity of its surface rather than its weight, since for him it is the most suitable material "for realizing spaces created by rays of sunlight . . . [where] walls become abstract, are negated, and approach the ultimate limit of space. Their actuality is lost, and only the space they enclose gives a sense of really existing." [24] While the cardinal importance of light is stressed in theoretical writings of both Kahn and Le Corbusier, Ando sees the paradox of spatial limpidity emerging out of light as being peculiarly pertinent to the Japanese character, and with this he makes explicit the broader meaning he attributes to the concept of a self-enclosed modernity:

> Spaces of this kind are overlooked in utilitarian affairs of everyday and rarely make themselves known. Still they are capable of stimulating

(Overleaf) Figure 15. Siver Hut (architect's residence, interior), in the Nakano suburb of Tokyo, by Toyo Ito.

recollection of their own innermost forms and of stimulating new discoveries. This is the aim of what I call closed modern architecture. Architecture of this kind is likely to alter with the region in which it sends out roots and to grow in various distinctive individual ways. Still, though closed, I feel convinced that as a methodology it is open in the direction of universality. [25]

What Ando has in mind is the development of an architecture where the tactility of the work transcends the initial perception of its geometric order. Precision and density of detail are both crucial to the revelatory quality of his forms under light. Thus he wrote of his Koshino Residence of 1981:

Light changes expressions with time. I believe that the architectural materials do not end with wood and concrete that have tangible forms but go beyond to include light and wind which appeal to our senses. . . . Detail exists as the most important element in expressing identity. . . . Thus to me, the detail is an element which achieves the physical composition of architecture, but at the same time, it is a generator of an image of architecture. [26]

As one can see, the ideological range of the so-called Japanese New Wave has oscillated from one extreme to the other—from the aestheticized negativity of Isozaki to the ontological, existential position assumed by Ando. Somewhere in the intervening spectrum one would have to situate both the liberal rationalism of Maki and the anthropological structuralism of Hara. In all this, Ito emerges as the unique synthesizer, the critical poet who combines certain aspects that can be found, to varying degrees, in the work of the other four. His Silver Hut is "negative," one might say, inasmuch as it distances itself, playfully, from Ando's somber existentialism and Maki's liberalism. On the other hand, it is "positive" in its inexpensive, erector-set functionalism and its maintenance of a strict enclosure.

*Late Modernism 2: The Iberian Modern Movement, 1950–1990*

The most recent incarnation of modern architecture, in Spain, begins in 1950, although an earlier heroic phase had, of course, happened there as elsewhere, above all in Barcelona with the so-called GATEPAC (Grupo de Arquitectos y Técnicos Españoles para el Progreso de la Arquitectura Contemporánea), which, as the Spanish wing of CIAM, believed in the integration of architecture with radical programs for social reform. The membership of GATEPAC included such important figures as Torres Clave and José Luis Sert. Founded in 1929, the group was able to realize a number of modest but uncompromisingly modern structures and three major theoretical housing studies prior to the disastrous upheaval of the Spanish Civil War. The last significant gesture of this architectural avant-garde was Sert's Spanish pavilion designed for the Paris World's Fair of 1937. This pavilion was the first occasion on which Picasso's *Guernica* was exhibited; commissioned by the Republican government, the painting and the pavilion conjointly served as a public rebuke to the international betrayal of the Republican cause.

A full decade of Fascist rule elapsed before modern architecture began to reassert itself in Spain. When it did so it emerged very slowly and surely, first with Francisco Cabrero and Rafael Aburto's rationally classicist Trades Union Building, erected in Madrid in 1950, and then with José Corrales and Ramón Molezun's Spanish pavilion built for the World's Fair in Brussels of 1958. The national desire for a return to both the cultural form and the social content of the Second Republic received major ideological impetus from the "Group R," an organization founded in Barcelona in 1952. This group, led by the architects J. M. Sostres and Oriol Bohigas, found itself caught between two rival agendas. On the one hand, it was obliged to revive the Socialist anti-Fascist values and procedures of GATEPAC, and on the other, it was intensely aware of the need to arrive at a more realistic and less doctrinaire form of architectural expression, one that would be accessible to the general populace. This double-headed program was first announced by Bohigas in his essay "Possibilities for a Barcelona Architecture," published in 1951.

The career of the Barcelona architect J. A. Coderch was typically Regionalist in this regard, inasmuch as it ranged from the direct evocation of a traditional brick vernacular, much in the late manner of the Finnish master Alvar Aalto (1898–1976)—see Coderch's brick-faced ISM apartment block built in the Paseo Nacional in 1951—to the pseudo-Neo-Plastic white rendered composition of his Casa Catasus built at Sitges in 1956.

Despite the ideological activity of the Catalan school, above all their critical magazine, *Arquitecturas-Bis,* the solid core of the post-Franco Modern Movement is largely grounded in the canonical works of four Madrilenian architects: Alejandro de la Sota's Governor's Building in Tarragona of 1957, Francisco Javier Sáenz de Oiza's Torres Blancas apartment building, completed in the suburbs of Madrid in 1968, Fernando Higueras's Munoz house built in Torrelodones in 1956, and last but not least, the organic Aaltoesque forms of Antonio Fernandez Alba's El Rollo Convent, erected in Salamanca in 1962.

The full range of the late modern eclecticism pursued in Spain over the last thirty years may be aptly characterized by these works, although the eclecticism in question does not involve the same level of stylistic repetition that one normally associates with the term. The Spaniards have synthesized the canonical works of the second generation of modern masters, Utzon, Aalto, Terragni, etc., as a way of transforming their own tectonic traditions. Their kind of creative synthesis is nowhere more evident than in Alba's El Rolla Convent, where an Aalto *parti* is mediated by more monumental masonry drawn from the work of Kahn. At the same time, this particular conjunction finds itself enriched by the time-honored Spanish tradition: a particular kind of local brick, the use of Spanish tiles, etc. That accounts for the solemnity of the exterior stonework and the crenelated effect of the tile capping to the stepped perimeter.

The work of Sáenz de Oiza has an equally organic origin, as we may judge from the decidedly Wrightian, clustered, cylindrical towers and balconies that make up the mass form of the Torres Blancas. Still indebted to the later Wright, but also influenced by the technical rationalism of the Neo-Miesian school, Sáenz de Oiza's Banco de Bilbao (fig. 16), built in Madrid in 1972–80, is an elegant freestanding office tower faced in pre-rusted, rustproof steel. It represents a level of refinement rarely attained in comparable American office development.

The most sophisticated of the Madrid architects to come to their maturity in the late fifties is undoubtedly de la Sota, above all for his Tarragona government building and for his Colegio Maravillas Gymnasium, Madrid, of 1962. However, in this instance, the primary references are Rationalist and Constructivist rather than organic. Thus, where the canonical works of Terragni and Mies find themselves reinterpreted in the Governor's Building in Tarragona, the Maravillas Gymnasium seems to derive its form from the early Soviet Constructivists and from the work of French metal fabricator Prouvé. Something of Aalto's is perhaps also present in the understated industrial manner employed for the main street elevations.

One of the prime pupils of Sáenz de Oiza has been José Rafael Moneo who, after the brief apprenticeship that he served with Utzon in Denmark in the early sixties, returned to Madrid to set up his own practice and to teach. Until recently his work has displayed a strong Scandinavian influence, in part stemming from Utzon, in part deriving from Aalto and Gunnar Asplund.

Where Moneo's first realized work, a factory in Zaragoza, was patently indebted to Utzon, his masterly Bankinter (with Ramón Bescós), completed in Madrid in 1975, is based on a synthesis of Nordic and American traditions. His description of this building reveals a good deal, not only about the subtlety of his own attitude, but also about the critical maturity of Spanish contemporary architecture taken as a whole:

> Bankinter . . . rises upon a site in the Castellana, one of the streets with
> most character in Madrid, next to a small, eighteenth-century palace
> of delicate workmanship. Its restricted size shows the respect involved
> in its planning as an unobtrusive background against which the palace
> would assume greater importance . . . [However] it must, then, be clear
> that . . . the influence of the setting to which the work of architecture is

(Opposite) Figure 16. Banco de Bilbao, Madrid, by Sáenz de Oiza.

subject—do[es] not prevent the appearance of those disciplinary procedures on which ultimately depend the formal structure of the object.

In Bankinter some of these principles are well known . . . the
emphasis placed on proportion, the interest shown in the definition of
the various elements, the consideration for the construction, and the
desire to give due value to the different materials . . . in Bankinter
I have not, I hope, fallen into the temptation of concentrating on
separate parts. [27]

This exemplary combination of contextual sensitivity and tectonic
rigor will be repeated by Moneo on an even more monumental and
ambitious scale in his museum for Roman antiquities, built in Mérida in
1978–84. This is a work of such synthetic complexity that it is hardly
possible to trace the origins in its forms, although in more general terms
it is simultaneously indebted both to the nineteenth-century warehouse
tradition and to antique Roman brick construction, and even to memories of medieval urban form. With regard to the last, one may even
claim that this blank, brick, buttressed massing serves to compensate, as
it were, for the medieval core that Mérida never had.

Respect for topography, tectonic form, and differentiation of material are three salient characteristics that are invariably found in the best
of recent Spanish architecture. These qualities are repeatedly inflected
to different degrees in the works of many contemporary Spanish architects, ranging from Helio Pinon and Albert Viaplana's Sants Station
Plaza, Barcelona, of 1983 to Esteve Bonell Costa and Francesc Rius
Camps's Velodrome, Barcelona, of 1984. A comparable tectonic and
topographical intensity links works as diverse as an exposed-timber
shelter erected on a mountain site near Madrid in 1979 to the designs
of Javier Velles, or the small house built by Pep Llinas at Bagur, near
Gerona, in 1980. In both instances what counts is the precise layering
of the spatial volumes involved, the exactitude of the constructional
logic, the delicate articulation of the joints, and last but not least, the
integration of the entire work into the topography.

Throughout the past fifteen years Spanish architects have designed
remarkable public spaces, of which Luis Pena Ganchegui's El Peine del
Viento Concourse at San Sebastián of 1977 is perhaps the most exemplary. Here we have one of the very few instances of a successful recent
collaboration between a sculptor and an architect, since the entire plaza
has been designed as a setting for Eduardo Chillida's monumental
sculpture *Wind Combs.*

Clearly, the overall scope of the Spanish civic achievement transcends
this uniquely artistic work. It is found on an everyday basis in many
public works both large and small, ranging from Elias Torres's Mora
d'Ebre hospital of 1987 to the model middle-class housing known by
the name Las Cocheras, realized in the Sarria district of Barcelona in
1968 to the designs of Coderch.

Spain has virtually rebuilt itself since the late fifties; there are hardly any building types that Spanish architects have not tackled over the past three decades, with the result that Spain is virtually the only developed country today that is able to display a total catalog of exemplary modern building types. This achievement represents a building culture in which "star" architects are of much less consequence than the fact that the entire society displays a capacity to build works of exceptional quality. Style per se is of less importance in Spain than the fact that the works are resolved at an uncommonly high technical and material level. This, together with the sophisticated and intelligent articulation of the social brief, seems to be able to transcend building culture while still remaining "stylish."

Naturally, Iberian building culture is not limited solely to the activities of the late Spanish Modern Movement, a fact to which the recent work of the School of Porto bears adequate testimony. The primary representative of this school as a critical architect is the Portuguese Alvaro Siza Vieira, whose career began with a small swimming pool, the so-called Quinta da Conceição, Matosinhos (1958–65), conceived as a public "temenos" bounded by walls and set within the confines of a lush nineteenth-century park. Nothing could be further from the deceptive imagery of so-called Post-Modern architecture than the tactile unphotogenic delicacy of this work.

Thus, Siza makes us aware through his critical practice that building is to a large degree contingent, that any construction is topographically and temporally predetermined, and that all one can do is to modify the fabric of the moment as it lies suspended between one historical instant and the next. He has perhaps never expressed this Heraclitian, existential insight more laconically than in his prose-poem of May 1979, entitled "To catch a Precise Moment of the Flittering Image in All its Shades."

> Most of my works were never fulfilled; some of the things I did were carried out only in part, others were profoundly changed or destroyed.
> That's only to be expected.

> An architectonic proposition, whose aim it is to go deep into the existing transforming trends, into the clashes and strains that make up reality . . . can't follow a linear evolution.

> Nevertheless, and for the same reason, that proposition can't be ambiguous, neither can it restrain itself to a disciplinary discourse, however sure it seems to be. . . .

> That may be the reason why only marginal works . . . have been kept as they were originally designed. . . .

> But something remains. Pieces are kept here and there, inside ourselves, perhaps gathered by someone, leaving marks on space and on people, melting in a process of total transformation. [28]

For Siza, the notion of transformation in architecture implies a wide and complex field of action. The scope of this action passes from the circumstantial (and hence organic) modification of rational-schematic types, as these are inherited, to the subsequent physical transformation of an actual urban or rural context through a specific intervention.

This concept of transformation is only too evident in the Alcino Cardoso house that Siza built in the Village of Moledo do Minho, Portugal, in 1971. Here he demonstrated for the first time his peculiar facility for revitalizing old fabric through a new original work. Thus, the agrarian rustic spirit of this old viticulture building remains virtually undisturbed, while it is, at the same time, totally transformed from its former year-round peasant occupation to its current use as a weekend house for a middle-class family. The key to its success lies mainly in the character of the low wing that has been added, at a sunken level, so as to maintain the original mass form of the complex as it was. The new and the ruined are thus seamlessly combined, and it is only through the reuse of traditional stone supports for the pergolas, as the pillars for a portico to the swimming pool, that a sense of conscious artistry becomes evident. Siza's resistance to any vulgar transformation of the site is evident in his successful fight against a proposal to widen the existing access road and to replace the old and barren vines with orange trees.

This hypersensitivity to the transformation of a fluid and yet specific reality renders Siza's work more layered and rooted than the scenic tendencies of the Barcelona school. By taking Aalto as his point of departure, Siza has grounded his buildings in the configuration of a specific topography and in the fine-grained texture of the local fabric. To this end, his pieces are tight responses to the urban land- and seascape of the Porto region. Other important factors are his deference toward local material, craftwork, and the subtleties of local light, a deference which is sustained without falling into the sentimentality of excluding rational form and modern technique. His approach is patently tactile and tectonic, rather than visual and graphic, from his Beires House built at Povoa do Varzim (1973–76) to his Bouça Residents' Association Housing in Porto (1973–77). Even his small urban buildings, of which the best is probably the Pinto e Sotto Maior Bank built at Oliveira de Azemeis in 1974, are topographically structured.

## Conclusion: Late Modernism: Regionalism versus Revivalism

The potential of both Regionalism and Rationalism to degenerate into Revivalism is brought out by the all-too-worldly success of the Catalan architect Ricardo Bofill, who passed rather lightly from the modern Catalan brick aesthetic he had inherited, so to speak, from the critical

Aaltoesque work of Coderch, to embrace the vagaries of monumental Neoclassical pastiche. We find these, say, in his so-called Les Espaces d'Abraxas apartment building (fig. 17) erected in Marne-la-Vallée, near Paris, in 1983, a work in which the escape stairs, half-housed in glass, are treated as though they are the surrogate columns of a hypothetically Classical facade. It is all too evident how a totally different ideology separates the early from the later work of Bofill's studio, the so-called Taller de Arquitectura, the style of which has degenerated over the years, despite its enduring commitment to the creation of public urban form. Thus, a whole world distinguishes the poetic organicism of Walden 7 (1970–75)—Bofill's would-be housing collective on the outskirts of Barcelona—(or the equally organic expression adopted nearby in the housing of Bofill's studio within the silos of a disused cement works) from the latent Classicism already evident in his residential quarter known as Les Arcades du Lac, in the new town of St. Quentin-en-Yvelines, France, constructed during the latter half of the 1970s.

Over the last decade, this incipient pseudoclassical revival has become a dominant mode, particularly in Anglo-American countries, where modern culture as a whole has been always less able to exercise a decisive hold over the received ideology of the society.

The general rise of a reactionary anti-modern position, from both a cultural and a political standpoint—the so-called New Conservatism—feeds directly into the current Classical Revival in architecture that first manifested itself in England, with the second National Gallery competition of 1985–86 won, significantly enough, by the American Robert Venturi, and with the public tirade that Prince Charles launched against modern architecture in the previous year.

Over the last six years, Classical Revivalism has made itself felt at many different levels, in one-shot private country houses, in Neo-Beaux Arts axial landscape design, and most forcibly perhaps in late multinational, capitalist downtown development. Here we can see its presence only too clearly, not only in fragmentary one-shot high-rise buildings, but also in the paradigms of global exurban expansion that we now encounter in Battery Park City, New York City (fig. 18), or in the Canary Wharf district of London. In each instance, the architecture has been reduced to a kind of skin-deep, "classical" packaging of the Productivist Neo-Miesian high-rise plan type of the 1950s. We are witness to a moment in which dressed stone revetment covers over the minimalist, curtain-walled silence of technocratic skyscraper form; a kind of "white noise" of pseudoclassical moldings and elaborate pinnacled tops serves to both mask and market the product as if it were nothing but one more giant commodity. The intention is to overcome universal megalopolitan alienation through gigantic Biedermeier illusion representing the fictitious continuity of bourgeois culture. These buildings arise out of a pretense that nothing has really happened to disturb the evidently

Figure 17. Les Espaces
d'Abraxas apartment
building, Marne-la-Vallée,
near Paris, by Ricardo Bofill.

fragile security of the bourgeois world as this was last asserted with true confidence at the beginning of this century—the brief triumph of Western Imperialism before the apocalyptic disaster of the first fully industrialized global war. In America this moment was personified in the state capitals of the last decade of the nineteenth century, and in the White City as imagined by Daniel Burnham in his Plan of Chicago under the direction of the Commercial Club, published in 1909. To return to these images contributes nothing whatever to the stability of our own historical moment, and to evoke the general possibility of recovering this lost ideal is a deceptive and meretricious fiction.

It is an irony of recent history that contemporary Revivalism seems to manifest itself only in terms of the Classical tradition, as opposed to the Gothic Revivalism of the last half of the nineteenth century and the first decade of this one. The differences between these two "revivalist" moments, separated by over half a century, is not without ideological significance. Thus we find that the English Gothic Revival, as a fore-runner of the socialist Arts and Crafts Movement, was a critical position that was as antithetical to industrialization as it was hostile to the representative "classical" style of imperial power. However, these latent sociopolitical implications were by no means the only issue attending the nineteenth-century "battle of styles," for evidently a style always has a

Figure 18. Two views of Battery Park City, New York City. (Below) World Financial Center, by Cesar Pelli & Associates. (Opposite) Artist Ned Smyth's colonnaded court installation, "The Upper Room," in the esplanade of Battery Park City.

direct effect on the intrinsic quality of the architecture. Obviously, a given syntax will permit certain spatial relations and not others. Thus, it is a characteristic of the Arts and Crafts and its organic legacy that its irregular additive format favored more inflected forms of spatial assembly, ones that were more responsive to the needs of evolving liberative institutions than those volumetric sequences normally afforded by the axial rigidities of classical form. Descending as a tradition from the Arts and Crafts through Wright and Aalto, this is still basically the same critical, organic line to which Critical Regionalism has made frequent recourse during its development.

Be that as it may, it has to be recognized that the current revival of classical language in architecture represents some sort of reaction against the seeming bankruptcy of abstract modern form, just as the return to figurative elements in recent painting directly expresses the exhaustion of the avant-gardist line in modern art. However, as the wide range of expression now covered by fine art would indicate, in this hyperpluralist situation no particular ideological standpoint seems to have any priority over any other, or at least not for any length of time. We are brought to confront the extremely disturbing fact that all cultural forms tend to become distracting aesthetic commodities rather than manifestations of lasting value. This is ever more the case, the more cultural form becomes divorced from spiritual content, or the more it is removed from any collectively held values. Once it is denied the underpinning of ethical value or sociopolitical commitment, architecture tends to be reduced to these basic alternatives: either to the "silent" economically maximized expression of techno-scientific instrumentality, that is to say, Productivism, or to emerge as an aestheticized version of the same. In this regard the current Classical Revival may be seen as a mildly effective and reassuring mask. That there is nothing of significance lying behind this mask save for an instrumental shell is all too evident.

In my view, a locally inflected culture of form offers one of the few ways of escaping from this impasse, particularly for architecture, since architecture is a public art by definition. However, the preconditions for such a development are not so readily available, for these depend in their turn on the evolution of decentralized forms of sociopolitical autonomy, and on the maintenance of a dialectic between the received values of the technological civilization and the more fundamental ethical values of rooted cultural identity. The architectural production of the Iberian Peninsula would seem to be exemplary from this point of view. It is surely no accident that the collective strength of this work is due in some measure to the current devolution of power in Spain, although we have also to bear in mind the evident economic prosperity of the society and the fact that the values of the vestigial "city-state" still remain as a nexus of identity and political independence. Perhaps these, in the last analysis, are the preconditions, without which architectural culture of quality and depth cannot be sustained for long. Good architecture depends as much upon the quality of the clients as on the architect, and where the former, as a society, is either degenerative or culturally underdeveloped, work of enduring quality can hardly be achieved.

---

1. Louis I. Kahn, "Towards a Plan for Midtown Philadelphia," *Perspecta* 2 (1953), p. 23.

2. Romaldo Giurgola and Jaimini Mehta, *Louis I. Kahn* (Boulder, Colo.: Westview Press, 1975), p. 224.

3. From an interview with H. P. Daniel van Ginkel, "The Animal World," *Arts Canada* (Spring 1961), as reproduced in *What Will Be Has Always Been: The Words of Louis I. Kahn*, ed. Richard S. Wurman (New York: Access Press, 1986).

4. *Louis I. Kahn*, p. 187.

5. Maria Antonietta Crippa, *Carlo Scarpa: Theory, Design, Projects* (Cambridge, Mass.: MIT Press, 1986), pp. 131, 132, 149.

6. In *Carlo Scarpa: The Complete Works*, ed. Francesco Dal Co and Giuseppe Mazzariol (New York: Rizzoli International Publishers, 1985), p. 283.

7. Paolo Portoghesi, "Carlo Scarpa," *Global Architecture* (Tokyo) 50 (1979).

8. Hannah Arendt, *The Human Condition* (Chicago: University of Chicago Press, 1958).

9. Charles Jencks, *The Language of Post-Modern Architecture* (New York: Rizzoli International Publishers, 1977; 4th ed., 1984).

10. Ibid., p. 125.

11. As quoted in *Contemporary Architects*, ed. Ann Lee Morgan and Colin Naylor (Chicago and London: St. James Press, 1987), p. 291.

12. In Paul Ricoeur, *History and Truth* (Evanston, Ill.: Northwestern University Press, 1965), pp. 271–84.

13. *Zodiac* 10 (1962), pp. 112–14.

14. Emilio Ambasz, *The Architecture of Luis Barragán* (New York: Museum of Modern Art; Boston: distributed by New York Graphic Society, c. 1976). p. 9.

15. Clive Bamford Smith, *Builders in the Sun: Five Mexican Architects* (New York: Architectural Book Publishing Company, 1967), p. 74.

16. Raleigh, N.C., Student Publication, XIV, no. 5.

17. Fumihiko Maki, "Japanese City Spaces and the Concept of Oku," *The Japan Architect* 265 (May 1979), pp. 50–62.

18. In *A New Wave of Japanese Architecture,* ed. Kenneth Frampton (New York: Institute for Architecture and Urban Studies, 1978), p. 38.

19. Ibid., p. 68.

20. Tadao Ando, "New Relations Between Spaces and the Person," *Japan Architect* 254 (June 1978), p. 13.

21. Ibid. pp. 12–13.

22. *Japan Architect* 301 (May 1962), p. 8.

23. Ibid., p. 9.

24. Ibid., p. 12.

25. Ibid.

26. Tadao Ando, "Koshino Residence," *Space Design* (June 1981), p. 15.

27. *Contemporary Architects,* p. 608.

28. Ibid., p. 845.

# Gender and Science: 1990

## Evelyn Fox Keller

Evelyn Fox Keller received her doctorate in theoretical physics from Harvard University with a dissertation in molecular biology. She then devoted the next decade to research in mathematical biology. In the mid-1970s her interests turned to questions in the history, philosophy, and sociology of science. She is currently a professor in the departments of women's studies and of rhetoric at the University of California at Berkeley.

Professor Keller is best known for two books, *A Feeling for the Organism: The Life and Work of Barbara McClintock* (1983) and *Reflections on Gender and Science* (1985), as well as numerous articles in theoretical physics, molecular and mathematical biology, feminist theory, history of twentieth-century biology, and the philosophy of evolutionary biology. She has received numerous awards and fellowships, including the Radcliffe Graduate Medal, a Rockefeller Humanities Fellowship, and an Institute for Advanced Studies Fellowship. When not working, her interests turn to family, friends, music, and the California landscape.

## I. Introduction

### a. The meaning of gender

Schemes for classifying human beings are necessarily multiple and highly variable. Different cultures identify and privilege different criteria in sorting people of their own and other cultures into groups: They may stress size, age, color, occupation, wealth, sanctity, wisdom, or a host of other demarcators. All cultures, however, sort at least many of the human beings that inhabit that culture by sex. What are taken to be the principal indicators of sexual difference as well as the particular importance attributed to this difference undoubtedly vary, but, for obvious reasons, people everywhere engage in the basic act of distinguishing people they call male from those they call female. And for the most part, they even agree about who gets called what. Give or take a few marginal cases, these basic acts of categorization do exhibit, at least when applied to adult human beings of reproductive age, conspicuous cross-cultural consensus: different cultures will sort any given collection of such people into the same two groups. For this reason, we tend to say that there is at least a minimal sense of the term *sex* that denotes categories given to us by nature. [1] One might even say that the universal importance of the reproductive consequences of sexual difference gives rise to as universal a preoccupation with the meaning of this difference.

But for all the cross-cultural consensus we may find around such a minimalist classification, we find equally remarkable cultural variability in what people have made and continue to make of this demarcation; in the significance which they attribute to it; in the properties it connotes; in the role it plays in ordering the human world beyond the immediate spheres of biological reproduction; even in the role it plays in ordering the nonhuman world. It was to underscore this cultural variability that American feminists of the 1970s introduced the distinction between sex and gender, claiming the term *gender* to denote the meaning of "masculinity" and "femininity" a given culture attaches to the categories of male and female. [2]

The initial intent behind this distinction was to highlight the importance of nonbiological (i.e., social and cultural) factors shaping the development of adult men and women, to emphasize the truth of Simone de Beauvoir's famous dictum, "One is not born, but rather becomes, a woman." Its function was to facilitate a shift in attention away from the time-honored and perhaps even ubiquitous question of the meaning of sexual difference (i.e., the meanings of masculine and feminine), to the question of how such meanings are constructed. In Donna Haraway's words, "Gender is a concept developed to contest the naturalization of sexual difference." [3]

Very quickly, however, feminists came to see, and, as quickly began to exploit, the considerably larger range of analytic functions that this multipotent category is able to serve. From an original focus on gender as a cultural norm guiding the psychosocial development of individual men and women, the attention of feminists soon turned to gender as a cultural structure organizing social (and sexual) relations between men and women, [4] and finally, to gender as the basis of a sexual division of cognitive and emotional labor that removes women, their work, and the values associated with that work from culturally normative delineations of categories intended as "human": e.g., objectivity, morality, citizenship, power, often even, "human nature" itself. [5] From this perspective, gender and gender norms come to be seen as silent organizers of the mental and discursive maps of the social and natural worlds we simultaneously inhabit and construct—*even of those worlds that women never enter.* [6]

This double shift—first, from sex to gender, and second, from the force of gender in shaping the development of adult men and women to its force in delineating the cultural maps of the social and natural worlds these adults inhabit—constitutes the hallmark of contemporary feminist theory. Beginning in the mid-1970s, feminist historians, literary critics, sociologists, political scientists, psychologists, philosophers, and soon, natural scientists as well, sought to supplement earlier feminist thought with an enlarged analysis of the ways in which privately held and publicly shared ideas about gender have shaped the underlying assumptions and operant categories in each of these fields. I have myself described contemporary feminist theory as

> a form of attention, a lens that brings into focus a particular question:
> What does it mean to describe one aspect of human experience as male
> and another female? How do such labels affect the ways in which we
> structure our experiential world, assign value to its different domains,
> and in turn, acculturate and value actual men and women? [7]

With such questions as these, feminist scholars initiated an intensive investigation of the traces of gender labels evident in many of the fundamental assumptions underlying traditional academic disciplines. While their earliest efforts were confined to the humanities and social sciences, by the late 1970s the lens of feminist inquiry had extended to the natural sciences as well. Those assumptions that posited a dichotomous (and hierarchical) structure tacitly modeled on the prior assumption of a dichotomous (and hierarchical) relation between male and female—e.g., public/private; political/personal; reason/feeling; justice/care; objective/subjective; power/love; and so on—came under particular scrutiny. The object of this endeavor was not to reverse the conventional ordering of these relations, but to undermine the relations themselves—to expose to radical critique a worldview that deploys categories of gender to rend the fabric of human life and thought into a multiplicity of mutually sanctioning, mutually supportive, and mutually defining binary oppositions.

### b. Feminism and science

The inclusion of the natural sciences under this broad analytic net posed special opportunities, special difficulties, and special dangers, each of which requires special noting. On the one hand, the presence of gender markings in the root categories of the natural sciences (e.g., mind and nature; reason and feeling; objective and subjective) is, if anything, more conspicuous than in the humanities and social science. At the same time, the central claim of the natural sciences is precisely to a methodology that transcends human particularity, that bears no imprint of individual or collective authorship. As Georg Simmel put it, more than sixty years ago,

> The requirements of . . . correctness in practical judgments and
> objectivity in theoretical knowledge . . . belong as it were in their form
> and their claims to humanity in general, but in their actual historical
> configuration they are masculine throughout. Supposing that we describe
> these things, viewed as absolute ideas, by the single word "objective,"
> we then find that in the history of our race the equation objective =
> masculine is a valid one. [8]

Yet Simmel's conclusion, while perhaps unobjectionable as description of a cultural history, alerts us to the particular danger that awaits a feminist critique of the natural sciences. Indeed, Simmel himself appears to have fallen into the very trap that we are seeking to expose: In failing to specify the space in which he claims "validity" for this equation as a *cultural or even ideological space,* his wording invites the reading of it as biological. By referring to its history as a "history of our race" without specifying "our race" as late-modern northern European, he tacitly elides the existence of other cultural histories (as well as other "races") and invites the very conclusion that this cultural history has sought to establish: namely, that "objectivity" really is a privileged possession of the male of the species.

The starting point for a feminist critique of the natural sciences is thus the reframing of this equation as a conundrum: How can the scientific mind be seen at one and the same time as both male and disembodied? How can thinking "objectively," i.e., thinking that is defined as outside the self, impersonal and self-detached, also be understood as "thinking like a man"?

One might suppose that, properly posed (i.e., as a conundrum), such questions have a special urgency for any woman seeking to participate in such a tradition as a scientist. But experience shows otherwise. Women scientists, it turns out, are just as capable of living with submerged contradictions as are other people. Indeed, precisely because of its historical force I would suggest that the cultural equation between "objective" and "masculine" demands of many, if not most, women scientists a quite particular effort to submerge (or deny) the normative contradiction that, for them, such an equation implies.

To take my own case as an example, before I could even *see* this equation as a conundrum in need of analysis, and not simply as a proposition subject to either truth or falsity, I needed to undergo a critical shift in consciousness, as it were acquire another identity, alongside that of a woman scientist. I needed to understand that it was not only things that could have force in the world, but also ideas, beliefs, and even words. Only then could I see the popular association of science, objectivity, and masculinity as a statement about the world that referred not to the bodily and mental capacities of individual men and women but rather to a collective consciousness; as a set of beliefs given existence in the real world not by bodies but by language, and through language granted the force to shape what individual men and women might (or might not) think and do. For me, as for a number of my contemporaries, it took the lens of feminist theory to focus my thinking about science on gender as a cultural rather than biological imperative—as a set of ideas capable of exerting force in their own right, and in their own space, i.e., in the space of ideology and culture.

But this was just a first step. An effective analysis of the role of gender ideals in the history of modern science requires more than a recognition of the social character (and force) of "gender." It requires, as well, recognition of the social character (and force) of the enterprise we call "science."

*c. The meaning of science*

Although people everywhere, throughout history, have sought reliable knowledge of the world around them, only certain forms of knowledge and certain procedures for acquiring such knowledge have come to count under the general rubric that we, in the late twentieth century, designate as science. Just as "masculine" and "feminine" are categories defined by a culture, and not by biological necessity, so too, "science" is the name we give to a set of practices and a body of knowledge delineated by a community. Even now, in part because of the great variety of practices that the label "science" continues to subsume, the term defies precise definition, obliging us to remain content with a conventional definition—as that which those individuals we call scientists do. Yet, despite conspicuous disciplinary and historical variations, we can nonetheless identify the broad normative dimensions of this venture in its current form—the values, goals, and assumptions that comprise the ideology of modern science; we can even trace their development from the particular upheaval we roughly identify as "the scientific revolution."

For recognition of the conventional character of modern science, feminist theorists have relied heavily on developments over the last three decades in the history, philosophy, and sociology of science. An extensive literature, initially stimulated by the publication of Thomas S. Kuhn's work on scientific revolutions in 1962, has irrevocably altered our understanding of the dynamics of scientific growth. [9] Kuhn's major contribution was to show that the transformations in the history of scientific thought which we call "revolutions" cannot be explained by the arrival of a better theory according to any purely internal criteria. "Ordinarily," he writes, "it is only much later, after the new paradigm has been developed, accepted, and exploited, that apparently decisive arguments are made." [10] Science may be progressive in the sense that the investment of scientific energy is technically productive, but the change in direction that new theories dictate, and the change in worldview they lead to, reflect not logical or empirical necessity but an admixture of scientific and extrascientific needs. The direct implication of such a claim is that, not only different collections of facts and different focal points of scientific attention, but also different organizations of knowledge and different interpretations of the world are both possible and consistent with what we call "science."

Since 1962, an enormous literature has accumulated as historians and sociologists have sought to display the extrascientific forces at work in the definition and growth of scientific knowledge. Throughout almost all of this work, however, two omissions remain notable: one is the contribution of gender, understood now as a social category, and the other, surely related, is the entire dimension of the personal.

Feminism thus makes a unique contribution to both traditional and revisionist studies of science in two respects: It not only focuses our attention on the gender basis of the division of emotional and intellectual labor assumed in traditional scientific discourse, and even in recent social studies of science; it also encourages the inclusion of concerns that have traditionally been assigned to women—not as "a woman's perspective," but as a critical instrument for examining the roots of those dichotomies that isolate such a perspective and deny its legitimacy. Feminism thus seeks to enlarge our understanding of the history, philosophy, and sociology of science through the inclusion of just those domains of human experience that have in the past been relegated to women: namely, the personal, the emotional, and the sexual.

In short, the conjunction of feminist theory and the social studies of science enables us to see that women, men, and science are created, together, out of a complex dynamic of interwoven forces. It confronts us with the task of examining the roots, dynamics, and consequences of the interacting network of associations and disjunctions that together constitute what might be called the "science-gender system." It leads us to ask how ideologies of gender and science inform each other in their mutual construction, how that construction functions in our social arrangements, and how it affects men, women, and science. From this perspective the proper subject of gender and science thus becomes the analysis of the web of forces that supports the historic conjunction of science and masculinity, and the equally historic disjunction between science and femininity. It is, in a word, the conjoint making of "men," "women," and "science," or, more precisely, how the making of "men" and "women" has affected the making of "science."

While many approaches to such a venture are both possible and necessary, [11] even a minimal analytic framework must include the following dimensions: a historical analysis of the role of gender ideals in the development of the norms and values of modern science; a psychosocial analysis of the development of men, women, and scientists in the same cultural context; and a philosophical analysis of how the norms and values of modern science affect the actual production of scientific theory. In the next section, I will illustrate the first, historical, approach with a brief discussion of the discursive politics of the "scientific revolution" in seventeenth-century England. For a discussion of the psychosocial dynamics by which the shared norms of gender and science contribute to the development of actual men and women, and to the process of selection by which some of these men and women become scientists, I refer the reader to Part II of my book on this subject. [12] Finally, in the remaining sections, I will turn to the philosophical questions (in many ways, the most difficult and the most pressing) of how the norms and values that science has absorbed from the larger culture in which it has been embedded have helped shape its growth. Here the issues far exceed the concerns of feminism, and the questions that arise are questions that have become critical for anyone currently working in the history, philosophy, or sociology of science.

## II. Gender and the origins of modern science

Central to the activity of naming science is the naming (or characterization) of the scientific knower, of that which is to be known, and of the relation between the two that is supposed as making knowledge possible. These acts of naming—of mind, nature, subject and object— inevitably structure the field of scientific inquiry in some degree of consonance with the larger social field such names (underlying images) evoke.

The first step in a feminist analysis of science is thus to call attention to the marks of gender that have been so prevalent throughout the history of scientific discourse and ask how they have functioned in the cognitive and social politics of scientific growth—to ask, in particular, how they have served to delineate and order the domains of mind and nature, reason and feeling, objectivity and subjectivity, which, once delineated and ordered, in turn helped redefine and reorder the domains of masculine and feminine.

Although the naming of material nature as female, and mind as male, was hardly new to seventeenth-century culture, these commonplace metaphors were cast in new relations—relations that fit the rhetorical needs of the founding fathers of modern science as they sought to establish a new cognitive politics in a changing world. When Henry Oldenburg wrote in 1662 that the intention of the Royal Society was "to raise a Masculine Philosophy . . . whereby the Mind of Man may be ennobled with the knowledge of Solid Truths," [13] he was on the one hand drawing on conventional understandings of "Masculine," "Mind," and "Truth," and, on the other hand, contributing to their transformation. Necessarily Oldenburg couched his appeal in language already familiar to his compatriots, thereby contributing to a larger discursive reconfiguration that was by then well under way.

In seventeenth-century England the meanings of "mind" and "knowledge," "man" and "woman," "God" and "nature," as well as the relations obtaining between these various categories, were all under contestation. The self-imposed task of the men who called themselves natural philosophers was both to describe and to prescribe a set of relations that could plausibly claim superiority to those that had obtained in the past. And in this effort the language of gender provided Oldenburg and his colleagues with a central and effectively inexhaustible metaphoric resource. To a considerable degree they were already drawing on the rhetorical accomplishments of their predecessor, Francis Bacon. In the context of Bacon's memorable prose, only a "virile" mind, properly cleansed of all traces of femininity, could effectively consummate his ideal of a "chaste and lawful marriage between Mind and Nature." [14] Bacon envisioned a "chaste, holy, and legal wedlock" with "things themselves" that promised to generate "a blessed race of Heroes and Supermen," a union uniquely capable of "leading [man] to Nature with all her children to bind her to [his] service and make her [his] slave." [15]

What was at issue for both Bacon and his successors was not the identification of nature with woman, wife, or mother, nor the identification of mind with man, husband, or father; in his time, each could be taken for granted. Rather, what was at issue was the relation *between* mind/man and nature/woman that could plausibly promise to yield the kind of knowledge/power imagined as capable of establishing man's dominion over nature, [16] a new science distinctive from that of the "sham philosophers" of old precisely by virtue of its special potency— in Bacon's own words, "A Masculine Birth in Time." Inevitably the character of mind/man and nature/woman—in short, the meanings of "mind," "nature," "masculinity," and "femininity"—were also at issue.

Where Bacon's rhetoric focused on the forms of proper marital congress between mind and nature (e.g., "constraint," "vexation," "hounding," "conquest") that would reveal nature "in her innermost chambers," fifty years later Robert Boyle could presuppose such forms and focus, instead, on the impotence of nature thus revealed. In "A Free Inquiry into the Vulgarly Received Notion of Nature," Boyle argues not only that it is "more consonant to the respect we owe to divine providence, to conceive . . . God [as] a most free, as well as wise agent . . . than to imagine, as we commonly do, that God has appointed an intelligent and powerful Being, called nature, to be as his vicegerent," but also, that his own scientific investigations show that "if there were such a thing, she must be said to act too blindly and impotently, to discharge well the part she is to be trusted with." [17] Furthermore, he adds:

> the veneration, wherewith men are imbued for what they call nature, has
> been a discouraging impediment to the empire of man over the inferior
> creatures of God: for many have . . . looked upon it . . . as something
> of impious to attempt, the removing of those boundaries, which nature
> seems to have put and settled among her productions. . . . [18]

For Boyle, science and religion conjoin to demand the recasting of "nature" as nothing more venerable than "a great pregnant automaton," [19] a machine whose works it is not only our right but our duty to examine, to emulate, and to excel.

\*       \*       \*

The many social and political factors that informed the philosophical debates attending the institutionalization of modern science in seventeenth-century England constitute a familiar subject for historians of science. But if modern science evolved in, and helped to shape, a particular social and political context, it also evolved in conjunction with, and helped to shape, a particular ideology of gender. We may have become accustomed to the equating of mind, reason, and masculinity, as well as to the dichotomization of mind and nature, reason and feeling, masculine and feminine; but seventeenth-century readers were considerably less so. These conjunctions and disjunctions were in part created by the particular discursive strategy employed by the founding fathers of modern science. And of course, the success of their discourse, in turn, attests to its consonance with concurrent transformations in the larger social, economic, and political arena.

The distinctive features of the role (and meaning) of gender in the rhetoric of men like Bacon, Boyle, and Oldenburg are cast in high relief by juxtaposing their discourse with that of their chief contenders, the Renaissance alchemists. In the decades preceding the founding of the Royal Society, natural philosophers may have been united in their enthusiasm for a "new science," but they were hardly united in their visions of what such a science might mean. Many and sundry interests and beliefs—as yet only partially sorted, and often coexisting in individual minds—might schematically be described in terms of two competing philosophies: the hermetic and the mechanical. In the hermetic tradition, material nature was suffused with spirit; its understanding accordingly required the joint and integrated effort of heart, hand, and mind. By contrast, the mechanical philosophers sought to divorce matter from spirit, and hand and mind from heart. In line with these distinctions, another stands out with prominence: where Bacon's metaphoric ideal was the virile superman, the alchemist's ideal was the hermaphrodite; where Bacon (and Boyle and Oldenburg) sought dominion over nature, the alchemists sought power through "cohabit[ing] with the elements"; [20] where Bacon appealed to conjugal chastity to advocate a disjunction between mind and nature, the alchemists, invoking the same marital metaphor, chose for their root image coition, the conjunction of mind and matter, the merging of male and female.

In hindsight, it is easy to dismiss Renaissance alchemy for its lack of "scientific" merit. But at the time, the very meaning of "scientific" was still under negotiation. If the alchemists had few tangible successes to their credit, the same must be said of the mechanical philosophers of their day. Indeed, the very terms in which the contest between these two competing schools was conducted reveals how inappropriate it may be to apply current standards retroactively. Perhaps especially revealing of the inadequacy of a contemporary perspective are seventeenth-century debates over witchcraft in which, at least in one decisive episode, certain mechanical philosophers insisted on the reality of witches, while the alchemists demurred. For the latter, all phenomena could be interpreted as a manifestation of God, while for the former, some things could only be understood as the work of the Devil: witches, through their omnivorous sexuality, provided direct testimony to Satan's ever-dangerous presence. [21]

At issue for Joseph Glanvill, a participant in this debate and also one of the chief propagandists for the Royal Society, was not simply truth versus falsity but also proper versus improper knowledge. Glanvill warned that true and pious scientists must not be tempted to pursue

Barbara McClintock (b. 1902), American cytogeneticist whose researches of the forties and fifties, recognized in the award to her of the Nobel Prize (1983), reflected what her biographer, Evelyn Fox Keller, author of this essay, calls "a feeling for the organism." This sprang from her sense of nature as both generative and resourceful in its development, not as something blindly obedient to what we call scientific "laws."

the "recondite knowledge" that belongs to Satan but must "take care to keep themselves with the Bounds of sober Enquiry." [22] So too, Henry More saw the alchemists' penchant for "tumbling and trying tricks with . . . Matter" as clearly exceeding philosophical propriety. [23] In allowing a kinship between knowledge and erotic sexuality, between experimental and spiritual knowledge, alchemical science not only failed to demarcate Nature adequately; it failed to demarcate the domain of proper knowledge and, accordingly, the domain of "true" knowledge. A century earlier, Paracelsus had written that one "discovers the curative virtues of remedies" by "true love," [24] but now Glanvill wrote, "[W]here the *Will* or *Passion* hath the casting voyce, the case of *Truth* is *desparate.* . . . The *Woman* in us, still prosecutes a deceit, like that begun in the *Garden;* and our *Understandings* are wedded to an *Eve,* as fatal as the *Mother* of our *miseries.*" [25] Truth has no chance, he concludes, when "the *Affections* wear the breeches and the *Female* rules." [26]

The issues under dispute had little direct relation to the actual politics of sexual domination, but they had a great deal to do with the evaluation of what was regarded as feminine, with the appropriateness of "feminine" traits for men and, perhaps especially, with their place in the new definitions of knowledge—in short, with ideologies of gender and science. Throughout Europe, prevailing concepts of gender had been subtly shifting for over 200 years, and by the end of the seventeenth century the plasticity and fluidity of gender roles that had previously been acceptable was considerably reduced. Definitions of "masculine" and "feminine" were becoming polarized in ways that were eminently well suited to the growing division between work and home required by early industrial capitalism. A new kind of wedge was being driven between the spheres of men and women, to which the rhetoric of the scientific revolution both responded and contributed.

In accordance with the growing division between masculine and feminine, public and private, work and home, modern science opted for an ever-greater polarization of mind and nature, reason and feeling, objective and subjective; in parallel with the gradual desexualization of women, it offered a deanimated, desanctified, and increasingly mechanized conception of nature. In so doing, science itself became an active agent of change. If new criteria of rationality and objectivity, along with new aims to dominate nature, supported the growth of a particular vision of science, they also supported a new definition of manhood. Given the subsequent successes of modern science, now defined in opposition to everything female, fears of both Nature and Woman could subside. With the one reduced to its mechanical substrate, and the other to her asexual virtue, the essence of *Mater* could be tamed and conquered and the Baconian vision of masculine potency confirmed.

## III. A skeptical rejoinder

A working scientist who happened to read the preceding discussion might well shrug his or her shoulders and say, "Well, perhaps, but what does all this have to do with what scientists actually do?" All my observations so far have been about scientific (rather, about metascientific) discourse, and perhaps about subjective motivations, but not about either the practice or theoretical achievements of scientists. Such a reader might also object that, even as discourse, all my examples are dated: they only illustrate the ways in which (some) people have talked about science and nature in the past, not how they talk in the present. These points are well taken, assuming them to have been made in fact, and they need to be addressed.

The second objection can be addressed with relative ease. While it may be true that the prevalence of gender imagery in scientific discourse has considerably abated since the seventeenth century, it has not yet, even today, disappeared. Rather, it might be said that the metaphoric structures the natural philosophers of the seventeenth century helped put in place have so permeated our contemporary world that we hardly notice them anymore. While the basic associations of nature with female, and of mind with male, have been a virtual constant of scientific culture ever since that time, they have come to be so taken for granted as to appear not at all noteworthy. Certainly, norms of gender have undergone considerable variation since the seventeenth century, and at no time have they been either uniform across differences of race and class or entirely binding for particular individuals. The meanings of terms such as *mind, nature, male, female* have been neither invariant nor binding. What matters for the history of our dominant intellectual traditions, however, is the durability, vitality, and force of the metaphoric structure in which they are coupled. The disjunctions between mind and nature, between reason and feeling, between objective and subjective, that were forged with seventeenth-century metaphors of gender are, if anything, stronger and more durable in contemporary scientific culture than they were then. Indeed, so sturdy have they now become that they may no longer need traditional tropes of sex and gender for their maintenance.

In the late twentieth century—in part as a result of contemporary feminism, and in part as a result of internal expansion—science is no longer seen as, and indeed can less and less be said to be, a world of men only. It is a world of men and women (though still mostly men, and predominantly white and middle-class at that) who display certain cognitive facilities—what until very recently we called "thinking like a man" but no longer do because such rhetoric has itself come to be recognized as discriminatory. Despite this twofold (linguistic and occupational) move toward equity, however, the questions put forth by feminist theory still stand: What have *already been* the consequences, for the development of science, of the historic exclusion of those values and human talents which that same history has relegated to the world of women? What have been the consequences of labeling scientific cognition as "thinking like a man" (over the 300 years in which such labels persisted) for the definition and practice of scientific thought? What about the kind of thinking (or whatever mental activity that phrase was intended to bracket) that, as part of their traditional cultural and material work, most women inhabiting such a cultural space perforce had learned to do?

Fifteen years ago, when feminist theorists first began to articulate such questions, the task seemed in some ways easier. To the extent that the occupational and linguistic worlds of the dominant culture were then still divided along the traditional line of sex, to the extent that science in particular remained a bastion not only of masculine virtues but also of male privilege, it seemed possible (although exceedingly problematic just because of its normative implications) to employ the term *women* to connote the values and virtues that had been excluded in their name. It was even possible, then, to hope that the demise of a gendered discourse of science would pave the way for a more human (i.e., "gender-free"), and accordingly more humane, construction of science. In the intervening years, however, it has become abundantly clear how much easier it is to integrate a few women and words than it is to respond substantively to the challenge posed by a different set of values, namely, the values of the culture these women and words necessarily had to leave behind. What was thought to be the problem has proved only to be the symptoms of it. The cure of these, partial though it is, is clearly not enough. Science shows no sign of being changed either by the inclusion of more women, or by our self-conscious attempts to remove the marks of gender from its discourse.

Does this mean that the skepticism of our hypothetical working scientist is justified? That finally (to return now to the first objection), language, the ways in which we talk *about* science and nature, is not relevant to the actual practice and theoretical achievements of science? Hardly. What the lack of change means is that our ordinary ways of speaking do not directly translate into the practice of science, any more than our conventional norms of gender are directly transferred onto the bodies of men and women. It merely underscores the necessity of another level of analysis, moving beyond the exposure of the place and rhetorical function of gender imagery in the history of modern science, to an analysis of how that imagery, along with the cultural norms it conjoins, has affected the actual cognitive and material development of science. More generally yet, it necessitates an analysis of the role of language and ideology in the day-to-day production of scientific theory and practice.

## IV. The problem of language and ideology in science

The "doing" of science is a gripping and fully absorbing activity—
so much so that it is difficult for anyone so engaged to step outside
the demands of the problems under investigation to reflect on the
assumptions underlying that investigation, much less on the language
in which such assumptions can be said to "make sense." Keeping track
of the arguments and data as they unfold, trying always to think ahead,
demands total absorption; at the same time, the sense of discovering or
even generating a new world yields an intoxication rarely paralleled in
other academic fields. The net result is that scientists are probably less
reflective of the tacit assumptions that guide their reasoning than any
other intellectuals of the modern age.

The success of their enterprise does not, at least in the short run,
seem to require such reflectiveness. [27] Some would even argue that
that very success demands abstaining from reflection upon matters that
do not lend themselves to "clear and distinct" answers. Indeed, they
might argue that what distinguishes contemporary science from the
more amateurish efforts of their seventeenth-century forebears is precisely its recognition of the dual need to avoid talk *about* science, and
to replace "ordinary" language by a technical discourse cleansed of the
ambiguity and values that burden ordinary language, as the modern
form of the scientific report requires. Let the data speak for themselves,
these scientists demand. The problem with this argument is, of course,
that data never do speak for themselves.

It is by now a near truism that all data presuppose interpretation.
And if an interpretation is to be meaningful—if the data are to be
"intelligible" to more than one person—it must be embedded in a
community of common practices, a community in which the meaning
of terms and their relation to the "objects" to which the terms point
is shared. In short, interpretation requires a common language, in science as elsewhere.

Sharing a language means sharing a conceptual universe. It means
more than knowing the "right" names by which to call things; it means
knowing the "right" syntax in which to pose claims and questions,
and even more critically it means sharing a more or less agreed-upon
understanding of what questions are legitimate to ask and what can be
accepted as meaningful answers. Every question carries with it tacit sup-
positions and expectations that limit the range of acceptable answers to
those which only a properly versed respondent will recognize. To know
what kinds of explanation "make sense," and what can be expected to
count as "accounting for," is already to be a member of a particular
language community.

But if there is one feature that distinguishes scientific from other
communities, and is special to scientific discourse, it is the assumption

that the universe scientists study is directly accessible, that the "nature" they name as object of inquiry is unmediated by language and can therefore be veridically represented. On this assumption, "laws of nature" are beyond the relativity of language—indeed, they are beyond language, encoded in logical structures that require only the discernment of reason and the confirmation of experiment. Also on this assumption, the descriptive language of science is transparent and neutral; it does not require examination.

Confidence in the transparency and neutrality of scientific language is certainly useful in enabling scientists to get on with their job; it is also wondrously effective in supporting their special claims to truth. It encourages the view that their own language is absolute and, in so doing, helps secure their disciplinary borders against criticism. Language, assumed to be transparent, becomes impervious.

Perforce, then, it falls to others, less enclosed by the demands of science's own self-understanding, to disclose the "thickness" of scientific language, to scrutinize the conventions of practice, interpretation, and shared aspirations on which the truth claims of that language depend, to expose the many forks in the road to knowledge that these very conventions have worked to obscure, and, in that process, finally, to uncover alternatives for the future.

Under careful scrutiny, the hypothesized contrast between ordinary and scientific language gives way to a recognition of disconcerting similarity. Even the most purely technical discourse turns out to depend on metaphor, on ambiguity, on instabilities of meaning—indeed, on the very commonsense understanding of terms from which a technical discourse is supposed to emancipate us. Scientific arguments cannot begin to "make sense," much less be effective, without extensive recourse to shared conventions for controlling these inevitable ambiguities and instabilities. The very term *experimental control* needs to be understood in a far larger sense than has been the custom—describing not only the control of variables but also of the ways of seeing, thinking, acting, and speaking in which an investigator must be extensively trained before he or she can become a contributing member of a discipline.

Even the conventional account scientists offer of their success has been shown by recent work in the history, philosophy, and sociology of science to be itself rooted in metaphor: The very idea of a one-to-one correspondence between theory and reality, or of scientific method as capable of revealing nature "as it is," is based on metaphors of mind as a "glassy essence," and of science as a "mirror of nature." Simple logic, however, suggests that words are far too limited a resource, in whatever combinations, to permit a faithful representation of even our own experience, much less of the vast domain of natural phenomena. [28] The metaphor of science as "mirror of nature" may be both psychologically and politically useful to scientists, but it cannot be taken to be correct. Nor can it be assumed to be particularly useful for a philosophical understanding of how science works; indeed, it has proven to be a positive barrier to our understanding of the development of science in its historical and social context. It is far more useful, and probably even more correct, to suppose, as Mary Hesse suggests, that "[s]cience is successful only because there are sufficient local and particular regularities between things in space-time domains where we can test them. These domains may be very large but it's an elementary piece of mathematics that there is an infinite gap between the largest conceivable number and infinity." [29]

In much the same sense, the idea of "laws of nature" can also be shown to be rooted in metaphor, a metaphor indelibly marked by its political and theological origins. Despite the insistence of philosophers that laws of nature are merely descriptive and not prescriptive, they are historically conceptualized as imposed from above and obeyed from below. "By those who first used the term, [laws of nature] were viewed as commands imposed by the Deity upon matter," the *O.E.D.* states, "and even writers who do not accept this view often speak of them as 'obeyed' by the phenomena, or as agents by which the phenomena are produced." [30] In this sense the metaphor of "laws of nature" carries into scientific practice the presupposition of an ontological hierarchy, ordering not only mind and matter, but theory and practice, and, of course, the normal and the aberrant. Even in the loosest (most purely descriptive) sense of the term *law*, the kinds of order in nature that laws can accommodate are restricted to those which can be expressed by the language in which laws of nature are codified. All languages are capable of describing regularity, but not all perceived, or even all describable, regularities can be expressed in the existing vocabularies of science. To assume, therefore, that all perceptible regularities can be represented by current (or even by future) theory is to impose a premature limit on what is "naturally" possible, as well as what is potentially understandable.

Nancy Cartwright has suggested that a better way to make sense of the theoretical successes of science (as well as its failures) would be to invoke the rather different metaphor of "Nature's Capacities." [31] In apparent sympathy with Hesse, as well as with a number of other contemporary historians and philosophers of science, she suggests that an understanding of the remarkable convergences between theory and experiment that scientists have produced requires attention not so much to the adequacy of the laws that are presumably being tested, but rather to the particular and highly local manipulation of theory and experimental procedure that is required to produce these convergences. Our usual talk of scientific laws, Cartwright suggests, belies (and elides) the conceptual and linguistic work that is required to ground a theory, or "law," to fit a particular set of experimental circumstances, as well as the material work required to construct an experimental apparatus to fit a theoretical claim. Scientific laws may be "true," but the question remains, what exactly are they true of? In Cartwright's account, they are true of highly contrived and local circumstances, reflecting the particular products of human workmanship at least as much as they reflect preexisting invariances of nature.

## V. Gender, language, and the "doing" of science

These philosophical revisions offer us a background against which to return to and reframe the particular concerns of this essay. Our original question about the influence of a gendered discourse on the historical development of modern science can now be reformulated as two separable questions: The first, that of the role of public and private conceptions of gender in the framing of the root metaphors of science, belongs to feminist theory proper, while the second, that of the role of such metaphors in the actual development of scientific theory and practice, belongs to a larger inquiry in the history and philosophy of science. Earlier, I sought to respond to the first question by way of historical examples of explicit appeals to conceptions of gender in the naming of science and nature. By undermining the realism and univocality of scientific discourse, the philosophical groundwork initiated by Kuhn and continued more recently by Hesse, Cartwright, and many others, now makes it possible to respond to the second question, and at least to indicate the kind of analysis that would be necessary to show how such basic acts of naming have helped to shape the actual course of scientific development, obscuring if not foreclosing other possible courses.

The most critical resource for such an inquiry is the de facto plurality of organizing metaphors, theories, and practices evident throughout the history of science. At any given moment, in any given discipline, abundant significant variability can be identified along the following four closely interdependent axes: the aims of scientific inquiry; the questions judged most significant to ask; the theoretical and experimental methodologies deemed most productive for addressing these questions; and, finally, what counts as an acceptable answer or a satisfying explanation. Different metaphors of mind, nature, and the relation between them, reflect different psychological stances of observer to observed; these, in turn, give rise to different cognitive perspectives: to different aims, questions, and even different methodological and explanatory preferences. Such variability is of course always subject to the forces of selection exerted by collective norms, yet there are many moments in scientific history in which alternative visions can survive for long enough to permit identification both of their distinctiveness and of the selective pressures against which they must struggle.

One of the clearest such instances in my own research is provided by the life and work of the cytogeneticist Barbara McClintock. McClintock offers a vision of science premised not on the domination of nature but on "a feeling for the organism." [32] For her, a "feeling for the organism" is simultaneously a state of mind and a resource for knowledge: for the day-to-day work of conducting experiments, observing and interpreting their outcomes—in short, for the "doing" of science. "Nature," to McClintock, is best understood in terms of its largesse and prodigality; accordingly, her conception of the work of science is more consonant with that of exhibiting nature's "capacities" and multiple forms of order, than with pursuing the "laws of nature." "Laws" of nature name nature as blind, obedient, and simple; at the same time, they name their maker as authoritative, generative, and complex. In contrast, I suggest that the conception of nature as "orderly," and not merely as law-bound, permits nature itself to be seen as generative and resourceful—by definition, more complex than we can either describe or prescribe. In this alternative view, nature can come to be seen, as it was by McClintock, as an active partner in a more reciprocal relation to an observer, equally active, but neither omniscient nor omnipotent.

Inevitably, such a relationship between mind and nature suggests a different style of inquiry, no less rigorous but more modest, encouraging one to "listen to what the material has to tell you," rather than assuming that scientific data are self-evident. Following the development of McClintock's research enables one to see, as well, how this quite different naming of nature organizes an entire array of procedural and methodological differences, beginning with differences in the questions she asked, leading to the privileging (and even the perception) of different kinds of data, and ending, finally, with her identification of a radically different mechanism, and principle, of genetic organization. To McClintock, the study of gene structure, and even of the mechanisms of replication and transcription, are subsidiary to questions of function and organization. Genes are neither "beads on a string" nor functionally disjoint pieces of DNA. They are organized functional units whose very function is defined by their position in the organization as a whole. Thus, an adequate understanding must include an account of how genes function in relation to the rest of the cell and, of course, to the organism as a whole. In turn, a conception of cells (or chromosomes) as organized functional units embedded in still larger functional units encourages forms of perception normally reserved for organisms like ourselves. In McClintock's style of research, intimacy and even identification with the objects of scientific research are put to productive "cognitive" use. [33]

McClintock is now widely credited with the "discovery" of genetic transposition, a process of genetic rearrangement that she saw as critical to the organism's developmental and regulatory needs. But before she could be said to have discovered this phenomenon, her mainstream colleagues, employing the different practices and speaking the different language of an increasingly alien community, needed first to concur that such a phenomenon existed.

As it happened, this concurrence took almost forty years. [34] From a historian's point of view, that lag provides an invaluable opportunity to explore the nature of the gap—linguistic, methodological, conceptual—that had impeded consensus; from the point of view of an advocate (as I freely confess to be), it is the fact of ultimate consensus that proves invaluable, that legitimates her story as a resource for us in the first place. History is strewn with dissidents and deviants, not unlike McClintock, whose erasure is readily justified by the conventional narrative of science. Without the validation of the dominant community, her particular claims and the vision of science which had guided them would, equally, be dismissed as mere "mistakes," misguided and false steps in the history of science.

It is also the case, however, that that very validation invites other kinds of misreading: The story of McClintock's life and work is neither a story of error, nor that of a lonely pioneer who was unaccountably able to see directly into nature, to grasp the truth "ahead of her time." Her accomplishments are entirely accountable in terms of the work she performed; the ultimate value of these accomplishments, however—that which we all too casually call "truth"—depended not on her special vision but on their acceptance by the community around her. The philosophical perspective employed here suggests that the arrival of that consensus cannot be understood in terms of self-evident truth claims, but rather must itself be accounted for in terms of greater or lesser convergences of language and practice. [35]

Of greatest importance for this essay, however, is the reminder that this story ought not, indeed cannot, be read as the story of a woman, attached by her sex both to nature and to the arts of "feeling" and "intuition," who, because of that attachment, was able to bring to science the missed virtues of "women's ways of knowing." The details of McClintock's actual life and work belie all three of these readings, but perhaps especially, they belie this last reading. Instead, they point to a story of diversity, multiplicity, and difference: of a woman rebelling equally against the conventions of science and the conventions of gender. The distinctive resources she brought to science were no more attached to her sex than they were to divine inspiration. They derived instead from a conception of nature and science that called upon many of the human concerns and the cognitive and emotional assets that had been historically excluded from science in the name of "masculinity," but which, by virtue of her unconventional naming of "science," "nature," and "woman," she was able to put to productive use as a working scientist. In the face of linguistic conventions that posit nature as the object of masculine prowess, and women and science as mutually exclusive categories, it may well be that McClintock had a particular (sex-based) need to reconceive the categories of "woman," "science," "mind," and "nature," a particular desire to liberate herself and her work from a history of normative constraint. In principle, however, the project and values of such a reconception are available to anyone and have, in fact, been embraced by many others, both male and female.

## VI. Conclusion

Still, the largest and most difficult question remains, and I have left it for the conclusion. McClintock's vision of science may be aesthetically and emotionally appealing, and may even have worked well for her, but her success pales before that which has accrued to the history of mainstream science, gendered though it may have been. Indeed, if I were to continue the story about transposition to the present day, I would have to admit that the principal utility of this discovery has proven to lie not in the conceptual revolution she had hoped would come, but in a domain in every way antithetical to McClintock's vision, namely, in genetic engineering. In the last few years, in part thanks to the techniques made possible by genetic transposition, it is the successes and technological prowess of molecular biology rather than of McClintock's vision of science that have captured the scientific and popular imagination. In the process, the very meaning of genetic transposition has been redefined, but against such redefinition, there appears to be little recourse: how, after all, can one argue with success?

By now, we may be well persuaded that the domain of natural phenomena is vastly larger than the domain of scientific theory as we know it, leaving ample room for alternative conceptions of science; that the accumulated body of scientific theory represents only one of the many ways in which human beings, including the human beings we call scientists, have sought to make sense of the world; even that the successes of these theories are highly local and specific. Yet, whatever philosophical accounts we might accept, the fact remains that the particular vision of science that men like Bacon helped articulate has, over the course of time, more than fulfilled Bacon's prophecies, yielding a kind and degree of power that surpasses his wildest dreams. Science as we know it works exceedingly well. The question is, can any other vision of science be reasonably expected to work as well?

Feminist studies of science share with other recent efforts in the history, philosophy, and sociology of science the task of finding a way to integrate the various influences on scientific development of social and political forces, psychological predispositions, experimental constraints, and cognitive demands. Feminist studies also share the task of accounting for the technological efficacy of science. If we can no longer appeal to the simple picture of science as a mirror of nature, if we are to acknowledge the importance of other, extrascientific factors in shaping the development of scientific theory, how then are we to account for the extraordinary degree to which such theories can be said to "work"?

One response has been to challenge the connections between formal theory and practical success that have been claimed for science. I suggest a rather different approach, requiring one further shift in our analytic focus. Until now, the primary focus of our analyses has been on science as representation, rather than as a set of tools for intervention, for materially altering the world around us. Feminist theory may have helped us to re-envision science as a discourse, but not as an agent of change. As such, it tacitly supports the dichotomy between representing and intervening, between scientific truth and its consequences, that is itself part of our scientific heritage. What is needed most urgently, I suggest, is a better understanding of what it means to say that science "works," above all, of what it is that science "works" *at*. What is needed is a reexamination of the meaning of "success."

Scientific theories do undoubtedly impinge on the real, but they do so more loosely and more selectively than we had thought, effecting some kinds of changes rather than others. If scientific theories are produced in a particular discursive tradition, by particular groups of people interacting among themselves, with nonscientists, and with nonhuman subjects, then the effectiveness of the resulting theories must be judged in terms of all the interactions which generate them. These interactions, both social and technical, produce an interlocking system of needs and desires demanding at least partial satisfaction by any theory or research program that is said to "work." But if the efficacy of science, or its consequentiality, is located in the satisfaction of these needs and desires, we must also consider its intentionality, located in the production of this particular system of needs.

A certain amount of the work that a successful theory or research program must do can be described in strictly human terms. It must be able to generate jobs and doable problems; it must offer explanations that provide aesthetic and emotional satisfaction; it must work rhetorically to recruit students, to "win allies," to get grants. In short, it must have the power to persuade a number of different constituencies— the funding agencies, the scientists themselves, potential recruits, the public at large—with interests that are themselves multiple, overlapping, and shifting.

For a research program to survive, however, it must satisfy the desires that motivate it, at least well enough to keep it going. In the short run, a stable network of interests might be well enough satisfied more or less independently of any particular interactions with the nonhuman world: Jobs, satisfying explanations, doable problems might all be generated by the strictly human (and rhetorical) work of a research program. But over the long run, the promises held out must be made good in terms of scientists' direct interactions with their world of nonhuman subjects. By the internal ethic of science, explanations must provide at least some predictive success in order to remain satisfying, and by the social and political ethic justifying their support, this predictive success must enable the production of at least some of the technological "goods" the public thinks it is paying for.

The truly remarkable thing about contemporary science (especially physics and molecular biology) is that it has been able to realize so many of these needs and desires, that it has produced a body of theory that matches the world well enough to satisfy this network of overlapping interests. That success bears testimony, above all, to the resourcefulness of scientists. Out of their interactions with each other, with the public at large, with their own heritage, and with a judiciously culled set of "facts" about the inanimate world, they have succeeded in producing tools which appear to dissolve nature's resistance to our own needs and desires.

But in marveling over their extraordinary success, we need also to consider the almost equally remarkable particularity (perhaps even singularity) of such needs and desires, of our selection of which natural phenomena to engage for experimental and theoretical inquiry (i.e., what it is we seek to know about), and of the social arrangements that facilitate the convergence of these needs and choices. It is only with the recognition of such convergences that we can begin to ask our question about alternatives: How might the unmistakable resourcefulness scientists have displayed be employed toward the fulfillment of other desires, satisfying a convergence of human interests that would be yielded by different social arrangements, producing a science that could be said to "work" differently?

Even so reformulated, however, this question conceals yet another. Feminists have irrevocably undermined our sense of innocence about the aspiration to dominate nature without, however, answering the question of just what it is that is wrong with dominating nature. We know what is wrong with dominating persons—it deprives other subjects of their right to express their own objectivities—and we may indeed worry about the extent to which the motivation to dominate nature reflects a desire for domination of other human beings. [36] But a salient point of a feminist perspective on science derives precisely from the fact that nature is not in fact a woman. A better pronoun for nature is surely "it," rather than "she." And it is not obvious what is wrong with seeking, or even achieving, dominion over things per se.

Perhaps the simplest way to respond to this final objection is to point out that nature, while surely not a woman, is also not a "thing," nor is it even an "it" that can be delineated unto itself, either separate or separable from a speaking and knowing "we." What we know about nature we know only through our interactions with, or rather, our embeddedness in what we call nature. It is precisely because we ourselves are natural beings—beings *in* and *of* nature—that we *can* know. Thus, to represent nature as a "thing" or an "it" is itself a way of talking, undoubtedly convenient, but clearly more appropriate to some ends than to others. And just because there is no one else "out there" capable of choosing, we must acknowledge that these ends represent human choices, for which "we" alone are responsible. The question then becomes: What are the particular ends to which the language of objectification, reification, and domination of nature is particularly appropriate, and perhaps even useful? And to what other ends might a different language—of kinship, embeddedness, and connectivity, of "feeling for the organism"—be equally appropriate and useful?

To ask about alternative aims for science in the late twentieth century is no idle or merely academic pursuit. Scientists have shown themselves to be smart enough to learn what they need to know to get much of what they, or we, thought we wanted, and at least some of us are alarmed. Something has gone terribly wrong. The very prowess of modern science confronts us with the fact that, somehow, we forgot to factor our own survival into our objectives for scientific knowledge. Perhaps it is not too late to reconsider, to rename and redefine the venture that has shown itself to be such a formidable resource; to recast the project of science in language that codifies a commitment to survival—our own as well as that of the world around us—as our first priority.

---

1. A somewhat different view is given by Thomas Laqueur, *Making Sex: Body and Gender from the Greeks to Freud* (Cambridge: Harvard University Press, 1990).

2. *See,* e.g., Gayle Rubin, "The Traffic in Women: Notes on the 'Political Economy' of Sex," in *Toward an Anthropology of Women,* ed. Rayna R. Reiter (New York: Monthly Review Press, 1975), pp. 157–210.

3. Donna J. Haraway, "Geschlect, Gender, Genre: Sexualpolitik Eine Vortes," in *Viele Orte, Überall?: Festschrift für Friegga Hauge,* ed. Kornelia Hauser (Berlin: Argument-Verlag, 1987), pp. 22–41.

4. *See,* e.g., Rubin, op. cit., and Catherine A. MacKinnon, *Feminism Unmodified: Discourses on Life and Law* (Cambridge: Harvard University Press, 1987).

5. In the most recent literature, discussions of gender have become yet more sophisticated as feminist scholars have begun to shift their focus away from the unifying force of gender norms within particular culturally homogeneous systems, to such inhomogeneities as class and race prevailing within ostensibly unitary cultures. But within the confines of those few worlds that can be said to be culturally homogeneous—such as, e.g., the almost entirely white, upper- and middle-class, predominantly Eurocentric world of modern science—analysis of the force of gender and gender norms remains relatively straightforward. Indeed, the very exclusivity of this tradition provides one of the few cases in which, precisely because of its racial and class exclusivity, the variables of race and class can be bracketed from the analysis. It must be remembered, however, that the concept of "gender" that appears in such an analysis is one that is restricted to a particular subset of "western" culture.

6. *See,* e.g., Sandra G. Harding, *The Science Question in Feminism* (Ithaca, N.Y.: Cornell University Press, 1986), for a useful summary of these multiple yet interacting meanings of the term *gender.*

7. Evelyn F. Keller, *Reflections on Gender and Science* (New Haven, Conn.: Yale University Press, 1985), p. 6.

8. Simmel, quoted in Karen Horney, "The Flight from Womanhood," in *Women and Analysis,* ed. Jean Strouse (New York: Dell, 1975); reprinted (Boston: G. K. Hull, 1985), pp. 171–86.

9. *The Structure of Scientific Revolutions* (Chicago: University of Chicago Press, 1962), (but *see also* Norwood R. Hanson, *Patterns of Discovery* [Cambridge: Cambridge University Press, 1958], and the even earlier work of Ludwick Fleck, *The Genesis and Development of a Scientific Fact* [Chicago: University of Chicago Press, 1979]).

10. Kuhn, p. 156.

11. While I draw heavily on my own work in this essay (*see* especially *Reflections on Gender and Science,* op. cit.), other approaches have been developed in the work of Carolyn Merchant, *The Death of Nature: Women, Ecology, and the Scientific Revolution* (San Francisco: Harper and Row, 1980); Brian Easlea, *Witch Hunting, Magic and the New Philosophy* (Brighton, England: Harvester Press, 1980); Ruth Bleier, *Science and Gender* (New York: Pergamon Press, 1984); Ann Fausto-Sterling, *Myths of Gender* (New York: Basic Books, 1985); Harding, op. cit.; and most recently, Londa L. Schiebinger, *The Mind Has No Sex?: Women in the Origins of Modern Science* (Cambridge: Harvard University Press, 1989) and Haraway, *Primate Visions: Gender, Race, and Nature in the World of Modern Science* (New York: Routledge Press, 1989).

12. Keller, op. cit., 1985.

13. Oldenburg, quoted in Easlea, p. 70.

14. *The Refutation of Philosophies.* Quoted in William Leiss, *The Domination of Nature* (Boston: Beacon Press, 1972), p. 25.

15. Benjamin Farrington, "Temporis Partus Masculus [A Masculine Birth in Time]: An untranslated writing of Francis Bacon," *Centaurus* I (1951), pp. 197, 201.

16. In the seventeenth century, these were all still promissory notes.

17. *The Works of Robert Boyle,* ed. Thomas Birch, vol. 4 (London: A. Millar, 1744), pp. 362–63.

18. Ibid., p. 363.

19. Ibid., p. 373.

20. Agrippa, quoted in Frances A. Yates, *Giordano Bruno and the Hermetic Tradition* (Chicago: University of Chicago Press, 1964), p. 136.

21. An excellent account of this particular debate is given by Thomas H. Jobe, "The Devil in Restoration Science: The Glanvill-Webster Debate," *ISIS* 72 (1981), pp. 343–56.

22. Glanvill, quoted in Jobe, p. 350.

23. More, *Enthusiasmus Triumphatus* (London, 1656), p. 36.

24. *Paracelsus: Selected Writings,* ed. Jolandt Jacobi (Princeton, N.J.: Princeton University Press, 1951), p. 73.

25. Glanvill, *The Vanity of Dogmatizing* (London, 1661), pp. 117–18; reprinted by Facsimile Text Society (New York: Columbia University Press, 1931).

26. Ibid., p. 135.

27. For an especially interesting discussion of this general phenomenon, *see* Gyorgy Markus, "Why Is There No Hermeneutics of the Natural Sciences? Some Preliminary Theses," *Science in Context,* 1 (1987), pp. 5–51.

28. Mary Hesse points out, "Neurons come in billions and their possible linkages in megabillions, while the words of a language come only in thousands and sentences cannot in a lifetime be long enough to match the antics of the neurons. There can't be a word or a sentence to cover every particular thing." ("Models, Metaphors and Myths," *New York Times,* Oct. 22, 1989, p. E24.)

29. Ibid.

30. *O.E.D.,* s.v. "law." The discussion here is adapted from the introduction to Part III, Keller, op. cit., 1985.

31. Nancy Cartwright, *Nature's Capacities and Their Measurement* (New York: Oxford University Press, 1989).

32. McClintock's own words, as well as the title of my book on this subject, *A Feeling for the Organism: The Life and Work of Barbara McClintock* (New York: W. H. Freeman, 1983).

33. Her own account of how she was able to see details of chromosomal structure that others had missed is striking: "I found that the more I worked with them, the bigger and bigger [the chromosomes] got, and when I was really working with them I wasn't outside, I was down there. I was part of the system. I was right down there with them, and everything got big. I even was able to see the internal parts of the chromosomes— actually everything was there. It surprised me because I actually felt as if I was right down there and these were my friends. . . . As you look at these things, they become part of you. And you forget yourself." (Taken from Keller, 1983, p. 117.)

34. McClintock was awarded the Nobel Prize for Physiology or Medicine in 1983 for work she began in 1945 and brought to first general publication in 1951. The long delay in recognition constitutes the principal subject of my book on McClintock's life and work (op. cit.), appearing only a few months before her Nobel Prize was announced.

35. There remains a very serious question, especially in McClintock's own mind, of the extent to which such convergences can in fact be said to have taken place, and accordingly, of the extent to which the meaning McClintock attached to "transposition" is consonant with the current use of that term. For further discussion of this question, as well as of other issues pertinent to her research, *see* Keller, op. cit., 1983.

36. This indeed is the argument of my psychosocial analysis in Part II of *Reflections on Gender and Science,* op. cit.

# Mental Images in Cognitive Psychology

Eva T. H. Brann

Since 1957 Eva T. H. Brann has been a tutor at St. John's College in Annapolis, Maryland, where she is now dean. Born in Germany, she received a bachelor's degree in history from Brooklyn College and a master's in classics as well as a doctorate in archaeology from Yale University. She has published numerous lectures and articles on various of the Great Books, a translation from the German of Jacob Klein's *Greek Mathematical Thought and the Origin of Algebra* (1968), and a collection of essays, *Paradoxes of Education in a Republic* (1979).

Ms. Brann's most current work has been on a book entitled *The World of the Imagination,* which is to appear in the fall of 1990. Her interest in cognitive psychology and mental images arose from this project. The book is a comprehensive consideration of the imagination in the major disciplines, and it is intended to help in establishing the object of its study as the central human faculty.

## I. The problem of mental images

If you ask people to imagine their childhood home, and then question them about the way in which they recall it, they are very likely to say something like this: "I saw it in my head; it was clear as a picture." Or alternatively: "I tried to call up the image, but it had gone fuzzy."

This way of speaking implies certain linked beliefs: That, when asked to recall memories or, for that matter, to imagine objects described to us, we think that we *see* something; that we see it "in our head" or *mentally;* that we see it in the manner of a picture or of an *image* of something; and that we are *somehow the wiser* for being able to summon up and see a mental image.

Now most people assume that there is substance of a sort to these beliefs and would be surprised to learn that they have been under heavy attack in this century, both in philosophy and psychology, as mere illusions, having no reality. But so they have come to be regarded in some quarters. The school of thought called "Philosophy of Mind" and likewise Behaviorist psychology are skeptical of their existence. Behaviorism will be briefly taken up later under the main business of this article, which is the investigation of mental images in "Cognitive Psychology." Here, it will be useful to give a sample of the philosophical attack as it appears in the work of Gilbert Ryle. To anticipate the gist of Ryle's argument, it is that people are mistaken as to the mental images they think they have. We do not really see internally, Ryle maintains, nor are there any immaterial pictures, any *mental images* to be seen in the mind. There is neither any evidence nor any need for such objects. There is no evidence because mental images are entirely internal and invisible, impossible to verify. And there is no need because they are not essential to explaining the overt behavior of the people who think they have them.

But before I go on, a word should be said about the general human importance of this assertion. To begin with, the denial that people "see things in their heads," or, more romantically, that they have imaginative vision, runs counter to ordinary opinion. It marks a willingness of the contemporary academy to set aside common "folk" psychology and its implications for the sake of philosophical rigor. This puts philosophy at odds with common understanding. Second, if human beings have no capability for internal seeing, that is, for visualization and imagining, then all cognition is reduced—not, to be sure, inevitably and necessarily, but very conveniently—to some sort of symbol-manipulation. This means we do not "see" in our minds, as we suppose, but that we only "think," and think blindly, somewhat like a computer.

By cognition is here meant whatever processes are involved in knowing. Traditionally, the mental image plays a mediating, and therefore a central, role in the coming-to-be of knowledge. It plays the middleman between perception and intellect, preparing and submitting the shapes of the world to the thinking soul. With this image-interface denied, the mind is held to face the world immediately, that is to say, in its own verbal or reasoning mode. All the products of imaginative seeing (such as painting) or visualization (such as novels) have their cognitive ground cut from under them. What happens when we are asked to use our imagination becomes practically inexplicable.

To return now to Ryle's attack on the existence and the cognitive usefulness of mental images, it is set out in his book *The Concept of Mind* (1949). This is one of the founding works in the "Philosophy of Mind," sometimes called "philosophical psychology." The direction of that philosophy is indicated by Ryle's treatment of the imagination as something which can only be expressed in terms of a rigorous adherence to the observable facts of mental life.

The general purpose of his book is to expose the falsity, and even the absurdity, of an "official doctrine," purportedly stemming from Descartes, which Ryle calls "the dogma of the Ghost in the Machine." An important part of this dogma is supposed to be that the mental life of the mental ghost that works the bodily machine, while open to itself by introspection, is totally hidden from the other ghosts in their own machines. Hence "mental-conduct verbs," such as "knowing," "believing," "remembering," and also "imagining," are quite inaccessible to, but also quite incorrigible by, anyone other than ourselves, insofar as we claim to be engaged in such activities.

The phrase "mental-conduct verb" intimates that imagining will be treated as a sort of inner behavior, though Ryle would really like to circumvent internality altogether. For example, in order to give evidence of what we take to be visual recall of an object, it is sufficient that people produce creditable drawings. Additional information about our supposed visual image is unnecessary. Unhappily, imagining is mostly an undemonstrative activity, and this kind of evidence is seldom available. How then to speak of it at all? Since Ryle does not maintain on principle, like a crude Behaviorist, that only external behavior is ever to be taken into account, he can compromise his position a little in the case of the imagination and allow for *some* sort of "inner" or mental happening.

Ryle's account of mental images is given in the chapter of his book slyly called "Imagination" (VIII)—slyly, since "there is no special Faculty of Imagination." Rather, there are various ways of imagining. If the general attack is on Descartes, the particular butt in this chapter is Hume's notion that ideas are in the mind, that they have inherent qualities like degrees of vivacity, and that they are shadow-sensations—weak sensation-images [*A Treatise of Human Nature*, I, i, 1].

The opening question of Ryle's chapter might indeed be thought to be the proper preoccupation of everyone who thinks about mental images:

> Where do the things and happenings exist which people imagine
> existing?

This question is declared spurious. What is to be done instead is to describe what people "see in the mind's eye" or "hear in their heads." For Ryle admits that they do this, without however conceding that entities like visual or auditory images exist in fact. But why do people talk as if they had such images? Why do they insist on analogizing seeing and "seeing" in the mind's eye?

It is an unfortunate consequence, Ryle answers, of the preeminence of sight that our imagination-language is largely drawn from vision. Since there are real simulacra—real pictures, portraits, photographs—in the visual world, people are induced to speak of visual mental images as if they really had them; since there are no dummy smells or tastes, the question of mental equivalents does not arise when they are imagined.

Furthermore, real picture-seeing, such as looking at photographs, often stimulates internal "seeing," but that does not mean that the latter belongs to the same genus as picture-seeing. As Ryle puts it, "to see is one thing; to visualize another."

"Seeing" and "picturing," though useful concepts, are, then, not to be taken as entailing the contemplation of inner pictures.

> Roughly, imaging occurs, but images are not seen . . . True, a person
> picturing his nursery is, in a certain way, like a person seeing his nursery,
> but the similarity does not consist in his really looking at a real likeness
> of his nursery, but in his really seeming to see his nursery itself, when he
> is not really seeing it. He is not being a spectator of a resemblance of his
> nursery, but he is resembling a spectator of his nursery.

Suppose there were what Ryle calls "special status pictures" inside the head. Then a child who sees her doll smiling would be seeing "a picture of a smile" but not seeing the smile where the doll is, which is absurd.

How then do people *seem* to see their nurseries or have ghost tunes running through their heads? One answer Ryle gives is that they are not really seeing but "seeing." Another reply, though really a nonanswer, is that the question is about the wires and pulleys the ghost uses to work the machine and requires no answer, because no account of interior or occult processes is necessary. Ryle has no need of a hypothesis so unprovable as that of mental images.

His positive answer starts from the claim that "seeing" images is only one of many widely divergent meanings of imagining. There is no nuclear operation called by that name. The meaning pertinent to "seeing" is pretending, or make-believe. Thus the child that plays bear pretends to be a bear by growling and stomping. It engages in a mock performance. Such part-playing has an interestingly dual description: The child is intelligently being a brute; it is being bright and brutal simultaneously. But this does not involve pictures or shadow-sensations. In imagining, the pretending includes a "refraining" from overt conduct. Ryle insists that silent pretenders do not show anything to themselves or watch themselves seeing anything. What people do is to engage in a kind of rehearsal which does not involve ghost pictures or tunes but involves "fancying" themselves hearing or seeing, listening for a tune that they have learned and not forgotten, knowing and thinking how the tune goes. It follows that such fancyings do not materially aid cognition; they are themselves the mere, willful side effects of knowledge.

Thus, visual memory and revisualization are finally just knacks which we expect of most people and in "high degree of children, dress-designers, policemen and cartoonists." In any case, they come into evidence only in verbal description; as images they are perfectly private.

This is not the place to analyze Ryle's argument against mental images as playing a role in using one's imagination. Such a critical analysis might, for example, point out that in Ryle's account the correlative of the activity and the objects of the verb "to imagine" are tacitly suppressed. We might ask questions such as these: What is being listened to? Who is pretending what to whom? Moreover, how can "refraining" leave so vivid a psychic remainder? Visualizing, Ryle says, is like a silent soliloquy which is "a flow of pregnant non-sayings." What, we might ask, does this account signify besides the resolve to look at mentation in a strictly negative way and from the outside? What does the reference to "description" betoken but a claim that "mental conduct" is heavily verbal?

On the other hand, there might be another way to deal not only with the Rylean attack on the images of the imagination but also with far subtler ones which lie outside the scope of this exposition, such as those of Wittgenstein (1949) and Sartre (1940). What if there were experimental evidence to show that we really and usefully do "see images," in some ordinary sense of these words, when we use our imaginations?

## II. Cognitive science

And indeed, as the *philosophical* arguments against the imagination have been elaborated and subtilized, something curious has happened: the cudgels for the existence of mental images have been taken up in a fairly new *science,* namely cognitive psychology. It does seem strange that a philosophical school that prides itself on its attention to observable fact should find itself opposed to laboratory science, but it is *really* strange if the science is an actual, result-producing science. In any case, the findings of this science might well obviate the argument mounted in philosophy. Whether that is indeed the case is what we are about to see. But first something must be said about the new science of images *as* a science.

Now if there is—as there ought to be—something astonishing in the mere conception of an experimental science of the soul in general, then the actual development of such a science of the imagination in particular is that much the more amazing. It might, to a lay proprietor of a soul and an amateur of the imagination, even be repugnant. Doctor Johnson, who complained that he was distracted by the virtuoso exhibition of an acrobat, was reminded by his companion that the feat was, after all, very difficult. "Difficult!" was his rejoinder, "I wish it had been impossible." So too might someone absorbed in that most elusive, evanescent, gauzy of inner activities recoil at the regimentation required to prepare the imagination for the laboratory and shudder at the exposure in store for so private a power.

In vain; the science does exist, and it is fascinating. The results themselves, ingeniously obtained and gratifyingly nontrivial though they may be, have not yet yielded, and perhaps never will yield, either a really comprehensive or a completely confirmable theory. Theory, however, is in one way the least of it, since the preparations and preliminaries are themselves deeply interesting. For as always, when science comes to deal with the soul, methodology becomes absorbing.

The science of physical nature came about, Kant says, when investigators began to force her to answer their questions [*GBWW,* Vol. 42, p. 6c–d], putting her to torture, so to speak. The inquisition into psychic nature has a prior task, namely, to force her into the open, to make her show herself to begin with. The capture of the imagination as an observable piece of nature starts with devising ways to extract measurable evidence concerning imaginal structures and processes. Indeed it begins even further back, with the tortuously difficult formulation of criteria for the existence of mental images.

The science in which imagery investigations take place is called Cognitive Psychology. Cognitive Psychology in turn belongs to a group of new or renewed disciplines including Artificial Intelligence, Communications Theory, and Linguistics, which make up Cognitive Science. "Cognition" in this context is not what it is traditionally in philosophy, namely the acquisition of intelligible truth. The unifying "cognitivist" view is rather that knowing is *information processing.* This belief, leading to many theories, amounts to what historians of science currently call a paradigm—a paradigm being to scientists about what a worldview is to the intellectuals, namely the prevailing frame of hypothesizing.

Cognitive science, then, is the setting of cognitive psychology. Indeed the latter might be said to be a specification of the former, at least with respect to imagery. In it the complex, embattled issues of cognitivism become simpler and sharper, whether as hopes or as hypotheses. A prime example of such an issue is functionalism, the prevailing, though not unchallenged, cognitive stance concerning the "mind-body problem," which is whether the mind is itself physical or is separable from the brain (Churchland 1984; Block 1978).* Functionalism is a sort of Neobehaviorism in that a mental state is understood as a disposition to act in certain ways, given certain sensory inputs. It differs from Behaviorism, old style (which is the claim that nothing concerning the mind is of consequence except overt behavior), in allowing individual mental states to exist and to be themselves the causes and the results of other mental states. Furthermore, it considers the mental functions as separable from their physical realizations. A human brain, a Martian brain, a computer, and a mere program all might "embody" the same functional economy, so that no type of mental state has one unique necessary embodiment. The point is that in cognitive psychology the hope is strong and the hypothesis general that to each particular mental state or event a corresponding brain state can be matched. In that hope for a real, visible embodiment of their theories by the functioning brain, cognitive scientists are true to the pattern of the grander new sciences: Copernicus in his day bought trouble by claiming reality rather than mere hypothetical adequacy for his heliocentric orbits.

Information processing is an approach to cognition which supports the functionalist obliteration of the distinction between human and ahuman mental states and events. With respect to psychology, the word *information* is not to be taken very stringently. It does not here have the precise quantitative sense used in communication theory, nor yet the general formal meaning according to which information is whatever puts an organism or a system into a new state of readiness for response. The most immediately apt tenor of the term is broad: Information is anything that is representable, where the latter term refers not to the capability of an external element to be re-presented inside the system but to any inside state or event which is there to be processed (MacKay 1969). Thus "information" does not necessarily involve any matching of thing and thought.

"Processing," the central cognitive term, then means any transformation of such representations, be it by elaboration or reduction, by storage or retrieval, applied in sequence or in parallel, from top down or bottom up. The kinds, stages, and routes of the processing are the preoccupations of cognitive science. The chief tool in imagery exper-

---

*This and similar references are to works listed in the bibliography.

iments, it will turn out, is the measurement of reaction times. Now the very fact that mental processes take measurable time suggests a possible physical underpinning, though such a correspondence of mind and brain is far from being established, as will be seen later.

It follows that "cognitivism" has two related problems particularly relevant to imagery. The first concerns the place of *consciousness* in information processing and of its imagery aspect—the "mind's eye," in particular. The second is the problem of *representation* in general, and of the representational type to which imagery in particular belongs. It should be said that the cognitivist theoreticians, who straddle the barbed wire fence between philosophy and science, get into fascinating tangles about these matters. On the philosophical side there are old epistemological questions which seem to be experimentally intractable, while on the psychological side there are new experimental results which don't make much of a whole with human experience. A consequence is the odd indecision of the literature about the life-stage that cognitive psychology has reached, especially with respect to imagery. Has it run its course to a conceptual standstill, or are its quandaries the growing pains of lusty youth? This is, for the present, an open question.

The first problem, that of consciousness, is, it seems, a lost cause for cognitive science. At least the theorists' dealings with it are mostly acrobatic—involved contortions and death-defying leaps. Consequently, for imagery the experiments are on the whole more illuminating without a theory of consciousness than with it. Nonetheless a word must be said about this theory.

The attempt of cognitive science is to catch consciousness within the concepts of information processing, eschewing traditional terms such as soul, self, and also subject (except in the experimental sense), and their associated insights. For example, the Kantian assumption that the possibility of self-consciousness is a condition of consciousness is not at all an accepted axiom of cognitivism.

The difficulty cognitive science has with consciousness, and a fortiori with self-consciousness, is related to the locus of its interest, which is below or behind consciousness. Most cognitive processes are, in fact, unconscious in the sense that they are not experienced by the knower. However, "unconscious," though it is the current word, is not quite the best one. For the Unconscious to which Freud accustomed the world, that pandemonium of asocial passions, is still conceived as of a piece with consciousness, whatever may be its ultimate biological basis. Though it is an interdicted region of the soul, its libidinous contents can be forced up into self-knowledge.

The cognitive unconscious, on the other hand, is not primarily passionate or emotional. In fact, the cognitive study of emotion has not gone very far. Furthermore, though aspects of it can on occasion become conscious—trains of thought having run underground for long stretches may slowly surface, and imagery may make sudden epiphanies before the mind's eye—the cognitive unconscious is conceived, not as in itself mental, but rather as the explanatory mechanism of mental activity (Richardson 1980, 38). Since the reconstruction of cognitive processes is the proper preoccupation of psychology and artificial intelligence, the consciousness question is an extraneous worry forced on the practitioners of these sciences by a philosophical hope: They want, while working out the information processing hypothesis, to shed light on the human being as well. This valiant attempt to be truly Janus-faced—philosophical among philosophers, and scientific among scientists—may, however, be impossible by the very nature of the enterprise. The functional or materialist version of consciousness may clash with a philosophical inquiry into its nature.

There is, to be sure, one area of unavoidable contact between philosophy and science in imagery investigations. Such experiments begin with the informal assumption that people can form, have, and report a mental image. They therefore, willy-nilly, begin with an "autophenomenological" moment—a point, that is, at which subjects observe themselves and give an introspective account of their own inner appearances. So the strait gate and the narrow way to mental processes is through self-conscious reports of conscious experience. However, such introspection is particularly obnoxious to science because it seems so private: it is so idiosyncratically "mine," so imperfectly communicable, so incorrigible. Hence the faster it can be left behind, the better. A self-report of a mental representation is taken to imply reliably only that *something* is going on, but no *what* (Harman 1978).

So, while experimenters do not gainsay the fact of an imagery *experience*, they try to circumvent it for purposes of determining the efficacy and nature of imagery. It is relegated to being an epiphenomenon which rides piggyback on the causal unconscious processes; the conscious experience is an inessential by-product or, more sophisticatedly, an "emergent" phenomenon. Emergence is the most acrobatic or magical of all the notions absorbed by cognitive science. It applies to an experienced whole which is quite other, and in some sense more, than the sum of its parts. It is useful because the elements of a scientific analysis never do quite synthesize into the object of common experience. For example, individual sensory stimuli often cannot account for the actual look of patterns or their "gestalt." This total impression is therefore termed an emergent property. After the fall taken by holistic experience, "emergence" is to put Humpty Dumpty together again.

An alternative to such leaps to higher levels is to regard consciousness as a "control element" in a system in which it is characterized merely in terms of its special access. Daniel Dennett is the author of a cognitive theory of consciousness (1978), here set out in an abridged schema: There are several functional areas in consciousness. For example, there is a perceptual component which takes sensory input and stores percepts in the memory component. Functionally above these is the control component which has access to them all. It directs the perceptual function through the focusing of attention, it sends commands to perform speech acts to the speech components, and it is in control of their execution. Above all, it directs inquiries to and receives replies from memory. The control component can introspect, for introspection is said to be nothing more than the control subroutine of addressing questions to and processing answers from memory.

Now such a specifically cognitive theory of consciousness, whether one finds it attractive or not, is interesting in the present context because it would effectively inhibit imagery investigations, for there is "no room in the subpersonal explanation of the perceptual process . . . for images" (Dennett 1981, 54). Mental images, by their very nature, require to be "perceived" and recognized *as* images. If the mind's eye is nothing at all but a metaphor, all reason for holding on to the term *imagery* is gone. On the one hand, it makes no sense to speak of an "unseen" or unconscious image (unattended to, yes, as in unconscious wish-fantasies of psychoanalysis). On the other hand, no verbal report can adequately represent a specific image any more than words can render a spatial picture without remainder; words may do perfect justice to thoughts but never to sights. So the imaginal representations have actuality nowhere if not before the subject's inner eye.

Such mental "seeing," however, would have to be an adjunct of consciousness. As the subject sees by means of the organic eye which is excited by stimuli, so it "sees" with a mind's eye which shares some of the perceptual processes of vision but works in the absence of external stimuli. Now, not only do imagery-havers maintain that inner seeing is just what they do experience but, what has more weight in this context, the experimental evidence to be presented in Section IV can be reasonably interpreted to confirm their claim.

Here then, is a probably intractable perplexity: There is the experience of imagery, a particular kind of consciousness marked by sometimes vivid inner representations which are peculiarly private in having no really adequate externalization such as thought has in linguistic utterance. There are also, as will be shown, experimental results to suggest that there are representations which have just the pictorial characteristics imagers say they do. But the traditional understanding of consciousness as the agency for and through which mental states and events like imagery have their being is not easily assimilable into the information-processing framework of cognitive science. For that is quintessentially explicit, analytic, and inhospitable to categories of inwardness. In particular, the strongly representational consciousness before and to which picturelike mental states and events appear—the "mind's eye"—is a standing embarrassment and stumbling block. Con-

103

sequently, a rigorous cognitivist theory of consciousness like Dennett's, which is thoroughly appropriate to the cognitive science mode, appears in certain respects to be at odds with the experimental work done in cognitive psychology. The fallout from this circumstance will turn up in the imagery investigations described below.

The second problem of cognitive science which is of special importance in dealing with mental images is that of representation. Mental imagery, we would think on the face of it, is the re-presentational experience par excellence. Its very name implies copying and correspondence. But that, for cognitive science, is just the difficulty. It seems to be agreed that this central notion of the science, representation, is terminologically muddled and conceptually perplexed in the extreme (Mandler 1983; Palmer 1978). Here follows a brief attempt to present the issue.

Cognitive scientists generally adhere to the representational view of mental states and events. Again, on the face of it, this fact would seem to mean that the paradigmatic scientific tack bypasses the prevailing philosophical tendency as it presses headlong on the other way. For the tendency, already evident in Ryle, is to deny that there are mental representations such as images. This philosophical denial is a flight from representationalism, understanding the mind as a mirror of nature—as so constituted that its ideas correspond more or less to the objects of the world. Cognitivist representation, on the other hand, does not necessarily include a "semantic" relation, that is, a reference to the world. Jerry Fodor has sharpened the cognitivist theory of representation by a blunt admission of "methodological solipsism" (1980). Methodological solipsism refers to the claim that the very methods of cognitive psychology preclude mental representations from being understood as having any reference to the external world.

Fodor's thesis is that the processes open to treatment in cognitive psychology must be not only representational but representational in a particular sense. They are *computational,* by which is meant that they are both symbolic and formal. "Symbolic" is here taken in the most minimal sense. It means nothing more than that the processes operate on elements of some sort. "Formal" means that the processes work by explicit logical, syntactical rules, or by mathematical transformations. The latter are included precisely to take care of imagistic processes such as the "mental rotations" which will play so central a role in the imagery experiments described below. The burden of the formality condition, however, is the absence of semantic properties. No truth, reference, or meaning is involved in these computational processes. Fodor's "rational" psychology is traced back to Descartes, who could offer no binding external criterion for distinguishing true from hallucinatory mental representations, depending instead on the inner coherence of the representational system. It is an alternative to the older "naturalistic" psychology that aimed at a study of the semantic, causal relations of stimuli to the soul.

Such a rationalistic psychology does exist. An example is the impressive project of having a computer "live in"—namely operate on—a simple world of block shapes. The point is that the blocks need not actually be *there*. The computer arranges its internal data and operates on them *as if* there were a real world. Its world is solipsistic, entirely internal. Fodor thinks the chances for regaining a naturalistic psychology are slim: "computational psychology is the only one that we are going to get" (1980, 66).

It remains to say why the formality condition is all psychology has to work with, or why a naturalistic psychology, that is, one in which the mind is related to the world, and which is also scientific, is thought not to be in the cards. The reason is, simply, that there exists no semantic science in the required sense, no possibility of specifying the relations that hold between a particular mind and the world's object in a scientific, that is to say, a law-instantiating, way. This science is lacking not because people are too spontaneous for such a psychology but because they do not yet possess so complete and public—so scientific—a description of objects that a lawful link between them and their mental representations is possible. Such a descriptional link would relate the representation to the thing by virtue of what both truly are. Before that is worked out—supposing it were possible in principle—we'll all be gone. In the meanwhile, naturalist experimenters cannot know what their subjects have in mind when they receive instructions and make reports on the stimuli. It should be said that Fodor's extremist thesis, while it is very influential, has also raised a storm of objections (Fodor 1980).

What matters here is, however, the bearing of the thesis on the practice of imagery investigation. Fodor's example of a psychological research strategy grounded in a solipsistic methodology is a simulation project in artificial intelligence, in which computers "live" in a world of their own that has no reference to the external world. Imagery experimenters, on the other hand, are normally as semantic as can be. They always begin with some expectation of a correspondence between the stimulus picture and the mental representation. The experimenters cannot help but assume that they and the subject are looking at the same object, and that at the instruction "Form an image!" the subject intends to and does form an image which is somehow true to the picture shown. It is a fascinating situation. Productive experimental practice once again runs counter to central tendencies of current philosophy, and what is stranger yet, to the sincerest theory of its sponsoring science. It is not, it seems, a standoff to be resolved by settling who tells who what's what. Mental imagery may well be unreachable by a "rational psychology," or by any philosophy which eschews representations in the strong sense, namely representations which correspond to something in the real world.

Working psychologists consequently tend to employ the term *representation* with two meanings. The first is the one explicated above: the elements and structures of cognition with the processes that operate on them. The second is the traditional meaning: "A representation is a spatial or temporal configuration of symbols which is conventionally regarded as standing in a certain relationship to something else. Mental images are representations in just this sense" (Richardson 1980). The "certain relationship" is elucidated by another definition belonging to the same group: One configuration represents a second when the former preserves some of the internal relations of the latter (Palmer 1978).

A last brief word about representation in general. The objects of the external world present themselves primarily under two aspects: as continuous and extended shapes and spaces, with their colors and other perceptible qualities; and as discrete, nameable, and countable items with their many kinds of relations. Pictures and diagrams fairly naturally represent the former, words and conventional symbols the latter. The most self-explanatory of representations is the picture or model which preserves similarity, while words in sentences and symbols in formulas represent the world in terms of its elements and their syntax, both requiring certain conventions. The two genera of internal representations whose possibility is generally accepted in cognitive psychology follow this lead. There is an "imagistic" or pictorial, and a "propositional" or verbal, code.

Along with representation, "code" and "encoding" are the key notions of cognitive science. Encoding refers to the way information is readied for internal processing. For example, it can undergo selection (as when only a part of the stimulus is admitted) or elaboration (as when words are remembered through the formation of imagery) or rewriting (as when the binary digits 11 are read as 3; Bower 1972, 87). But above all, information is encoded in the sense of being transposed into either the imagistic or propositional code.

A perplexing question arises: Is there an actual imagistic mental code, and what is its nature? It is a question from which the propositional code is immune, since from the point of view of evidence, human language is trusted to represent a corresponding mental encoding. From the point of view of its physical realization, the elements and the syntax of language are easily conceivable as mediated by the neural networks and firings of the brain. But above all, from the computational point of view, the artificial languages of computers offer excellent models for study. Consequently there are numerous species of propositional or computational encodings, and the only question is which of them are most adequate.

It is otherwise with the imagistic code. External evidence for imagining is much less direct and trustworthy. There is at present no neural account of specific visual memories. Computers still have a hard time with complex perception-based pictures. Furthermore, propositionalists stand ready to account for the experience of depictive imagery as a mere epiphenomenon coming on top of descriptive encoding, while they impugn the very possibility of imagist encodings. That is to say, they might admit that we have pictures in the mind, but they do not think that they are a serious cognitive code.

The best hope for the claim that there is imagistic encoding is the fact that there is actually a computational model of mental imagery. The experimental evidence which it incorporates is described below. The arguments for it in principle are largely computational-convenience arguments such as are exemplified in the common experience of answering, say, geometric questions. A propositional proof and its imagistic diagram are "informationally equivalent," since they say the same thing, but they are "computationally non-equivalent," for in simple cases, like the Euclidean theorem which asserts that the base angles of an isosceles triangle are equal [Book I, Proposition 5; *GBWW*, Vol. 11, pp. 4b–5b], people can answer much faster by looking at the picture than by thinking through the proof (Palmer 1978).

It will be argued below that the imagistic computational theory has at bottom nothing much to do with imagistic, that is, picturelike, mental representation. It turns out to be really only a claim that mental encodings cannot be narrowly syntactic but must include mathematical structures like arrays and matrices and their special transformations, which describe spatial layouts.

The crux of what might be called the "imagistic representation" scandal is thus just the "inner picture" experience. The latter is the complement to the "mind's eye" perplexity, the internal "seeing" discussed above, since "pictures" are what the imaginer "sees." However inaccessible and inarticulate they may be, internal likenesses are what most people have the incorrigible sense of seeing. These likenesses are felt to be genuine spacelike similarities, preserving that essential extendedness which is lost in any verbal or numerical symbolization. Moreover, such imagery does carry information in the precise sense mentioned above: It puts those who have it into a new state of readiness to know or to act.

The following parts of this article will illustrate, alongside some wonderful experimental discoveries, the insoluble bafflement of cognitive science in the face of experience in general and of spacelike representations in particular. It will turn out to be no local difficulty but a perplexity of deep significance, reflecting equally on the nature of imagery, of our cognitive constitution, and of the science itself.

## III. Cognitive psychology

The imagination becomes the object of science by the strictest criteria under the succinctly revealing title of "Mental Imagery." "Imagery" signifies that the having of images in general rather than their mode of being or their individual quality is at stake. "Mental" here signifies that imagery is to be investigated in terms of the cognitive structures and processes of the mind understood as a function of the brain, rather than as a faculty of the soul. The heading naturally implies that the subject of mental imagery exists, though its chief proponents prudently abstain from defining it beforehand: Since the features of the mental image are about to be discovered, that would be premature. Imagery is thus treated as a namelike term, anchored in some phenomenal entity in the world, but not an immediately definable one. For one would hardly wish to commit its meaning to some set of properties which on further inquiry might prove mistaken (Kosslyn 1980, 469). The investigation here reported is based upon nothing more than an assumption that mental imagery does occur.

One more preliminary point. The science of mental imagery comes within cognitive psychology, which in turn is part of cognitive science, as has been said. Here is a way to distinguish the latter two. The chief aim of cognitive science is to mimic and even to outdo the capabilities of the human mind, as in artificial intelligence, but not necessarily by means of its actual specific structures and processes. In cognitive psychology, on the other hand, the factual functions of the human mind are to be discovered. If it proves ultimately impossible to attach these functions to specific brain events, cognitive psychology will fade out, as have other schools of experimental psychology. Not so cognitive science, for it has no life-or-death stake in the exact correspondence of neurophysiology with imagery.

When psychology first tried to turn itself into an observational science in the last quarter of the nineteenth century, imagery was its chief preoccupation. That was quite understandable since ever more refined introspection was its main technique of inquiry, and introspection by and large yields nothing in greater profusion than imagery. For it is probable that our mental life is almost continuously filled with images, noticed or unnoticed (where "unnoticed" does not necessarily mean unconscious but merely unattended to). Moreover the various kinds of mental activity shade into each other: percepts into imagery, imagery into dreams, dreams into hallucinations (Holt 1972).

But not only the seamless and apparently universal experience of imagery itself was a spur to naturalistic observation. The investigation of thinking also pointed the new science to imagery, since this enterprise was projected on a philosophical background that was powerfully representationalist in general and Humean in particular. Hence thinking itself was regarded as the operation of the mind on ideas which are, in Hume's terms, "faint images" of sense impressions organized by laws of association [*A Treatise of Human Nature,* I, i, 1]. The "science of immediate experience," as its founder Wilhelm Wundt called psychology, was to analyze the elements of consciousness and to specify these laws. Of these enormous and acute descriptive and analytic efforts, scarcely an echo remains except in the classificatory terms for imagery, such as visual, eidetic (after-image-like), hypnagogic (presleep), and hallucinatory.

But one of the earliest and certainly the most frequently cited works on imagery already foreshadowed that drastic "ostracism" of images from psychology (Holt 1964), which brought this first phase to a close. In 1883 Sir Francis Galton, who introduced statistics into psychology, conducted a study by means of a questionnaire sent out to one hundred men. He asked his subjects, about half of whom were distinguished scholars and scientists, to image mentally their breakfast table of that morning. Slightly over 10 percent, among whom the men of distinction figured largely, claimed never to have had any imagery. This finding, never reduplicated, nonetheless raised a new possibility, that of "imageless thought."

In the first decade of this century, "imageless thought" became the doctrine of a school, the Würzburg school. It was observed that the introspective reports of conscious mental content during problem solving did include images and vague sensations. But these were thought to be insufficient to account for the subjects' judgments or performances. Evidently, the operations of thought were not fully conscious and the conscious imagery was often not functional. It followed that the significance of imagery was diminished, while the old method of introspection began to be discredited as being inadequate to the investigation of the unconscious. Imagery was about to disappear from psychology for half a century.

Disciplined introspection, careful protocols, data collection by questionnaires and other psychometric techniques, which treat imagery features as measurable traits and are still used in memory studies, were the methods of this first phase. In its devotion to method and measurement this tack is certainly at least science-flavored. But while it yields many interesting observations, it does not seem to lead to suggestive models. Consequently it is conducive to that anxious frame of mind familiar to the trade as "physics envy." What would be the qualifying characteristic of a "real" science of psychology?

At this point it makes sense to try to articulate those most fundamental features the science of cognition must display in order to be as "real" as a science as physics is (on the assumption that there is none more real), and, further, how cognitive psychology does display it. Indeed, each new science seems to stay remarkably close to something like these requirements.

Science requires that immediate experience and its commonsense conclusions be regarded as strictly provisional and penetrable, so that sensory experience is a mere surface indication. It is an epiphenomenon only, somewhat like a colored buoy floating above a lobster pot: it shows that something is below to be hauled up, no more.

A science of subjectively conscious experience is therefore a contradiction in terms. The real science of cognition must bypass self-consciousness and manipulate the reports of the experiencing subject. So the subject taken philosophically, that is, the conscious self, becomes an "S," a "subject" taken psychologically—that is, an informant. This subject reacts to instructions by speech or by pressing buttons, but its introspective reports are not taken as the last word on the conditions and events of its mind.

Correspondingly, the object of inquiry, too, must be publicly available. It cannot be a merely inward event. It must rather be understood as a phenomenon with some dimension measurable in space and time. It must, further, present itself as an instance of a rule or a kind (rather than as a unique incident), capable of figuring in a general theory. Accordingly, in cognitive psychology ways are found to externalize the mind, to force it to become a public phenomenon with measurable dimensions and to frame research programs in terms of models which express general mental features.

Since the single phenomenal dimension of the mind is time, the most powerful technique of cognitive psychology is chronometry, the measurement of reaction or response times. Now while in physics time is the prevalent independent variable, in cognitive science time is most often dependent on distance. The end however is the same: the discovery of functions to incorporate in a model of the structures and processes of the mental system. The ultimate hypothetical expectation is that the temporal evidence can be given a spatial basis, that is to say, that it can eventually be fitted into a spatiotemporal physical neural system.

However, cognitive psychology is unlike physics in that subject and "subject," the observer and the observed, are the same in kind—conscious beings. So much the more is it necessary to the "objectivity" of the science that they should not be identical in number. No more than people can safely be their own judges can they be their own cognitive psychologists. The subject in the philosophical sense, the person, has to undergo a division of labor into the task-setting psychologist and the responding "subject."

The surface reason for cutting people's reports of their conscious experience out of the enterprise is simple, though perhaps surprising. People are demonstrably full of illusions and ignorance regarding the nature of their own mental events. Subjects often show surprise when told the results of experiments they have participated in; they didn't, as it were, know they had it in them.

The deeper reason is in fact the fundamental hypothesis of cognitive psychology. It is that one cannot in principle know one's mind, because it is a covert operation, ultimately a brain function, of which subjective experience is a kind of insubstantial facade.

Consequently, in imagery studies only this is initially presupposed about the participating subjects: They can, as indeed they claim they can, follow directions to "Image!" when it is explained to them that they are to picture things before their mind's eye (Kosslyn and Holyoak 1982). Furthermore, they can memorize a picture. These are large assumptions, for which the experiments are intended to tease out corroboration as they go. So, since the subjects' responsive utterance is an unavoidable factor in experiments, the point is to compel additional facts beyond the subject's awareness to emerge by rigorous control of the protocols of introspection.

Next it is necessary to find a way to draw out the object-contents of the mind, namely its representations. This a particularly tricky proceeding for visual imagery, since there is no way, as yet, to get inside the head, and there are special difficulties about getting imagery out. Words are in principle inadequate for describing pictures exhaustively, while in fact drawings are usually insufficient. Of course, the cognitive ideal would be to externalize images via the detection and projection of their patterns of cortical activity. Researchers dream about a device that would throw a person's imagery on the screen for all to see: a strange déjà vu in which a subject might be fed back its very own imagery as a percept simultaneously with having it (Shepard 1980).

The solution in imagery science is to regiment the mental image severely. The representations useful to the science are not the spontaneous, feeling-fraught shapes nor the delightful panoramic visions of the imaginative imagination, but memorized mundane pictures of isolated, usually uncolored, objects. In short, subjects are asked to memorize very boring drawings, not for pleasure but for business. It is thus that imagery is brought under control.

As has been said, the theory of "reaction times" is the bread and butter of imagery studies (Klatzky 1980). Subjects are asked to perform some precise mental task or to solve a well-defined problem in the hope that the measured reaction times will reveal whether imagery was being used—that is, scanned, rotated, or otherwise transformed—and if so, what in particular its "privileged," that is, imagery-specific, features might be. These methods produce significant results precisely because subjects are often not conscious of time differences in their imagery processes—for instance, that it really takes longer to image a scene than an item (Kosslyn 1983, 100).

However, there is an aspect which makes imagery somewhat intractable to scientific treatment and which, hard though the experimenters try, they cannot get around. It is the pictorial likeness of the representations they deal with (Anderson 1978). The methods have to assume, and the experiments continually corroborate, that having imagery is somehow like seeing, that is, like visual perceiving, and that it is somehow like seeing pictures. Indeed the very naming of the subject implies such a hypothesis.

The picture metaphor seems to cause continual confusions and cross-purposes. It thus becomes the more necessary to outline in the broadest possible strokes the notion of a picture in general, and to see how it applies to mental imagery.

To begin with, a picture is physically seen. There is evidence that mental imaging is akin to perceptual seeing. Two obvious points of similarity are revealed by introspection and corroborated by experiment: Imagery is "scanned" by the mind's eye just as the physical eye runs over the visual scene, and it is "seen" from various points of view, that is, the viewer perceives the visual object in terms of various perspectives. While having images is obviously unlike seeing in that it does not cease—in fact it often starts—when the eyes are closed and perception stops, yet it is a fact that even people blinded in childhood still imagine visually. Moreover, such differences between seeing and imagining will turn out to be, if anything, favorable to the picture metaphor of visualization: imagining is in certain respects more like picture-viewing just because it is less like perceptual inspection.

Images, quite aside from their perceptlike features, and taken as purely internal representations, have these pictorial qualities: They are apprehended as not being what they represent, or to put it another way, as being re-presentations and not the objects themselves; they are copies or replicas of original objects. They require, it will be shown, an appropriate field or medium upon which to appear, just as material pictures need a canvas. Such a medium will set a limit of resolution: Too small an area is no longer a significant part of the mental image, just as close-up details of a painting blur, whereas original bodies remain almost indefinitely and continuously accessible to optically enhanced inspection. Mental images lack their own principle of natural motion just as painted pictures do; such translations or transformations as they display, they seem to undergo passively, and their motion is as much the act of the imager as of the image. As mentioned above, they often incorporate one or more points of view, like perspectival paintings; moreover, the aspectual properties of the image can be separated from the viewer's own perspective, as in picture viewing. Again like pictures, images are compositions, that is, parts are accentuated or omitted and shapes transformed; just as with paintings, they are intrinsically interpreted, significant.

There are also, of course, obvious ways in which mental imagery, though quasi-visual, is *not* picturelike: A picture has a material substrate like canvas, which is itself in space, while the mental image is directly inscribed on the imaginal medium. Mental images, unlike pictures, are not, after all, entirely passive under scanning; they sometimes give the appearance of transforming according to intrinsic rules: that is, of having proper motions. And, of course, unlike most kinds of material pictures such as aging photographs, they fade out and are regenerable; they can, as people well know, become blurred and fuzzy, and then be revivified.

At this point it has to be said that no cognitive scientist takes the picture analogy as anything but a metaphor. None thinks that the mind's eye is literally some sort of organ, viewing an internal exhibition. Yet the very method of the experiments which follow is an implicit acknowledgment of the pictorial hypothesis, insofar as the stimuli used are nearly always themselves pictures. The reason is not only that pictures in their rigidity are the best way to regiment image memory. There is also a sense that pictures are themselves the most characteristic product of the imagination and are therefore the presentations most likely to elicit its peculiar properties. So the question becomes just how to understand the picture analogy.

## IV. Experimental discoveries about mental imagery

Scientific psychology is nothing if it is not experimental. With respect to mental imagery, the trick was to design experiments whose results could be interpreted as pertaining to the inner phenomenon—if it existed to begin with. The hope was then that the actual results might show some significant regularity which would simultaneously prove the existence and display some features of mental imagery. That project proved to be possible.

The bulk of the work I am about to describe was done by Stephen Kosslyn (1980) and set out by him in a very accessible book called, in deliberate opposition to Ryle, *Ghosts in the Mind's Machine* (1983). The experiments about to be recounted are the most exemplary, the simplest, and the most easily describable. They are mostly concerned with the "privileged" properties of mental images, namely those that distinguish visual imagery from other forms of representation. It should be said right now that the results—for example, the functions discovered—seem to stand fast, but the interpretation continues to be the center of a storm of debates.

Kosslyn guides certain lines of his experimentation by means of a "decision tree," a device that is particularly appropriate, since the problem of imagery presents itself in terms of downward branching yes or no issues. The top node is defined by the issue of "not epiphenomenal [phenomenal] vs. epiphenomenal" (Kosslyn 1980, 93). Are images cognitively effective or just along for the ride?

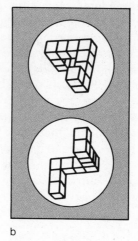

a        b        c        Figure 1

This way of putting the issue begins by admitting the experience of imagery and then asks if it is useful. Roger Shepard, the inventor of the basic technique of imagery experimentation, began with the sense that a mental event so universally reported by humans must be an adaptive function. In a memorable moment he suddenly saw a way of testing whether imagery might involve a structure-preserving mental modeling of the world and might therefore be employed in practical problem solving rather than remain mere random and idle mimicry (Shepard 1981).

The way was this: Since rigid rotations form so large a part of the physical motions in our experience, it might be possible to make their mental counterparts disclose themselves through time reactions. Subjects were shown pairs of perspective drawings of three-dimensional block shapes, armlike figures with right-angled bends, built up of ten cubes stuck face to face (fig. 1). A random half of the pairs were mirror images of each other. This meant that although they were locally—that is part by part—similar, they could not be brought into congruence by any rigid rotation (c). The rest were identical. For each pair the two members were drawn at different orientations, such that they might be brought into comparable or coincident positions by a rotation either in the picture plane (a) or in depth (b).

Subjects were to begin at a signal to inspect the drawings of the pairs and were to press a "same" or "different" switch to stop the reaction timer as soon as they had reached a judgment.

Reaction times, when graphed, displayed a beautifully clean linear function. The times taken to make the judgment were directly proportional to the angle of rotation required to make the orientations the same or comparable, from 0 to 180 degrees. Different subjects had slightly different personal rates of rotation, but the rates were individ-

114

ually constant; whether the rotations were in the picture plane or in depth, the average rate of mental motion was 60 degrees a second.

The results were clearly interpretable as showing that a moving image, a mental model of the rotation, was used to solve the problem of comparing the figures. Presumably they were first brought into like orientation and then either compared piecemeal or superimposed (Shepard 1981, with Metzler, chap. 3).

Other experiments showed that the rotations were indeed continuous through intermediate positions. Shepard's associate, Lynn Cooper, asked subjects to rotate mentally some well-defined plane shapes which they had been asked to memorize. Other shapes were then presented for comparison. Judgments were fastest when the test shape was presented in the orientation calculated to have been reached by the mental image at various angles of rotation. Clearly the mental image was rotated as a whole over all positions.

The alternative possibility would have been to compare the pictures feature by feature. This imageless procedure would have resulted in very different time functions. It was a strategy evidently not spontaneously preferred. Nevertheless, the interpretation of these results in terms of imagery use has been impugned on the grounds, applicable *mutatis mutandis* [with due modification] to most of the experiments, that subjects have enough tacit knowledge of physical motions like rotation to produce an internal wordlike description. It is thought that such verbal renditions might mimic the stages of the transformation by discrete symbolic computations in the time needed to perform a real rotation. However, this attack presents various difficulties. If discrete acts of understanding are involved, why is not the 180-degree rotation the fastest rather than the slowest, since conceptually it is a simple flip? Why do we generally compute at a rate of 60 degrees per second, a rate certainly not determined by any law of external motion? But above all, the verbal explanation is not at all the most straightforward one, and it is clearly driven by considerations other than the most economical explanation of these results.

There exist profuse variations on these experiments leading to many detailed inferences concerning the nature of images. For example, it seems to be the object itself which is mentally rotated and not its plane picture or its retinal image. This is indicated by the finding that the images of solids presented as plane drawings preserve proper perspective under mental rotation. Hence it is not the intrinsic conceptual structure of the object that is being immediately displayed but its apparent "visual" shape. Furthermore, images of objects variously arranged in three-dimensional space are mentally seen as in a picture plane, since the scanning times of these objects are proportional to their two-dimensional picture plane distance (Kosslyn 1983, 155). Evidently some imagery is indeed "seen" from a point of view, just as a picture, or, for that matter, a view, would be. It follows that the plane aspect of an image carries some three-dimensional information, for even without the opportunity to reach into actual space for further experience, novel imagery objects with geometric structures can be internally rotated to reveal, for example, their backsides. The fascinating but problematic implication of these discoveries is that while a mental image has pictorial characteristics, an imaged object has a status analogous to that of an actual object and may display itself, as it were, to our admiring gaze independently of prior perceptual knowledge.

A further problem arises over the "mental motion" implicit in these findings. The mental rotation rate appears not to mimic any natural motion but rather something like the deliberate turning of an object in one's hands. But then where does the specific uniform rate come from? And suppose the motions of mental objects did mimic, say, the acceleration of natural objects, should one say that tacit knowledge was at work or that some sort of imaginary mass was controlling the motion? Both puzzles will be discussed below.

Shepard's first round of rotation experiments concentrated on cognitive effectiveness and merely broached the question concerning the privileged or constitutive properties of mental imagery and its motions. The series that deals with these properties systematically is by Kosslyn. Perhaps it would be more accurate to say that his experiments are largely designed to test whether the mental events elicited by instructions to image do have depictive character—whether they are indeed *images*. Consequently the first question is: Do they in fact have the kind of spacelike dimension or extension that can in some sense be scanned?

In these experiments, in contrast to the Shepard series, subjects do not keep the stimulus picture before them while doing the rotation; instead they memorize drawings. What is more, subjects are asked not to move the figures mentally but to scan them. This technique is carefully devised, first, to avoid the contamination of the imaging process by ongoing perception, and, second, to get a handle on the agent of the mental motion.

Subjects memorized a fictive map of an island in which seven features, such as a hut, a tree, and a beach, were schematically depicted, each at a different distance from all the others (fig. 2). Subjects were to focus on one certain location in the island. At the naming of a second feature they were to locate it by a glance, then to make a black speck move as fast as possible from the first to the second, and finally to press a button as soon as it had arrived. The results showed that "scanning" times increased linearly with the distance from the original location. The subjects were evidently doing something analogous to visual scanning.

A double check was run. Since plus-or-minus-seven had long been known to be the number of items that can be stored in short-term memory, it was possible that subjects might simply be remembering the features as a list of names and checking the destination feature against this list. In that case, it was predicted, reaction times would no longer vary with distance. This time subjects were not asked to scan the map, but just to respond as fast as possible without necessarily using imagery. The result was that no discernible function connected times and distances; whatever they were doing, the subjects were not scanning.

The conclusion is that mental imagery is scannable, hence somehow spacelike or extensive (Kosslyn 1980, 43).

Pictures are seen on a medium like canvas or paper. If mental images are indeed picturelike, they too may have a medium analogue. The notion of a mental medium is old. In the *Theaetetus* Plato uses the metaphor of a wax tablet, capable of receiving impressions with different degrees of sharpness in different people [*GBWW*, Vol. 7, p. 539a]. Guided by this figure, Kosslyn has devised experiments that would force the imagistic medium, if there was one, to reveal its features.

Pictures have a limit of resolution. The canvas, being grainy, will not take strokes below a certain size; the painted image itself is also grainy, since it is composed of brushstrokes. Moreover, the eye is incapable of discerning parts that are too small. The image as a whole therefore has a limit of resolution, on approaching which details become harder and harder to make out. In Kosslyn's experiment on mental images these three factors are not discriminated, but the whole effect is attributed to a mental medium. The point is to see if this limit-effect is demonstrable.

Subjects were bidden to image a target animal, say a rabbit. They were to picture it at correct relative size, first as next to an elephant,

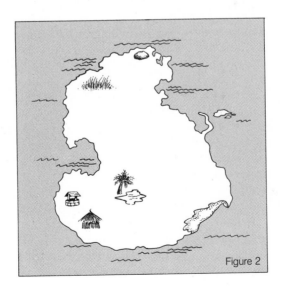

Figure 2

and then as next to a fly. The assumption was that the larger animal would crowd the smaller one into a tiny part of the imaginal space. The hypothesis of a mental "grain" predicts that tiny features are harder to "see" and therefore take longer to make out. And so it proved: Reaction times for reading the features and answering questions about the comparatively small animals were longer. Now most people have more bunny than fly information handy, because they feel more affectionate toward the former than the latter. Lest results be influenced by this fact, subjects were also asked to image a huge fly next to a tiny target animal, with the same result: The small animal took longer to report. The results were interpreted to mean that the medium has, in some sense, a grain. Of course, this is being guided by the medium metaphor with a vengeance. Introspection suggests that what takes time in "seeing" tiny images is rather the focusing of the mind's eye than the inspection of the grainy image. But as we will see, Kosslyn has motives for not making that interpretation.

This experiment was now extended to counter the claim, always lying in wait, that the chronometric results have an alternative nonimagistic explanation. Suppose subjects were expending the capacity of their short-term memory on storing the features of the larger animals, so that they had to dig into long-term memory for answering questions about small animals such as: Does a fly have a mouth? Suppose, moreover, it was not the largeness of the animal image that made for fast answers but the "associative strength" of features, namely how strongly one term calls up another, as "elephant" does "trunk."

These objections were tested by pitting "associative strength" against size. It can be ascertained that most people associate claws more closely with cats than they do heads. Thus, when cats are mentioned, they think of claws more immediately than of heads, although heads are much larger. Subjects were asked whether certain specific features belonged to certain animals. Without imaging instructions, the stronger association of features made for shorter response times. With imagery instructions, the greater size of the features did. Evidently, when subjects were using imagery, the medium's grainy characteristics came into play (Kosslyn 1983, 58).

Material pictorial media, like canvas and paper, have both definite size and shape. The mental medium too is not unlimited, as the fact that a large animal crowds out a small one indicates. Can the dimensions be more definitely determined?

The size of the medium, just like the perceptual field, is appropriately measured by the visual angle it subtends (fig. 3). Here is a simplified account of the main experiment determining that angle. Subjects were asked to memorize line drawings of different-sized animals. Larger animals were drawn larger but correct proportion was not preserved. Among them was a rabbit, a dog, a cow, an elephant. The participants

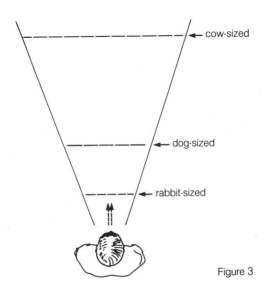

Figure 3

were then asked to take a "mental walk" toward the images and to place a real tripod at that distance from a wall at which they judged the animal image to be when it began to overflow the mental screen. The result was that the various distances at overflow were roughly proportional to the real-life sizes of the different animals. These distances, the dimensions of the animal, and a little trigonometry together gave the visual angle subtended by the medium as roughly 25 degrees.

The shape of the medium was also measured by a "mental walk," this time toward a foot-long ruler imaged once horizontally and then vertically. It overflowed sooner in the vertical dimension, showing that the medium is roughly elliptical.

In these experiments it was found that imagery was fuzzy toward the edges of the medium, and that the area of greatest acuity was small and roughly circular (Kosslyn 1980, 73, 84).

Is the image space thus discovered really a canvaslike medium or rather just a quasi-perceptual field? There is one obvious indicator of the difference between the mental medium and a material medium: It is impossible to tear a piece off an image as off a photograph. A mental image cannot be mutilated through its medium, which, in effect, is therefore less, not more, concrete than the image it underlies. What this circumstance indicates is that the medium mimics the perceptual field. That field, too, is roughly elliptical because of the horizontal setting of our eyes. It too subtends roughly the same visual angle, and it too has a similar area of acuity. But then, of course, the very conception of a mental walk presupposes that the mind's "eyes" have their quasi-visual field, just as the organic eyes look out on a delimited part of the world.

Imagery is notoriously unstable. It is both fleeting and changing. It fades continually and quickly, especially when fixated, as one can tell by mentally staring at the center of an image. This is the mental analogue to perceptual "adaptation," which occurs where neurons overused by staring at an object stop firing, so that the image fades. Eye movement is necessary to sight. An experiment featuring the memorized image of three concentric blobs showed that when the mental gaze was fixed on the largest blob, the middle blob was more "adapted out" than when the gaze was first fixed on the innermost one. Evidently fixating on an area "adapted" the whole of the medium within it, showing that the medium works as a whole (Kosslyn 1983, 67).

In the laboratory, imagery comes into being through time and in parts and is transformed continuously. A deliberately formed image does not arise suddenly as a full-blown panorama. Imaging is less like the sudden epiphany that seizes a seer and more like the compositional process engaged in by a painter.

The next experiment consequently deals with the temporal forming of imagery. Once it had been established that experienced imagery is indeed a quasi-pictorial representation, the next issue or node on the decision tree was: How is imagery stored when we are not experiencing it, and how is it retrieved from long-term memory—as a whole, or in parts?

For the experiment to show that forming images takes time, subjects learned first to draw and then to image a series of squares. Each square was six times the area of the preceding one. The largest was just large enough to overflow the mental medium. They were then asked to imagine various animals filling the different squares. (In fact they were to imagine each animal in all the squares, in order to prevent variations in complexity from affecting response times.) The results were straightforward: Larger animals took more time to image. Probably this means that images are retrieved medium-section by medium-section and not all at once as a unit, or size would not matter.

On the other hand, the amount of mental ink used, so to speak, for drawing an image does not affect recall-time. For when subjects were asked to image an equilateral triangle inscribed in a larger one, they took less time to interpret the figure in the terms just described than when asked to see it as three triangles around a central one (fig. 4). Had the mere amount of drawn line mattered, the times should have been identical. Unlike the pictorial medium, the imagery medium does not bear a fixed quantity of "paint," that is, of activated area (Kosslyn 1980, 97).

Other experiments showed more ways in which images are generated in sections. Elements can be sequentially recovered from memory and overlaid or "glued" to make a whole. Parts are added, not with reference to any coordinate system of the medium, but directly to the

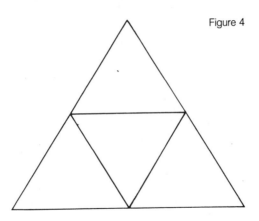

Figure 4

image already present. They are, as it were, not disposed aesthetically in mental space, but contextually in relation to the figure. Furthermore, Shepard and Cooper (1981) had earlier shown that larger angles of mental rotation take longer; now it was shown that larger images took longer to rotate (Kosslyn 1980, 290). Since, in addition, more complex images took longer to generate, while complexity failed to affect rotation times, the inference was that images are shifted as a whole rather than continually regenerated at new positions. Yet such incremental shifting also introduced incremental error. People reported that after rotating images through large angles the images grew deformed; presumably some realignment then occurred.

In general, transformations come in two classes, "field-general" and "region-bounded." The first means that the whole imagery content of the field shifts; the second means that only the local contents change. Transformations in each class have analogues in the other. Zooming is field-general; imaging the enlargement of an object is its region-bounded analogue (Kosslyn 1980, 341). This duality suggests once again that the mind's eye and the mental space are, somewhat mysteriously, obverses of each other: Either the mental medium or the mental eye may move.

The findings under this last heading, the generation and transformation of imagery, are the best grist to the mill of the computational model which is the crux of Kosslyn's work. The ambition of cognitive research is finally not to collect descriptive features of imagery but to provide a global theory. Moreover, it is in the nature of cognitive science to conceive of theories as essentially embodied in models. For models are incarnations of abstract principles which work, which can be run as a program. Kosslyn was first brought to his computational theory by a crude but serviceable computer-mind analogy in which the physical computer served to suggest the elementary components of an imagery theory. It consisted of a TV screen, analogous to our experienced mental image space where the surface images appear; a central processing unit analogous to our long-term memory, which stores the deep representations that are called up onto the mental screen; and an interpretative processing device analogous to the mind's eye, which scans the surface images.

Kosslyn makes careful methodological discriminations, among them the distinction between the aspects of a model which embody the theory and the irrelevant areas which belong to the model, insofar as it is a particular embodiment. The physical computer itself is such an irrelevancy, and in his full-fledged model Kosslyn comes to the point of abandoning the indeed increasingly doubtful computer-brain analogy. In fact the brain does not effectively enter these studies at all, while it is only the functional aspect of the computer which models the mind. In sum, the model actually involves not a computer-brain analogy but a program-mind analogy.

Here is a sketch of the program model: It provides for two structures and for many processes. The first of the structures is an active memory matrix. This matrix is the imagery medium which models the experienced imagery. A display screen for externalizing the imagery can be added but is not integral to the model. The second structure is a long-term memory with storage facilities for information, which can be either of a potentially visual type, such as pairs of coordinates for points in the image space, or of a nonvisual type, such as files listing features under category headings.

The actual memory is a matrix of cells with filled or unfilled locations from which an external picture can be generated on the screen. In computer terms, this storage device, intermediate between the central processing unit and the display screen, is a "visual buffer." This structure incorporates all the properties discovered: shape, size, fading, limit of resolution. The last, for example, is obtained as a bonus from the fact that the number of cells is exceeded by the number of dots which represent the "ink" of the image. This means that points sometimes overlap and cannot be resolved.

The propositional long-term memory stores lists with the most strongly associated features on top, so that when an item is called by category name, these come up fastest. Thus, CAT PRP, which calls the propositional file on cat, will get up "claws" before "head."

Images are generated, inspected, and transformed by a variety of processes. For example, the IMAGE process is used to generate images. It first checks the propositional file for the name of a basic skeletal image, such as the body of a car, which is in turn used by the PICTURE process to activate the proper coordinates in the surface matrix at a requested size or location. Further processes fill in parts, such as tires.

The model generates ways to simulate the observed behavior and to predict the properties of images. But it is more than a mere device for predictions. It provides an account of underlying processes at work in the having of imagery. Moreover, it embodies the basic theory that the mind has cognitive structures and processes of a picturelike nature. The model also helps to uncover indeterminacies and contradictions in the submodels, the devices for accounting for specific behavior, and it suggests further inquiries.

No doubt it is marvelous to see a computer screen mimic, however crudely, our own imaging. But what the theory behind the model does not pretend to do is to give the "deep reasons" for our imagery capacities (Kosslyn 1980, 477). Nor can it claim that these structures and functions are those actually and literally underlying imagery. One might say that it is similar to a Copernican hypothesis of epicycles more than to a Keplerian theory of real orbits. It is a possible, not a real, explanation.

## V. The interpretation of mental imagery findings

The compound hypothesis required for imagery study to get under way was that there are mental representations, both structures and processes, and that some of these behave like images. Both assumptions were regarded as ranging from unassailable to indefensible in the debate going on in philosophy and cognitive science. This debate, passionate enough before, becomes rousingly involved when an attempt is made to cash in on the promise, so often made in those disciplines, to refer problems from the conceptual to the experimental domain for final solution. For then the argument picks up additional complexity from controversies internal to experimental psychology itself.

One such complication comes from the claim that all mental representations are propositional, and that the results presented cannot prove otherwise. This propositionalist claim puts the experimental science of mental imagery on the defensive from its very inception, by forcing it to stop before it even begins. Before trying to discover the properties of its objects, cognitive psychologists must show that they in fact exist, that we have mental images at all. They must try to do this without depending on people's self-reports. Thus Galton's innocent old procedure of just asking people is put out of commission. It may seem like a fatal first move, but such strong challenges to ordinary experience as are mounted by the successors of the Behaviorists have the force of a bear hug: Disengagement requires desperate measures.

To give the problem of existence some scientific bite, it is necessary to establish a conceptual criterion for distinguishing mental imagery from other representations. Spacelikeness comes to mind. Yet to show that anything can be spacelike without being spatial (no one claims that mental images are literally, somatically spatial) is a subtle philosophical task. So without clear conceptual marks of imagery, the problem of its existence cannot be met head-on in cognitive psychology—though, as we have seen, it can scramble itself into very plausible conclusions.

This is the moment to delineate in more detail the two camps of the imagery debate carried on within cognitive psychology. They have been alluded to before, but a more explicit distinction between them will help to establish the desired criteria for calling something a mental image. The battle is formulated around the nature of the mental "code." Is it exclusively "propositional," or is there also an "imagistic" code? Obviously, what is at stake is the existence of mental images.

The propositionalists (whose chief proponent is Zenon Pylyshyn) think that the elements of cognitive representations are wordlike, discrete symbols, organized by categories, which come together in verbalistic descriptions. The imagists, on the other hand, posit at least some representations that are spacelike, not subordinately organized but extensive and continuous, and which represent objects by depiction-preserving resemblance. Imagists, of course, admit that cognition is also verbal: they adhere to a "dual-code" theory.

To understand the difference between the two schools, it is necessary to see how the term *proposition* is understood in the propositionalist code. A proposition is more abstract than a verbal sentence, since it may be expressed in several linguistic versions. Consequently this code is not precisely verbal but rather wordlike. Propositions are taken as having truth values; they are either true or false. They are made up of various kinds of discrete symbols and formed according to explicit rules of syntax by which their well-formedness can be tested. They have something that can be read as a predicate-argument structure; thus they shouldn't be mere arrays or lists (Anderson 1978).

Images, on the other hand, are precisely *not* what propositions are: They are not abstract but concrete, since each image is a quasi-sensory particular. Neither are they unequivocal, since in contrast to a formal proposition, an image can sometimes be "read" in diverse ways—as is, for example, a trick picture in which various figures suddenly stand out. Images are not either true or false, except in conjunction with a proposition. They are not discrete, but rather spacelike and continuous, so that a part of an image is still an image, whereas a part of a proposition is no longer a proposition. This is so because, while the latter are formed according to general syntactic rules, images are governed, if by any rules at all, by gestalt laws, laws of visual organization. Such laws organize the whole representation at once, "holistically," rather than sequentially or coordinately, as do syntactic rules. Moreover, images seem to be capable of an intrinsic fuzziness, while propositions (as distinct from actual human speech) are definite. On the other hand, images cannot be noncommittal, that is, simply blank, about the appurtenances of a visible feature, while propositional representations can be simply silent. For example, except in degenerate cases like stick figures (Block

1981a, 14), a head in an image is either crowned by a hat or not; the sentence needn't say.

The positive marks of imagery are precisely those collected in the experiments above: having a sized and shaped and grainy medium within which is inscribed a depictive structure activated part by part and subject to definite transformations.

These, then, are the two chief sides of the debate. The debate itself begins with a propositional attack on the imagist position, an attack which is largely theoretical. There are not many clear experimental findings in favor of propositionalism, but here is an important one. It is the so-called congruity effect. When subjects are asked which of two large items is the larger, they respond measurably faster than when they are asked which of two large items is smaller, that is, when the asking and the response categories are mismatched. This effect would seem to indicate that not the image but the categorization matters. However, Kosslyn explains the effect in terms of the recalibration of the mental comparison mechanism for imagery, a process which might take just as long as would category rematching. He shows that both processes are at work in parallel, "racing" each other. Whichever gets there first wins out. For example, when two memory representations are in the same size category, it is fastest to compare the images directly without considering the categories (Kosslyn et al. 1980).

Some of the theoretical objections on the propositional side (Pylyshyn 1978) are as follows (here listed with the imagist rebuttals in parentheses): The imagery model still relies on self-reports, which propositionalists eschew on principle. (However, some cooperative response on the subject's part seems unavoidable in either case.) The imagery code is computationally cumbersome to store, on account of the indefinitely large amount of information in an image. (However, it is unclear why a description of a visual memory would be more parsimonious than a depiction. Imagine exhaustively describing a picture, especially in a symbolic code that was true enough to the particularity of an image to generate an individuated symbol for every item in it.)

Another theoretical argument is that, if there are two codes, they must be readily translatable into one another. For example, images can be described, descriptions can summon images, and sometimes people even forget whether the original source of information was visual or auditory. Such translatability seems to require a third, more abstract code as a common basis and this "interlingual" code would be essentially propositional. (The objection to this argument is analogous to Aristotle's "third man" criticism of the Platonic forms [*GBWW*, Vol. 8, p. 587c]: If two codes need a third to be related, then that third in turn needs yet another code to relate it to either one, and so on to an infinite regression. Thus any coding becomes impossible.)

There are also two methodological arguments against all imagery experiments at once. One is the claim that they are all contaminated by "task demands," which means that they reveal nothing about having imagery but only something about the expectations built into the task. For example, suppose it is the case that subjects cannot do mental rotations on very complex block figures unless they find a way to reduce the complexity of the task. Suppose they do this by discovering at a glance that large parts of the figures are the same and then comparing the rest piecemeal. One might conclude that Shepard's figures were of just the right complexity for this process to mimic rotation times (Yuille 1983a). (However, the imagist side in fact allows for such feature-by-feature comparison where that is easiest. Moreover, it can parry the task-demand objection by showing that generally subjects are kept in careful ignorance of the point of the experiment and cannot guess the results (Kosslyn 1980, 458; Pinker and Kosslyn 1983).

The other methodological argument against imagery experiments is this: It has been proved formally that for any apparently imagistic process, say rotation, an equivalent propositionalist explanation mimicking it can be constructed. As for processes, so for shapes: Any form can be encoded propositionally. For example, the letter $R$ can be seen as a whole figure, but it can also be described algebraically, in terms of points, straight and curved line segments, and angles (Anderson 1978, 268–69). It turns out to be a matter of trade-offs. To get an imagistic interpretation, one keeps the structures "holistic" and makes them bear much implicit information, thus keeping processes simple. To get propositionalist readings, one makes the elements spare, symbolic, and explicit, with well-defined but complex transformations (Pylyshyn 1978). Seen from this angle, the whole problem is reduced to computational preferences. But that does not make imagery studies futile (Johnson-Laird 1983, 151). After all, to show the impossibility of proof isn't to show that neither side is right. By the criteria of straightforwardness, closeness to common experience, and plausible accounting for the peculiarities of structures and processes, the imagist side does better.

Finally, the deepest anti-imagist argument is that from "cognitive penetrability," which is Pylyshyn's phrase (1981, 159–60). It signifies the fact that the influence of beliefs penetrates both perception and imagery. Neither percepts nor memory images are strictly veridical, but they are vulnerable to transformations depending on "tacit" knowledge. For example, people usually recall a panoramic scene not as an evenly distributed surface but hierarchically, in terms of a total initial impression whose detail can be recalled by using the whole as a cue. Or again, in an experiment reminiscent of those Jean Piaget did on children, subjects were shown trick photographs of pitchers tilted at various angles whose fluid levels were not horizontal. Over half the subjects failed to "see" anything wrong, although they correctly perceived that the levels were not parallel to some shelves in the pictorial background. In post-experimental interviews it emerged that those and only those subjects recognized the trick who could clearly articulate the principle of fluid-level invariance. Thus, only those who tacitly knew the rule for the correct situation could recognize a wrong one. The others were blind to it, although they must have seen that the fluid levels in tilted containers remain horizontal often enough in real life.

In short, what we know affects what we see, and similarly, what we imagine. Images do not represent percepts photographically but in an interpretative transformation. Our propositional knowledge informs imagery. (However, the imagist rejoinder goes, the imagery theory was never meant as a crudely photographic one. It explicitly specified that when convenient, images can be "categorized," that is to say, read propositionally—or interpreted—rather than scanned imagistically.)

All in all, then, the arguments against the dual-code theory, in which propositional and imagistic processes race or supplant each other, seem to be answerable, and the experimental evidence seems to favor it (Kosslyn 1980, 363). Here, to end with, is a very simple and telling experiment in favor of a dual coding in which both thinking and imaging processes figure. When first asked how many windows there are in their houses, most people will take a mental walk and count as they conjure up the facades imagistically. However, when asked the same question later in the day they will have the answer handy propositionally, in terms of a digit. Before long, however, the number is apt to be forgotten. Evidently, in some cases, picture memory is not only more long-term but better for active recall than is verbal memory.

## VI. Conclusions and consequences

The mental imagery issue, then, carried on in terms of the "How many codes?" question, tends to a conclusion favoring the existence of imagery. Yet there remain deep obscurities and perplexities which become even more intriguing once the cognitive effectiveness, and by implication the existence, of mental imagery is accepted. The outstanding questions are: How really is mental imagery a bearer of knowledge? Just what is the literal sense of the "mind's eye" metaphor? What actually is the object which the mind's eye sees, and what is the nature of that seeing? Just what moves in mental motion and by what laws?

One might demand that once the fact of imagery is granted, all the metaphors should be literally interpreted. But then the difficulties detailed above start all over, only now in dead earnest—and that is how they will be taken here.

First, then, how do we know or learn by means of mental images? Just what do they contribute? Insofar as they are merely recalled percepts, their function, if not its explanation, is simple. They can act in two ways: They can serve as a kind of mental photo album which simply brings back visual memories (fact retrieval), or, more actively, they can help to solve problems that have a spatial aspect (mental models). I am hewing to the cognitive line here in taking cognition as information processing. Of course, the imagination might also be the source of revelations for which "information" would be something of a misnomer. But that sort of vision is not the present topic.

Insofar as an image is straightforwardly a restored percept or memory (as indeed it normally is in the laboratory), it is a perceptual stand-in and is used as perception is used. In this case having a mental image is cognitive just as perception is having knowledge, namely insofar as some purposeful focusing, transforming, analyzing, categorizing, or feature reading is occurring (Kosslyn and Pomerantz 1981). Good examples for images as perceptual stand-ins come from elementary geometry. The famous old problem of "doubling the square"—put to such cognitively suggestive use as in Plato's *Meno* [*GBWW,* Vol. 7, pp. 174–90]—can be intuitively solved by imagining the corners of a square which has been circumscribed about another square to be folded in so as to cover the internal square, just as one might do with a piece of paper.

But images are not normally percept-photos for most people. They are rather very much "cognitively penetrable"; that is, they arrive already shot through with tacit knowledge and nonconscious intentions. Here arises the continually perplexing question: Does imagery give even marginally more than it gets? In other words, are images also to some degree cognitively *im*penetrable? Are they at all autonomous bearers of knowledge? Although imagery often renders no small service by incorporating and bringing out unnoticed detail, hidden designs, and unspoken cognitions, yet the imagist ideal would aim higher. It would be realized if images, quite independently of the subject's fund of propositional knowledge, so transformed, anticipated, or accented perceptions as to reveal something genuinely new, just as dreams were once thought to reveal not the subconscious of the dreamer but the nature of things.

Imagists often do cite anecdotes in favor of this power of imagery, especially from scientific discovery (e.g., Shepard and Cooper 1981). Einstein himself, in a famous letter to Jacques-Salamon Hadamard, insisted that the "combinatory play" of the imagination "seems to be the essential feature in productive thought." One of those thought- or rather imagination-experiments, whose paradoxical implication first preoccupied Einstein at sixteen, is the mental image of a physicist riding a beam of light with a mirror held at arm's length before him. In our context, the question concerning this ingenious image would be: Does the rider learn that the mirror is blank by inspecting his own imagery, or does he imagine it that way because he already knows that the reflection can't outrun him (Einstein 1949)?

So, granting imagery various ancillary cognitive uses, these deepest matters remain unresolved: Can we have veridical images of circumstances previously unperceived or in principle unperceivable? For example, having never come across a square while its corners were being folded in, could we image the process, not in the sense of constructing it rationally by thinking, but of finding it in the image medium by looking? Or can we at least read perceptual memories more discriminatingly than we apprehended the original percept itself? To take a physical instance, could we "see" in visual memory the parabolic trajectory of a ball whose orbital rule had escaped us in visual tracking? Or, at the very least and vaguest, does our mere having of images itself perhaps tell us something about the constitution of an imageable world? These cognitive questions shade into philosophical perplexities, which is to say that they may be in principle unamenable to empirical resolution. They certainly are nowhere near resolution now.

Next, how is the "mind's eye" metaphor defanged and deployed in imagery research? Mental imagery invites talk of "seeing" more spontaneously and properly than does any other kind of conscious awareness, and it is more seriously involved in the problems of consciousness. Thus on the one hand, we do have the experiences of internal seeing and of correlated objects of inner sight, while on the other, no cognitive scientist wants to admit an organ of internal sight or wants to distinguish literally the process (the imaging) from the product (the image).

In a way, the "mind's eye" flap is a red herring. The mind's eye is a pseudo-organ that "sees"; however, although the physical eye is a real enough organ, it doesn't see, being merely a transducer of stimuli. So the "organ" question is a diversion. The mind's eye is only a subproblem of the problem of consciousness. Not the "mind's eye," but the "mind's I," is at issue, to borrow a dreadful pun from Douglas Hofstadter.

Nonetheless, image investigators feel obliged to take up the problem, or, more precisely, to show that imagery representation is possible without the absurdity of an internal agent of sight. In fact, the title of Kosslyn's second book on imagery, *Ghosts in the Mind's Machine,* is a borrowing of Ryle's phrase for any inner agent of awareness, including the mind's eye. One point of Kosslyn's book is to reassert mental, especially imagistic, representation against Ryle, while taking the teeth, or better, the eyes, out of that offensive homunculus, that little watcher within, and sending him packing: "Goodbye Homunculus" is one of his chapter titles. However, the internal seer, the mind's eye, is not so easily dismissed.

In the cognitive computer model, the "mind's eye" is thought of as the interpretative function which reads the imagery space, the cell matrix. It determines, for example, if this space contains points meeting the rule for the image of a straight line, and it computes similarities or searches for identifying features (Pylyshyn 1978). The trouble is that this work is just not what the mind's eye of common parlance does. That eye sees. It genuinely gazes. So whatever ghost is being exorcised, it is not the mind's eye of experience.

Furthermore, the computational model itself incorporates some strange exchanges of functions. One such is the rather unnatural assignment of the resolving power, as well as of size limitation and of shape, to the "medium." After all, acuity, visual angle, and field of vision would normally be said to belong to the organ of sight rather than to its visual object. Similarly the scanning operation is assigned to the image itself. It is an imaginal translation transformation; the image itself moves across the buffer (Kosslyn 1980, 329), which certainly contradicts our ordinary experience of imaging. To be sure, the model does embody features which replicate the feel of internal image viewing. For example, it identifies the summoning and the seeing of an image, which do merge in the process of visualization. (Oddly enough, Kosslyn was surprised at the experimental finding that inspection was part of the generating process [1983, 103].) But with respect to the forcible reassignment of functions from mind's eye to medium, one might say that the ocular ghost hadn't been so much exorcised as sacked.

The question, "Exactly what is the image-object?" is thus just the obverse or complement of the "mind's eye" problem. Image and inner eye stand and fall together. Once the (admittedly troubling) notion of internal perception-like seeing is proscribed, the image itself can no longer display itself as a quasi-spatial inner appearance inscribed into a medium possessing a sort of quasi-physical extension.

Then what is there left for the image to be? Recall that the "visual buffer," the medium function, is modeled as a matrix of cells for storing active memory points. Now this matrix is actually in no way spatial. It is in fact only a list of coordinates that are under certain constraints. These are interpretable as locations yielding, when activated, image configurations which when displayed have just the properties that have been experimentally discovered. It is these coordinates that are inspected by the computational analogue to the mind's eye. The matrix is thus, on the one hand, not propositional, since it has no syntactic rules, no predicate argument form, and no truth values. Yet, on the other, neither is it truly spatial, since it is digital—that is, a discretely numerical list rather than a resemblance-preserving continuum. It is a nonpropositional digital structure which shares certain formal properties with space.

In fact, the medium matrix is really intended to be a *quasi*-quasi-space: It only functions as if it were the sort of image space that is in turn experienced as if it were a perceptual space. As Kosslyn puts it: "something does not have to *be* a picture to *function* as one" (1983, 22).

An image is "emergent," meaning that it is a whole different from its constitutive parts. For the list of activated coordinate points does not at all resemble the image emerging from them.

But this is leaping lightly over a philosophical abyss. One might insist that the image has not really emerged until it has been traced as an appearance in an extensional space. One might urge that the coordinate "points" are not yet the graphic dots from which an image can emerge, precisely because they are just number pairs and not actually spatial locations or loci. From that nonmetaphorical, literal point of view the term "visual buffer" is a kind of doublespeak, glossing over a question as old as the Pythagorean inquiry into the relation of arithmetic to geometry: Doesn't the full notion of space have to include, besides its formal structure, a material element, namely its very extension? Couldn't one say that nothing can satisfyingly represent a spatial structure except another spatial structure?

If one answers yes to this question, the computational model will not ultimately seem to be about image spaces and the depictions therein at all. On the other hand, if one opts for the negative, as Kosslyn does, the argument for the cognitive convenience of processing "holistic" representations, on the ground that their information is on patent display and directly available to inspection, is much weakened. The patency, belonging as it does to the material side of space, is now gone, and who knows whether the full-blown matrix structures are very convenient or quicker to process than a propositional model would be? What is also gone is any bond of similarity between external and internal representations. The breaking of that bond is a loss cognitive science isn't quite up to mourning.

Shepard, the originator of cognitive imagery study, faces exactly this question: "In just what way are images spatial objects?" He, together with Susan Chipman, proposes to answer it by means of the notion of a "second-order isomorphism" (Shepard and Chipman 1970). A first-order isomorphism is one which preserves shape. Old-fashioned portraits are isomorphic with their sitter. He cites philosophers like Wittgenstein as discrediting the possibility of access to such mental imagery. But since his experiments show that there *is* something isomorphic about imagery, he introduces a "functional" or second-order isomorphism. It is not a relation of similarity of shape between an original and its image, but instead between *relations* among external objects on the one hand and their mental images on the other. Such a relation of relations is like an old-fashioned proportion. For example, square A has to square B the same relation as number a to number b, and this sameness of relation holds although numbers are not shaped like squares, indeed not shaped at all. Shepard calls the internal set of relational events, which might be no more than a specific activation of neurons, a functional relation. And now the problem is even more acute than it was for the medium matrix.

For although this hypothesis does avoid all talk of mental images being squarish, the price is that it also avoids determining them at all. Now the answer to the original question—in what does the spacelike, similarity-preserving nature of mental images consist?—is that the experienced images themselves are not at issue at all, but only their interrelations. Surely that is not a very satisfying answer.

The last question—"Just what is mental motion the motion of, and what are its laws?"—is, of course, intertwined with the problem of the image-object. To the propositionalists, there is an epistemological pitfall in imagery studies, namely the tendency to yield to an "objective pull." Objective pull is a Quinean phrase meaning that mental motions tend to be taken as the movements of the objects represented rather than as the motions of their representations (Pylyshyn 1978). Such an approach is said to have no explanatory power because it attributes the mental event to the properties of the natural object. For example, it might attribute an image motion to the inertia of the body represented rather than to the cognitive mechanism. This attribution is mistaken, for that mechanism "has no access to properties of the represented domain *except insofar as they are encoded in the form of the representation itself*" (Pylyshyn 1981, 171). Here is a succinct and extreme expression of what one might call, tit for tat, the "solipsistic pull" of cognitive science, namely the tendency to cut off the mental representation from any objective influence.

There is a large class of experiments by both sides (Pylyshyn 1978; Kosslyn 1980; Yuille 1983a) showing that the mental motion rate is not quite a constant, but bearing out a guess Locke ventured long ago, namely that such motion must undergo rather limited variation [*Essay Concerning Human Understanding; GBWW*, Vol. 35, pp. 155b–62a]. Mental rotations done in the presence of the perceptual stimuli are slower than those done from memory. The mental rate decreases appreciably from the 60 degrees per second mentioned above as the conceptual complexity of an imaged solid increases. Such results might seem at first be interpretable as being anti-"holistic," that is, anti-imagistic. A conceptually complex structure requires more propositional material to be processed, which takes time. However, so do the corresponding image-reading operations. A holistic reading, though done in no syntactic sequence, is yet not necessarily done all at once.

Oddly enough, in spite of the cognitive solipsism of some of its proponents, it is an implication of the propositionalists' view that people's imagery does in fact often stay close to external nature, since for them the "image" is just a simulation in propositions of the way they believe things are. Kosslyn tested this hypothesis, that experience informs such simulations, by having subjects handle two stimuli, a heavy lead-filled soft-drink bottle and a very long, light dowel. They were then asked to rotate them mentally in two ways, first by picturing the objects as

physically turning and then by mentally rotating their imaginal representations. Both objects were to be thought of as pinned through
their center to an imagined dial, and a button was to be pressed as
they passed each 45-degree mark. According to Pylyshyn's view, the
two imaged motions should come to the same thing—a simulation of
the natural motion. In each case the bottle should show some inertial
effects at the beginning and end of its rotation, and the dowel none.
But Kosslyn predicted that in the second, the "turn the image" run,
the dowel should take longer than the bottle. This result was expected
because, as has been shown, rotation is a "region-bounded" transformation, namely the sort in which not the whole image field but only
the image is transformed, and in these transformations large areas take
longer to process. And that is what happened. The image underwent
an image motion, not a simulated naturalistic one (Kosslyn 1983, 149).

Note that Kosslyn insists that in his theory, too, it is the image-object
and not the dynamic object which is moved. Indeed that is what even
the most unrefined notion of having an image implies, namely not having the dynamically real objects within: "Yet did not I by seeing draw
them into myself, when with mine eyes I beheld them" [Augustine,
*Confessions; GBWW,* Vol. 18, p. 75b]. Nonetheless, Kosslyn's theory
does take account of some of the many subtle variations in the subject's
relation to the image: Sometimes we do recall it as a memory replica
of a real free motion. We also see ourselves moving it with a motion
controlled by our own hand. We watch it reveal itself freely to our wondering gaze. We constrain it to move with a merely mental motion. We
scan the inert image. We take a mental walk around it. Sometimes the
motion is localized; sometimes the whole field undergoes translation;
sometimes it teems with localized motions.

The best imagery theory to date cannot be said to have unraveled
the mysteries of mental motion and to have reknit it into a coherent
theory. However, what has been gained is a phenomenology of internal
motions, which no future philosophical inquiry can ignore.

To the question: "What is to be learned about the imagination from
the science of mental imagery?" a curt answer might be: "Nothing very
new or very firm or very relevant to the common experience." But
there is more to it than that.

It might seem that imagery study, like so many psychological investigations, merely succeeds at what older Russians used to call "discovering
America." That is to say, it confirms belatedly and laboriously what had
long been known to ordinary people, namely that we have a certain
kind of mental picture which we use for doing tasks, to solve problems,
and to entertain ourselves. However, the science confirms common
belief not only by parrying the objections of nonbelievers but also by
specifying and filling out the notion of mental imagery. To do the latter, the enterprise employs a method of "convergent operations." That

means that it goes after its object from all sides by ad hoc experiments designed to establish at the same time—progressively and in tandem—both the definition of the concept *and* the properties of the object. The outcome is impressive precisely because, with certain revealing exceptions, it provides a controlled corroboration of ordinary intuition.

What this method cannot do is to prove rigorously the existence of its assumed object. But it can so vigorously delineate one kind of imaging capacity as to make its existence highly plausible. The imagery of cognitive psychology is of the instrumental variety, yet it surely throws some light even on unregimented common reverie—the sort of imagination dismissed by cognitivists as "warm and fuzzy." Although this experimental project cannot convince the purists who have propositionalist agendas, the imagist side seems to have the edge with the profession, and for the general reader the results are impressive. Even if it is only a skeletal, functional, mundane, and memorized—in sum, laboratory-bred—imagination which is here revealed, yet it is one with indefeasible features. Moreover, some of these discoveries concerning the size, shape, motion, generation, and fading of images are surely not accessible to mere introspection.

Aside from positive results, the imagery debate, including even its deadlock, is itself revealing. Perhaps the argument has run itself into the ground; perhaps that constitutes a "crisis" which demands a shift in terms, perhaps even a shift away from the cognitive approach (Yuille 1983a). But any new terms are likely to run into the same trouble. For they will equally reflect the intractable cognitive question—cognitive in the larger, philosophical sense: What and how many are the roots of human consciousness?

Now, while cognitive science forces explicitness and precision about the issue, the issue in turn forces the science to display its defining limits. One of those limit assumptions is the materialism universal in cognitive science. Kosslyn's popular book (1983) bears the subtitle "Creating and Using Images *in the Brain*" (my emphasis). There is little about the brain in the book except its picture. Neurons are referred to with respect to the image matrix, but a precise connection between the computational model and brain functions is nothing more than an ardent hope—ardent because the model's theory truly explains nothing until its structures and processes can be fitted to the brain as its neural functions. In the imagery context this holds particularly for the "visual buffer" and for the mental motions of imaging which may reasonably be expected to have some relation to the rates of neural processes. The expectation of succeeding in this liaison is the fundamental assumption of the science: In modern cognitive psychology:

> we describe these neural patterns [those excited in perception] . . . in
> a vocabulary more abstract than actual neural firings, namely, in the

vocabulary of mental representations and the computational processes that act on them. We then identify mental entities, such as percepts or images, with particular representations (factoring out of the problem the nature of the qualia, or subjective experiences, associated with visual processes, since they are as intractable as a scientific problem can be) . . . (Pinker and Kosslyn 1983, 57).

As was said, the actual doing of it is so far mostly conjectural. It follows that the future will tell, and what it will tell is of extreme interest. It will tell whether the structures and processes reached by going through consciousness can also be observed from the material end—whether mind is in observable detail a function of the brain. It is hard to see how this inquiry could proceed without establishing what those functions are, and, in particular, whether they include a spacelike component. And that is what the science of mental imagery seems to have done.

As for consciousness itself, it remains uncaught either way. Claiming that the brain imagines is something like saying that the mouth eats—a suggestive figure, but not a sufficient account.

## Bibliography

Works fundamental to the study of mental imagery are starred.

Anderson, John R. 1978. "Arguments Concerning Representations for Mental Imagery." *Psychological Review* 85:4, 249–77.
Block, Ned J. 1978. "Troubles with Functionalism." In Savage, 1978.
——. 1981a. "Introduction: What Is the Issue?" In Block, 1981b.
*——, ed. 1981b. *Imagery.* Cambridge: MIT Press.
——, ed. 1981c. *Readings in Philosophy of Psychology.* Vol. 2. Cambridge: Harvard University Press.
Bower, Gordon H. 1972. "Stimulus-sampling Theory of Encoding Variability." In *Coding Processes in Human Memory,* edited by Arthur W. Melton and Edwin Martin. Washington, D.C.: Winston and Sons.
*Churchland, Paul M. 1984. *Matter and Consciousness: A Contemporary Introduction to Philosophy of Mind.* Cambridge: MIT Press.
Dennett, Daniel C. 1978. "Toward a Cognitive Theory of Consciousness." In Savage, 1978.
——. 1981. "The Nature of Images and the Introspective Trap." In Block, 1981b.
Einstein, Albert. 1949. *Albert Einstein: Philosopher-Scientist,* edited by Paul A. Schilpp. Vol. 1. La Salle, Ill.: Open Court (1970), 280.
*Flanagan, Owen J., Jr. 1984. *The Science of the Mind.* Cambridge: MIT Press.

*Fodor, Jerry A. 1981. *Representations: Philosophical Essays on the Foundations of Cognitive Science.* Cambridge: MIT Press.

——. 1980. "Methodological Solipsism Considered as a Research Strategy in Cognitive Psychology" (with commentary and response). In *The Behavioral and Brain Sciences* 3:63–109; also in Fodor, 1981, without commentary.

Harman, Gilbert. 1978. "Is There Mental Representation?" In Savage, 1978.

Holt, Robert R. 1964. "Imagery: The Return of the Ostracized." *American Psychologist* 19:4, 254–64.

——. 1972. "On the Nature and Generality of Mental Imagery." In *The Function and Nature of Imagery,* edited by Peter W. Sheehan. New York: Academic Press.

Johnson-Laird, Philip N. 1983. *Mental Models: Towards a Cognitive Science of Language, Inference and Consciousness.* Cambridge: Harvard University Press.

Klatzky, Roberta L. 1980. *Human Memory: Structures and Processes.* 2nd ed. San Francisco: W. H. Freeman and Co.

*Kosslyn, Stephen M. 1980. *Image and Mind.* Cambridge: Harvard University Press.

Kosslyn, Stephen M., G. L. Murphy, M. E. Bemesderfer, and K. J. Feinstein. 1980. "Category and Continuum in Mental Comparisons." In Seamon, 1980.

Kosslyn, Stephen M., and James R. Pomerantz. 1981. "Imagery, Propositions, and the Form of Internal Representations." In Block, 1981c.

Kosslyn, Stephen M., and Keith J. Holyoak. 1982. "Imagery." In *Handbook of Research Methods in Human Memory and Cognition,* edited by C. Richard Puff. New York: Academic Press.

*——. 1983. *Ghosts in the Mind's Machine: Creating and Using Images in the Brain.* New York: Norton.

MacKay, Donald M. 1969. *Information, Mechanism and Meaning.* Cambridge: MIT Press.

*Mandler, Jean M. 1983. "Representation." In *Handbook of Child Psychology: Cognitive Development,* edited by Paul H. Mussen. Vol. 3. 4th ed. New York: John Wiley and Sons.

Palmer, Stephen E. 1978. "Fundamental Aspects of Cognitive Representation." In *Cognition and Categorization,* edited by Eleanor Rosch and Barbara B. Lloyd. Hillsdale, N.J.: Lawrence Erlbaum Associates.

Pinker, Steven, and Stephen M. Kosslyn. 1983. "Theories of Mental Imagery." In Sheikh, 1983.

Pylyshyn, Zenon. 1978. "Imagery and Artificial Intelligence." In Savage, 1978; also in Block, 1981c.

*——. 1980. *Mental Imagery and Human Memory.* New York: St. Martin's Press.

*———. 1981. "The Imagery Debate: Analog Media versus Tacit Knowledge." In Block, 1981b.

*Richardson, John T. 1980. *Mental Imagery and Human Memory.* New York: St. Martin's Press.

*Ryle, Gilbert. 1949. *The Concept of Mind.* Chapter VIII. New York: Barnes and Noble, Inc.

*Sartre, Jean-Paul. 1940. *The Psychology of Imagination,* translated by Bernard Frechtman. New York: The Citadel Press, 1965.

Savage, C. Wade, ed. 1978. *Minnesota Studies in the Philosophy of Science.* Vol. 9. Minneapolis: University of Minnesota Press.

Seamon, John G., ed. 1980. *Human Memory: Contemporary Readings.* Oxford: Oxford University Press.

*Sheikh, Anees A., ed. 1983. *Imagery: Current Theory, Research and Application.* New York: John Wiley and Sons.

Shepard, Roger N., and Susan Chipman. 1970. "Second-Order Isomorphism of Internal Representations: Shapes of States." *Cognitive Psychology* 1:1–17.

———. 1980. "The Mental Image." In Seamon, 1980.

*Shepard, Roger N., and Lynn A. Cooper. 1981. *Mental Images and Their Transformations.* Cambridge: MIT Press.

*Wittgenstein, Ludwig. 1949. *Philosophical Investigations.* 193–214. New York: The MacMillan Company, 1953.

Yuille, John C. 1983a. "The Crisis in Theories of Mental Imagery." In Yuille, 1983b.

*———, ed. 1983b. *Imagery, Memory and Cognition: Essays in Honor of Allan Paivio.* Hillsdale, N.J.: Lawrence Erlbaum Associates.

# Reconsiderations
# of Great Books
# and Ideas

# Tragedy and Comedy

## Harvey D. Goldstein

This is the second time that Harvey Goldstein has appeared in *The Great Ideas Today,* the first having been in 1982 when he provided a survey of twentieth-century theories of literature—requiring discussion of structuralism, deconstruction, post-structuralism, and other difficult topics. Literary theory, indeed, is Mr. Goldstein's field, but his main interest has been in the eighteenth century, and he has written at length on, among other subjects, the *Discourses on Art* by Sir Joshua Reynolds, selections from which were reprinted in our volume for 1976.

A graduate of the University of Chicago and Northwestern University, Mr. Goldstein has taught literature and its theory at Williams College, Brandeis University, the University of Rochester, and the University of Southern California at Los Angeles, from which he retired this year.

Now immersed in studies of Plato and eighteenth-century empiricism, he lives in Beverly Hills, not far from two of his three children. His interest in Great Books goes back to his days at Chicago, where he was a student of R. S. Crane, Elder Olson, and others of the University of that time.

# In the beginning—Comic and tragic visions in Genesis 1–5

Aristotle's *Poetics* is probably Western culture's most influential discussion of tragedy. Although Aristotle, there, shows almost exclusive concern with the form of tragedy, he nevertheless does make a few significant observations about tragic matter, identifying the pathetic and fearful as the necessary material cause of tragedy. Pity he defines as the feeling involved in unmerited misfortune, while fear results from the misfortune of one like ourselves (1452b30–1453a20; *GBWW*, Vol. 9, pp. 687c–88b).

He is brief and, as such, suggestive. The tragic emotions derive from the conditions of human life. The definition of fear further suggests that these feelings and the realities that give rise to them are universal. The definition of pity emphasizes a lack of justice in tragic suffering—tragic misfortune is undeserved. Although Aristotle says little about comedy, it can be argued that comic matter is neither painful nor destructive to the viewer (1448a32; p. 682b). The comic differs from the tragic primarily on the question of justice.

Comedy and tragedy are, of course, artistic forms. But both rest on different ways of seeing reality, and both manifest different visions of reality. Indeed, from the beginning, from the stories of the creation in the first few chapters in Genesis, mankind has portrayed the universe in these two different ways. Thus, when Hamlet explains to Rosencrantz and Guildenstern the crucial differences between his present tragic condition and his former optimistic attitude, he deals in exactly the same set of terms that characterize the optimism and "tragedy" in the first two chapters of Genesis. Hamlet's earlier hopefulness rested on a view that emphasized man's closeness to divinity: man was godlike in apprehension, angelic in action, infinite in faculties. Now, however, Hamlet's rejection of the human condition recognizes only man's finite limitations: the paragon of animals is no more than the quintessence of dust (II, ii, 300–304; *GBWW*, Vol. 27, p. 43d). [1]

The first five chapters of Genesis show that the tragic vision emphasizes death, isolation, a lack of ultimate meaning both in human life and in the universe, a failure of community, whereas the comic vision stresses community, communion between humanity and the cosmos, the value of human life, and tends to suppress death as a horror.

Genesis 1, affirming the goodness and beauty of the universe, the transcendent wisdom, power, and goodness of the Creator, points, as does the happy Hamlet, to man's kinship with the divine. It is an optimistic story, that optimism clearly rendered in the repeated judgments that the creation is good. Indeed, it is "very good." Moreover since those judgments are made by an infinitely wise and benevolent deity, they cannot be wrong. Inasmuch as it is in the image of such a deity that man is created, nothing can be wrong—with God, with His universe, with man, with man's place in that universe.

The first creation story contains all the elements necessary for celebrating the human condition. When God is omnipotent, omniscient, and good, human life cannot be seen as tragic. It is noteworthy that Hamlet, in fact, goes beyond tragedy when late in his play he reaffirms to Horatio God's omnipotence and omniscience (V, ii, 48; p. 68b). When Heaven is ordinant in human affairs, all life makes sense. If "there's a special providence in the fall of a sparrow" (V, ii, 230; p. 70a), the universe cannot be "foul and pestilent," a "congregation of vapours." If a divinity shapes our ends, even a vision of Alexander's noble dust stopping a bunghole may become an affirmation (V, i, 225; p. 66d).

The deity of Genesis 1 knows exactly what He is doing. His act and intention are one. No shadow falls between His conception and His creation. The Thirty-third Psalm celebrates the creation that needed no labor, the surpassing act that made the heavens by God's word alone, that created the heavenly hosts merely by the breath of God's mouth: "he spoke, and it came to be; he commanded, and it stood forth" (RSV 33:9). Such a creator and such a creation can have no place for suffering.

Nor is God's transcendence made inhuman in this story. Divine greatness may, as in the Book of Job, produce a painful abyss dividing God from man. But no such suggestion disturbs the happiness of the vision here. God is transcendent, yet He is also concerned with man. And man's condition almost spans the gulf between creature and creator, for man is created in the image of his creator. A fourfold repetition emphasizes the closeness of human nature to that of divinity: "God said, 'Let us make man in our image, after our likeness.' . . . So God created man in his own image, in the image of God he created him" (Genesis 1:26,27).

Further, despite man's being the image of divinity, his place is established comfortably in the world. The author of the story carefully eliminates any possibility of tragic alienation. Man is created with all his meaningful connections. From the beginning, he is provided the central fulfilling relationship—an enriching union of sameness and other. Both man and woman are created in the image of God. Cocreated, both are equal, but made male and female and so able to give each other the delight and excitement that results from a union of contrasting qualities.

The human being is also provided meaningful connection with the rest of his environment. God blesses him in his endeavors and gives him dominion over the entire earth—the fish of the sea, the birds of the air, and every thing that creeps upon the land. Man, then, not only belongs to the world, but the world, in effect, belongs to man. If, as Marx said, it is man's nature to realize himself in his work, man's work in Genesis 1 affords him complete and easy opportunity for such realization. It is his God-given task. Told to subdue the earth, he subdues a friendly earth without a struggle. His needs and the objects of his instincts may, in fact, lie outside him. But they are in harmony with him, and the products of his labor belong to him. He is told to master nature; both God and nature cooperate with man to bring about that mastery.

When the narrative of Genesis 1 picks up in Genesis 5, the optimism is enriched with other meaningful human connections. Death, although it is there, is softened by longevity. And man is further fulfilled by continuity. "May you live to see your children's children" is a Jewish blessing. Adam lives to see eight generations of offspring, and all of these live to interact with each other as adults. Part of the pain of the human condition as we know it is, in contrast, our fundamental isolation from both our past and our future. Our lives must seem like fragments, for we have no knowledge of our consequences and only an abstract and imperfect knowledge of our sources. This kind of estrangement from meaning is prevented in the first creation story. For the nine generations from Adam through Lamech, both past and future are experienced as lived knowledge. Patrimony and legacy—for us so doubtful—are known concretely. This continuum of generations provides human life with yet other fulfilling harmonies, with other enriching relationships of similarities and differences, other significant expansions of self into otherness. In the comic scheme of the first creation story, the earth is indeed a "goodly frame" and man, in all respects, is "the beauty of the world! the paragon of animals!" as Hamlet says (II, ii, 310, 319–20; *GBWW,* Vol. 27, p. 43d).

When Hamlet loses the mirth appropriate to this sort of vision, man becomes for him merely "the quintessence of dust." And it is man's state as dust that Genesis 2 emphasizes, as distinct from Genesis 1. Almost all the elements that constructed the optimism of the first creation story are absent or are reversed in the second version. Man is sorely limited by being dust, and significantly God, too, seems limited. No more talk about the goodness of the creation, the creation of man in the image of God. The notes are changed to tragic, stressing man's Adamic nature and destiny. [2]

Even more fundamental to the changed view of life in this second story is the different vision of the deity it provides. Kafka declared to Max Brod that for God there is infinite hope, although there is no hope for man. Such a view contains a basic core of optimism. For—

as also the Book of Job suggests—even if the human role in the divine scheme is humanly hopeless, it is still somehow acceptable so long as divinity and His scheme are in control. The chorus in Sophocles' *Oedipus the King* expresses the same realization, preferring that an innocent Oedipus suffer terrible and undeserved punishment rather than for the oracles to prove false and for the navel of the earth to be destroyed (*GBWW*, Vol. 5, p. 107c–d). The most terrible thing is the absence of divine order. It is this terror that shadows the second creation story in Genesis 2. The divine order is less certain and controlling there than in the first story, and the divine power is clearly diminished.

The second story—as is well known—seems to begin in the second half of Genesis 2:4. The different view of the godhead is apparent at once. No longer transcendent, God now seems subject to reality: He is unable to cause vegetation until there are both rain and a man to till the soil. The exalted deity of Genesis 1 had created without hands, without labor. But does the Lord in this story "create" at all? The word is not used. Rather, He "makes" or "forms"—a potter's act. And, like the potter, He needs the clay. In the anti-tragic vision of the first creation, man had been created in God's image. In the earthbound world of this story, God seems anthropomorphic—shaping His creatures from mud, walking in the cool of the day. Painfully human, too, is the jealousy He feels toward His own creatures. Afraid that man might eat also of the fruit of the tree of life and become like Him, God banishes man from the Garden primarily to prevent his attaining godhead. Nor does God's envy of human beings stop at this point. The Lord of Genesis 11, who fears what men might achieve once they have built the tower, who scatters men and confuses their language because He fears "this is only the beginning of what they will do; and nothing that they propose to do will now be impossible for them" (11:6), is clearly the same anthropomorphic God that stamped His nature on the second creation story. Like a human being, the Lord makes mistakes in His creation, regrets them, tries to rectify them. No longer omniscient, He proceeds by trial and error. Whereas the God of the first story created man male and female, the Lord, here, creates man single, only later discovering that it is not good for man to be alone. And His attempt to find man a fit helper seems bumbling. After He forms every beast and every bird and fails by this procedure to find man his proper helper, God finally makes woman. No statements here about the goodness of the creation; God now is "sorry that he had made man on the earth" (6:6), and He declares that man's imperfection is part of man's original nature: " 'the imagination of man's heart is evil from his youth' " (8:21).

Man's imperfection is, in fact, inherent in the nature of man's creation. The dust—or ground—plays as defining a role in this creation as does the deity. Like all other flesh, man is shaped from the ground, and the ground is so much man's essence that the name man (*Adam*) is cognate with the word for ground (*adamah*). Man is formed from the earth like a piece of pottery, animated only when breath is breathed into his nostrils, his earthy nature and destiny intensified when he is given the task of tilling the earth. Nor is there in this narrative any suggestion that he is to subdue the earth and master it.

Man's condition as the image of God, his role as God's vicar on earth, had precluded tragedy. May not the role of breathing mud make tragedy inevitable? Freud locates the three sources of human misery as the self, the outer world, and our relations with other humans. We may add a fourth—our relations with the godhead. Both the self and nature are inadequate for Adam's happiness. Though of the earth, Adam never seems harmoniously or comfortably connected with it. Even before the fall, he is so lonely and dissatisfied that the Lord recognizes the evil of his isolation. Further, he remains separate from the beasts the Lord brings him for companions. Might not the serpent's behavior indicate that some of nature is hostile to man even before the fall? Certainly the presence of the forbidden tree indicates that danger to man is built into man's original environment. At any rate, in the tragic scheme of this narrative, the fall condemns man to constant enmity with the world around him.

The culmination of a perfect creation, in harmonious relations with an omnipotent and omniscient God, with a fulfilling earth, and with each other, the human beings of Genesis 1 could not have sinned. And because they had been given no command, no prohibitions, sin was a logical impossibility. The piece of mud of Genesis 2, dependent on God for his breath, on the earth for his essence, seems from the start to want something else. And from the start, sin is made possible when man is tempted, ordered to avoid the temptation, and threatened with terrible punishment if he fails. In this way, something of an adversarial relation seems always to exist between man and God.

It has been argued that there were two primal sins and two primal curses. Disobedience, by bringing death, doomed every human life to a tragic conclusion. The second sin is Cain's murder of Abel, which cursed us to the other basic tragic fact, our fundamental isolation, our antagonism to each other. But Adam was isolated from the start. And the intimacy of Adam and Eve begins marred by the conditions of Eve's creation. An afterthought, made from man as man was made from the mud, she is dependent on man for her very nature. She is a secondary creature whose inferior status becomes intensified after the fall. After the fall, shame also will contaminate intimacy. Yet shame, too, seems immanent from the start. The text makes clear that once there were sexes, human nature in its sexuality was something to feel guilty about, that the human body was somehow dangerous. Adam and Eve were unashamed of their nakedness only because, in their innocence, they did not know they were naked.

The tragic view of this narrative is implicit in its account of the creation. It becomes more profound and more all-encompassing with the fall. The fall puts human beings in a painful relationship with every aspect of their lives. The world becomes hostile, survival difficult, the work involved in survival destructive to the human spirit, a burden to the human body. The ground—the very ground from which he was made—is now cursed for man's sake. The earth—the source of his life—becomes man's enemy, bringing forth thorns and thistles for him. Condemned to the pain of hard labor, he seems condemned, too, to the futility of a life that labors only for survival and that must end in death. Man's origin had been the dust. Now his only destiny is dust.

Where does this narrative offer any solace to the human being? Is there any suggestion that the other animals are anything but alien to humanity? Man and the serpent, for example, are in everlasting antagonism, permanently sentenced to harm each other.

The central human relationship is now the most problematic; it is upset by guilt, shame, recrimination, and anger. Its harmony is also upset by inequality: man's rule over woman must, in some measure, establish man and woman as adversaries. Love now becomes contaminated also by pain. Woman is condemned to desire her husband, and that desire leads to the multiplied agony of childbearing. This narrative's vision of the disharmony of the human condition recognizes even a basic disharmony within the human being's own emotions, an antagonism of the body with itself.

In the optimistic pattern of the first creation story, progeny was a crucial element connecting human beings to each other, to the world, and to God. Human progeny was part of the providential order, an important aspect of man's task of filling and subduing the earth. No suggestion of such meaningful order brightens the view of the second story. Here, the human being is not told to have children, nor has he been given the destiny of subduing the earth. It seems that children may serve only to punish the woman with the pain of bearing them. Indeed Adam and Eve's first two children bring them nothing but loss.

Edgar, in *King Lear*, observes that "the worst is not / So long as we can say, 'This is the worst' " (IV, i, 30; *GBWW*, Vol. 27, p. 269d). The circumstances of man on earth become even more puzzling, painful, and alienated as the second creation narrative moves into Genesis 4. Genesis 1 had established the Sabbath as a ritual uniting human behavior to divine behavior, a way, as it were, of keeping in touch with God. But in the second story, it is not easy to know what God wants. Why is Cain's offering rejected? Cain clearly does not know. And God's explanation is Delphic in its obscurity and evasiveness. The Lord, here, might well seem arbitrary and perhaps capricious. And Cain, a petulant, angry, and jealous child, acts without any moral sense.

"Adam and Eve Driven from Paradise," by Masaccio (1401–28). *The fall puts human beings in a painful relationship with every aspect of their lives. The world becomes hostile, survival difficult.*

The murder of Abel is the paradigm of egocentricity. Brotherhood is overwhelmed by frustration. The ties of kinship do not bind. The pattern of human life that Cain's act establishes is the Hobbesian one: "a perpetual combat for honor, riches, and authority," where we have "a great deal of grief in keeping company." The action of Genesis 4 intensifies man's tragic alienation. As Adam and Eve had been driven from their home, so Cain, their surviving descendant, is separated from his home. Homelessness, it seems, is established as a constant aspect of the human situation: Cain is condemned to be a fugitive and a wanderer. The earth is made even more alien to man, cursed once again, this time not to reward Cain's tillage. The first sin caused man to hide himself from God's presence. Man's estrangement from God is now apparently complete as Cain is forever driven from God's face. There is not a single mention of God in the Cain genealogy. A record of "man abandoned to his own devices," it stands in painful contrast to the fulfilling harmonies of the Seth genealogy in Genesis 5. The life of men cut off from God and directed only by self-interest seems a Hobbesian "war of everyman against everyman," when Lamech boasts: "I have slain a man for wounding me, a young man for striking me. If Cain is avenged sevenfold, truly, Lamech seventy-sevenfold" (4:24).

Nietzsche pointed out that the desirable tragic pattern "turns [lamentation] into a song of praise." [3] Tragedy does not seek to evade the horrors of human life, but at the same time it does not succumb to those horrors. Rather, it celebrates the human being who despite his inevitable failure tries to triumph over them. Something of this sort seems to take place in the Cain genealogy. Man's own devices turn out to be no small thing. They almost triumph over God's curse. Cursed to be a fugitive and a wanderer on the earth, Cain marries, has a family, builds a city. Condemned to labor fruitlessly for the earth's yield, the tribe of Cain raises cattle, forges instruments of iron and bronze, and seems, on its own, to husband nature. Cut off from God, the descendants of Cain create the arts. Deprived of both the earth's cooperation and the divine presence, they reach a condition of independence. They make civilization, and they almost transcend the state of breathing mud.

Nevertheless the triumphs of tragedy are seldom real. Rather they are dramatic gestures, only symbolic achievements in the face of real doom. *The Iliad,* perhaps the greatest of all tragedies, again and again sharply reminds us of this fact. We are told, for example, that Hector's dead body, which will soon be consumed on his funeral pyre, does not stink, and is not damaged, despite the twelve days when it was abused by the Greek troops: "fresh with dew he lies. . . . So it is that the blessed immortals care for [him], though he is nothing but a dead man" (XXIV, 419, 422–23; cf. *GBWW*, Vol. 4, p. 175d). [4] And Sarpedon, urging Glaucus to heroic action, argues that because they are mortal they need to get or give glory before they die. The glory of a dead man may be merely a metaphoric accomplishment, but such metaphors are the only accomplishments available to a mortal being. The last episode of the second creation narrative in Genesis also faces up directly to this tragic reality. The descendants of Cain who build the tower of Babel build it in order to make a name for themselves, not for any pragmatic ends, but precisely because they are aware that they soon will be scattered to the ends of the earth (11:4).

Reputation for pragmatic ends is a comic pattern. An instrument of *will*, the comic vision accepts life and its standards, and it values success by those standards. In tragedy, on the other hand, reputation has its most significant role within the inevitability of failure. For the most part, tragedy denies the validity of worldly success. Tragedy, where we win only in symbol and lose in reality, "sing[s] of human unsuccess"— and at its best, as in *The Iliad* or the second creation story—"in a rapture of distress." [5]

From the beginning, then, the Old Testament provides these two contrasting visions of man's condition and his fate. Further, it identifies the essential features that characterize those visions. It is curious that this is, more or less, paralleled by the two different ways in which *The Iliad* and *The Odyssey* see the world, and the defining elements by which they render their conceptions. Here, Hebraism and Hellenism come close together.

## Plato and Aristotle on tragedy

The Greeks, unlike the Hebrews, also give us important discussions concerning tragedy and comedy and, in Aristotle's *Poetics*, the analysis that probably has most influenced the Western world's ideas about these literary types. Yet Aristotle, on these subjects, seems only formal. For example, although he derives his concept of the complex plot, with its patterns of reversal and recognition, from *Oedipus the King*, he seems to value that plot merely for the pleasure of achieving surprise within probability. He does not seem to notice that, as the *Oedipus* dramatizes man's ignorance and helplessness in relation to the godhead and the inevitable frustration of all human intentions, reversal is what that play is all about. It is content as well as form. The tragic vision of the *Oedipus* focuses on the painful limitations of human intelligence. Thus the plot device of recognition is part of that play's subject: how little any human being—even the unriddler of the sphinx—can recognize, even about who he is, and what he says and does.

Aristotle's concern is with the ways that dramatic form transmutes unpleasant and destructive matter into beauty. For that reason, it seems, his discussions of matter must be limited. His brief remarks about pity and fear as the material causes of tragedy, or the ridiculous as the matter of comedy, do not come near the human realities within those two forms. Only in his observation that pity results from undeserved misfortune, the awareness that in this world misfortune might well be undeserved, does the *Poetics* come close to any suggestion about the tragic nature of human life. Aristotle's discussion focuses instead on the human need to transform reality, and, thus, on the poetic art itself—its nature and function. Mimic representations of "ignoble" animals, "by disclosing to intellectual perception the artistic spirit that designed them, give immense pleasure to all that can trace links of causation . . . for each and all will reveal to us . . . something beautiful. Absence of haphazard and conduciveness of everything to an end are to be found in Nature's works" (*On the Parts of Animals*, bk. 1, chap. 5, 645a9–10, 23–24; *GBWW*, Vol. 9, pp. 168d–69a). In the *Poetics*, Aristotle is not concerned with the chaos, the pity, or the terror of human life, but with its transformation. His emphasis on form thus makes poetry only a mimetic reality, and the art of tragedy itself becomes an instance of real woe turned into a merely symbolic—because, in this case, a purely formal—triumph.

In the artistic vision, Nietzsche comments that "content—our life included—becomes something merely formal." [6] And Aristotle observes that matter, once it is informed, is no longer matter but "part of the formula of the form" (*Metaphysics*, 1035a; cf. Vol. 8, p. 558b).

On the other hand, Plato, who had conflated tragedy "on the stage," with that "on the greater stage of human life" (*Philebus*, 50; *GBWW*, Vol. 7, p. 630b), showed small interest in tragic form. Whereas Aristotle absorbed content into structure and often defined end as the achievement of form, Plato had subordinated design to ethical or political purpose, art to reality, and concluded in that way that tragedy is not useful to the state or to human life (cf. *The Republic*, X, 607; p. 434b).

Plato's rejection of tragedy is fundamental; it refuses the reality of human suffering and denies the tragic aspects of human existence. Once again, Nietzsche's remarks are pertinent. Nietzsche points out that the antithesis of the tragic disposition is the Socratic disposition: Tragedy recognizes "whatever is awful, evil, perplexing, destructive, and ominous" in human life, while the Socratic position stresses "the optimistic, rational, and utilitarian." Nietzsche concludes that Socrates' "dialectical drive toward knowledge and scientific optimism turns tragedy from its course." [7] Plato, himself, had argued the same antithesis. Not only does philosophy "banish the cry of sorrow by the healing art" of reason (*The Republic*, X, 604; p. 432c), but the philosopher (in the *Laws* as well as in *The Republic*) literally banishes the tragedian from the community. Indeed, says Plato, the issue in this ancient conflict is "great . . . whether a man is to be good or bad" (608; p. 434a).

Although Plato attacks poetry as a whole, it is clear that the primary object of his attack is the tragic vision. He does not, as the famous closing passage in the *Symposium* demonstrates, distinguish between comedy and tragedy as literary types (223; p. 173c). Yet, his conception of comedy is limited to laughable things, things which are painful and out of place. And comedy of this sort, because it emphasizes the hurtful and discordant qualities in the universe, is, in fact, close to tragedy. Plato's own "Aesopian fables" (as Nietzsche calls the dialogues), on the other hand, express another sort of comic vision: All things work for the good. It is Dante's vision in his *Divine Comedy* (*GBWW*, Vol. 21); it is the comedy of the first chapter of Genesis. Miguel de Unamuno labels Descartes's skepticism, "comic doubt . . . the doubt of a man who acts as if he doubted without really doubting." [8] And Plato, in this sense, is profoundly comic, for he affirms the ultimate meaning and perfection of the gods, the world, man's role in the world. The *Gorgias* presents the scheme of the universe in similar happy terms to those of Genesis 1: ". . . communion and friendship and orderliness and temperance and justice bind together heaven and earth and gods and men, and . . . this universe is therefore called Cosmos or order . . ." (508; *GBWW*, Vol. 7, p. 284d).

It is the absence of such order that the tragic view stresses about human life. Tragic man does not dwell in Plato's "land of health"; he does not "receive the good in everything" (*The Republic*, III, 401; p. 333b). Accordingly, Plato dismisses tragedy as "irrational, useless, and cowardly" (X, 604; p. 432d).

The aspects of the tragic vision on which Plato concentrates his criticism are the nature of the hero, the attitude toward death, the explanation of suffering, the pattern of justice, the view of God.

Examining the solipsism that characterizes the tragic protagonist, Plato singles out Homer's portrayal of Achilles as impious and false (III, 391; p. 327a–b). The tragic protagonist is torn apart. On the other hand, a true hero exhibits "the true simplicity of a rightly and nobly ordered mind and character" (400; p. 333a). The tragic protagonist such as Achilles is self-involved and self-indulgent. A true hero subordinates the self to God, justice, duty, law, and community. The Socrates of the *Apology, Crito,* and *Phaedo* is, it seems, the paradigm of such a just and manly hero (*GBWW*, Vol. 7, pp. 200a–51d).

In the same way, when Plato attacks Homer, whose characters find death tragically fearful, and declares that ". . . the good man will not consider death terrible to any good man" (*The Republic*, 387; p. 325b), the image that contrasts most sharply with Achilles is the dying Socrates, "freed," as Nietzsche says, "by knowledge and argument from the fear of death." [9]

Whereas tragedy questions the pattern of universal justice asserting that the wicked "spend their days in prosperity" (Job 121:13), and that the rain falls on the just and the unjust alike, Plato specifically attacks such a position: "the gravest mis-statements" are that "wicked men are often happy, and the good miserable; and that injustice is profitable when undetected" (*The Republic*, III, 392; *GBWW*, Vol. 7, p. 328b). Like Job's comforters, Plato insists that God can never be the cause of evil: The poet "must devise some explanation of them [sufferings] . . . he must say that God did what was just and right" (II, 380; p. 322c).

The attitude toward God is a central issue that determines a tragic or optimistic view of the world. Its attitude toward God is Plato's major quarrel with tragedy. The Athenian Stranger calls it vicious to deny God's existence or his righteousness. *The Republic* insists on the same argument: God must be presented as truly good; no good thing is hurtful; God and the things of God are in every way profitable. Plato stresses his opposition to tragedy in this regard: "the good is to be attributed to God alone; of the evils the causes are to be sought elsewhere . . ."; therefore, "we must not listen to Homer," who ascribes the cause of evil to God (II, 379; p. 322b).

### *The Iliad* as tragic paradigm

Plato focuses on Homer, and especially *The Iliad*, when he illustrates the faults of tragedy. *The Iliad*, perhaps more than any other work, exhibits all of the essential elements of the tragic vision. Suffering is the given of that poem, and human life is constantly shown in terms of its pain and futility. The gods seem both responsible for human grief and helpless before the reality of it.

The Trojan War, of course, is the extreme situation that, placing man at the edge of doom, intensifies the terrors of living. Yet the war is a metonymy for human life. Simone Weil observed that in *The Iliad* "all men, by the very act of being born, are destined to suffer violence." [10] So in Joseph Heller's *Catch 22*, the Second World War makes it easy to learn "Snowden's dirty little secret"; but the war did not create the reality of that secret. "Man was matter. . . . Drop him out a window and he'll fall. Set fire to him and he'll burn. Bury him and he'll rot like other kinds of garbage." [11] Snowden's terrible wound tears open the veil obscuring that grim reality, and, in the same way, the deaths in *The Iliad* graphically reveal how slight the difference is between a man and a thing.

The tragic vision of *The Iliad* constantly penetrates to the horror beneath. Hades, lord of the underworld, fears the effects of seeing ultimate truth: "Poseidon, might break the earth open / and the houses of the dead lie open to men and immortals, / ghastly and mouldering, so the very gods shudder before them . . ." (XX, 63–65; cf. *GBWW*, Vol. 4, p. 142d).

In tragedy, says Nietzsche, "illusion is the only possible mode of redemption." [12] Perhaps in *The Iliad*, there is no redemption. But illusion is what seems to keep human life going. Much of the greatness of *The Iliad* as tragedy may lie in its rich tensions between the drama of human aspirations and relationships that are played out in the realm of illusions, and the poem's constant reminders of that other realm where all human actions are seen as no more than illusions. The grave proves the child, love, marriage, country, heroism, all ephemeral.

Hector, who has been called the "guardian of perishable values," and who knows that those values he guards must soon perish, illustrates this aspect of man's plight. For Hector, while he recognizes necessity, also denies it. He is painfully aware that soon "there will come a day when sacred Ilion shall perish, and Priam, and the people of Priam," and that his wife will be led off to slavery "in tears" (VI, 448–49, 455–56; cf. *GBWW*, Vol. 4, p. 44c–d). Yet, within a moment of expressing that recognition, he prays that his baby will someday "be . . . pre-eminent among the Trojans . . . and rule strongly over Ilion" (VI, 477–78; cf. p. 44d). Because he can pray that fantasy, Hector is able to continue in battle.

Aeschylus tells us that when Prometheus gave man fire, he also gave us an equally important gift; he took away from us the knowledge of the day of our death "so that we could build houses and break horses." Only by denying the day of their death had Hector and Andromache been able to love, marry, have their child; only by his deliberately blind commitment to illusions had Hector been able to fight gloriously. When Hector dies, Andromache's great cry, in a sense, does "break the earth open." Holding the baby before the corpse, Andromache exposes the tragic interdependence of human achievement and illusion when she exclaims "You cannot help him, Hektor, any more, since you are dead. Nor can he help you" (XXII, 485–86; cf. *GBWW*, Vol. 4, p. 160c). Freud defined mental health as "love and work." The tragic vision of *The Iliad* reveals the hollow grounds on which the human ability to do either rests.

To accept the human condition, it is, of course, necessary to accept death, not merely to deny it. The comic disposition, one way or another, overcomes the terror of the terminal and isolated self. The dying Socrates affirms by "reason and argument" an eternal and divinely ordered harmony in which the individual soul has its proper and meaningful place. Likewise Saul Bellow's Charlie Citrine, in *Humboldt's Gift,* rests his optimism on a kind of determined faith: "There is far more to any experience, or relationship than ordinary consciousness, the daily life of the ego, can grasp. You see, the soul belongs to a greater . . . life outside. It's got to." [13] Affirming an all-embracing reality that gives significance to self-consciousness, Plato condemns the tragic view for finding death terrible.

In *The Iliad,* on the other hand, human beings see death as the greatest evil. It is "the hateful darkness" (V, 47; cf. *GBWW*, Vol. 4,

In *The Iliad, "Zeus . . . wets the earth with 'tears of blood . . . for the sake of his beloved son,' Sarpedon,"* here shown, in a detail of a sixth century B.C. Greek kylix painting, being borne to heaven by the gods of Sleep and Death.

p. 30c); the dying spirit "goes down into Death's house mourning her destiny" (XVI, 856–57; cf. p. 121c). And the gods, also, grieve over man's mortality. Thetis laments her son's destiny as bitterly as any mortal mother. Zeus sorrows over the deaths of Hector and Patroclus, and he wets the earth with "tears of blood . . . for the sake of his beloved son," Sarpedon (XVI, 459–60; cf. p. 117a).

Death is the absolute that defeats all human enterprise. Because death is final and completely destroying, Achilles declares that neither heroic accomplishments nor all the treasures of Troy are worth the value of his life, which "cannot come back again . . . once it has crossed the teeth's barrier" (IX, 408–9; cf. p. 61b).

The horror of death is the horror of annihilation: "There is no mind at all in Hades." And, most terribly, death obliterates not only the person but the meaningfulness of all his connections. The poem's constant stress on the death of fathers and sons shows how insubstantial both legacy and patrimony ultimately are.

"There is no way out, around, or through" the narrowness of human necessity. All alternatives are unhappy. Iphidamas will never have delight in his bride, though he had "given much for her" (XI, 243; cf. p. 74c). The boy, Astyanax, "will never come of age" (XXIV, 728; cf. p. 179a). The aged Priam will be devoured in his own courtyard by his own dogs, of "all sad mortality, . . . the sight most pitiful" (XXII, 76; cf. p. 156a). Survivors are left with bitterness and pain, with "sorrow passing endurance" (XXIV, 708; cf. p. 178d).

Faced with the realities of loss, grief, and death, Achilles summarizes the human condition saying, "we live in unhappiness, but the gods themselves have no sorrows" (XXIV, 526; cf. p. 176d). And the gods agree with this judgment!

Zeus regrets that the immortal horses were given Achilles, observing that "among all creatures that breathe on earth and crawl on it there is not anywhere a thing more dismal than man is" (XVII, 446–47; cf. p. 126c). In terms similar to Job and to Ecclesiastes, Apollo emphasizes the triviality and evanescence of human beings: "insignificant mortals, who are as leaves are, and now flourish and grow warm with life, and feed on what the ground gives, but then again fade away and are dead" (XXI, 463–66; cf. p. 153a).

Achilles may blame the gods for having spun a bad destiny for "unfortunate mortals," but it is not altogether clear that divinity is in fact in firm control of human fate. The godhead's unhappiness at human unhappiness might well indicate that. The relationship between human events and the gods' will is, finally, murky. Zeus sends Agamemnon a deceptive dream. Hera would "eat Priam and the children of Priam raw." Ares is a "maniac who knows nothing of justice." Athena involves herself in Diomedes' battles and in Achilles' defeat of Hector. Yet none of this intervention seems to change the outcome of the war or even to accomplish anything very important. Achilles would kill Hector without Athena's help. Diomedes, in fact, wounds Ares. Zeus is helpless to save his own son. Apollo can try to keep Troy from falling before destiny, but he cannot prevent that destiny. And Zeus, too, must consult necessity which he seems powerless to change. The gods brawl among themselves, and although Zeus is Zeus he can be tricked by Hera.

Divine omnipotence seems somehow limited; divine wisdom and goodness are very uncertain indeed. What is finally most telling, there does not seem to be any providential justification behind human suffering. All human plans are frustrated, all human intentions are defeated. Parents are left childless, children are orphaned, wives are widowed—many will be killed or sold into slavery—and all this irrespective of human effort, desires, or virtues. It is this indifference to human enterprise and merit that, above all, makes *The Iliad* tragic.

### The Odyssey as comic paradigm

In contrast, *The Odyssey,* which picks up the story of *The Iliad,* announces its very different vision as early as the poem's thirty-second line:

> . . . mortals put blame upon us
> gods, for they say evils come from us, but it is they, rather,
> who by their own recklessness win sorrow. . . .
> (cf. *GBWW,* Vol. 4, p. 183b–c)

Indeed, even the invocation, in line seven of Book I, declares that Odysseus' men were "destroyed by their own wild recklessness" (cf. p.

183a). It is immediately apparent that in *The Odyssey* men have important control over their destinies. Justice is the way of the gods and of the world, and life, therefore, makes human sense and is, at least partly, designed to fit human desires. If *The Iliad* is the first Greek tragedy, *The Odyssey*, as Longinus suggested, provides a pattern for comedy.

Plato attacks *The Odyssey* along with *The Iliad*. Yet, *The Odyssey* renders a view of cosmic justice that Plato should have applauded. Nietzsche points out that a central formulation of optimism, and certainly of Socratic optimism, is that only the virtuous are happy. It is a central formulation of *The Odyssey*, and it is there affirmed by gods, men, and by the plot itself.

The Book of Job is tragic because in its world "the wicked live, reach old age, and grow mighty in power" (21:7). Their children are established, they achieve prosperity; without fail, their bulls breed and their cows calve. They die completely at ease. All the while, virtuous men may die in bitterness of soul, never having tasted good. Job's is a universe indifferent to justice.

In the comic world of *The Odyssey*, on the other hand, well doing produces well-being, not only for the person, but also for his family and his nation. Odysseus summarizes this when he tells Penelope that a blameless and God-fearing man receives an abundance of barley and wheat from the earth, fruit from the trees, fish from the sea, "because of his good leadership, and his people prosper under him" (XIX, 113–14; cf. *GBWW*, Vol. 4, p. 290b).

Moreover, in this poem there is never any sad uncertainty about values. Men know precisely what conduct is good and what is evil: "when a man is harsh himself, and his mind knows harsh thoughts, all men pray that suffering will befall him," but "when a man is blameless . . . the friends he has entertained carry his fame widely to all mankind" (XIX, 329–34; cf. p. 292c). Even more important to the poem's cosmic optimism, the gods share the same desires for human behavior that men do, and men know what the gods want. The human agents are sure that the "blessed gods have no love for a pitiless action, but rather they reward justice and what men do that is lawful" (XIV, 83–84; cf. p. 261a). Furthermore, the gods' active involvement in the ethical scheme is constant. Even the evil suitors acknowledge that " 'the gods watch . . . to see which men keep the laws, and which are violent' " (XVII, 487; p. 282a). Human behavior is a principal concern of the godhead: "Zeus . . . beyond others is outraged at evil dealings" (XIV, 283–84; cf. p. 263a).

Despite the violence graphically detailed in the destruction of the suitors and of the disloyal servants, the reader is directed to feel no compassion. For "they were destroyed by their own wild recklessness" (I, 7; cf. p. 183a). In the same way, we are told at the very beginning that Aegisthus' death is payment for his vile deeds.

*"Nor is Odysseus himself exempt from this universe of law. He brings about the encounter with the Cyclops when, driven by greed and desire for adventure, he ignores the advice of his shipmates."* Line engraving (1805) after a drawing by John Flaxman.

The various sufferings the Argives experience on their voyage home further show the inevitability of retributive justice: "Zeus in his mind devised a sorry homecoming for the Argives, since not all were considerate nor righteous" (III, 132–33; cf. p. 194b–c).

Odysseus' men also bring their evil destinies on themselves. From the first adventure with the Kikonians to the holocaust following Thrinacia, their destruction results from their own actions. They would have left Ismaros with booty and women if they had followed Odysseus' good advice and quickly escaped, "but they were greatly foolish and would not listen" (IX, 44; cf. p. 229c). Envy and misguided selfishness bring the sailors to open the bag of winds. Elpenor's own stupidity causes his death. Despite the warnings of Teiresias and Circe, and despite their own oaths, Odysseus' men, driven by recklessness, "dared a deed that was monstrous" by killing the oxen of the sun (XII, 373; cf. p. 254a). They pay for this impiety with their lives.

Nor is Odysseus himself exempt from this universe of law. He brings about the encounter with the Cyclops when, driven by greed and desire for adventure, he ignores the advice of his shipmates. He is, in fact, ultimately responsible for the whole long and difficult voyage home. Having escaped Polyphemus under the safe anonymity of "Nobody," he could have remained safe if he had remained anonymous. But he makes himself a target for Poseidon's wrath when his boastfulness causes him to identify himself. He never again overcomes prudence with pride and reveals himself prematurely.

Aristotle defines tragedy as a rendering of pity and fear, and he identifies the source of pity as undeserved misfortune. In the just and orderly world of *The Odyssey,* there is no pity, for misfortune is not undeserved.

There is no fear either. Some time ago, Ronald S. Crane, discussing "The Plot of *Tom Jones,*" developed the notion of alarm as the comic analogue of fear. [14] Alarm is what we feel for dangers that we know the protagonist will escape. *The Odyssey* makes certain that our apprehensions about Odysseus never pass from alarm into fear. As early as the seventeenth line of the poem, the reader is told that he need not worry about Odysseus' ultimate well-being. Zeus guarantees his safety and his return. We know immediately that for the hero this is not to be a tragic epic. All the gods will "work out his [Odysseus'] homecoming, and see to it that he returns." Even Poseidon, we are told, will put away his anger, for "all alone and against the will of the other immortal gods united he can accomplish nothing" (I, 76–79; cf. pp. 183d–84a).

The reader, in fact, is never allowed to forget the safeguarding presence of divinity. The episode with Circe, for example, has no real danger, for before Odysseus enters Circe's house, Hermes promises him to "find you a way out of your troubles, and save you." When Odysseus, then, encounters Circe he is protected by the "good medicine" (X, 286–87; cf. p. 239a). There can be no apprehension.

Apprehension is also diminished by the prophecies of Teiresias and Circe. Both forecast Odysseus, despite obstacles and delays, a successful destiny. How great is the danger of a man who will die peacefully "in the ebbing time of a sleek old age" (XI, 136; cf. p. 244c), surrounded by his prosperous people? Circe, moreover, provides Odysseus with careful instructions on protecting himself from the Sirens, Scylla and Charybdis. "Resourceful" Odysseus is hardly a man abandoned to his own devices.

It is of major importance to the comic quality of the action that until the landing in Ithaca the only adventure we actually witness is the dangerous voyage from Calypso's island to Scheria. And even here, Odysseus is not abandoned. Calypso helps plan his journey; Ino aids him; Athena brings him to safety. All the adventures that Odysseus recites at Scheria have no fear. They are, after all, over with and we know that he has already escaped. We cannot worry over the safety of a man who is safe. The most the Great Adventures can arouse in us is the hypothetical fear of alarm.

With the landing in Ithaca we move into the present. And although this signals a shift from the unreality of the fabulous world, Homer takes great care not to permit the tragic emotions to take over. At the very beginning of the domestic action, Athena announces to Odysseus, and to us, that she will be at Odysseus' side, that "we two [will] go to this work," which is the killing of the suitors (XIII, 394; cf. p. 259a). The god then proceeds to give Odysseus detailed advice about his strategy in Ithaca, ending her speech with the assurance that Telemachus, too, is safe and watched over, having "no hardship" (XIII, 423; cf. p. 259c). The suitors' ambush of Telemachus is a comic ambush. Athena guarantees that it will not happen. At every stage of the developing encounter with the suitors, Athena plays a direct intervening role.

In the comic universe of *The Odyssey*, heaven is ordinant in human life; heaven's will is unified and benign. On the other hand, in *The Iliad* an important aspect of life's terror resulted from the uncertain and apparently capricious rule of a godhead that was divided, overcome by its individual passions, at war with itself. Perhaps the *Theomachia* (the Battle of the Gods in *The Iliad*), which did not resolve that poem, did resolve the heavenly disorder. For *The Iliad*'s "son of devious-devising Kronos" (IV, 75; cf. p. 24d), has become in *The Odyssey* "Father Zeus," ruling a harmonious family, in firm and just control, knowing and guaranteeing the course of the universe. It does not seem too much to suggest that God is omnipotent and omniscient in this poem.

A united godhead is now tied to man: rituals connect humanity directly to divinity; human institutions have divine sanction. Because these institutions are validated by divinity, they are never challenged or doubted. In *The Iliad*, rituals had been no more than desperate gropings in an impenetrable dark. Man never knew whether the gods accepted or rejected his offerings, whether the signs he thought he received were true or false. Nor could his human institutions support him. These were, after all, breaking apart. Troy was about to fall; relationships were being disintegrated; community would soon be obliterated. Similarly, Achilles' challenges to the institutions of rule and to the code of heroism were never answered in that poem. Finally, nothing seemed "worth the value of [one's] life" (IX, 401; cf. p. 61b).

In contrast, *The Odyssey* so thoroughly grounds both ritual performance and the right maintenance of human institutions in ultimate reality that Telemachus receives instruction in proper behavior from the godhead itself. Propriety is neither trivial nor arbitrary. The same forms of behavior that bind men into community establish communion between men and gods.

Justification by works is a deeply optimistic doctrine. Not only does it put man in charge of his own condition, it assumes that man always knows what the godhead wants, and that the gods will always reward his doing well. This is the homocentric assumption held by Job's friends, the assumption that shapes the lovely fairy-tale world of the first four verses of Job. *The Odyssey* so completely accepts the doctrine of works that it never distinguishes between piety and pragmatism. Proper conduct gets its material rewards from both gods and men.

Material well-being, in fact, has a central place in the pattern of order and harmony. Human opulence connects man to the opulent condition of the godhead. Odysseus admires the richness and stability of both Circe's and Calypso's palaces, just as Telemachus responds to Nestor's and Menelaos' estates. Alcinous' estate is a human Olympus, and thus an ideal human situation. In the comic universe of *The Odyssey,* when decorous and prosperous, human life is very good indeed!

Human life is so desirable that Odysseus twice rejects the prospect of immortality in order to return home and restore himself to human values. In *The Iliad,* on the other hand, both men and gods often observed the sadness of the human condition, and men agonized over their finite limitations. Hector prays that he might escape from those constraints and be like Athena or Apollo. Sarpedon wishes he were ageless and immortal like the gods. Achilles tries to transcend the human state. In that poem, as has long been recognized, the godhead functions as an absolute against which the human is measured and found wanting: the *Theomachia* ends in a spanking; while men are dying painfully on the hard ground, Zeus and Hera lie down on a soft bed of dewy clover, crocus, and hyacinth. In that poem the only way that men can attempt to bridge that infinite chasm is by becoming "godlike," an entirely metaphoric condition.

Because in *The Odyssey* men are clearly in the image of god, there is no chasm to be spanned. Significantly, in this poem the godhead makes no comments on the unhappiness of the human condition. In fact, the comparisons between men and gods seem almost weighted in favor of the human. Not only do the gods care about human affairs and involve themselves directly in their outcome, gods also seem to depend on man and to need him. They take pleasure in human company. Indeed two goddesses couple with Odysseus and each offers him immortality if he will become her consort. Gods desire the burnt offerings that come from men. Hermes complains that his voyage to Ogygia took him far from human civilization: "there is no city of men nearby, nor people who offer choice hecatombs to the gods, and perform sacrifice" (V, 101–2; cf. p. 209a). "No, I am not a god, . . ." Odysseus announces to Telemachus, "but I am your father" (XVI, 187–88; cf. p. 274a). The poem makes it clear that this is for him the better role.

The comic spirit of *The Odyssey* shows itself in the poem's constant celebration of human life. The human being belongs in his world and is in fulfilling relationships with it. Only the "barren sea" is inhuman and is therefore rejected by both gods and men. Odysseus may be famed as a mariner, but the salt sea is empty and without community. The land is human and offers both crops and society. Odysseus says: "There is nothing worse for mortal men than the vagrant life" (XV, 343–44; cf. p. 269c).

Although Odysseus is the archetypal voyager of Western literature, although his tale of the Great Adventures has long had a disproportionate fame, the poem's most importantly defining images are of things fixed: Olympus "stands firm and unmoving forever . . . and is not shaken" (VI, 42–43; cf. p. 214c); Odysseus and Penelope's marriage bed is firmly established, built into the thick bole of an olive tree so that "there is no mortal man . . . who . . . could move the weight elsewhere" (XXIII, 187–88; cf. p. 314a).

Mutability is an important aspect of the tragic vision. *The Iliad,* for example, begins with a plague and ends in a funeral. But in *The Odyssey* references to human mutability are suppressed, and the poem stresses manifestations of stability. Aged fathers remain alive and vigorous. Sons carry on their fathers' values and virtues. Wives remain unchanged. Even after twenty years of separation, they remain faithful and lovely.

Closely related to this anti-tragic quality in *The Odyssey* is the poem's emphasis on the importance of society. Although Odysseus' men progressively fall away, and, after Thrinacia, Odysseus is left alone without any comrades, the universe of *The Odyssey* is profoundly public. Family and community are central motifs in that poem, as death is a central motif in *The Iliad.*

On the other hand, despite its crowded presence of Greek and Trojan hosts, *The Iliad* is profoundly private. When faced with his destiny, the individual there is alone and unsupported. Deiphobus' support, significantly, is an illusion that vanishes before Hector's final confrontation with Achilles. We may add that after that confrontation, Troy, Andromache, Astyanax become no more than illusions that for Hector have also vanished. Emerson observes somewhere that "for every seeing soul there are finally just two facts—I and the abyss."

Supported by an uncritical belief in society's values and a firm acceptance of his public role, the individual in *The Odyssey* never comes near that sort of insight. Although Odysseus journeys into the underworld, he never looks into the abyss. Characters in that poem do not struggle over ultimate questions. Achilles goes through the dark night of the soul, but Odysseus always knows who he is and what he wants, and he is always certain about his system of values. Odysseus' questions therefore are completely instrumental—how to succeed in terms of the accepted system: not what is the value of a man's life, but how to go about making that life better. When Athena praises Odysseus because he "reason[s] closely and keep[s his] head always" (XIII, 332; cf. p. 258c), she seems to give divine approval to precisely this aspect of Odysseus' intelligence. Odysseus only deliberates over ways and means; ends are taken for granted by both gods and men.

Similarly, whereas lamentations in *The Iliad* were over the hopelessness of the human situation, in *The Odyssey* lamentations are only over the immediate predicament.

Aldous Huxley, discussing the non-quotidian nature of the tragic vision, points out how thoroughly the comic world of *The Odyssey* accepts the reality of daily life. Only after they put away their desire for eating and drinking do Odysseus' men cry "for their beloved companions whom Skylla had caught out of the hollow ship . . ." (XII, 309–10; cf. p. 253b).

The opposition between ultimate and utilitarian concerns is crucial in determining the differences between tragedy and comedy. It influences the role of such important elements as wealth, success, honor, and even literature itself.

When in E. M. Forster's novel *Howards End,* Leonard Bast, having come to pragmatism through poverty, declares that "the real thing is money, all the rest is a dream," Helen Schlegel replies that he has forgotten about death: "Death and money are the eternal foes." "If we lived forever," she tells him, "what you say would be true. But we have to die, we have to leave life presently." Death, she concludes, "shows . . . the emptiness of money." [15] In contrast to Bast's utilitarian judgment, Helen looks at wealth in ultimate terms, where dream may matter more than the quotidian real. The ultimate vision exposes the meaninglessness of money when faced with mortality. Achilles rejects Agamemnon's offer of prizes on the same basis: wealth can be had for the lifting, it can be grabbed and taken away, but death is absolute, once a man's life is lost it cannot come back again.

On the other hand, the comic world of *The Odyssey*—where abundance clearly makes life better—puts its greater emphasis on wealth. Menelaos would give two-thirds of his possessions if "the men were alive who died in . . . Troy" (IV, 98–99; cf. *GBWW,* Vol. 4, p. 200a). The qualification is crucial. The sanity of the poem cannot permit a man to give up all his goods. The hero's major task, after all, is to increase the affluence of his estate. Odysseus' wanderings may have lost him the riches he won at Troy. But the tale he tells in Scheria brings him prizes greater than those he lost. Wealth is so important in the poem that much as Odysseus longs to return home he tells Alcinous that he would be willing to remain in Scheria even for a year, if then Alcinous would speed him home with many "glorious presents, . . . there would be much advantage in coming back with a fuller hand" (XI, 357–59; cf. p. 246d).

The continuity of inheritance, furthermore, gives wealth an importance transcending individual life. Odysseus wishes Arete not only prosperity but also the ability to bestow prosperity upon her children. Even death is made acceptable when one leaves to his son wealth, fame, and a legacy of right conduct.

The dead Hector and the soon to die Astyanax cannot, as Andromache exclaims, help each other anymore. But Odysseus and Telemachus clearly do help each other. Not only do they together destroy the suitors, but even before his return, Odysseus already helps his son. His friendships make Telemachus welcome by both Nestor and Menelaos. In the final confrontation with the suitors' families, Laertes, Odysseus, and Telemachus manifest, in their unity, an important image of continuity. The theme of inheritance is made explicit when Odysseus rallies Telemachus, reminding him about "the blood of [his] fathers," telling him that they "in time past all across the world have surpassed in manhood and valor." When Telemachus promises that he will not shame that blood, Laertes rejoices: "What day is this for me, dear gods? I am very happy. My son and my son's son are contending over their courage" (XXIV, 508–9, 514–15; cf. p. 322b–c).

Much as in the Seth genealogy of Genesis 5, inheritance and longevity in *The Odyssey* almost overcome death. Nestor and Laertes have already reached old age and remain vigorous. [16] Odysseus has been promised a sleek old age, in whose ebbing he will die surrounded by his prosperous people; his descendants will thrive. Furthermore, whereas in *The Iliad* death is violent and painful, death here, for the heroic characters at any rate, is "soft"; Apollo's arrows are painless. In *The Odyssey,* where quotidian values seem to be all that matter, all horrors—even the horrors of death—are muted.

Reputation, legacy, and patrimony help bind the human universe into cosmos and order. Reputation also functions in another and very utilitarian way. Because of his father's reputation, Telemachus receives fine gifts at both Pylos and Sparta. His own fame frequently gains Odysseus recognition, reception, and prizes. His tale of the Great Adventures augments his reputation, gains him transportation to Ithaca, and wins him great material rewards. It might be suggested that heroic reputation has greater utility than does heroism itself. After all, the story that Odysseus tells at Scheria earns him wealth greater than all he won at Troy.

Is Odysseus a bard like Demodocus, the blind singer of *The Odyssey* VIII? His performance follows that of Demodocus as afterdinner entertainment. Further, he tells a story of an Argive hero that, in a sense, continues Demodocus' tales of the heroes at Troy. But Demodocus takes his theme from the great deeds of famous men and receives a chine of pork as a reward. Odysseus, whose reward is great wealth, creates a story about himself, constructs his own identity with his tale. We may well wonder whether the Adventures are anything more than a tale Odysseus invents for the sake of manipulating his audience. Is he not always inventing tales for that purpose? Perhaps even more than the great voyager, Odysseus is, in fact, the great narrative artist. Athena's praise of his deceptions and "thievish tales" occurs shortly after the episode at Scheria. The business of a man is business, and Odysseus knows the business value of saying many false things that were like true sayings. Along with being a poem about family, home, wealth,

*The Odyssey* is also about storytelling. Its attitude toward storytelling is another important aspect of the comic spirit of this poem.

Both *The Iliad* and *The Odyssey* seem, in fact, to advance theories of literature appropriate to their condition as tragedy and comedy. *The Odyssey's* theory of literature is explicit. In *The Iliad* the literary doctrine is only hinted. Furthermore, *The Iliad* seems to suggest both an affective and an ontological theory of tragedy. Perhaps they come together, for both involve transcending quotidian limits.

*The Iliad*, which looks at human life in ultimate terms, stresses life's utilitarian hopelessness. This is the aspect of tragedy that Nietzsche emphasizes when he observes that the penetrating insight of the tragic vision makes us "realize that no action . . . can work any change in the eternal condition of things." Tragedy, he goes on, which shows us the impossibility of human happiness, "makes us always aware of the ghastly absurdity of existence." Yet it does not turn us to despair; rather, there is something saving in this vision. "The tragic myth," Nietzsche declares, "delivers us from our avid thirst for earthly satisfaction" and affords us, instead, a redemption that is completely symbolic, a redemption in fiction. [17] There is no earthly satisfaction in the glory that Sarpedon's death bestows on Patroclus, in Patroclus' death, in Hector's dead body. A tragedy such as *The Iliad* celebrates victories

"We may well wonder whether the Adventures are anything more than a tale Odysseus invents for the sake of manipulating his audience." Odysseus (right) importuning Penelope, in a fifth century B.C. Greek terra-cotta relief.

and accomplishments that are only metaphoric: the entirely figurative state of being "godlike," the merely poetic triumph of Hector's fresh and dewy cadaver. The action of *The Iliad* quickly turns a human being into a thing. But *The Iliad* is a work of art, and in art a thing becomes transformed into an aesthetic object, an image of a different and further value.

Yeats celebrates Hamlet and Lear who "Do not break up their lines to weep." Their existence, after all, is not earthly but is in the aesthetic realm of tragedy. For that reason "Hamlet and Lear are gay; / Gaiety transfiguring all that dread." [18]

"Only as an esthetic product," says Nietzsche, "can the world be justified to all eternity." [19] Can it not be argued that something like this view of artistic mimesis is, in fact, present in *The Iliad*? For one thing, does not the poem as a whole transfigure pain into aesthetic form? Further, and of more direct pertinence, the one-hundred and fifty-nine lines devoted to the Shield of Achilles seem specifically to focus on a theory of artistic imitation (XVIII, 458–616; cf. *GBWW*, Vol. 4, pp. 134d–36c). By means of its intricate artistry the Shield is able to represent the entire universe—the sun, the constellation, the ocean, all the activities of man in both peace and war—on its limited surface. The artist—Hephaisthos or Homer—has accomplished this by selecting representative details out of the world's unintelligible chaos of infinite possibilities and then arranging these on the Shield in a formal pattern that gives them coherence and meaning. The real world, of course, could not be contained on the Shield. Instead, the Shield manifests the intelligibility and organization of a mimetic world. In this way, the Shield directs our attention to an aesthetically transformed universe.

*The Iliad*'s mimetic theory of art seems to anticipate Aristotle's. May it not be argued that its affective theory of tragedy anticipates a possible reading of Aristotle on catharsis?

"Expose thyself to feel what wretches feel," says King Lear (III, iv, 34; Vol. 27, p. 264c), and at that moment he expands himself from self-concerned pathos into tragedy. He also suggests a function that tragic suffering may have, not only for the characters but also for the audience. Nietzsche observes that "individuation should be regarded as the source of all suffering." [20] But source is not end. The movement of tragedy takes the sufferer beyond his individuation.

*The Iliad* provides the paradigm of this basic tragic process. In the last book of that poem, the aged and grieving Priam, having penetrated the enemy lines, enters Achilles' tent and tries to ransom Hector's body. Priam has lost some forty sons; he is soon to lose his nation and his life. Falling before his great enemy, he calls attention to the depth of his suffering: "I put my lips to the hands of the man who has killed my children" (XXIV, 506; cf. *GBWW*, Vol. 4, p. 176a). And Achilles, absorbed in his own mourning for Patroclus, wrapped up in the horror

*"Hamlet's rejection of the human condition recognizes only man's finite limitations: the paragon of animals is no more than the quintessence of dust."* Sir Laurence Olivier as Hamlet in a motion-picture version of the play (1948).

of his own mortality, responds to the pitiful figure before him. He lifts Priam from his knees, places him in a chair and sits beside him:

> . . . you and I will even let
> our sorrows lie still in the heart for all our grieving . . .
> Such is the way the gods spun life for unfortunate mortals,
> that we live in unhappiness . . .
>
> (XXIV, 522–23, 525–26; cf. p. 176d)

Freud has said that the aim of psychotherapy is to restore the patient to the unhappiness common to mankind. That is what Priam and Achilles do for each other. They redeem each other from the solipsism of their personal despair. Is it too much to suggest that the spectator is also restored, that by witnessing this movement in the characters, the spectator is also transported out of his solipsism? Confronting the common human condition by means of tragedy rescues the spectator from the isolation of his private woes.

When the chorus in the *Agamemnon* declares that "Zeus has laid it down that wisdom comes alone through suffering" (177–78; cf. Vol. 5, p. 54a), the kind of wisdom it is talking about has nothing to do with instrumental reasoning. In fact, by the time that the tragic protagonist has reached insight through suffering he is usually beyond the possibility of any pragmatic improvement. Rather, the Aeschylean chorus is referring to the entirely poetic "wisdom" of recognizing one's humanity, an understanding that is well beyond utility. It is, in a way, beyond ordinary consciousness, beyond "the daily life of the ego."

While tragedy takes us from our concern with earthly satisfaction, the comic spirit of *The Odyssey* is completely involved in this life, its satisfactions, successes, victories. And literature, which is presented here as utilitarian and hedonistic, is given a central role in *The Odyssey*'s celebration of this world. Along with "the feast . . . and dances and changes of clothing and . . . hot baths and beds" (VIII, 248–49; cf. *GBWW*, Vol. 4, p. 224d) storytelling is part of life's delightfulness. Indeed, "the lyre [was by] the gods made to be a companion of feasting" (XVII, 272; cf. p. 279d). Like the feast, literature is an aspect of the ceremoniousness that unites men in community. Like the feast, too, literature gives pleasure. Pleasure, in fact, is the chief and constant element in *The Odyssey*'s talk about tale-telling. The bard, Phemius, "pleases himself" as well as his audience. The god gave Demodocus "song surpassing in power to please," and the Phaiakians "joyed in his stories" (VIII, 44–45, 91; cf. pp. 222c, 223a). Because of the pleasure they bring, "with all peoples on earth singers are entitled to be cherished." Pisistratus may "have no joy in tears after dinnertime" (IV, 194; cf. p. 201a), but for the most part, when satisfied by literature, even the longing for lamentation becomes "lovely." Hearing tales of Odysseus, Penelope takes "her pleasure of tearful lamentation" (XIX, 213; cf. p. 291b).

In *The Iliad,* suffering is a final reality; there is no way out of personal sorrow but to recognize the sadness of the overall human condition. In *The Odyssey,* on the other hand, suffering and sorrow become the stuff of literature, and in that way they are the basis of delight. Dangers are experienced and then remembered: as memories they are no longer dangerous. Turned into entertainment, sorrow is detoxified. *The Odyssey*'s orderly optimistic universe supplies a humanly valuable function for destructive events. Alcinous observes that even the Trojan War was spun "for the sake of the singing of men hereafter" (VIII, 580; cf. p. 228c).

Eumæus directly addresses the relationship of stories and suffering, and, at the same time, he expresses a theory of literature as hedonistic. His remarks also make it clear that telling stories is an important aspect of man's function in society: the good guest and the good host entertain each other. Literature, and the pleasure it brings, creates human relations. To be an able storyteller is a desirable attribute of a good guest.

It is also, in fact, a desirable attribute of a good husband. The shade of Odysseus' mother directs her son: "remember these things for your wife, so that you may tell her hereafter" (XI, 223–24; cf. p. 245b). And we witness Odysseus wooing Penelope with his tales. It seems that storytelling is a significant element in the art of constructing a good marriage: "When Penelope and Odysseus had enjoyed their lovemaking, they took their pleasure in talking, each one telling his story" (XXIII, 300–301; cf. p. 315b).

Similarly, after the pleasure of food and wine, a guest provides entertainment with talk, telling where he comes from, and about the sorrows he has been suffering. Eumæus points out a practical function of exchanging stories: Nights are long, too much sleep is boring, but when enjoying tales there is "no need to go to bed before it is time" (XV, 392–94; cf. p. 270a). Eumæus makes the connection between sorrows and entertainment explicit:

> . . . we two . . .
> shall entertain each other remembering and retelling
> our sad sorrows. For afterwards a man who has suffered
> much and wandered much has pleasure out of his sorrows.
>
> (XV, 398–401; cf. p. 270a)

The view of literature, the attitude that finds even sufferings useful because they can be turned into good stories, is a paradigm of *The Odyssey*'s comic optimism.

It can, of course, be argued that a universe containing the Cyclops, Læstrygonians, Scylla and Charybdis has too many terrors for comedy. J. R. R. Tolkien comments about *Beowulf* that the heroes come and the heroes go, but the monsters go on forever. [21] *Beowulf* is a tragedy, and Tolkien's observation is directed to its basic tragic nature. With the defeat of the hero, the aura of futility this casts over his earlier victories, the projected after-history of the decline of the nation, *Beowulf* looks directly into the abyss. But in *The Odyssey* the hero triumphs and survives; the projected after-history is of happy and prosperous domesticity and a prosperous people. There may be monsters, but no look into the pit darkens that poem's optimistic vision.

## Other comic types

Optimistic comedy, the kind of comedy that characterizes *The Odyssey* or the first creation story of Genesis, is clearly not the only comic type. There is also, for example, a comedy of pessimism, the strong pessimism that Nietzsche assigns to tragedy. It does not avert its gaze from the darkness of life, but at the same time, it accompanies that gaze with laughter. Woody Allen's *Annie Hall* or his *Love and Death* can be taken as examples. Like tragedy, this comedy finds death terrible, divinity uncertain, the universe morally indifferent, the person alienated from the universe and even from his most intimate attachments. *Annie Hall* begins with a joke about the misery and brevity of human life: "The food at this place is really terrible, . . . and such small portions." It ends with a joke about relationships: "they're totally irrational and crazy and absurd . . . but, I guess we keep goin' through it because most of us need the eggs." God is an "underachiever." Death is "even worse than the chicken in Kretsski's restaurant." This is the comedy of laughable things, things that are painful and out of place, that Plato, in the *Symposium,* identifies with tragedy. Like tragedy, and unlike *The Odyssey,* this kind of comedy is beyond utility. Unlike *The Odyssey,* this is a comedy that rests on the tragic elements of pity and fear.

There is yet another comic type that stands in contrast to the optimistic comedy of *The Odyssey* or the first creation story. It is found in a comedy that "cover[s] the abyss with grass and spangle[s] the grass with flowers and make[s] believe." [22] The make-believe of *A Midsummer Night's Dream* constructs that sort of lovely and decorative covering. It might be called the comedy of consolation, where love and poetry, the realm of the imagination, create the conditions that make life delightful—a delightfulness that transcends life's quotidian reality.

We know *The Odyssey*'s monsters only as ingredients of Odysseus' good stories. Their existence is merely fictional, and therefore the monsters do not affect the comic optimism of the poem. In *A Midsummer Night's Dream,* on the other hand, the terrors are real, [23] while the consolations belong to a fictional realm of fairy, love, and poetry. Despite the laughter and despite the happy ending, the play never lets us forget that the real world contains dangerous elements: bright things that come quickly to confusion; the wretch that lies in woe who is put

(Above) Diane Keaton and Woody Allen in *Annie Hall* (1977). *"Like tragedy, this comedy finds death terrible, divinity uncertain, the universe morally indifferent, the person alienated . . . even from his most intimate attachments."* Similarly, in *A Midsummer Night's Dream, "the terrors are real, while the consolations belong to a fictional realm of fairy, love, and poetry. Despite the laughter and despite the happy ending, the play never lets us forget that the real world contains dangerous elements."* (Opposite) Mickey Rooney as Puck in the movie version of the play, made in 1935.

in remembrance of the shroud; the dust of reality that Puck is sent to sweep behind the door. On the other hand, the "bringer of the joy" is entirely an invention of the fancy. Love may as easily result from the fairies' potion as from any other cause; it doesn't matter. It is "an airy nothing" upon which human needs and desires have bestowed a "habitation and a name." This is very different from the love of Odysseus and Penelope, rooted in common things, deliberately constructed and maintained with art and intelligence by two persons who are established as worthy partners for each other.

Like *A Midsummer Night's Dream, The Tempest* is a comedy of consolation. Like *The Odyssey,* it is a comedy of homecoming. The purity of *The Odyssey's* comic optimism may be seen in contrast to *The Tempest,* for both works sound many of the same comic themes and share many of the same comic attitudes. Each work creates a comic plot with a happy ending of return and restoration, and more importantly, each expresses a belief in a cosmic order of justice and in the active involvement of divinity in human affairs: the powers do not forget, destiny instruments the lower world. In that its threatening seas turn out to be merciful, that, despite all apparent injuries, no harm is done ("not so much perdition as a hair"), in the "miraculous" way that "all things work for the good," *The Tempest* seems a very pattern of optimism.

Yet the comic vision of that play is strangely vexed. Heaven had seemed ordinant in human affairs, but does the power of Providence turn out to be only Prospero's "rough magic"? The moral nihilism of Antonio and Sebastian, their indifference to the ties of kinship, provides an element of darkness more frightening than anything in *The Odyssey* (a danger that recalls the Hobbesian world of Genesis 4). Furthermore we may wonder whether the reconciliation with Antonio and Sebastian might not shake the play's ethical scheme. Are they, in fact, sufficiently redeemed for forgiveness? Caliban is rejected, but is he any less redeemed? Indeed, what effect does the ambiguous, often touching role of Caliban have upon the comic quality of the work? Mankind seems beauteous to Miranda, but only because she lacks experience: Mankind is new to her. This is hardly the optimistic view of humanity that was held by the pre-tragic Hamlet when man was "like an angel! . . . like a god!" Prospero's famous comments about the brevity and insubstantiality of human life would not be inappropriate to the pessimism of a Woody Allen film. Prospero is restored to his dukedom, but the happy ending is disturbed. After all, Prospero's "every third thought shall be the grave." The comedy is a problematic artifact. The real world emerges as scary and somewhat sad.

The real world, on the other hand, is precisely what *The Odyssey*— as well as the first creation narrative—celebrates. Its "deep comfort of the world" is a primary differentia of the comedy of optimism. Despite the element of the fabulous in the story of the Great Adventures, despite the embodied presence of divinity in human events, the important world of *The Odyssey* is everyday life. Marriage, family, home, community afford the person his significant and fulfilling circumstances. The activities connected with domesticity—carpentry, farming, keeping accounts, managing the details of an estate, preparing and serving food, telling tales—give the individual that meaningful work by which he masters his environment, realizes himself, and achieves a readily available happiness.

---

1. When seen in conjunction with I, ii, 129–59 (*GBWW,* Vol. 27, pp. 32d–33a), this speech clearly contrasts Hamlet's tragic vision with his former attitude.

2. Cf. John Milton, *Paradise Lost* (IX, 1–6; *GBWW,* Vol. 32, p. 247):

> No more of talk where God or Angel Guest
> With Man, as with his Friend, familiar us'd
> To sit indulgent, and with him partake
> Rural repast, permitting him the while
> Venial discourse unblam'd: I now must change
> Those Notes to Tragic . . .

3. Friedrich Nietzsche, *The Birth of Tragedy* (Garden City, N.Y.: Doubleday & Company, Inc., 1956), p. 31 (cf. *GIT* 1983, pp. 396–469).

4. I have used Richmond Lattimore's translations of *The Iliad* (Chicago: University of Chicago Press, 1951) and *The Odyssey* (New York: Harper and Row, 1967) throughout this article.

5. W. H. Auden, "In Memory of W. B. Yeats."

6. Nietzsche, *The Will to Power.*

7. Ibid.

8. *Tragic Sense of Life* (New York: Dover Press, 1954), p. 107.

9. Nietzsche, *The Birth of Tragedy,* p. 93.

10. "The Iliad; or, The Poem of Force" (reprinted from *Politics,* November 1945), p. 11.

11. (New York: Dell Publishing, 1976), p. 456.

12. Nietzsche, *The Birth of Tragedy,* p. 10.

13. (New York: Avon Books, 1976), p. 321.

14. *Journal of General Education,* January 1950.

15. (New York: Vintage Books, n.d.), pp. 238–39.

16. It might be argued that Nestor is old in *The Iliad,* but he is ten years older in *The Odyssey.* Furthermore, his age is a limitation in *The Iliad* when he must be rescued by Diomedes (VIII, 99–120; *GBWW,* Vol. 4, p. 52c–d).

17. Nietzsche, *The Birth of Tragedy,* pp. 51–54.

18. "Lapis Lazuli."

19. Nietzsche, *The Birth of Tragedy,* p. 42.

20. Ibid., p. 66.

21. *Beowulf: The Monsters and the Critics.* Proceedings of the British Academy, XXII (1936), p. 34.

22. Louis MacNeice, "Venus' Speech."

23. For the terrors of *A Midsummer Night's Dream,* cf., among much else, Lysander's speech (I, i, 141–44; *GBWW,* Vol. 26, p. 353d) and Puck's speech (V, i, 378–97; pp. 374d–75a).

# The New Pythagoreans III:
# The Scientists of the Mind (Part One)

## Thomas K. Simpson

Thomas K. Simpson has appeared frequently in *The Great Ideas Today*.
Until last year, when he retired from teaching, he was a tutor at St. John's
College, in Annapolis, Maryland, and Santa Fe, New Mexico. Currently he is
conducting seminars on the idea of nature with members of the Maryland
Department of Natural Resources. Under a grant from the National Endow-
ment for the Humanities, he has been working also on an edition of papers
on the electromagnetic field by James Clerk Maxwell, designed to make
Maxwell's text accessible to readers without special training in mathematics
and sciences. Other projects include a study of Leon Trotsky's *History of
the Russian Revolution* and a computer investigation of a claim by Jules-
Henri Poincaré that nothing in principle prevents consistent intuitions of non-
Euclidean geometry, including those with dimensionality greater than three.

Mr. Simpson's education was at the Virginia Polytechnic Institute, at St.
John's, at Wesleyan University, and at Johns Hopkins University, where he
earned a doctorate in the history of science and technology. He is pictured
above at a science exhibit with his son, Eric, a professional photographer.

Two previous essays, one devoted to physics and the other to the sciences of life, have explored the transformation which seems to have operated upon the *idea of science* in our time—by which I have meant those now five decades since the onset of World War II. [1] I hope the previous studies have offered convincing evidence that science at its very roots has in fact undergone such a transformation, which seems best characterized on the whole as a *liberation:* quantum mechanics in its fruition as nuclear physics has led the way in freeing us from notions of strict determinism, naive "objectivity," or the materialism of small, hard atoms. The greatest scientists, we should hasten to remark, probably never thought of their work in such reductive terms, but the common perception and the social grip of the old way, which I have characterized as a "Glacial Age," has been severe. In many ways explored in the previous essays, this icy grasp is now being relaxed, with the prospect that first the physical sciences, and now the biological sciences in their train, are entering upon an altogether new era in which they are prepared to join in shaping the overall, restless intellectual and social strivings of our time.

Some initial perceptions led me to identify the new way of the sciences as "Pythagorean," and I think on the whole that has proved an illuminating insight. Following this hint, the first essay took Plato's *Timaeus* (*GBWW,* Vol. 7, pp. 442a–77c) as characterizing the Pythagorean vision of a world and man's place in it; of course no literal archaism was intended, but the classic text offered a rich point of reference for an investigation, and the leads it provided seemed, nearly all of them, fruitful. How might they now be summarized?

The beginning, the myth said, was with unity, form, wholeness, the good. All things, starting with soul, were constructed on principles of number and symmetry: the elaboration of the diatonic order in music became the mythic model for the structure of ourselves and of the cosmos, ultimately in a single system which could be known only in its organic completeness. There was a dark side: number closed upon itself in the contradiction of the irrational, and that intractable closure bespoke a realm of Necessity, shaken in the womb of becoming and bearing the prospect of a perpetual undoing of the cosmic weave. [2] From the interworking of Same and Other was born Time, the moving image of eternity, and with it the linear flow of our human discourse.

Many things separate us from that old myth—perhaps so utterly that we can never again even quite comprehend it. But features of it bear strikingly on the revelations of past decades in the sciences: in physics first, the primacy of form, number, symmetries and asymmetries—and with these, the liberation from reductionist notions of brute "matter." It is hard to realize, but inescapable: at the foundation of things we are no longer dealing with anything like that "matter" which once seemed to us so hard and elementary. Kicking the table leg for reassurance is interesting, but no longer relevant to this fundamental proposition. Now, instead, a sense of almost mythical wholeness pervades the efforts of contemporary physicists to think first of the unity of a primal plasma, from which the diversity of particles is derivative, emerging in the new mythology during the "first three seconds" of the universe. It seems indicative that we are searching now in our laboratories for "signatures" of particles rather than for the entities themselves—for computer constructions, the terms of whose existence lie in principle beyond the horizons of imaginable experience.

Perhaps most telling of all these transformations has been the demand for a deep revision of our notions of cause and effect, with the dawning recognition that we must learn to think from the beginning in terms of whole *systems*. Causality must, it seems, be derived from such larger wholes as the primary entities, rather than built up in the old style from pushes and pulls among isolated, atomic components. [3] It is this last insight which commanded special attention in the second essay, devoted to the life sciences; there the "world food problem" turned out to be a *systematic* concept which was tragically self-defeating when analyzed in lesser terms, without regard to the world food system as a whole. That ultimate unity of all forms of life which was the first principle for Timaeus seemed to reappear as well in the almost inconceivable interrelationships inscribed in the DNA and the proteins, while they are now understood better semiotically than materially as two modalities of life as *text*. All of these concepts press hard upon our regressive social and political forms, which they tend at every point to challenge and contradict. It was perhaps inevitable, therefore, that each of the two preceding essays has ended with a sense of sharp negation: the promise of the new scientific insights, with their implications for ourselves and our life and thought as a community, tends everywhere to be canceled in practice by social thought which, unlike thought in the sciences, seems still deeply in bondage to a glacial era of its own.

We turn now to a new effort, this time to consider the "sciences of the mind," and as we do so, an initial disclaimer is in order. Any attempt to look synoptically at "the sciences," as we are doing in these essays, is of course doomed to the hazards of fragmentary sampling and arbitrary preoccupation: one cannot be expert, or even decently informed, over a wide range of the sciences at once. This is especially true of the sciences of the mind, which, however rich in their parts, do not yet cohere in a single body of theoretical insight. Prudence would urge that one master a small portion and observe a respectful silence about the rest. But there is also a role for the effort to recover some perspective on the whole, on behalf we might say of "Everyman," the liberal artist, who though he cannot be master of these matters, deserves something more than the ordinary in the way of bulletins of current information. I am very willing in this sense to undertake the fool's errand, as messenger to Everyman. We seem to hear resonances of tales out of the depths of our tradition, suggesting clues to the meaning of this strange new world, otherwise so unfamiliar. Like Prospero, in *The Tempest,* we may be witnesses to some destined meeting of what is oldest in our tradition with what is most new.

Again in this case of our contemporary sciences of the mind, I suggest there is something interestingly Pythagorean at work. Acting on that intuition, I propose that we begin our new investigation by recalling a text which is at once deeply Pythagorean, and devoted to the question of the mind and its modes of knowing—Plato's dialogue the *Theaetetus* (*GBWW,* Vol. 7, pp. 512a–50c). I turn to this text because, while it deals explicitly with the question of "knowledge" and the classifier's shelf labeled "epistemology"—and while few scholars might think of it initially as Pythagorean—I think we will soon find that it is a gateway to the broadest questions about the mind and its functions and shares in the realm of mind the essential worldview of our original Pythagorean text, the *Timaeus.* We will discuss it, though only briefly, with an eye to certain themes which may today still underlie our studies of the mind. Then, with these enduring themes in view we will look— admittedly, very selectively—at a few works of people who call them- selves "biopsychologists," "neurophysiologists," "etologists," or more simply, just "psychologists"—scientists of the psyche. My hope is that as a result, though we will find few formal answers, we will be able to achieve some sense of new perspective on old questions about ourselves and our minds, and some sense as well of important new forms which the *idea of science* is taking in our time.

Following this reading of the *Theaetetus,* our task divides into two parts: the first will deal with laboratory investigations of perception itself, and certain striking theories which follow upon them. In this we track the pattern of the dialogue, for as we shall see, Theaetetus' first answer to the question of the definition of knowledge is that "knowl- edge is perception." The second will look deeper, into the domain of the unconscious, into motivations and instincts, and the genetic, evolu- tionary history which underlies them. It is the first part which appears here, together with our account of the *Theaetetus.* Part Two, which will begin with a discussion of the work of Freud and Jung, is promised for the next edition (1991) of *The Great Ideas Today.*

## I. The *Theaetetus*

In what is evidently one of Plato's artful fictions, the conversation reported in the dialogue called *Theaetetus* is described as having taken place when Socrates was on the point of going to his trial, and thence to imprisonment and death. The discussion which forms the body of the dialogue begins when he is introduced to a young man, Theaetetus, who becomes the principal respondent in a dialectical investigation of what might be the most central of human questions: "What is knowledge?" Systematists, as we have observed, thus tend to classify it as a dialogue on epistemology. If we wonder whether other matters, such as love, justice, or courageous devotion, would be humanly more revealing as objects of investigation than knowledge, the dialogue might have us ask: ". . . but how do we *know* that this is love, and not its surrogate, that this is justice, or that this courage will remain secure, when tested?" In this sense, knowledge is the key to all our questions. Perhaps it is only if these objectives to which we devote ourselves are real and thus knowable, that life can have meaning. And it is just such questions as these, of the human virtues, which this dialogue does pose—implicitly if not explicitly—if only by keeping always before us the example of Theaetetus himself, whose devotion and courage are surely genuine, knowable, and grounded in Being, if anything is.

There is thus an interesting complexity about the discussion from the outset: for it does not consist solely, or even primarily, in that formal pursuit of the definition of knowledge which is its announced concern. Much more, it is a direct encounter with the problem of knowledge, by way of the presence of Theaetetus. The young man has been brought to Socrates by Theodorus, his teacher of geometry, with the warmest of recommendations: he is said to have already proved himself an excellent learner, and indeed, very much *like Socrates himself*—even to the point of sharing Socrates' distinctively unaesthetic snub nose. [4] This claim is to be put to the test. So the real question of the dialogue, beyond the official investigation of the definition of knowledge, is what we might call the framing inquiry, the examination of Theaetetus. The dialogue's overt question has closed on itself: rather than "What is knowledge?" *in general,* it becomes the immediate and exact concern, human and almost mystical, "Who, in truth, is Theaetetus?"

In many dialogues we see the finest citizens of Athens put to such a Socratic test, and we see many fail, for it is hardest of all in life to acknowledge that one is in error and has something to learn. Theodorus, for example, utterly lacks courage when the questioning is directed to him. If Theaetetus on the other hand is in truth the person of intelligence and courage Theodorus would project, then we must find at the base of his Being some rock on which this character is founded: and it is about that bedrock of human truth which any one of us might really be asking if we join in the philosopher's formal inquiry, "What is knowledge?" Knowledge may be a question of ideas, but here as in the dialogues generally, we pass or fail the test of knowledge as we meet the idea in some most present and immediate encounter.

This question concerning Theaetetus is asked of course not primarily about his body, though that is specifically and importantly involved, but about his soul; and thus if this young man measures up to the promise of Theodorus, we will in examining Theaetetus in fact be examining what the human soul can be, at something close to its best. He is spoken of from the outset as an object of genuine wonder. [5] There is indeed something of the classic sense of *form*, the *eidos*, in this: Theaetetus stands before us as the very type of the human—and thus, it might be our hope, as an image of ourselves. He comes, then, as an object of question and wonder: and the question of Theaetetus is the question of ourselves. And too, if Theodorus is right about a resemblance he thinks he sees between examiner and examinee, a likeness which Socrates himself seems to perceive and enjoy, then the soul being revealed by stages as the dialogue proceeds will reflect that of Socrates as well— and this will be a dialogue in some curious sense of Socrates *with himself,* perhaps that "inner discourse" of which thought is said, later in the dialogue, to consist (*GBWW,* Vol. 7, p. 538a). If so, the dialogue in its circling must curiously transcend time to incorporate a lifetime, since the elder Socrates is in this view seen interviewing his own youth concerning a Socratic question—a question which, as it is never simply answered, properly embraces lifetimes. Perhaps a Socratic dialogue is never destined to become a discourse among the elders, the wise ones, which we sometimes wish for ("The real discussion in the Academy," which people envision) but inherently remains an interview which knits up lives. Is it not rightly cast in the mode of a challenge and invitation of the young by the old, of those who are arriving, on the part of those who are leaving?

Thus universalized—and I think we do no violence to the intimacy of the dialogue by interpreting it in these universal terms—it becomes an inquiry into the human soul itself, or after all, not so much a work of epistemology as a Platonic *psychology.* Other dialogues, in which the soul is the explicit object of inquiry, present themselves more directly as psychological—*The Republic* as metaphor for the just soul (*GBWW,* Vol. 7, pp. 295a–441c), the *Phaedrus* (*GBWW,* Vol. 7, pp. 115a–41c) imaging the phenomenology of the soul in love—but here we study the soul simply at its most central work, of seeking to know the world. If so, we may reasonably assume that it will pose, in Socrates' timeless way, those questions which will be operative, but so much harder to recognize, in our contemporary investigations of the sciences of the mind—and we need make no apologies for beginning our modern inquiry with this digression into a more speculative past.

The *Theaetetus* will ask then in all seriousness *who we are,* in terms of the question, what it is to know the world. Other creatures live in the world and use it, but we, if not exclusively at least characteristically, move in the world by way of knowing it. What does it mean to make that claim? That is the overall question which the *Theaetetus* sharpens for us yet leaves us to take in turn to our modern scientists of the mind. The dialogue, as we shall see, begins with a discussion of sense perception, then moves on to naming, and then finally to the forming of full thoughts housed in "sentences." Throughout, we seem to have assumed this outcome of the inquiry, that knowing will be coextensive with such articulate predication, for our effort is to *know* "knowing"— by asserting its definition! The full significance of this search for ourselves as knowers may strike us as we see that on the reverse of this coin of knowledge is stamped the word *Being*. Is there something in the world to be known—something real and lasting, and worth thinking about or living for? Do we ourselves, like Theaetetus, possess that integrity of Being which would make us knowable? Surely even in our modern, scientific world such questions remain appropriate, and the answer might be yes.

*The Eleusinian way*

Interestingly, Plato begins, not with the discussion between Theaetetus and Socrates itself, but with a certain precise, very different encounter, in a meeting much later between a certain Euclid and Terpsion, in Megara. From the evidence of the dialogue itself, it would seem that we stand then at the very point of Theaetetus' own death: the one who will narrate the dialogue, Euclid of Megara, has walked a very long way beside a stretcher bearing the dying Theaetetus homeward to Athens. He has thus led, or dispatched him in the role of Hermes, Soul-leader, the soul's guide to another world. [6] Theaetetus has been wounded in battle and has fallen victim, as well, to disease. He has conducted himself bravely, and this valor is said to have verified certain mantic words of Socrates, sprung from the conversation recorded here, that Theaetetus would, if he lived, one day prove himself an excellent man. Thus for Euclid, this occasion of the ending of Theaetetus' life becomes a reminder of its intellectual beginning, on the occasion of a conversation long before, with Socrates—the ending of the student's life serving then significantly to provoke *reminiscence* of its own beginning, which was at the same time the point of ending of his teacher's.

We are looking directly at the substantive meaning of the Pythagorean "reincarnation" of souls, always hovering over the Platonic dialogues: namely, the community and perpetuity of soul through generations. This last journey with Euclid is Theaetetus' Eleusinian rite of passage, as his conversation with Socrates was his mystical intellectual coming-of-age. A geographer might note that the road Euclid has walked beside

Theaetetus, from Megara toward Athens, and then the return alone, has taken him once through Eleusis on the way up, and once again, through Eleusis on the way down. The way up and the way down, beginning and ending, are one and the same.

It is in the very sentence in which he speaks of this soul-leading that Euclid says he is *reminded* of Socrates. As we learn in the *Meno* (*GBWW*, Vol. 7, pp. 174a–90c), where "recollection" plays a central role, this word, *reminiscence,* is the centerpiece of the Pythagorean answer to the question of *knowing*—we "know" in this world only because hints here remind us of things we have known in another. [7] Thus memory, which links past with present in this life, also mythically links one world with another: the world of flux and appearances, with a world in which Being is well grounded. In the Socratic mythology, only such human cycling and this community of the generations makes *knowledge* possible. In this way the answer to the dialogue's question is deeply founded at the outset, before the question itself has even been asked.

Does such mythical Eleusinian medicine seem too strong as our introduction to a modern discussion of the psyche? Is it hopelessly "unscientific"? I propose that it is not: that just as we found in physics that there is no limit to the depths of the mysteries of order and symmetry which have replaced the idea of "matter" and now constitute all we can know of the elementary particles and the substances of the world, so here even more in the domain of mind, there will be every invitation to invoke bold theoretical orders. Only very strange stories—perhaps even very old ones—could hope to save the astonishing data now coming from the neurophysiological laboratories.

*Socrates as editor*

We begin, then, appropriately, with a most solemn conversation between Euclid, who as it happens is carrying with him the text of the dialogue we are about to hear, and Terpsion, who has been eager to hear it. We are first carefully told the origin myth of the dialogue: it was, it seems, related to Euclid by Socrates himself, written down by Euclid from memory, and then again corrected by Socrates—so we know it was, in a sense, savored by Socrates, evidently in the last days of his life, during his imprisonment. Does Plato ask us to imagine Socrates, so traditionally the nonwriter, blue-penciling the text which we have before us? (If so, we must add, he may well have invented it or adjusted it to meet the demands of his dream of a Theaetetus.) What does this mean, that Socrates should be represented as having taken such an interest in the precise preservation of this particular dialogue? Perhaps it is a gift of love to Theaetetus—very likely, as who could be more attractive to Socrates than this young man, who learns with such winning devotion, initiative, and comprehension? But even if it is that, might it not be at the same time the most accurate definition

Socrates could leave of the soul and its act of learning? Superficially viewed, the dialogue ends, as we shall be seeing, in failure: very simply, no definition of knowledge is discovered which meets the test of the argument. But may not this failure in one mode, the literal, be only an index to victory in another? Socrates may have carefully left for us here his full, if tacit *answer* to the question, "What is knowledge?" And that is the question on which any inquiry into the human psyche, ancient or modern, must ultimately be founded.

### Seeing, naming, and thinking: aisthesis, onoma, *and* logos

Once we have turned from this short but telling introduction to the reading itself, Euclid explains that we are to be spared the complications of the narrative mode: it will be presented directly as drama, omitting the repetitive formula, "He said . . .". We must wonder again why Plato thus entangles his careful arguments with such dramatic involvements—complicating attentions to the detail of the human scene. Many plausible suggestions can be offered: the dialogues are thereby rendered more vivid or more humanly interesting; we ourselves, at the remove now of millennia, are drawn once again into the scene, so that the questions and arguments leap over time, born again in our own minds. But I suspect that in the present context of our concern with psychology, we can say something more definite, having to do with the nature of words.

Words can mean in the way of *logos*—that is, the sentence, in which a thought is fixed in the form, S is P, a predicate P asserted of a subject S. Such will be the burden of the argument of this dialogue, which is dedicated to achieving an accurate thought, in the predicative form, "Knowledge is . . .". But words work otherwise as well: they may more simply name a person or a thing, or paint a scene. In this case, no formal thought is spelled out, yet through such words, outside of their predication and *logos,* we may be drawn to see or feel, or to know. They are descriptive, suggestive, evocative; they are hints which evoke reminiscence: such are the words of Plato's careful scene-painting. Let us then distinguish two modes of the word, calling the first way, of predication or *logos,* "syntactic" (the Greek word means that words are ordered together); and the other way, in which words stand on their own without predication, without that specified ordering toward other words—and thus must *mean* by metaphor, character-painting, or scene-painting, or suggestion—"paratactic" (the words standing "*para,*" or side-by-side). It is very important to the intent of this dialogue, I believe, that it begin thus paratactically, and that invocation rather than propositional thought is in this sense the environing, dominant mode. If we now set these proposed modes of knowing in order, what emerges is something very much like the plan of the *Theaetetus* itself. The first—Theaetetus' first definition of knowledge—is perception, simply seeing or hearing. The second is designation, for example of the objects of perception, in naming. The third is that of the fullness of thought, in the formulation of the sentence in which one thing is formally predicated of another. We shall have much more to say about each of these, and it is striking, the extent to which they will prove powerful guides to the modern study as well as the ancient. In the most general way, we may anticipate by suggesting that they look like the great domains of the "right brain" (the right cerebral cortex; perception), and then respectively in the left brain, Wernicke's area (naming), and Broca's area (predication or syntax). Whether broad suggestions of this sort will bear useful fruit, however, we shall have to see.

We will, then, follow the fates of these themes first through the *Theaetetus* itself, and then into the modern world. As we do so, we can be clearest if we refer to them by the names they take in the dialogue: *aisthesis* (sensation, perception); *onoma* (name); and *logos* (sentence, predicative thought, argument). The English equivalents I offer here are merely suggested tags: what these terms mean, we shall have to see.

### Theaetetus as mathematician: Naming the nameless

The setting of Theaetetus' dialogue is important in another respect, for he comes to Socrates from a truly astounding experience with Theodorus, the geometrician. We are told that it is Theaetetus who has worked out a way of classifying the lines which are called incommensurable, meaning that they do not have a ratio expressible as the ratio of a number to a number (*GBWW*, Vol. 7, p. 515b–c). But *logos*, which is sentence or thought, is also the term for ratio; thus those lines which have no expressible ratio are nonrational or "irrational," the Greek for which is *alogos*. [8]

Theaetetus' project is of the greatest difficulty and significance, and yet almost inaccessible to modern readers, as it is no longer quite possible to perceive the problem with which Theaetetus and Theodorus were confronted. Our modern, casual facility with the irrational numbers has made the basic problem almost invisible. We have spoken of this in connection with our reading of the *Timaeus* in an earlier essay, but it will be very much worth our while to review the matter in more detail, in this new context, for it lies close to the center of the question of the mind's effort to know the world. [9] At the heart of the Pythagorean mystery, at least in its mathematical aspect, if that indeed is not the heart of the whole, lies the problem of the *alogos*—that which cannot be spoken, or more strictly, that about which predications cannot be made. But a predication makes a sentence—a *sentencia*, which is no more than Latin for a "thought"; *sententia* translates the Greek word *logos*. Thus the *alogos* presents itself at first blush as the unthinkable, but more reflectively, the unspeakable, or the mystical—for the mystical is precisely that before which one must be silent (Greek: *muein*).

We are about to stumble over a confusion of names, so it will be as well to pause to acknowledge the intriguing difficulty. We need to speak of "Euclid's" *Elements* (*GBWW*, Vol. 11, pp. 1–396). It appears that there was a deep and most reasonable medieval tradition which confused the Euclid of Alexandria, who was the author or assembler of the *Elements,* with our Euclid of Megara, who hosts this dialogue. What a creative error of a more playful tradition! The blessed scholars of the Church, licensed to be a bit cavalier about their centuries (and misled, perhaps, by misconceptions seeded in this way by Plato), were able to make an identification which is one of those greater truths that escape history. For the study which Theaetetus carried out under Theodorus is identified—by the same solemn scholars who dispel the medieval naïveté—as having in fact been incorporated as Book X of the *Elements* of the Alexandrian Euclid. And further, to our Theaetetus is assigned as well the triumphant and most celebrated Book XIII, the final book of the *Elements,* in which the regular solids are constructed. Throughout the constructions, the lines called *alogos,* irrational, are carefully identified and tracked. Thus this Theaetetus, here presented as at once young man and dying hero, is also one of the great mathematicians of our Western tradition. It is only an incidental misfortune that he devoted his efforts to the solution of a mathematical problem which happens to be no longer visible as having ever been a problem at all, and hence receives little recognition for his triumph!

As we will now try to show, the *alogos* is at the very heart of the question of knowledge—and hence, we might say, of the dialogue's construction of Theaetetus himself, very much as it is at the heart of the construction of his icosahedron. And in case the reader of the present essay begins to fear that we have lost altogether our way to the modern sciences of the psyche, let me offer my assurance, for what it is worth, that the same question, quietly as always, underlies much of our modern investigation of the psyche. It is one of those questions which change form but will not, and should not, go away.

What, then, is this mathematical discovery on which Theaetetus' project is built? It is the demonstration in the first book of the Alexandrian Euclid's *Elements* which is, quite rightly, known to the world as the Pythagorean Theorem, namely that in the right triangle, the squares on the two sides are together equal to the square on the hypotenuse (Book I, Proposition 47; *GBWW*, Vol. 11, pp. 28–29). This is of course well known (though not necessarily well demonstrated) by all schoolchildren: in the specially interesting case of the "equilateral" right triangle, the relationship can be grasped by the eye in a single drawing (fig. 1). [10] What lurks immediately is a mystery appropriately left silent by Euclid: in the case, for example, of the equilateral triangle of figure 1, if a number measures each of the equal sides, than *no number will measure the hypotenuse.* No number? The same schoolchildren are

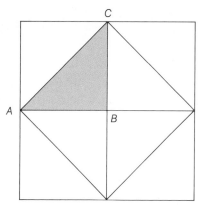

Figure 1. The equilateral right triangle, drawn to show by inspection that the square on the hypotenuse *AC* is twice the square on the side *AB*.

ready to assert that a number measures the diagonal, only it is an *irrational number,* in the case of the unit square written $\sqrt{2}$. [11]

But wait! What is a *number*—what, that is, is the *definition* (*logos*) of a number? Euclid, in the arithmetic books of the *Elements,* is quite clear: "A *number* is a multitude composed of units" (*GBWW,* Vol. 11, p. 127, Definition 2). Our irrational "number," $\sqrt{2}$, does not fit this definition, for the corollary we have cited means that here *is no unit* (however small), such that one multiple of it will measure the sides, and another the hypotenuse, of the equilateral right triangle. The two lines, side and diagonal, are utterly *incommensurable.* [12] To write the $\sqrt{2}$, the Western tradition has long since fudged the definition of number. One famous way of doing that is by means of Dedekind's "cut," a method based on limits; a device essentially equivalent to Dedekind's was used by Euclid in Book V—a book apparently supplied by yet another delegate of Plato's Academy, Eudoxus—but *not at all as a definition of "number."* [13] Eudoxus makes it possible to speak of a *ratio* between our two incommensurable lines, but we are not thereby allowed to avoid the fact that they are not numbered. What this means in turn is that though we are equipped to refer to two ratios as being "the same" with one another, we have no way to say what that "ratio" *is.* To express a ratio, we need to say what its two elements are, as two numbers (the ratio of two lines is 2:3, for example, if when a unit-line measures one of them 2 times, the same unit measures the other 3 times). If we cannot come up with any such number pair to measure a given pair of magnitudes, then the ratio, though we may be confident it exists, remains unexpressible, or *alogos.* [14]

We cannot speak it, which is to say: we cannot give its definition. Can we *know* it? Well, that is exactly the center of our Pythagorean interest. We can *see* it in the figure, but we cannot know it expressly,

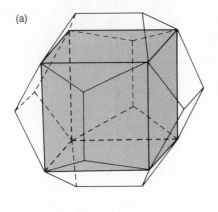

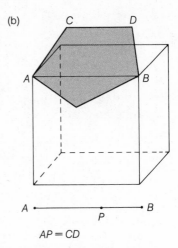

$$AP = CD$$

Figure 2. The dodecahedron, which as Euclid shows incorporates an underlying cube (a). In (b), if the edge of the cube is taken as a unit (*AB*), then the side of the dodecahedron (*CD*) is the irrational line Theaetetus named the *apotome*. Their ratio is the "golden section."

in the sense that we cannot say or define it. We know it, in terms we used earlier, perhaps *paratactically*—not as a set explanation, but somehow . . . we see it in its relationships in our figure. Yet Eudoxus' theory shows us that it exists and makes it possible to work with it, even build a science based on it! The tradition normally thinks of this as a *mathematical* triumph of Plato's Academy, but we can see it is more than that. It is a crucial clue to the insight that things we cannot define or say—which are *alogos,* and thus before which we must remain silent, as in the mysteries—nonetheless do exist and are knowable.

Now, this is the domain over which Theaetetus has achieved special and personal triumph. Simple theorems show that each irrational line, such as the diagonal of the equilateral triangle, spawns an infinity of others, and indeed, infinities of infinities—all incommensurable with the line we have taken as our unit. [15] Theaetetus has developed a general system for classifying—that is, *naming*—these irrationals. He has brought the *alogos* under the control—not of *logos,* for that is what cannot happen—but, at least, into the domain of the name, the *onoma.* He has classified and named the irrationals and then, it seems, tracked them into their places in the regular solids of Book XIII, where they, the irrational, inhabit the most rational and beautiful—presumably, the most knowable—of figures (fig. 2).

The most rational is infused with the utterly irrational, the most speakable and knowable with the utterly unknowable and unspeakable: that is the heart of the Pythagorean mystery, and it is a thread which runs through not only the Platonic dialogues but the tragedies as well. [16] Thus the founding myth of Athens, Aeschylus' *Oresteia,* is infected with the furious creatures who bear doom through the generations of the House of Atreus; they are so amorphous the gods themselves cannot utter names for them. [17] But in the final play of the trilogy, Athena, the Theaetetus of the tragedy, finds a way, which it seems surprises her as much as her Athenians—and hence is only partially persuasive—to bring them to accept a name, the "Eumenides," the Well-Minded Ones, and to take their places in the construction of the new Athens of civic justice and the law courts. The place of the Eumenides in Athens is almost exactly correspondent to that of Theaetetus' irrational lines in the Book of the Regular Solids. In each case, the rational is founded on the irrational, the speakable on the unspeakable: and the triumph of the conversion must be profoundly celebrated. The crucial, first task is to bring an unspeakable infinity under the discipline of word, by *naming* it; the first victory is that of *onoma;* the more questionable victory of *logos* comes later. The fact of this incorporation, by which the unspeakable will be brought to accept a name, is the principle of the saving mysteries. The one mystery is at the same time very bright and very dark: that is why this dialogue, in which Theaetetus shines so brightly, is at the same time framed by deaths, knit even more closely by the curious chiasma in which the younger death is seen first, the elder last.

## The struggle for the name

Throughout the present essay we will be following the tracks of this strange power to bring the world under the spell of human knowing. The first stage, mystical and as it turns out utterly crucial, is preverbal; but when language enters as the instrument of knowing, then the first step is this use of the name as instrument: the power, granted to Adam, to command the world by way of naming introduces that space between knower and object in which all the development of the world of intellect can ultimately arise.

I suspect that generally in the dialogues a rejected answer is seldom simply "wrong." Perhaps, in dialectic, it is impossible to be simply wrong! In any case, Theaetetus is by no means altogether in error when he gives his first answer to Socrates' question, "What is knowledge?"— namely, that knowledge is *aisthesis,* sensation or perception (*GBWW,* Vol. 7, p. 517b). It will not be long before that proposition of Theaetetus' meets its refutation, in the recognition that if our powers are to be identified with sensation, then all sensation being in perpetual flux, there will be nothing which can endure existence or *bear a name.* This is the implication, the argument shows, of the doctrine of Protagoras, and it leaves each person isolated as the measure of all things, which are by the same token no things at all. Thus from the question of perception, of *aisthesis* itself, the discussion quickly shifts to the question of *onoma,* of the name—for in such a world of utterly fluid perceptions, there will be no objects firm enough to be the bearers of definite names: there is nothing to receive and retain one name, one word. Protagoras immerses us in another sense in *a struggle for a name*—which is, at the same time, the struggle for some Being with the stability to retain a name.

One hint, however, that Protagoras' position is not quite as false or utterly insupportable as it at first seems comes in Socrates' mock invocation of the Mysteries. As if in an Eleusinian ceremony, we turn to Protagoras, who it seems was Theodorus' friend, to rejoin the living for a bout of Socratic questioning (*GBWW*, Vol. 7, pp. 522b–24c). There emerges a disturbing insight concerning the Protagorean relativity of entities to one another—one active, the other passive: Protagoras is supposed to be wrong, but this Protagorean relativity seems true! For as Socrates suggests, he and Theaetetus are so conjoined: he as teacher is, he says, passive, while Theaetetus, the student, is the source of the ideas, and hence active. The existences of Socrates and Theaetetus *are* joined in a Protagorean relativity: they *are* bound to one another, and this by way of the very flux of the argument. That, we might reflect, is what dialectic is: the paired reasoning of two persons, "two going together," as Socrates says elsewhere. And it is striking, too, that it is precisely in dialectic that man most truly becomes the measure—for the testimony of the "one witness" in the dialectical argument is decisive; if he fails to say yes, the conclusion is not granted and the argument fails. We see the ambivalent truth of "man the measure." If we are measures separately, then everything is true and nothing is true; but if on the other hand we measure by seeing through to Being, which is the same for all, then that measurement becomes the insight which lies at the foundation of all knowing. These are the two modes of *aisthesis:* as commitment to flux which undoes Being and frustrates all naming, or as silent insight to that Being which underlies all knowing. This is the double truth of *aisthesis.*

### The good as benchmark

What is the significance of the fact that Socrates, hosting a mock mystery in which Protagoras is fetched back to life, undertakes to wear the mask of Protagoras himself and present the proposition that "man is the measure of all things?" He does this in the first instance for Theodorus, who is not only a mathematician but was a friend of Protagoras' as well. Theodorus it seems must be made to suffer the apparent contradiction between his friend's doctrine and his own science: for if man is the measure, then Theodorus' geometry is not possible. The possibility of science is at issue: if Protagoras' doctrine is valid, then Theodorus' life has no merit. [18] No one is excused from the Socratic judgment: Theodorus must suffer defeat with his "old friend" Protagoras, in order to be saved for science, and thus also for Theaetetus, his pupil in science.

The defeat of Protagoras in this dialogue could have been total, for his arguments come only from Socrates' mouth: it is therefore interesting that under Socrates' guidance, Protagoras' position is benignly modulated—a saving feature is included (is it gratuitously?) on Protagoras' behalf. For he is permitted to adjust his doctrine slightly but crucially, *on behalf of the good*—admitting that in matters of the better and the worse, not every man is a measure, but rather, we prize the opinions of those who know. Protagoras admits that all men acknowledge that some things *are* better, others worse—and with that admission, the gates are opened for us to pass beyond the Protagorean relativity. The same grace was granted once to Gorgias in the dialogue which bears his name: though he claimed for the rhetorician the task of persuading to one thing as well as another, he blushed to admit that he had omitted to preserve justice as a standard and, with revealing shame, implicitly acknowledged that he was a better man than he had claimed (*GBWW*, Vol. 7, p. 259b–c). [19] Let us say that the thread of the good runs through the argument concerning knowledge: our conviction that there are things which are better, and others worse, is stronger even than our conviction that the theories of geometry are true. Instances of the good and the bad are then the strongest Pythagorean hints that we do know certain things which have not been taught us.

We see, recognize, and in some way know the valor of Theaetetus in the argument, just as we see and somehow know the weakness of Theodorus, who will not undertake pursuit of the argument if there is any way to avoid doing so. We thus, looking at Theaetetus in our mind's eye, as the words of the dialogue paint him, see with eyes more powerful than those which *aisthesis* intends. Even at this distance, we do not need the impossible definition in order to know Theaetetus. But what crucially unlocks this power of knowing that is not spelled out in *logos* is the good, which shows through even in the manner of Theaetetus' responses to Socrates, or his initiatives in the conversation.

With such invocation of the Good as key to knowing, it might well seem that we had left behind any hope of connecting our Platonic reading with the modern sciences of the mind—for is it not the case that our modern sciences are "objective" and preserve a stance of value-free inquiry? Curiously, it appears to me that the opposite may be the case—that the sciences are at last very ready to address questions of subjectivity and value.

### The birth of logos

Theaetetus' first suggestion, that knowledge is *aisthesis,* has left us with uncertain success in the faltering project of naming. At one extreme pole, we have contemplated the utter flux espoused by Heracleitus, Protagoras, and in general, the Ionians (whose very name, *ion,* means "moving"). Only hinted here is the other pole, interestingly at the other "pole" of a world as seen from Athens, namely Parmenides in Italy. Parmenides, as that most difficult dialogue dedicated to him shows, brings us back always to Being. We are as silent about Being, because of its stasis, as we are about the Ionian flux, because of its motion. In another geographic image, we see that Athens is balanced in-between, as the point at which the two doctrines can be contemplated from a single center. Athens then marvelously symbolizes the birth of discourse, *logos:* for here at this center, the sentence (*logos*) can be shaped: the subject, about which varying things are predicated, itself remains constant, as the reflection of Parmenidian Being; the predicates bespeak change, accident, and motion and in their flux have nothing to say apart from the subject. In the joining of the two, however, arises the discourse which is hosted by Socrates: the *logos* in which something is said *of* something, the predicate *of* a subject, and a complete thought is born. Here in this dialogue, we are witnessing the birth of *logos,* the origin myth of human thought as captured in sentences, *sententiae.* The present dialogue is the weaving of just such sentences aimed at finding a *logos* which will encapsulate that ultimate thought, of what knowledge is. If things were as simple as that, the problem of Being, flux, and thought would have come to a happy resolution.

But of course, it is not so. Each definition Theaetetus proposes—each *logos*—he will see refuted in its turn; no definition will stand, and the project will utterly fail unless there is some form of thought which is not in *logos.* We thus witness in this dialogue both the beginning and the end of *logos:* its forming-up out of the flux, the articulation of a series of thoughts, and the passing-beyond all such predicative thought as it fails to catch just that truth, about knowing, which most interests us.

### Hesiod's wagon

It becomes a major concern of the argument to account for the fact that predications can be in error: perhaps memories are written on tablets, whose wax may be too hard or too soft to take the message well. Or perhaps words are like birds held captive in an aviary, from which we may draw in error and make false identifications in our predicating. The problem of error is crucial, because its other face is the possibility of truth: from visualizing the origin of false judgment, we turn to the question of the possibility of guaranteeing truth. Socrates' suggestion is that we undertake this by building up from secure elements, taking the model of constructing speech from letters to make syllables, then combining syllables to make words. It is a most attractive proposition, that we might indeed compose a world of truth this way; it is what we understand as the program of science, including no doubt the geometry which Theodorus and Theaetetus have been working out together.

Here is the root of the concept of orderly theory-building: to build knowledge from *elements,* which are themselves best known. The ques-

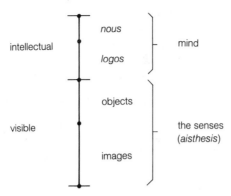

Figure 3. One interpretation of the Divided Line from Plato's *Republic*. Within the domain of the intellectual, the science of geometry belongs to the lower section, taking its first principles from the faculty called *nous*, the intellectual intuition, which does not employ argument.

tion converts, however, to one which is both central and elusive: what constitutes an entity, a Being in the world? Do we get entities in this way, by adding up secure parts—that is, in the dialogue's terms, is an entity achieved as an aggregation (*to pan,* the all), or as something which is a whole prior to its parts (*to holon,* the whole)? Socrates puts the problem in terms of Hesiod's legendary wagon, made of a hundred parts. Do the parts constitute the wagon, or is the wagon indeed something else? (*GBWW,* Vol. 7, p. 547d). As a further example, the word occupies an interesting place here, as it serves the argument both as model of the problem and as the object and essence of the inquiry. It on the one hand represents any being, made of elements (*stoicheia*); but on the other hand, it is the very entity on whose being the question of knowledge depends. How does a sound become a word? We cannot find the meaning of the word by studying and aggregating the sounds of which it is composed; it takes its meaning as a whole, and by a different route. The wagon is not to be grasped by aggregating the parts of which it is composed.

In this way, as we thus approach the end of the dialogue, we find ourselves once again at the beginning—our question is again, the simple word. A sound becomes a word only when it comes to *mean,* and that is not a question of aggregating sounds. It becomes clear that we cannot find a way out of the problem of meaning by building from least-parts. We must start with elements, but those elements will be themselves, wholes. Readers who recall the Divided Line of *The Republic* will see that we are at the starting point of a science such as geometry, which occupies the second part in the line of descent of the hierarchy of knowing (fig. 3). Its *elements* must be known first, from some prior source, or no geometry will ever be built. [20] But those elements are not least-parts but concepts which are themselves already essentially whole, such as *straight line,* or *number,* the *odd* or the *even. Aisthesis* must show them to us in images the eye can see; but unless that image triggers some recollection and we see through the image to the truth beyond, there will be only flux and confusion, once again the Ionian plague. *Aisthesis* becomes the occasion for intellectual insight, *nous.*

There is no sense here of the formal structure beloved of the modern algebraist; if this argument is right, the diagram will always be an essential part of the geometric demonstration. In the deeper mode of the duality of *aisthesis,* it functions as reminder and opens a direct way to insight into truths of the figures which it represents. In this sense, Euclid's *Elements* is a fundamentally dialectical work, in which Euclid asks the questions, and the reader plays the role of respondent. Turning to the figure, Euclid asks, "Is this not so?"—and the reader, seeing that it is, grants agreement. Reference to the diagram—whether on the page or in the mind's eye—thus often substitutes for and always in principle underlies argument in words, while the express argument never pretends to, or cares for merely formal completeness. Once again, in the geometry of Euclid as in the dialogues of Plato, we must use *aisthesis* in its penetrating, intuitive mode, invoking *nous* to see through to truths which underlie any truth expressed in words. This might seem to some a disturbingly un-Platonic position; Plato, as we know, inveighs against the poets! But that is one of the Platonic ironies long since explicated: the dialogues are throughout poetic, and since it is then within poetic that Plato inveighs against the poets, it must be that the poetic admits more than one mode. The Platonic poetic is to dialectic as the diagram is to the argument in the geometry of Theaetetus, which we know in Euclid's *Elements. Aisthesis* in this most serious mode, of tragedy, myth, or prayer, is not the distraction of the poet who merely plays with mirrors but the indispensable instrument of the philosopher concerned to mirror truth.

The dialogue ends, as we have anticipated, in apparent failure: no *logos* of knowledge has stood the test of the argument. But is that more than to say, *logos* is not the primary path between Being and truth? *Logos* must be silenced, if truth is to speak. We are returned to the opening sense of mystery, and the conviction we have called Pythagorean, modeled by Theaetetus' remarkable triumph, which is double. On the one hand, the darkness which he confronted: the truth is not in *logos;* there are relations in Being which cannot be asserted in speech, given definition, or in that straightforward sense, known. On the other, however: what thus seems darkness to *logos* can be charmed by naming, whereupon it reveals what is perhaps a much greater light. If it cannot be defined, still it can be hinted through image and paratactic speech in ways which approach ritual. To reach such powers of rite, it is necessary to pass through all the stages, as in this dialogue, which disabuse us of those things which speech and knowledge are *not;* and in the process, we must keep summoning by hint and successive allusion those resources we will need to have gathered in the end. This is the significance, it would seem, of the successive stages of the *Theaetetus,* leading as if in a great circle of refutations from *aisthesis* to *onoma* and to *logos,* but then in the grip of the final refutation, back to *aisthesis* once more.

## II. *Aisthesis* in the modern world

### *The eye*

As we turn now to the modern sciences of the mind, we may begin by following the thrust of Theaetetus' first proposal: that we know the world in the mode of *aisthesis*—sensation, or perception. Among the instruments of our sensation, it will be fitting, too, to choose the eye as the first organ for our study: both as physiological system and as a metaphor for "knowing," the eye will properly serve as a leading thread throughout this essay. [21] As a physiological system, the eye admits the tightest forms of laboratory study in every aspect: biochemical, physical, and neurophysiological. The interface with physics is so immediate that experiments can be controlled virtually to the level of the photon; while striking new advances in laboratory technology are well adapted to catch the eye in their instrumental nets. It is not surprising that this physiological domain of investigation has yielded brilliant results— taking the eye as a sensitive detecting instrument, tracking its ramifying neural connections, exposing it to carefully controlled stimuli, recording and interpreting the patterns in the cortex which result, even modeling aspects of this process in the computer. [22]

On the other hand, the eye as our chief avenue to whatever knowledge we acquire of the contents and makeup of the world becomes the object of that other kind of investigation, the psychological. Here our concern is with the experience of perception, subjectively observed, or measured by tests of performance and behavior, or analytic evidences of attention or cognition. The tense, always-problematic stretch between these two aspects of the sciences of the mind—roughly, the physiological and the psychological—is in a sense the axis on which the present essay must turn. The reader must be forewarned: to date, the fundamental questions in which we are most interested have not been answered, and it is almost as much a mystery as ever, how it is that we come to know, or invent, what we so confidently call the world. The first indications are that Theaetetus' initial impulse was very sound: *aisthesis,* quietly, has a great deal to do with whatever we come to verbalize confidently as knowledge of the world.

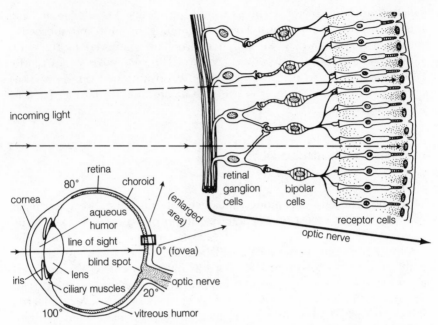

Figure 4. The human eye, with a detailed view of a section of the retina; the "living camera" and its "photographic film."

## The living camera

Perhaps the most helpful way to think of the eye is as a *living* camera, for although it is very far from being a merely passive recording instrument, it does on the other hand have an optical structure much like that of a Kodak. It has a lens of fair quality: it is very wide-angle, with a short, adjustable focal length and an iris which varies over a wide range in response to the ambient light level. The "film" is the retina, actually four melded photosensitive structures consisting of rod cells sensitive to low light but not distinguishing color, and three types of cone cells whose response curves center on as many distinct wavelengths, thereby making possible that qualitative distinction among lights which we call color. The retinal surface is three-layered, the sensitive rod and cone cells being found, strangely enough, on the back, farthest from the lens, while the ganglion cells which communicate the signals to the brain are in the front (fig. 4). There are said to be some 100 million photosensitive cells, yet only one-hundredth that number of ganglion cells: in between, by way of intermediate bipolar cells, there must thus be a dramatic gathering of many low-level rod and cone outputs to generate a single ganglion nerve signal to the brain. What is communicated, however, is not simply the *presence* of light. At the level of the retina, there is already organization of the information, or the first level of interpretation: the retina, it is pointed out, is embryologically a part of

194

the brain. Some cells act by inhibition, with the effect that the report from the retina includes information on contrasts which has the effect of revealing edges, and hence sharpening the definition of the image, introducing a contrast—an edge is, in a sense, an artifact, a construct of our sense process.

And how is this intensity information to be reported? It would be simplest to imagine that the nerve signal became an analogue of the light, the amplitude of an electrical signal in the optic fiber simply corresponding to the amplitude of the light detected by the retina— mapping the optical image into a direct electrical counterpart spread topologically across the optic cable. It is not, however, at all so simple. Nerve fibers carry their information in digital form—as trains of pulses essentially uniform in amplitude—so that from the outset some form of artful coding of the world is required. Amplitude information, picturing the world, has therefore to be translated in the output of the retina into new terms of pulse bursts and frequencies. This seems a crucial clue: perhaps we should say that we are from the outset not in reality engaged in picturing, but rather in interpreting and reconstructing a deluge of evidences, to *make* of them a "world."

The photosensitive film is not distributed uniformly over the retina: we get only very generalized, blurry information from most of our field of view. It is our Promethean way, it seems, to zero in intensively on just the forward view. A whole epoch of the evolution of the optical system ›follows the slow drift of mammalian vision, from the two broad, unco-ordinated worlds seen by the side-looking eyes of the horse or the cow, to the augerlike intensity of our human concentration, single-mindedly to the front. Interestingly, from an optician's point of view this means that we use the eye's lens at its best. A simple lens inevitably introduces aberrations; these are, however, least for points close to the axis and become greater at wider angles. We therefore do well to concentrate our cone cells, detecting the daylight scene in the fullness of what we call color close to the axis in the area called the fovea. Here the retina is rich in cells closely spaced for highest resolution. Having chosen at the outset as our human way this sharp but narrow view, we are left with a very general—and at the fringes, even colorless—sense of what is going on in most of the world. In the domains of the other senses as well, our strategy seems thus goal-riveted: we set a purpose, choose a target, and search it out, rejecting most of the world, and perceiving only what we anticipate and care to know about. We begin to recognize what is entailed in speaking of a "Kodak sprung to life"—become a searching, seeking, inquiring instrument. In this our human seeing, we thus function altogether differently from a camera—our eyes do not report neutrally what is before them but rather are always constructing for us a world to our own specifications, filling our orders for entities. Do we then make the world in our own image? Are we prepared

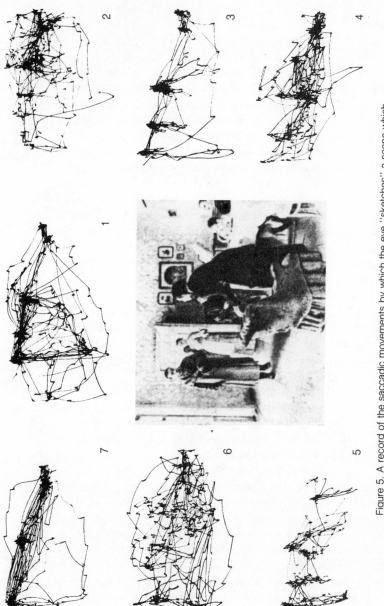

Figure 5. A record of the saccadic movements by which the eye "sketches" a scene which it is viewing, in pursuit of an interest. (1) The subject viewed the picture at center, without instructions. In successive trials, the same subject viewed the picture under instructions as follows: (2) Estimate the material circumstances of the family. (3) Give the ages of the people. (4) What were the family doing before the arrival of the "unexpected visitor"? (5) What clothes were the family wearing? (6) Describe the position of the people and objects in the room. (7) How long had the unexpected visitor been away from the family?

to see only what we or our primal ancestors have seen before, just what we are prepared to allow past the border-posts of a preconceived world? This would give Theaetetus' insight, that knowledge is *aisthesis,* an interesting twist. We see by way of knowing, rather than the other way around: what we see is already inherently somehow known to us. In the extreme, it here is rather confirmation of Kant: that things-in-themselves, whatever they are, are not in truth even spatial or temporal at all; their Euclidian character, for example, is the consequence of our special way of perceiving, the mode of our intuition. [23]

To utilize the narrow beam of our vision strategically and to respond efficiently to our ever-eager "search" orders, we have quick, complex control over movements of the eyes in their sockets. A set of six muscles is continuously setting the direction of the optical axis, at three levels of speed. Most rapid is a slight vibration, but perhaps humanly most distinctive is a bold, very fast saccadic jump at the rate of up to five per second. With this, we are always restlessly, unrelentingly scanning a scene—not at all, however, with the scanning routines of the TV raster, but with quick, arbitrary movements responsive to mercurial shifts of interest. In this way, we are constantly searching and appraising the scene. It is striking that a device which can follow and record these saccadic movements reveals us as in effect sketching the scene with our eye-beam, drawing pictures of our interests in the air (fig. 5). [24] Finally, slow movements of pursuit follow the motion of an object on which our interest has settled. This in itself is by no means as simple as it may seem, for as the head moves or the eyes pursue, light patterns fly over the retina, while the object must be perceived as an entity, persistent in time through the flux of impressions. Among the crucial inputs are those from the vestibular system, three orthogonal fluid canals in the inner ear, which by reference to gravity yield current information on head position and attitude. Even *stasis,* then—that crucial first stand against the Ionian flux—is not at all a given, but a work of art: the result of intricate computations of invariants in the transformations of the retinal data. Beyond all this, we adjust the directions of the axes of the two eyes to converge at an object's distance, and we position the lens in turn to bring the image at that distance to a focus on the retina. With this further computation, we in effect measure our optical reach into a world which, by that act, among others, we represent as three-dimensional.

What after all *is* "seeing," then? What does it mean, that we have a "lens" for sight, but none for hearing, touching, smelling? Sight, it would seem, is a very special way we have of sampling the world at a level of infinite detail which the other senses do not afford, poking at it with a tiny needle of investigative peering! The lens is a device shaped, the textbooks say, to generate an "image-point" for every "object-point" in the world. But actually, of course, the lens has no direct contact with any such object-points. From the sea of electromagnetic impulses in which it is immersed, a near-chaos of the electromagnetic field, any lens is extracting the statistical correlations which yield image-points for imputed object-points. As we shall see, the ear has no corresponding lens: and its construction of a "world"—its version of what we assemble as the one world—is, as we shall see, a construction of perhaps equal intricacy and delicacy, yet of a completely different sort.

### Strange images in the cortex

Most of us who have not thought greatly about the problem of perception intuitively adopt what is unflatteringly known in the literature today as the "Little Green Man" approach: we suppose that the problem is essentially cinematic—to *project* the world in all its aspects into the cortex, thought of perhaps as a kind of command center, where it can be viewed and assimilated by consciousness, the autocrat of our mental empire. Plato might seem to invite us to think in these terms, in speaking of the eye as the instrument by which the soul sees (*GBWW*, Vol. 7, pp. 534c–35d). Things are not so simple, surely, and perhaps not at all of this kind, though if we are to disparage this view, we

Figure 6. The human visual system. Within the optic nerve, all the information we call vision passes in the form of a structure of digital pulses.

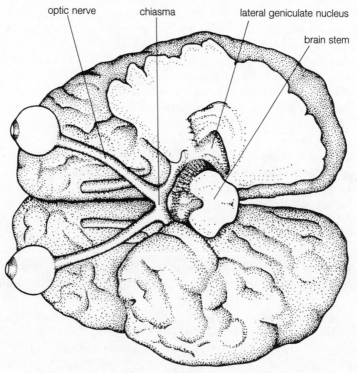

optic nerve     chiasma     lateral geniculate nucleus

brain stem

assume the challenge of replacing it with something more plausible. It will be very interesting to see, as we trace certain representative lines of modern reasoning in the sections which follow—to whom or what the Little Man has yielded his chair of conscious office!

Entirely new neurophysiological techniques perfected since World War II have made it possible to give answers to some major questions about the psyche which before that time could be matters only of pure speculation. Most impressively, it has become possible—by heroic means, electrical, biochemical, metabolic, radiological—to trace the pathway from a single nerve cell to its ultimate targets, with the result that astonishing patterns of neural connection have been mapped. There is, at the first stage, a way station between retina and cortex called the lateral geniculate nucleus (LGN), an impressive element of straightforward mapping (fig. 6). But altogether different principles quickly seem to take over as we move to the cortex itself, and these in turn dictate some very different understanding of the nature and function of the psyche. Thus, there is a point-to-point mapping of the retinal cells onto the LGN which might be very much like the expected TV screen. But as the signals pass to the cortex, presumably the dwelling place of our Little Man, the pattern is strangely broken up and reconceived. The "picture" which results in the primary visual cortex was worked out by David Hubel and Torsten Wiesel at Harvard, in perhaps the most celebrated single research effort of this kind. Let us look at the picture which they revealed. [25]

It may be most helpful to suggest at the outset that the problem, as soon as it reaches the cortex, is already ceasing to be an optical one. The picture which they revealed is reproduced in figure 7. This is not so much an optical, as an initial conceptual map. The two-dimensional array of the retinal surface is still respected in the two dimensions of the surface of the visual cortex. But what appears at the points of the cortical surface are not activations corresponding to light levels on the retina. Instead, there are reports of features of the retinal scene: a kind of conceptual dissolution has taken place, so that what is reported is an analysis by lines and the angles at which they are oriented, and motions which these are undergoing. They are organized in columnar fashion, as shown in figure 7, with the result that even a single line which is found out by the analysis is not represented in the brain as a line at all, but a series of patches corresponding to the cortical cells, within the columns, which have picked it up. What was to have been a "picture" is not that at all, but a now three-dimensional array organizing data about the world, of the sort which will really interest the mind.

We must remind ourselves: at this level of the primary visual cortex, we have taken only the first step on the path of our encounter with the world—and, unfortunately, the story is less clear with respect to the other, "higher" visual areas. Figure 8 (p. 201) gives some suggestion of

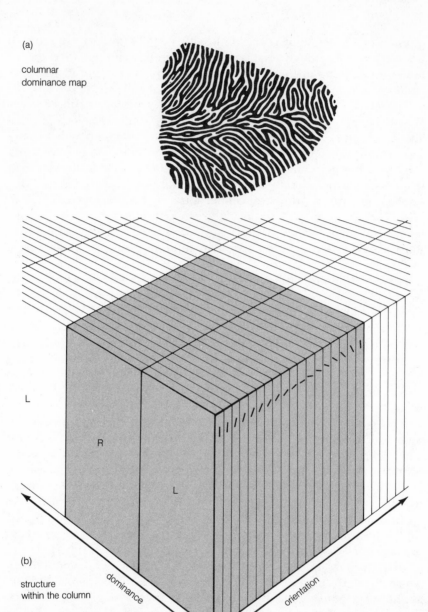

(a)

columnar
dominance map

L

R

L

(b)

structure
within the column

dominance

orientation

Figure 7. The ocular-dominance pattern of the visual cortex of a primate. In this "plan view," the banding distinguishes areas corresponding to the right and left eyes. (b) If the cortex in (a) is sectioned, each band is revealed as a ribbon (L or R) whose width extends through the thickness of the cortex. As we pass along the length of one ribbon, we encounter successive "columns," each dedicated to a specific orientation of the visual pattern. The arrow labeled "orientation" passes along the successive angles to which the system is sensitive. From "Brain Mechanisms of Vision," by David H. Hubel and Torsten N. Wiesel. Copyright © 1979 by Scientific American, Inc. All rights reserved.

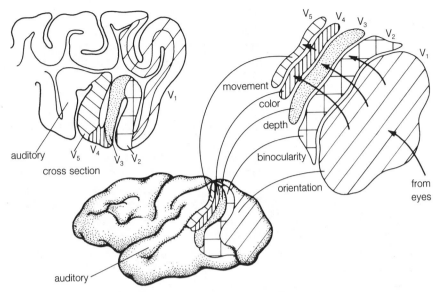

Figure 8. Successive levels at which visual information is interpreted ($V_1$–$V_5$), in the visual cortex of a monkey.

their various preoccupations, in terms of the features which they appear to extract from the data world. Registration is scrupulously observed, so that the topographical continuity of the world is not lost: it can be assembled, and one world emerge. But not cinematically. Evidently, the world is conceptual before it is optical: or better, it is never, in our consciousness, optical. To be seen, it has already to be known. Before a featureless scene, our eyes go blank—that is, unattended and unnoticed. A simple evidence of this is that the primary cortex ignores light levels: we might say, we correct for that, but actually it seems we never "see" it—unless, of course, we "notice" it—in which case, it has become in itself . . . a *feature!*

It was always striking, that deep in the roots of our languages, *knowing* has often been expressed through words which once meant *seeing.* That has been called an analogy, but we see now (yes: it is "e-*vid*-ent") that like so many other connections whose roots are only now becoming accessible to us, this was not an analogy: language was giving recognition to the fact that *seeing is knowing,* we "see" *by* knowing. When the picture does come up on the screen, it is *by definition* intelligible throughout—what is not intelligible, we never notice: or, when we do notice it (to prove that we can!), we see it as a problem, which is only to say, we have given it an intelligible frame to bring it up on the screen. It was once thought that we had "sensations," and that we then (by association) framed them up into objects. We begin to see how wrong that was! There is a great deal of knowing involved in seeing, before there is any speaking.

## The Eleusinian frogs

Often, we are able to learn a great deal more about the psyches of other creatures than about our own: we can probe and experiment with them in ways we cannot, or would not, with human subjects. Thus, Hubel and Wiesel's work was done on macaque monkeys, and it was thus about primate vision more generally, and not specifically about human vision, that we were concluding that perception of features of interest precedes, or is congruent with, sensation. Strong clues in this matter have been obtained as well in studying vertebrates much lower down on the psychic scale. Warren McCulloch and others studied the frog's vision by electrical recording from its optic tectum (an area just below the cortex, and the highest visual area in the frog) as visual patterns were presented to it. Four layers were identified in which an equal number of retinal nerve fibers terminated, again, in a column of good spatial registry. The optical system proved not to report "light" as such, but rather four broad features:

(1) local sharp edges and contrast
(2) curvature of edge of a dark object
(3) movement of edges
(4) dimming produced by movement, or
    rapid general darkening.

The first two were conveyed by unmyelinated nerve fibers; these lack a myelin outer coating and conduct nerve pulses very slowly on the neural time scale (20–50 cm/sec). The third and fourth, myelinated, conveyed pulses at much higher speeds: the fourth covering the short distance from eye to brain at some 10 m/sec—evidently, in a fraction of a millisecond. The four together, stacked in a column in their sequence of times, report not a seeing but an *event*. The first to arrive, the darkening, is evidently an alarm, an instant, indeterminate signal of preparation for attack or flight. When the remaining three are activated, the researchers concluded, they sum to constitute a signature: the identifying mark and precise location of a reassuringly small, moving object, a bug—by which attack is triggered and directed. It is not that the frog is surveying a scene and responds when the right object appears; it is evidently not seeing anything until an appropriate event occurs, and then it sees, not an object, but the event, stacked in time. Sensation is perception and is already working with preverbal *signs:* here, the "sign of the bug." [26]

Our human case, when it is eventually pursued through its cortical levels, will likely prove not less complex but more sophisticated than the pre-cortical vision of the amphibian. The frog is rigidly specialized as we are not: we pursue options in building a world, where the frog does not. But the principle that sensation is never bare, not of raw data or points of light but of features of interest, must carry through; if so, we build our world, not of the raw materials we imagined when we spoke of "sensation," but of *features,* shaped elements which are already *forms* (*eidei,* "seen things").

Was McCulloch's, then, an Eleusinian frog? [27] For it seems to be pointing our way back to something fundamentally Pythagorean, and a clue even to the mystery of dialectic itself. In terms of our dialogue, vision is reminiscent, in the sense that it sees through to entities. If we ask how we penetrate the sophistic facade of words to find the Being which underlies them and empowers language to speak of truth, these frogs seem to be providing a hint!

## The ear

We have two very highly developed, remarkably different systems for conjuring perceptual worlds. The eye, as we have just discussed, knows its world electromagnetically: it searches out its entities from the myriad nuances of the electromagnetic ether. As a marvel of physiological workmanship the eye has long been admired—Darwin is in awe of the power of evolution to have perfected such an instrument. [28] By contrast the ear, whose delicate detector, the *cochlea,* is utterly secreted from view, goes unappreciated—but like the eye, it is a gem of infinite subtlety. Though it becomes the primary medium of human language and thus deserves all honor as hereditary custodian of human thought, many of us have never seen the tiny spiral structure called the cochlea (fig. 9). Its task and its structure are worlds apart from those of the eye: it is a mechanical, as distinct from electromagnetic, detector, responding to the least variations of pressure in the air. Crudely speaking, if we were classifying detecting instruments into very broad pigeonholes, the eye would find itself beside radio receivers, and the ear with barometers. In another sense it might be thought of as a very precisely tuned pipe—though the inverse of a musical instrument, responding to, rather than producing sounds. Unlike the eye, it is not primarily concerned to locate objects in their spatial positions (though the paired ears do have that important secondary function). For us humans, at least, there is no "sun" for sound—no universal, irradiating white noise, corresponding to the pure solar light, whose reflections would become signatures of objects; and the ear has no lens to gather spatially coherent data. [29]

What, then, does the ear in fact seek to draw from its soft, seemingly rather vague aerial environment? Evidently, signals which are actively emitted by the natural world: tiny, complex vibrations of the gaseous medium we live in and breathe, which, rightly analyzed in ways the ear is better suited to do than the best of computers, bear signatures of their sources—of fire, terrifying or promising in its crackling; of water in its many modes, again as threat or promise, of splashing, beating, running; of the ambiguous wind; and of all the animate beings gifted

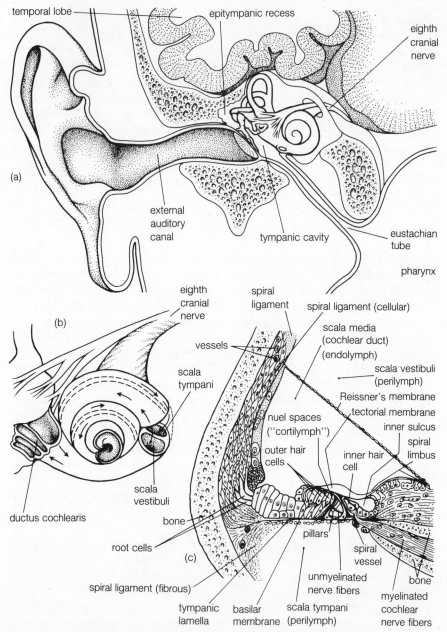

temporal lobe

epitympanic recess

eighth
cranial
nerve

(a)

external
auditory
canal

tympanic cavity

eustachian
tube

pharynx

(b)

eighth
cranial
nerve

spiral
ligament

spiral ligament (cellular)

scala media
(cochlear duct)
(endolymph)

vessels

scala vestibuli
(perilymph)

scala
tympani

Reissner's membrane

tectorial membrane

inner sulcus

nuel spaces
("cortilymph")

spiral
limbus

outer hair
cells

inner hair
cell

scala
vestibuli

ductus cochlearis

bone

root cells

pillars

spiral
vessel

(c)

bone

spiral ligament (fibrous)

unmyelinated
nerve fibers

myelinated
cochlear
nerve fibers

tympanic
lamella

basilar
membrane

scala tympani
(perilymph)

Figure 9. The human auditory system: (a) overall view, (b) the cochlea. (c) Cross section of one tube within the cochlea of a guinea pig.

to sign the air with calls aimed first to be heard by their own kind. Again in this world of sounds, we are dealing with *aisthesis* not as mere sensation but in its abundant magical power, surrogate and foundation of the lexical, to search out signatures, reminiscences of Being.

What is the physical nature of these signs, and what is the ear's task in detecting them? It is enough perhaps if we say that they are complex vibrations of a vast variety, corresponding to the lively motions of the surfaces of all the objects of the world—including of course those special organs of the insects and most higher animals, designed to activate the air with our squeaks, roars, barks, whistles, and clicks. Many of these are inaudible to us humans—the world is full of sounds to which we are deaf, just as the ether is dense with sights to which our electromagnetic eyes are programmatically blind. But vast numbers of others are, we are saying, for us signs of their types. To *read* such signs, what alphabet must the ear command? The answer seems to be that the cochlea must be a virtuoso in the analysis of vibrations: not simply to detect them, or to separate them crudely as the eye does with its three very broad bands of color, but to sort them with high fidelity and extreme rapidity. To this end, the vibrations with which the ear's drum responds to pressure waves in the air are introduced in turn into a fluid medium which fills the spiral turns of the cochlea. (It is evident that by switching from gas to liquid—from a soft to a hard medium—we get velocities up and wavelengths and dissipations down to more promising proportions.) Over the length of that tiny pipe, the frequencies are sorted so that hairlike detectors at the near end respond best to the highest frequencies, and those near the far end, the apex, to the lowest. This is the near equivalent of a Fourier analysis, yielding an ever-changing frequency spectrum (fig. 10). [30] Since it has to happen extremely rapidly (think of the fastest passages in a Bach violin suite, each note of which is rich enough in detail to preserve both "violin" character and separate attack), it is, mathematically viewed, a fast, real-time Fourier analyzer.

The cells of the nerve system which transmit this information pass through at least five successive synapses and a variety of interconnections before reaching the primary auditory cortex—the analogue of the optic lobe for vision. Materially, the data stream is of the same universal sort—pulse groups along axons—as that which reaches the optic lobes; but as we see, it bears information of totally different significance, and it demands processing in very different terms. It is strange and for most of us very difficult to think of alternative worlds in such bare "data" form: worlds-in-transit in their respective optical and auditory fiber bundles. Their material, the frequency-modulated pulse trains, the same: yet in the form of their coding, bearing the import of all divergence of the worlds of sight and sound. The pulse form is, one supposes, like a single alphabet, spelling out two companion sacred testaments.

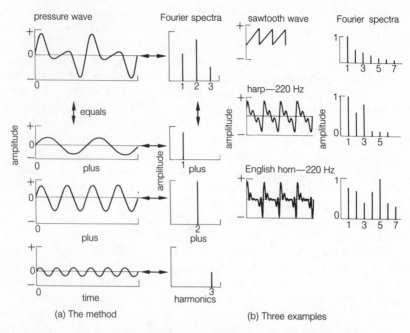

pressure wave     Fourier spectra     sawtooth wave     Fourier spectra

equals

plus     plus     harp—220 Hz

plus     plus     English horn—220 Hz

time     harmonics

(a) The method           (b) Three examples

Figure 10. The principle of Fourier analysis. In (a), air vibrations of a complex tone followed by its three components are represented on the left in graphs of pressure (amplitude) versus time. Alongside, on the right, these components are represented in the sound spectrum. The three components added together yield the resulting tone (top). In (b), three samples of such complex tones are given, each with its corresponding spectral analysis.

In the world of sound we are not, it would seem, looking for the *places* of things, at least not places in what we first think of as geometric space. Perhaps it should be said in all earnestness, however, that in looking for their identifying characters, we are in effect *giving* them places in a very real perceptual space of the ear's shaping. Such a space, without which, in the case of the deaf, it would be difficult to locate oneself physically, would of course not lack its own geometry. Certain analogies in the cortical structuring may encourage that point of view— frequency domains are edge-sharpened and topographically mapped in the auditory cortex, very much as features of spatial signals were seen to be topographically arrayed in the optical cortex. The cortex seems not to know that sound is not spatial. This may be some clue to the virtually inescapable analogy to "up" and "down," and to the sense of physical motion and pace in the auditory world, as we follow for example the excursions of a Bach partita. If we are to pursue this line of thought further for a moment, we may ask: what are the dimensions of auditory perceptual space? That would seem to mean: what are the most elementary features—the letters, the *stoicheia*—whose combinations define the specific forms of these auditory signals?

## Alternative auditory worlds

There seem to be two distinct answers to that question: one system, which we may call the *auditory system,* interprets the air waves in the spirit which we have anticipated; another, however, which we will turn to later, the *phonetic system,* takes a very different approach. The first, we might say, hears the qualities of sound as such; the second hears sound as speech. They are quite different processes and call for two independent plans of cortical processing. We take up the acoustic system first.

It is customary to think of a sound such as the sustained note of a musical instrument as consisting of a fundamental frequency, which determines its pitch, and a set of overtones—the octave above this, which is twice the frequency, then a further overtone, which is three times the frequency of the fundamental, another which is four times, and so on through the sequence of the whole numbers. A pure tone of sinusoidal waveform consists of the fundamental alone and has no overtones, but other sustained tones, such as those of the winds or the strings in our orchestras, derive their tone quality, or timbre, to a large extent from the distribution of these overtones. This is the point of view of Fourier analysis, of which we spoke earlier. A sustained vibration can be represented as a mathematical function of time, and it was Fourier's theorem that such a function can be analyzed into a fundamental and an appropriate series of overtones. This is the analysis our acoustic system so cleverly performs: it finds the pitch and interprets the overtone structure. Here is the answer to our question of elements: the auditory cortex lays out the world in terms which include the fundamental-and-overtone structure: we live in an auditory world which we catalog in part in a lexicon of such structures—we place sounds, we say, by their unique assemblages of these elements.

Thus far, we have spoken only of those sustained sounds which do in this way have pitch—a click, a bang, or a bump may not. These more fragmentary sounds have their own characters. In fact, as they mark the starts or stops of sustained sounds, they may be crucial in identification of those as well. Processing in secondary cortical areas seems to find the elements, the irreducible features, of these other modes of sound.

The modern electronic synthesizer—just one more mask of the ubiquitous computer—makes it possible to bring experimentation in these matters under strict, systematic control; in one experiment, for example, the sound of a dropping bottle was recorded—first bouncing, and then the sound of the same bottle breaking. [31] These are sounds immediately recognized as semantically distinct in our auditory lexicon. The synthesizer could then be asked to produce any sound in-between the two—between a bounce and a break (a break is a thousand tiny bounces)—and the lexicon in this way pressed to reveal its secrets of judgment (fig. 11). Similarly, mix-'n'-match musical instruments can

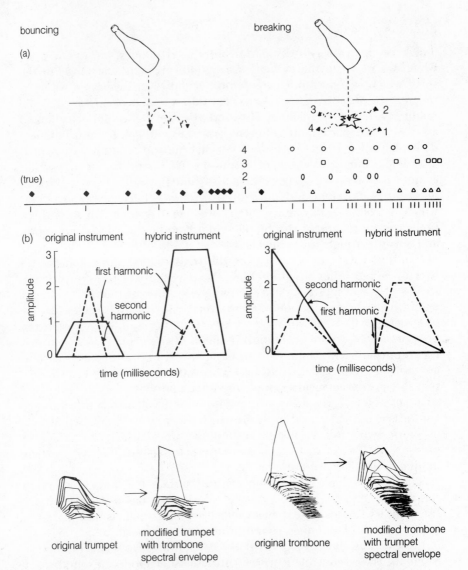

bouncing

(a)

breaking

(true)

(b)    original instrument    hybrid instrument

amplitude

3

2

1

0

first harmonic

second
harmonic

time (milliseconds)

original instrument    hybrid instrument

amplitude

3

2

1

0

second harmonic

first harmonic

time (milliseconds)

original trumpet

modified trumpet
with trombone
spectral envelope

original trombone

modified trombone
with trumpet
spectral envelope

Figure 11. (a) The acoustic difference between a "bounce" and a "break." The sound of
the breaking bottle is the composite of four fragments bouncing; each is analyzed into the
frequency distribution of its component overtones. (b) Mix-'n'-match musical instruments: the
trump-bone, and the tromb-pet!

be fabricated digitally, to unravel our criteria for placements of their sounds in tone-space. [32]

We are speaking, it seems, of a kind of semantic space: an auditory world of signatures, of events and creatures, of moods, threats, and invitations. As in the case of optical space, the signals do not come objectively as inputs to an observing mind: like the optic nerve, the auditory fibers pass through lower brain-stem centers where, as we shall see later, they are bathed in affective coloration—and thus come always as having been sought—and invested with interest; the cortex in turn alerts the listening system and directs ongoing attention. [33] We have amazing powers to "hear out" sounds we are thus attending to, in the midst of fields of distraction. [34]

It is revealing that earlier acoustic studies of the cochlea could be carried out only on preserved specimens; now that techniques have become available which make it possible to investigate the living cochlea—the living Stradivarius—at much lower pressure levels, it appears to be much more subtle and selective. [35] In the physiological mechanisms of selective attention, we recognize that listening is an act, involving searching for what we wish, and repressing what we do not wish to hear: this (not mere passive recognition) is evidently then the sign of intelligence in our hearing. As listeners to music, we care for, seek, and anticipate—we play the music which we hear. That must be the principle of the involvement which can so absorb us as we listen, and which makes music in principle coextensive with all meaning and human experience.

## Onoma: *The world of words*

We have been speaking of natural sounds, calls and signatures, a plenitude of meaning which makes a world and touches us deeply, surely, but *not yet language*. I find it surprising that a physiologically different system, even at the first level of auditory analysis, seems to be invoked with the advent of what we call speech, or phonetics. Speech would seem, then, to be a new and distinct step in evolution. This physical difference in our auditory process—correlated of course in evolution with the development of the components of our vocal apparatus for the production of speech sounds—consists in what might be termed the "liberation of the overtones." In place of the natural relation of the overtones with frequencies locked to the order of the natural integers, the physics of speech consists essentially in the manipulation of the vocal stream to produce artificial overtones in arbitrary frequency relations. The device—a truly brilliant invention—is to use the vocal chords to produce a sound stream which is not tonal but is a rich source of an abundance of overtones (this is the characteristic of a nasty sound, a buzz, or a rasp—our bare vocal chords sound pretty much like a duck quack). [36] From this cornucopia, resonant vocal cavities of our throat

209

and mouth select frequency bands for emphasis while rejecting others, assembling a sound structure as a composition of formants. The fact that auditory space now becomes plastic and responsive in this new way means that it can be inscribed with a new abundance of information: and that is the foundation of the very special, richly detailed physical system we call speech. Strictly, what we have said thus far has been a description of the shaping of the vowel sounds, which are distinguished by their formant ratios. The consonants, produced by various tricks we have of stopping and constricting the vocal stream with our teeth and tongue, equally open domains of semantic possibilities. They serve in part as transitional events in the rapidly modulated voice stream of the vowels: and it has been shown that they are not only incidental phenomena but already alert the psyche, setting anticipation by pointing acoustically to the next vowel to be expected (fig. 12). [37]

All of this repertory of possibilities is processed in areas of the cortex distinct from the primary acoustic. The first of these language areas, known as Wernicke's (fig. 13), seems to carry out processing of the sort just described. A further category of function, the culminating stage of language use, belongs to Broca's area, in the frontal lobe. We encounter here the phenomenon of *lateralization* to a striking degree. Broca's and Wernicke's areas are found only in the dominant hemisphere of the brain—for the majority, the left hemisphere (by chiasma, that which sees with the right eye, hears with the right ear, and controls the right hand).

There is a curious, inherent difficulty encountered in the physiological investigation of speech, not met, for example, in the case of optics. Normally, neurological research can be carried out upon laboratory

Figure 12. Sound analysis of the spoken phrase "Santa Claus."

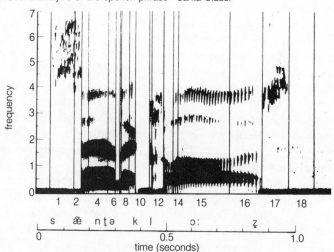

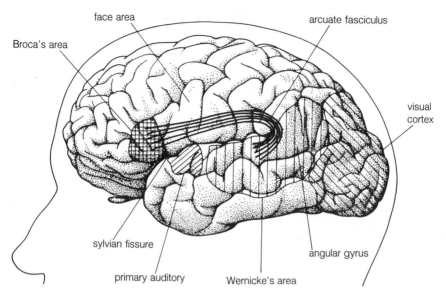

Figure 13. The language areas of the human brain.

animals, who, we must acknowledge, can be invaded, wired, modified, and sacrificed at will; by the astute choice of the model animal and appropriate translation of the results, a great deal can be learned about the human psyche. Thus, images could be photographed in the brain of the macaque—a creature in most ways very close to us—by a technique of exposing the subject to a visual pattern, then killing the subject and mounting the brain slice; in this way figure 7, which revealed so much about our visual cortex, was produced. Unfortunately for us— fortunately, perhaps, for the macaques—no creature shares with us the powers of human speech. [38] We have no model, and thus paradoxically we know less about those areas of our brains which are most distinctively our own, the speech areas, than we do about any of the others. How the speech areas process the rich data stream corresponding to the plastic vocal manipulation of air pressures is known thus far largely by inference.

Certain animal models have provided unexpected sources of suggestion. The bat, in its echo ranging, processes a frequency-modulated echo stream interestingly analogous to our stream of vowels and consonants, and its cortical topographical mapping corresponds to formant- and frequency-modulation ratios. Once again, this is a question of *features:* it is clear that the speech cortex is not interested in the world of sound as such, but in speech features of another, very different and special world. In this respect, speech has been perceived as a kind of vocal gesture. We *hear* sounds—hear, indeed, as we see: alert to significance and according to the regimens of our own preoccupations, not at all as raw sensation, which does not exist for us. Yet speech belongs to a further and distinct realm of significance. The acoustic domain is one world, the speech world is another. Speech is acoustically transparent; we *understand* speech, a very different matter. If we attend, as we say, to a friend's *words* as such, we are understanding speech. If we then notice a special quality which has momentarily come into her voice, and attend to that, we have switched systems and brain areas, from speech to acoustics—in which we may detect a far more important, nonspeech message. Always, in human discourse, we are at work to some degree in both domains. Intelligent reading works with acoustic meaning to fetch out, modulate, even invert linguistic. But without naming, the preverbal acoustic semantic, however deep, remains somehow dark.

## The birth of time

We have been speaking of the difference between the two worlds of acoustics and phonetics: but there is yet a world to go. We are working our way through the *Theaetetus:* first *aisthesis,* wordless sensation, then taming by *onoma.* There remains syntax, with the birth of whole thought, in *logos.* Acoustics gives us a natural semantic, full of meaning, but too close to the original—to the wind in the trees, the animal cry; not yet, as we say, articulate. We intuit them, as we say, "instinctively," and that is quite correct. By contrast, phonetics gives us an intentional semantic; perhaps it will be useful to say a *semiotic:* for now we can *sign,* and not merely *call.* Full speech now links these signs: that is by no means a question of simple addition, but an utterly new function, which has its own area of the brain. Syntax—the asserting one thing of another—is not done by juxtaposition. It is an act of thought of a new order: in some sense, the first act of thought. One thing, in some category of Being or Becoming, belongs to the other. "The sky," we say, "is blue." This is not "sky + blue"—but an intrinsic linkage: blue is a quality of the sky. In Broca's area that link is made: patients who retain the use of Broca's area, but have lost the use of Wernicke's, to that extent tend to make fluent, sentence-like but meaningless phrases. Those with Wernicke's area but lacking Broca's can use words meaningfully, but they lose the sense when it is crucially dependent on syntax. We see, incidentally, that the capability for language use is genetic; we are to some important degree born with a basic structure for grammar and semantic—in essence, a universal grammar and a universal phonetic alphabet—which manifests itself and takes shape at appropriate points in development. An infant does not learn words, as we once supposed, merely by imitation—it assimilates language from the environment with what is almost literally a "word-hunger." [39] We are born with a nervous system still indeterminate; over the first months of development, for example, a vast excess of potential neural connections is sorted out, in a selection process which in effect molds the genetic language universals into the specific, permanent shapes, and of course the sounds that go with them, of the mother tongue. [40]

We have not left the course of the *Theaetetus:* from that first human triumph of naming, we move as the dialogue does to the act of predication as the foundation of completed thought. The speech stream becomes divided into those speech signs we call words, which are first of all names, and then, by syntax, into phrasal groups which are based ultimately, in some deep structure, on that elemental act of thought, linking Being and Becoming, by *saying one thing of another* which was the culminating stage of Theaetetus' search. It is very interesting, then, that modern studies of the poetics of many cultures, whether written or simply oral, have shown that there is always something which can be recognized as a "line," and this marks with remarkable uniformity about three seconds on the clock. [41] The poetic line is the sentence of thought, woven into a verbal music. The same studies show that in an audience listening to a recitation of verse, individual thought pacings become entrained to a common meter, as of course they do as we listen together to music.

In another line of research, independent laboratory studies of our mental chronometry show that we assimilate the world in a hierarchy of times; our knowing of the world comes metered in a series of temporal stages. They begin at three-thousandths of a second, the least time between which we can discriminate events, the threshold of any knowing, and range to, again, about three seconds, that time it takes to absorb a thought. [42] It seems clear that some deep, inner brain-stem rhythms time all these mental cycles. [43]

In the sense that in syntax one symbol, the subject, immediately demands another, its predicate, and thus sets the motion of *logos*—thought—going, we could say that with what we have already called the *birth of logos* in syntax, comes also the *birth of time* in its most significant human measure. Thus although other far briefer times underlie it, perhaps we do not sense those as such; if it is thought which we experience as the first whole motion with a beginning, middle, and end, it may be that thought is the elemental act which gives rise to our human sense of time and thus clocks our mental life. For "time," Aristotle says, "is the measure of motion." (Motion does not occur "in time"; rather, time is the measure of the motion which is, humanly, always primary.) The motion of mind which forms a thought seems the paradigm of all motions: once a name is perceived as a *subject,* we have arrived at a genuine beginning, in that it demands a predicate in order to complete a thought—only with the completion of the act of predication does thought rest. The subject is then potentiality: it proposes and calls for an act of thought, and sets a motion going. The actualization of that potential in its potentiality, which Aristotle so persuasively identifies as *motion,* is the very act of predication—which is the act of thought.

Every real motion is like this act of thought: a complete entity, with its beginning, middle, and end. Large motions, such as dramas or lifetimes, are, if they achieve a certain perfection, unities on which thought might dwell. The *Theaetetus* is such a whole motion, and seems in its cycling never to rest, since we as readers enter upon that motion again today, the two thousand years intervening being in a sense, as nothing. Is not this ever-moving thinking in search of knowing the crux of our human life, its timing close to the heart of our vitality?

In *aisthesis* we encounter a natural being, a sight or a sound, normally reacting unconsciously with lesser or greater motions of love, courage, dread, anger, or alarm; with *onoma*, we name a being and can dwell on it, in its wholeness, mentally; in *logos*, it is as if the word becomes a seed of thought and springs to life; we move with it, it links with another, and we are able to attend to a level of knowing which corresponds to a weave of Being in world. If in all our sensing and thinking we are, as it has seemed, making a world, then with this birth of time and thought we begin to make a woven world. Our human world is that woven world, its weave always in mode of motion. It is an easy mistake though to imagine that *logos* is in any simple way final, or simply best. That was the lesson of the circling of the dialogue, knowing to be founded after all on its mystical beginning. Indeed, most of the Platonic dialogues circle back on themselves in somewhat this fashion, recognizing the original answer to the question, now stripped of its errors, at the end of the discussion, and realizing the deeper question to which that answer points when it is understood. It is so, too, in our modern sciences of the mind, as the remainder of this essay will seek to explore.

It is interesting to think for a moment of music in terms of these three auditory areas of the brain. Is it not tempting to suggest that music is syntactic and semantic, but if there is no text, largely skips semiotic? The closure of the musical phrase is surely that of Broca's area and *logos*, as the linkage of the musical phrase and the line of song seems to confirm. The correspondence of the structure of the musical phrase revealed in the musical theory of Heinrich Schenker and Victor Zuckerkandl to the act of thought in *logos*: the *dynamic* of tones, which energizes the diatonic order and is the root of music's power to move and inform us, is surely the same ultimate dynamic which motivates mind to the closure of thought. [44] As Karl Pribram has pointed out, there is a fascinating parallel between the deep structure of universal grammar, revealed by Noam Chomsky's transformational grammar, and the deep structures of musical compositions revealed by Schenker-analysis. [45] If we recall the correspondence we have seen between spatial and acoustic topologies in the respective cortical areas, we may suspect how deep the unity may be among the motions in speech, in music, and in space.

## III. Conclusion

Reflecting now on the *Theaetetus,* we might agree that it is a dialogue which takes place on two levels: that of the explicit argument, following the evolution of the definition of knowledge, but that other as well, hinted and in some way always secret, the level which I think we can rightly call deeper, of the Pythagorean mystery. The outcome of the explicit argument is literal failure, while the rescue of the human project comes from the environing mystery. In the simplest terms, it is what the textbooks call the Platonic "doctrine of recollection": there is no knowledge, and thus no grounding of the human experience in Being or truth, unless there is reference to a truth outside of the immediate discourse. The argument circles about its meaning, but, in the inner experience of the one witness in the dialectical argument, this remains unspoken. Modern students of the dialogues are annoyed by the readiness of Socrates' respondents to agree: they want to replace Theaetetus' "yes" with a "no," because no literal argument (no formal proof, by our cold modern standards) has guaranteed the agreement. They do not see, or care to see, that the "yes" may be genuine, warranted not by words but by a seeing which looks to a different source and bespeaks well-grounded conviction. That other seeing, "mystical" because it has no warranty in words, is what Plato calls the operation of *reason— nous*—the intellectual *intuition.* It is strangely related to *aisthesis:* for in the terms we have been using, the hints by which it is referenced are more nearly those which begin with simple vision or a single telling word, than those of a proposition or a connected argument. Of all the ironies which envelop the Platonic dialogues, perhaps this is the most interesting: that Plato, who most rejects poetic in its idle role of mere distraction, depends utterly upon it for the founding of his truth. The *Theaetetus* is essentially a work of poetic, for insofar as it is not that— not, in other words, empowered by a truth centered beyond the literal argument—it fails. And we have seen the sense in which this dialogue is coextensive with the life of Socrates, incorporates the Socratic project. The point is so simple: if words bear truth, they do so not syntactically, by linked statement and proof, but paratactically. Through some crisis of refutation on the first level, reference is forced or induced poetically to another, deeper level—one which, seen from the rational plane, will look mystical. That was the crisis prefigured in Theaetetus' encounter with the intractable in mathematics, the irrational, the *alogos.*

If we are to follow Theaetetus' lead in a serious sense, we cannot therefore be content with laboratory investigations of perception— however interesting their theories—or even with studies of the shaping of words and sentences in the language areas of the brain. We must begin anew and ask: does the deeper, Pythagorean plane of the Platonic project have any counterpart in the modern sciences of the mind? It is good to be able to report that the answer is a secure "yes," and to turn in the second part of this essay to those sciences which treat of the mind in its richer depths.

History here has worked one of its almost disconcerting parallels: where in the study of the physical sciences, the subject of the first of the essays of this series, we found that quantum mechanics had in the first half of the century now ending wrought a total transformation at the level of the foundations, we see now that Freud, over essentially the same period of time, accomplished a corresponding revolution in the foundations of the sciences of the mind. The Freudian theory of the unconscious is the quantum mechanics of the mind, in the sense that it totally transforms the terms and domain of discussion. It is not clear that Freudian theory in any of its successive transformations has ever taken complete theoretical form, but that is not a central concern: it has opened for inclusion in any scientific discussion of the psyche the deeper world of the unconscious, and the immense and decisive role of what Freud termed the drives. We now see that at the foundation of all the work of the psyche, transformed through a thousand sublimations, is the encompassing power of our caring, which may in the course of our lives take any form from abiding love, through steady purpose, to instant and violent emotion. We shall find that in one way or another some form of caring infuses all our acts, and that one of its manifestations is in the highly selective, directing principle which as we saw lies at the foundation of the human way of *aisthesis* itself.

Protagoras was rescued, by grace of Socrates' account, from the morass of "man the measure" through his acknowledgment of the power of the good: all men care for what is really, and not merely seemingly, best. This was a clue to the principle, which we found at the origin of the myth of the *Timaeus* as well, that all Being flows from the Good. This remains true. If there is anything in life to care about— if there is anything to know—it will be housed, not in words, but in the domain which words reference. Freud has shown us the way to the *alogos* in our time. The content of the world Freud opened is only beginning to unfold in a new era of the sciences of the mind, ready now to look unblinkingly into the realms, which we may call *deep*, which he has opened to our still-mystified view. Would it be out of order, then, to suggest that the analytic interview is in some way the Socratic dialogue of our time?

What is the emerging physiological ground of the psychoanalytic project set going by Freud and Jung? Part Two of this essay, scheduled to appear in the next edition of *The Great Ideas Today*, will follow some of the many paths that question opens. One leads into the world of the endocrinal system and, more largely, into the domain of neurotransmitters and the view of the brain as a chemical system—what we may call the pharmacopoeia of the mind. Another suggests the deep partitioning of the psyche, with concomitant questions of the unity of the self, revealed through research into the distinctive roles of the right and left hemispheres of the brain, and their spectacular mapping upon one another through a cable structure known as the *corpus callosum*. Yet another, guided by complications of psychoanalysis and learning theory in the direction of the developmental process, will look at emerging accounts of human instinct. This, finally, will take us to evolutionary theories of the origin of the human mind and the ultimate governance of physiology by the genetic molecule, the DNA, which appears here rather in the mode of an intricate and living text than of a chemical molecule in any more traditional sense. In this structure, still so new to theory that it utterly evades our conceptual grasp—at once archival and vital, most ancient and yet minute-by-minute most urgent—lies the nearest answer we can give to the search for a physiological seat of the passions or the archetypes that set our lives going. Physiologically, this is the "book of life" which is the deepest referent of the psyche. Here, surely, in this vibrant physical system which yet startled Schrödinger in being far more timeless than diamond, lies the modern version of the mysteries: this is our mainspring, and this is the silent source of all the meaning our uttered words can have, to which the *Theaetetus* points.

Such remarks in an earlier era would have seemed reductive and crass, a materialist surrogate for serious philosophical thought. Now, with the liberation of the sciences from the long sleep of objectivity and mere mechanism, we are on the verge of a new dialectic in which philosophy and the sciences must surely join. Who better could host this conversation than Theaetetus, who entered his dialogue with Socrates with his head still swimming in the vision of a new prospect, shifting the foundations of the sciences and of the very concept of knowledge in his own time? There is surely no end to myth and mystery: we need to incorporate them fully and, if we can, wisely, in our search for a more human future. With this aim in view, we will turn in another year, in Part Two of this essay, to this question of the foundations of the human psyche.

---

1. "The New Pythagoreans: Reflections on the Idea of Science in Our Time. Part I: The Physicists" (*GIT* 1988, pp. 162–221), and "The New Pythagoreans II: The Scientists of Life and the World Food Problem" (*GIT* 1989, pp. 162–232).

2. Discussion in the *Timaeus* turns to the works of Necessity at *GBWW*, Vol. 7, p. 455c.

3. N. David Mermin, "Spooky Actions at a Distance: Mysteries of the Quantum Theory" (*GIT* 1988, pp. 2–53).

4. Socrates' snub nose became a philosophical as well as an aesthetic tradition when Aristotle, in the *Physics*, explained the relation of form and matter in natural bodies by saying that form inheres in matter as snubness inheres in [Socrates'] nose (*GBWW*, Vol. 8, p. 270c).

5. The dialogue begins in this mode, and Theodorus in turn praises him, saying, ". . . I never knew any one who was his equal in natural gifts . . ." (*GBWW*, Vol. 7, p. 513b). The Greek at that point is more literally, ". . . so wondrously gifted . . . ," the term deriving from *thauma*, that "wonder" which suggests some combination of magic, amazement, and perplexity, and is taken by both Socrates and Aristotle to be the beginning of philosophy. Theaetetus says in response to perplexities during this dialogue, "I am amazed (*thaumazo*)," and Socrates says this assures that he is indeed a philosopher (ibid., p. 519b–c; compare Aristotle, *Metaphysics*, *GBWW*, Vol. 8, p. 500b–d). This same astonishment, I feel sure, motivates the sciences of the human mind, at their best, today.

6. The Greek word here is *propempset*—"sent him on his way"—a term used to describe the role of Hermes, Guide of Souls (*psychopompos*). Karl Kerenyi, *Hermes—Guide of Souls* (Dallas, Texas: Spring Publications, 1986). As Kerenyi points out, the finest example of this may be Hermes' role in accompanying Priam to the abode of Achilles, to make it possible to bring back the corpse of Hector, at the close of *The Iliad* (p. 9: cf. also *GBWW*, Vol. 4, pp. 174d–78d). I feel that Plato has this passage in mind.

7. This is the myth attributed by Socrates—no doubt in part in order to command Meno's attention—to ". . . certain wise men and women who spoke of things divine . . ." (*Meno*, *GBWW*, Vol. 7, p. 179d). In the dialogue, a slave boy has been led through questioning to perceive a certain geometric relation we will be discussing below; Socrates has carefully not told him the theorem and concludes, interrogatively, "And this spontaneous recovery of knowledge in him is recollection?" and "But if he did not acquire the knowledge in this life, then he must have had and learned it at some other time?" (ibid., p. 182d).

8. We meet this term, "*alogos*," at a crucial point near the culmination of the dialogue, at p. 547b, where it is translated "undefined," and at p. 548a, where it is translated "irrational."

9. The discussion in the earlier article was in somewhat different terms, though the problem is the same. There, it was cast in terms of the works of "Necessity" and appeared directly in terms of the tuning of the monochord (*GIT* 1988, pp. 177–81).

10. Our figure 1 is the very figure which was drawn to prompt the slave boy's powers of recollection in the *Meno* and is drawn here according to that text (*GBWW*, Vol. 7, p. 181a).

11. We see that if each side of our square were taken as of unit length, i.e., value 1, then their squares would each have the value 1 as well, and their sum, which is the square on the hypotenuse, would have the value 2. Then the side of that square, the hypotenuse itself, would have that value whose square is 2. We make a mark on the paper to indicate this, namely "$\sqrt{2}$," but what does that mark mean?

12. The proof is brief, but a little tricky; it is in the form of a *reductio ad absurdum*, meaning that we assume the contrary and show that it leads to an impossibility.

Thus: suppose that the side and diagonal of a square *are* commensurable; then if the number $p$ measures the side, there will be some other number, $q$, which measures the diagonal. Let these numbers be *in least terms*—that is, let them have no common factors (if they do, cancel them out, so that $p$ and $q$ no longer have any common factors). Now, we know by the theorem that $p_- + p_- = q_-$, i.e., $2p_- = q_-$. Then $q_-$ is an even number.

But then, so is $q$, for if it were not, it would be odd, and the square of an odd number is odd. But if $q$ is even, that means that there exists some other number, $m$, such that $q = 2m$. Substituting, $2p_- = 4m_-$, or $p = 2m$. Well then, $p$ is even, and there exists some $n$ such that $p = 2n$. But if $p = 2n$ and $q = 2m$, then $p$ and $q$ have a common factor after all! But they don't. QED.

Therefore, once and for all, no two numbers $p$ and $q$ of the sort we supposed can exist, and the side and diagonal of the square are utterly incommensurable!

13. This is done in Definition 5 of Book V, Euclid's book of ratio and proportion (*GBWW*, Vol. 11, p. 81a). This is the definition of *same ratio;* that is, it permits us to say that the ratio A:B is the same as the ratio C:D, but it does not permit us to know otherwise *what that ratio is*. The definition permits us to say, for example, that the side of a little square has the same ratio to its diagonal that the side has to the diagonal in a large square—but what that ratio *is*, we know that we do not know, by our proof in note 12!

14. It may be helpful to add that the Latin word *ratio* includes in its meaning both "reason" and "ratio" and thus regularly translates *logos,* as *irrationalis* translates *alogos.*

15. Thus, for example, Euclid, Book X, Prop. 13, tells us in effect that if two lines $p$ and $q$ are incommensurable, then the infinity of quantities given by $(m/n)p$ is likewise incommensurable with $q$—that is, one pair of incommensurables spawns an infinity of others. And Prop. 16 assures us that if $p$ is incommensurable with $q$, then $(p + q)$ is incommensurable with both $p$ and $q$ and hence becomes the launching point for another infinity of incommensurables! We begin to see what Theaetetus was attempting to deal with (*GBWW,* Vol. 11, pp. 220b, 202b). Book X, by the way, contains 115 propositions and presumably is never studied today by anybody.

16. To give just one example of this, the enunciation of Prop. 73 of Book X reads as follows:

> If from a rational straight line there be subtracted a rational straight line commensurable with the whole in square only, the remainder is irrational; and let it be called an *apotome* (*GBWW,* Vol. 11, p. 255).

This tells us that if we lay out the side of square on the diagonal, the leftover will be of this kind; in fact, the proposition demonstrates that it will not even be commensurable with the side in square, as the diagonal is—it is yet more deeply "irrational" than the diagonal itself! Thereafter, a whole genus of different sorts of apotomes arises.

17. The *Oresteia* trilogy consists of three plays: *Agamemnon, Choephoroe,* and *Eumenides* (*GBWW,* Vol. 5, pp. 52a–91d). The Furies, though they lurk in the first play, appear manifestly at the beginning of the third. Neither the Prophetess of the Oracle at Delphi, nor Apollo, can find names for them. The resolution begins with Athena, who is able to say "I know your race, and your names" (translated "This tells your title and your lineage," at *GBWW,* Vol. 5, p. 85d).

18. Theodorus has passed the argument to Theaetetus on the excuse that if the younger respondent fails, he will be "less disgraced" (*GBWW,* Vol. 7, p. 524c). Note that "science" here (exemplified by Theodorus' geometry) is simply *mathesis*—simply anything which can be taught, learned, and *known.*

19. Both Polus and, later, Callicles, the other two respondents in the dialogue, accuse Gorgias of having yielded to Socrates out of "shame" to admit that rhetoric concerned itself with the good.

20. As the difficulty of part and whole in relation to knowledge focuses, the issue of the *alogos* takes new, explicit form. The syllable cannot be known if the letters are not; but the letters have no parts, and thus no *logos*—they must be known, if anything is, but they are inherently "*alogos*"—they have no parts, to be linked by a defining predication.

21. It is significant that our words for "knowing" are almost inextricably linked with words for "seeing." In Greek, one of Plato's most crucial words, "the form," is *eidos*—from the root *eido,* to see. The verb itself, in its perfect aspect, means "to have seen," and thus, "to know." Another instance: "theory" (Greek: *theoria*) is a seeing before it is a knowing; a "theater" is a place for seeing, but also for wondering and, evidently, for speculation. A *speculum,* in turn, is a mirror!

22. A recent report concludes that neural-net computer models are getting beyond sheer modeling of familiar performance and are beginning to contribute significant predictions as new forms of learning algorithms are included. The report sees a new order of dialectic between computer modeling and the physiological laboratory and predicts significant results in the next decade (Marcia Barinaga, "Neuroscience Models the Brain," *Science,* Feb. 2, 1990, p. 526).

23. Thus Kant introduces the discussions of space and time in *The Critique of Pure Reason* with this question: "What then are time and space? Are they real existences? . . . or, are they such as belong only to the form of intuition, and consequently to the subjective constitution of the mind, without which these predicates of time and space could not be attached to any object?" (*GBWW,* Vol. 42, p. 24b). This last is the answer developed in the *Critique.* How it really relates to the neurophysiology of the eye, for example, seems a difficult question.

24. John Z. Young, *Programs of the Brain* (Oxford: Oxford University Press, 1978), pp.

117–24; Masao Ito, *The Cerebellum and Neural Control* (New York: Raven Press, 1984), chap. 27, "Saccade and Smooth Pursuit Eye Movements," pp. 389–405.

25. David H. Hubel and Torsten N. Wiesel, "Brain Mechanisms of Vision," in *The Brain: A Scientific American Book* (New York: W. H. Freeman, 1979), pp. 84–96; reprinted from *Scientific American*, vol. 241, no. 3 (September 1979), pp. 150–62.

26. J. Y. Lettvin, H. R. Maturana, W. S. McCulloch, and W. H. Pitts, "What the Frog's Eye Tells the Frog's Brain," in McCulloch, ed., *Embodiments of Mind* (Cambridge: MIT Press, 1985).

27. The way from Athens to Eleusis passed a swamp, where dwelt the frogs celebrated in Aristophanes' comedy. They become the seriocomic guides to the mysteries (Aristophanes, *The Frogs*, in *GBWW*, Vol. 5, pp. 564a–82c).

28. Darwin writes:

> To suppose that the eye with all its inimitable contrivances . . . could have been formed by natural selection, seems, I freely confess, absurd in the highest degree (*The Origin of Species; GBWW*, Vol. 49, p. 85).

29. Since vibrations in air have very long wavelengths by contrast with the extremely short waves of the electromagnetic medium, a lens is possible in small space for the eye, while it would have to be of Mount Rushmore proportions if anything comparable were devised for the ear! The ear, that is, is not confronted with a situation which admits spatial image formation, from which we might conclude that a word is a phonetic (mechanical) surrogate for a geometric (electromagnetic) object. A word may, that is, be the temporal counterpart of a spatial object. As we get into more intelligent communication with dolphins, we may begin to get a very different sense of the entities which belong to the construct world of yet a third medium, the sea.

30. Joseph Fourier was interested in the distribution of temperatures over heated bodies in equilibrium; he developed a method of infinite series to approximate the mathematical functions representing these distributions. The resulting theorem, since it addresses the mathematical function and not the physical phenomenon per se, is very powerful. Any reasonable single-valued, continuous function—such as sound vibrations in air expressed as functions of time—can be represented as accurately as we please by Fourier's series. It consists of a fundamental sine function, to which are added as successively diminishing terms of the series, sine and cosine functions whose frequencies are integral multiples of that of the fundamental. Fourier's work is set out in his *Theory of Heat* (*GBWW*, Vol. 45, pp. 165a–251a).

31. Stephen Handel, *Listening: An Introduction to the Perception of Auditory Events* (Cambridge, Mass.: The MIT Press, 1989), pp. 259–62. This, by the way, is an excellent volume on all aspects of the auditory system.

32. Ibid., pp. 245–57.

33. The complex relations of the auditory system are diagramed in Katharine B. and Kermit T. Hoyenga, *Psychobiology: The Neuron and Behavior* (Pacific Grove, Calif.: Brooks-Cole, 1988), pp. 146–49, 158–59, 160–67. Cf. also chapter 12, "The Physiology of Listening," in Handel, op. cit., pp. 461–545.

34. Cf., for example, Charles Watson and William Kelly, "Role of Stimulus Uncertainty in the Discrimination of Auditory Patterns," in David Getty and James H. Howard, Jr., eds., *Auditory and Visual Pattern Recognition* (Hillsdale, N.J.: Lawrence Erlbaum Associates, 1981), pp. 37–60.

35. Handel, op. cit., pp. 473–78. The functioning of the cochlea is immensely delicate and intricate, and as yet full of mysteries. The possibility that the hairlike receptors may be responsive to adjustment is discussed at Hoyenga, op. cit., p. 167.

36. This is the mathematical property, the result of Fourier analysis, of a discontinuous, mathematical function such as the "sawtooth" or "square" waveforms widely used in electronics.

37. Again, an excellent discussion of the mysteries of speech recognition is to be found in Handel, op. cit., chapter 5, "Sound Generation by the Voice: Speaking and Singing," pp. 134–62. It is a question of working with a variety of phonetic entities; Handel likens phonetic listening to the solution of a jigsaw puzzle, in which the intelligible objects are the pictures, while the pieces are the acoustic entities. Many clues are known, and we

solve the problem without difficulty on a daily basis, but science hasn't yet found out how! For those for whom this language is helpful, Noam Chomsky suggests thinking of the acoustic entities as eigenvectors in a finite vector space. Cf. his *Language and Mind* (San Diego, Calif.: Harcourt Brace Jovanovich, Inc., 1972).

38. It is important to note here two possible alternative speeches in dolphins, porpoises, and whales. As they become better known, the whole theory of speech, as well as that of perception, would seem likely to be fundamentally affected—a new perspective, then, on the liberal arts. John C. Lilly, *Communication between Man and Dolphin* (New York: Crown Publishers, 1987). *See also* the review volume: Joan McIntyre, ed., *Mind in the Waters* (New York: Charles Scribner, 1974).

39. John Eccles, "Cerebral Activity—the Freedom of the Will," in Eccles, ed., *Mind and Brain* (New York: Paragon House, 1985), p. 182.

40. Jean-Pierre Changeux, *Neuronal Man: The Biology of Mind* (New York: Pantheon Books, 1985), pp. 246–49.

41. Frederick Turner and Ernest Poppel, "The Neural Lyre: Poetic Meter, the Brain, and Time," (*Poetry Magazine*, August 1983, pp. 277–309.

42. Ibid.

43. Ibid. The authors speak of an "ergotropic/tropotropic" system of arousal and rest. We will allude further to brain-stem rhythmic systems later in this essay.

44. Heinrich Schenker, *Harmony* (Chicago: University of Chicago Press, 1954), p. xxv: "I should like to stress in particular the biological factor in the life of tones. We should get used to the idea that tones have lives of their own, more independent of the artist's pen than one would dare to believe." Victor Zuckerkandl states directly that "man is a musical animal" in *Man the Musician* (vol. 2 of *Sound and Symbol*; Princeton, N.J.: Princeton University Press, 1973), p. 7. The reality of the musical phrase as a dynamic entity is the basis of the theories of Schenker and Zuckerkandl. The foundations of this can be found in Renaissance theory: Gioseffo Zarlino, *On the Institution of Harmony* (1558).

45. Karl H. Pribram, "Brain Mechanism in Music," in Manfred Clynes, ed., *Music, Mind, and Brain* (New York and London: Plenum Press, 1982), pp. 21–35.

# PART THREE

# Special Features

# The End of the Conflict
# Between Capitalism and Communism

## Mortimer J. Adler

Mortimer J. Adler, who is editor of *The Great Ideas Today,* has had a lifelong interest in great books. Among many projects he has undertaken has been the editing, with Robert M. Hutchins, of Britannica's *Great Books of the Western World,* which will appear, before the end of this year, in a new and expanded edition of sixty volumes.

Himself a teacher for many years at the University of Chicago, and since 1950 at the Aspen Institute for Humanistic Studies, Dr. Adler is also the director of the Institute for Philosophical Research, which he founded. There he brought into existence the educational reform known as the Paideia Proposal, which aims at restructuring public education so as to emphasize coaching and discussion rather than the didactic teaching now chiefly found in classrooms. This project has since been taken over by the University of North Carolina at Chapel Hill.

Dr. Adler is the author of many books, among them *How to Read a Book* (1940, rev. 1972), *The Conditions of Philosophy* (1965), *The Difference of Man and the Difference It Makes* (1967), and *Intellect: Mind Over Matter* (1990).

## 1. The questions to be answered

In its August 1, 1988, issue, *The New Yorker* magazine published an article by William Pfaff about the Gorbachev reforms in the Soviet Union. The title of the article was "The Question Not Asked." The summer of 1988 was still fairly early in the upheaval occurring in the Soviet Union. Much has happened since then that was only prefigured in the first announcements of *glasnost* and *perestroika*. But the question that Pfaff said had not been asked in 1988 has still not been asked or answered.

To make that question clear, I must quote some passages from the article. "The true problem" before Mikhail Gorbachev, Pfaff writes, "is not 'reform' of the system and of the economy. He must discover a new basis of legitimacy for Soviet society and for its government. . . . The question not asked, which *has* to be asked, is: What will become of the Soviet Union and the Soviet system if it abandons its intellectual and moral foundations as untrue?" Pfaff later continues as follows:

> . . . This is a revolution disguised as radical reform that is meant to save the system. That it cannot remain mere reform, however, follows from the fact that the intellectual foundation of the system is contradicted and jeopardized by the nature of the reforms that are required. Gorbachev refers to Lenin to justify his program, yet the program undoes Leninism. [1]

Writing two years ago, Pfaff points out that Gorbachev at that point had somewhat obscurely described the purpose of his economic reform as "to assure, during the next two or three years, a transition from an overly centralized command system of management to a democratic system based mainly on economic methods and on optimal combinations of centralism and self-management." Pfaff follows that quotation from Gorbachev with another: "This presupposes a sharp expansion of the autonomy of enterprises and associations, their transition to the principle of profitability and self-financing, and the investment of work collectives with all the powers necessary for this."

Pfaff's comment on this is as follows:

> Gorbachev is determined to renew his system but is constrained to do so in terms of a doctrine that, although it purports to be the most

advanced and scientific description of reality that exists, actually does not account for how the modern industrial economy and industrial society work. [2]

And toward the end of his article, Pfaff tells us that

. . . If one takes the language of Gorbachev and his fellow-reformers to mean what it means in the West—"pluralism," "democracy"— they could be said to be attempting, by indirection, to re-start that evolution. But neither in Leninism nor in czarism is there the liberal or constitutional political precedent that the Soviet Union needs—one to which people might refer in attempting to find a new course.

Finally, Pfaff concludes with this statement:

. . . To break with that system [i.e., Marxism-Leninism] would leave Gorbachev and the reformers without a place to stand, a fulcrum from which to move society, a justification for their own power. They rule Russia by virtue of the Party, Leninism, Marxism. Yet the Party, Leninism, and Marxism are the problem. [3]

I agree with Pfaff that Gorbachev and his fellow reformers cannot succeed if they explicitly renounce Party, Leninism, and Marxism. For more than seventy years now the people of the Soviet Union have been inculcated with commitment to and respect for the doctrines of Karl Marx and Vladimir Lenin and for the Party. This borders on religious reverence and fidelity. They have nothing prior in their history except the autocracy of the Romanovs, and to this they wish never to return. The question not asked, the question that must be asked is, therefore: To what doctrines and institutions can Gorbachev and his fellow reformers appeal for the legitimacy of their proposals?

If they fail to find the answer, their successors—and it is almost certain that they will have successors in this century or the next— must succeed in finding it, for the people of the Soviet Union must be given the intellectual and moral foundations that can legitimate the *reform* of the system of totalitarian communism, or what may have to be described as its *replacement* by other political institutions and other economic arrangements. If *reforming* the system cannot produce the desired results, then *replacing* it must be resorted to. But how can that be done without a complete rejection of Party, Leninism, and Marxism?

The actions taken by Gorbachev at the end of 1989 and in the first months of 1990 appear to have moved *perestroika* in the right direction, both politically and economically, without his having to justify the steps he has taken by appealing to the canonical texts of Marx and Lenin. Though he may have bypassed the question raised by Pfaff, there is another question to be answered.

Marx and Friedrich Engels, like others in the nineteenth century, were socialists before they adopted that form of socialism they called communism. When the Eastern satellites of the Soviet Union—Poland, East Germany, Czechoslovakia, Hungary, and Romania—threw off their Soviet yokes, they proclaimed the tendency of their own internal reforms to be in the direction of socialist democracies. Marx and Engels, in *The Communist Manifesto,* declared progress toward democracy through the enfranchisement of the working class to be an indispensable step toward the realization of their socialist aims; and Lenin, in *The State and Revolution,* made democratic institutions inseparable from the ultimate realization of the socialist ideal.

In other words, Marx and Lenin were not wrong in all respects; nor were they entirely right. The Marxist-Leninist doctrine is not wholly true and sound; but neither is it wholly false and unsound. The millions upon millions of people who have lived under communism in this century have not been totally deluded, deceived, and misguided. Hence the other question to be answered by us as well as by Gorbachev is: What principles in Marxist-Leninist doctrine should be retained while others should be rejected? The choice is not between the extremes of All or None, but rather in the middle ground of partial retention and partial rejection.

There are elements in the doctrines of Marx and Lenin that have prevented (and always would have prevented) the Soviet Union from establishing the kind of economic equality that has always been stated as the communist ideal; that make it impossible to achieve political liberty and individual freedom for the people, to increase the supply of consumer goods to a point that raises the standard of living to an acceptable level, and to promote an economy with a plurality of competing economic agencies or associations; in short, with government regulation that is at the same time neither governmental nor controlling.

On the other hand, there are also elements in the doctrines of Marx and Lenin, no less fundamental than the ones which have to be rejected, which can and should be retained to provide the intellectual and moral foundations that would legitimate the radical reforms that would amount in effect to the substitution of democratic socialism, which is consistent with such reforms, for totalitarian communism, which is not.

## 2. The plan for the Aspen seminar

I have described my state of mind as a result of reading the Pfaff article and thinking about it in the fall of 1988. This led me to offer to conduct a seminar at the Aspen Institute in the summer of 1989 entitled "Capitalism, Communism, and Their Future." The proposed seminar was oversubscribed. Double the largest number that can be accommodated around the seminar table enlisted for it. I was asked to conduct the seminar twice in August of 1989, with approximately twenty-five persons in each of the week-long sessions. This happened before the first streaks of dawn glimmered in the darkness of the Cold War.

In planning for the seminar, I produced a volume of readings which, in order to avoid undue length, provided the shortest possible excerpts from the fewest texts that would cover all the salient points we had to consider in order to reach agreement or disagreement about the solution to the Pfaff problem, as I had finally come to formulate it for myself. I should report at once that in both seminars we reached agreement and shared understanding, by no means completely, but to an extent that is not often achieved in Aspen seminars.

The Appendix of this article contains the table of contents of the volume of readings prepared for the seminar. In that table of contents, readers will find not only the headings for the six sessions of the seminar but also the names of authors and the titles of the works assigned for each session. In the light of what happened in the course of the six days of discussion, I would now revise some of the language used in the headings for the sessions. For example, I would head Session III with the words "The Self-Destruction of Communist Socialism and Its Transformation into Privately Capitalized Socialism"; and I would change the heading of Session VI to "Conclusion: Coexistence or Convergence, Reform or Replacement."

I would add two further things. The first would point out that the word *capitalism,* when not modified by adjectives as in "private-property capitalism," or "state capitalism," designates a capital-intensive economy without specifying how the productive capital employed is owned and operated. The qualifying adjectives added to the word *capitalism* indicate just that—how the capital is owned and operated.

The second thing I would add is that the common future of what is now private-property capitalism and state capitalism (which is identical with Marxist or totalitarian communism) can be described by two phrases. The first of these names the future development of the economy of the United States, and the second names the future development of the economy of the Soviet Union. The first phrase is "socialized private-property capitalism." The second phrase is "privately capitalized socialism."

When the full significance of these two names is grasped, it will be seen how these future developments converge toward a common future that will include not only the United States and the Soviet Union but all the capital-intensive industrial economies of the world.

Following this section will be a series of sections in which I will try, as briefly as possible, to summarize the basic insights that developed in the course of the six sessions of the seminar. In presenting this summary, I will quote, as often as necessary, crucial passages from the texts read and discussed.

## 3. Labor and Capital as Forces in Production (Session I)

Before the first session on Monday morning, the participants gathered on Sunday evening for an introductory meeting. At that time, I had the opportunity to make some general remarks about the aim and conduct of the seminar. I will repeat here only four things that I then pointed out.

(1) The word *future* in the title of the seminar was not to be interpreted as an interest on our part in predicting what will happen in the years immediately ahead. We were not to be engaged in forecasting events to come. Our concern was rather what should or must happen if the improvements that are needed both in the Soviet Union and the United States are to be accomplished in a sound fashion. If this is not accomplished by Gorbachev and his associates, then it will have to be achieved by their successors. The same holds true for the present and future administration of the government in the United States.

(2) The basic terms in all practical problems are ends and means. What ends should be sought? What means should be chosen to attain them? Practicable, not utopian, arrangements and institutions should be the ideal ends sought both in the political and the economic order of affairs, and there should be consonance or harmony between the twin goals. When agreement is reached about the political and economic ideals to be sought, we can then move to the consideration of the means and the arguments *pro* and *con* with respect to them.

(3) The ultimate question that we would try to answer as we reached the end of the seminar might be phrased in the following manner. Should we be satisfied with the coexistence of diverse polities and economies in the Soviet Union and the United States, or should we hope for their convergence?

In the case of the Soviet Union, should the changes to be made be the reform of institutions that now exist there, or should the changes be more radical than that and amount to a replacement of the existing institutions and arrangements by new ones?

In the case of the United States, should we go much further than we have so far gone in the direction that was first initiated at the beginning of this century by such leaders as Theodore Roosevelt, Woodrow Wilson, Franklin D. Roosevelt, and Harry S. Truman; or should we continue to go in the opposite direction that we have followed under the leadership of Ronald Reagan and George Bush?

(4) Finally, I pointed out that while the word *democracy* was used as an honorific term by all the participants, its precise meaning was not sufficiently understood. This, I suggested, would become clearer to them when they no longer used the term *socialism* as a term of opprobrium and came to understand that democracy and socialism, far from being incompatible, are really two faces of the same ideal—the political and

the economic aspects of a justly constituted society, and one that would operate effectively to produce the conditions needed to enable all its members to lead good human lives. This point, as will subsequently be made clear, became the controlling insight of the seminar. It not only corrected the current mistaken identification of socialism with communism, but it also helped us to understand why totalitarian communism is the wrong means for achieving democratic socialism.

Like all introductory remarks at the opening of Aspen seminars, these four points probably fell on deaf ears. It would take the next six days of reading and discussion for the participants to achieve the requisite understanding of them. The following session-by-session report of the seminar will show just how it was achieved, with a remarkably high degree of consensus among the participants.

It would be impossible to present this report in the form of the questions asked and the answers given in the course of each two-hour session. Instead, what must be presented is a summary of the main points that were carried away from each session. In this presentation the personal pronouns "I" and "we" will be used—"I" for the things I pointed out in the explication of the texts, "we" for the things that the participants and I were in substantial agreement about as the discussion proceeded.

On Monday morning, we began our discussion with Chapter 5 in John Locke's *Second Treatise Concerning Civil Government* (1690; *GBWW*, Vol. 35, pp. 30b–36a). That is the chapter in which Locke advances his quite original labor theory of the right to property, a theory which should never be confused with Marx's labor theory of value. In fact, as I pointed out and we perceived, Locke's labor theory of property contained (more than 150 years before the publication of the *Communist Manifesto* in 1848) a refutation of the central mistake that Marx made in the formulation of the labor theory of value.

The seminar participants were given only Sections 24–29 of Chapter 5 to read, and for our present purposes I am going to quote here only Sections 26 and 27.

> Though the earth and all inferior creatures be common to all men, yet every man has a "property" in his own "person." This nobody has any right to but himself. The "labour" of his body and the "work" of his hands, we may say, are properly his. Whatsoever, then, he removes out of the state that Nature hath provided and left it in, he hath mixed his labour with it, and joined to it something that is his own, and thereby makes it his property. It being by him removed from the common state Nature placed it in, it hath by this labour something annexed to it that excludes the common right of other men. For this "labour" being the unquestionable property of the labourer, no man but he can have a right to what that is once joined to, at least where there is enough, and as good left in common for others.

He that is nourished by the acorns he picked up under an oak,
or the apples he gathered from the trees in the wood, has certainly
appropriated them to himself. Nobody can deny but the nourishment
is his. I ask, then, when did they begin to be his? when he digested? or
when he ate? or when he boiled? or when he brought them home? or
when he picked them up? And it is plain, if the first gathering made
them not his, nothing else could. That labour put a distinction between
them and common. That added something to them more than Nature,
the common mother of all, had done, and so they became his private
right. And will any one say he had no right to those acorns or apples
he thus appropriated because he had not the consent of all mankind
to make them his? Was it a robbery thus to assume to himself what
belonged to all in common? If such a consent as that was necessary, man
had starved, notwithstanding the plenty God had given him. We see in
commons, which remain so by compact, that it is the taking any part of
what is common, and removing it out of the state Nature leaves it in,
which begins the property, without which the common is of no use. And
the taking of this or that part does not depend on the express consent
of all the commoners. Thus, the grass my horse has bit, the turfs my
servant has cut, and the ore I have digged in any place, where I have a
right to them in common with others, become my property without the
assignation or consent of anybody. The labour that was mine, removing
them out of that common state they were in, hath fixed my property in
them. (*GBWW,* Vol. 35, pp. 30d–31a.)

I pointed out, as the discussion of this text began, that the crucial
words were *common* and *property*. The common included everything in
the environment that belonged to no one, but was available to all for
appropriation through the labor of hand and mind that anyone mixed
with the common to make the product of this mixture that individual's property, to which that individual alone had a right of possession,
excluding all others. The examples that Locke gives of primitive acquisitions of this sort were clear to all the participants.

I then concentrated their attention on a portion of the final paragraph of Section 27, which I reproduce below.

Thus, the grass my horse has bit, the turfs my servant has cut, and
the ore I have digged in any place, where I have a right to them in
common with others, become my property without the assignation or
consent of anybody.

I expanded this one sentence for the participants by the following
account of what Locke was, in effect, saying. Let the owner of the
horse, grass, turf, and ore be Smith. How did he acquire the horse as
his property? By going out into the wilderness, finding, capturing, and
taming the horse that thus became, by right of his labor, his private
property. Let us suppose that Smith, by his labor, has staked out his
claim to owning a plot of land on which there is grass, turf, and ore.

Schooling in the U.S.S.R. is excellent by U.S. standards. Most children graduate from high school with competence in science, mathematics, and foreign languages, notwithstanding their Marxist-Leninist social studies (no longer required).

Let us further suppose that, by his own efforts, he has cut down trees, fenced his land, and built some crude farm implements, such as a rake, a shovel, and a plow; and that he has also worked to make a harness for the horse he captured. With all these rightfully acquired possessions, appropriated by his labor from the common, Smith has himself for many weeks produced his own means of subsistence.

Then, one Sunday, while he is standing at his fence, along comes an itinerant, with a bag of personal possessions over his shoulder. Let his name be Brown. Smith asks Brown whether he would like to work for him next week, offering to give him room and board and a share of the wealth produced during the next six days of work. Brown finds the offer a fair one and accepts it, entering voluntarily into a labor contract with Smith. It is this voluntary contract that makes Brown the person referred to in the Locke passage quoted above as "my servant."

The word *my* here does not have the same meaning as it does in the phrase "my horse" or "my grass." There, "my" refers to private property rightfully acquired by Smith. But Brown is not Smith's private property; nor in fact is the word *servant* satisfactory, for Brown should more properly be described as Smith's employee or hired hand.

Communism's inability to provide consumer goods is well known. Queuing at stores—
stark and unappealing in themselves—is common in Soviet cities, where people wait
hours in line for whatever is available.

During the next week, when Brown works for Smith, his employer
decides not to do any work himself. He spends the entire week in his
house reading books. All the labor involved in the production of wealth
that week is done by Brown's labor on Smith's land, using Smith's horse
and other instruments of production (such as shovel, spade, plow, etc.).

At the end of the week, the total wealth produced is, let us say, the
quantity X. Smith gives Brown the share of that total wealth that he
contracted to give him as Brown's wages for a week of work. Brown
departs satisfied with Y, his agreed-upon share. This leaves Smith
with Z, the residue of X that is left to Smith after Brown has been
paid off.

I then pointed out that the instruments of production used by Brown
in working for Smith are capital. We agreed that everything that can be
used in the production of wealth, other than labor, is capital. We also
agreed that money is not capital but only an instrument of exchange
and a source of purchasing power. Money, in and of itself, is not an
instrument of production. We were thus quite clear about the two basic
economic terms—labor and capital. We avoided the mistake of calling
the labor power of men and women "human capital."

I then asked the group the sixty-four-dollar question. During the week in which Smith did not labor at all, and all the work productive of wealth was done by Brown, did Smith rightfully earn—without laboring—the wealth Z that was left to him after he paid Brown Y out of the total wealth X produced that week? If the answer to that question is affirmative, I said to the group, then a number of things follow that we ought to acknowledge and agree upon.

(1) One's own labor power of hand and mind is the only private property that is not acquired. It is each individual's birthright of natural property. This fact makes unjust the ownership and use of human beings as chattel slaves. Only consumable goods and capital instruments can be rightfully owned as private property.

(2) If an individual puts into productive operation the capital he owns, then, even if he does not work himself, that contribution to the production of wealth rightfully earns for him whatever share of the total wealth produced that is not paid to the laborers involved for the work they do. The nonworking capitalist is *not* unproductive. In other words, wealth can be acquired either (a) by working to produce it or (b) by putting the capital one owns into production, or (c) by the combination of both factors. Smith could have labored himself, along with Brown, instead of reading, and then more wealth than X would have been produced, and Smith's share of the total would have been larger than Z.

(3) Labor and capital are distinct factors in the production of wealth, and each deserves, by right, that portion of the wealth produced to which each contributes. Labor is the independent factor, in the sense that no wealth can be produced except by some labor input. Capital input by itself will not suffice. But the fact that labor is the independent and capital the dependent factor does not blur the distinct contributions that each makes to the production of wealth.

(4) The wealth that is rightfully earned by the productive use of the capital one owns refutes the view that what an individual receives from the productive use of capital is "unearned income." The profits or dividends of capital are earned income in exactly the same sense that the wages or salaries paid to labor are earned income.

These insights, I pointed out, challenge the correctness of all the basic propositions in Marx's labor theory of value. If these insights are sound, then it cannot be correct to declare, as Marx does, (a) that all wealth is produced by labor and labor alone, either by living labor or by the labor congealed in machines and other capital instruments; (b) that the portion of the wealth produced, taken by the owners of capital, is "surplus value"—an "unearned increment" that capitalists *steal* by their "exploitation of labor"; and (c) that capital, certainly the modern form of capital—the machines used in factories after the Industrial Revolution, not the simple hand tools used by laborers before the Industrial Revolution—cannot be rightfully acquired as private property.

I told the group that we would return to the third point (c) later when we discussed Marx in the third seminar, but if we agreed on the first two points—(a) and (b) above—we have already discovered serious mistakes in Marxist doctrine that should be rejected.

The seminar next turned to the discussion of a passage from Alexander Hamilton's *Report on Manufactures* (1791). He wrote this as our first secretary of the Treasury. I quote below the paragraphs to which we paid close attention. First this:

> The employment of machinery forms an item of great importance in the general mass of national industry. It is an artificial force brought in aid of the natural force of man; and, to all the purposes of labor, is an increase of hands—an accession of strength, unencumbered, too, by the expense of maintaining the laborer. [4]

I pointed out an error in this statement. The introduction of machinery cannot always be regarded as equivalent to an increase of hands, because in technologically advanced industrial economies, some wealth cannot be produced without the use of machines. But at an earlier stage of the Industrial Revolution, it is true that any increase in the production of wealth through the use of machinery could have been produced by an increase in the amount of labor employed. In other words, machinery is a laborsaving device. This led us to understand the division of all economies into labor-intensive and capital-intensive.

We concentrated next on the following passage:

> The cotton mill, invented in England within the last twenty years, is a signal illustration of the general proposition which has just been advanced. In consequence of it, all the different processes for spinning cotton are performed by means of machines which are put in motion by water, and attended chiefly by women and children; and by a smaller number of persons, in the whole, than are requisite in the ordinary mode of spinning. And it is an advantage of great moment that the operations of this mill continue, with convenience, during the night as well as through the day. The prodigious effect of such a machine is easily conceived. To this invention is to be attributed, essentially, the immense progress which has been so suddenly made in Great Britain in the various fabrics of cotton. [5]

The significance of the above, I pointed out, is its indication that with the Industrial Revolution the total amount of capital employed by a nation became the more productive factor and the total amount of labor became the less productive factor. [6] We agreed that, were this not so, the factories could not have effectively employed in the spinning industry women and very young children instead of men and, on the whole, a smaller number of workers than had been employed in spinning when that was conducted domestically.

We turned next to the *Preamble of the Mechanics' Union of Trade Associations,* promulgated in Philadelphia in 1827. Here, about twenty years before the *Manifesto* was first published, we find a statement of the labor theory of value—that labor and labor alone produces all the wealth that society consumes. The Philadelphia Mechanics ask: "Do not you, and all society, depend solely for subsistence on the products of human industry? . . . Do not all the streams of wealth which flow in every direction and are emptied into and absorbed by the coffers of the unproductive [the nonlaboring owners of capital] exclusively take their rise in the bones, marrow, and muscles of the industrious classes [the laborers]?" [7]

The laborers are being exploited by capitalists who, being themselves unproductive, get wealth that is an "unearned increment," a "surplus value" stolen from labor. But if this were so, then what the Philadelphia Mechanics should have asked for is all the wealth that labor alone produces. But they did not do that. They asked only for their fair share. I called attention to the following passage:

> . . . It is neither our intention nor desire to extort inequitable prices for our labor; all we may demand for this shall not exceed what can be clearly demonstrated to be a fair and full equivalent. If we demand more, we wrong the society of which we are members, and if society requires us to receive less, she injures and oppresses us. [8]

Their self-contradiction here caused us to ask ourselves whether the Philadelphia Mechanics really affirmed Marx's labor theory of value. I then pointed out other contradictions in the text. The writers observe that the introduction of machinery in the production of wealth has greatly increased the amount of wealth produced and, at the same time, "the demand for human labor is gradually and inevitably diminishing." [9] A diminishing demand for labor with an increased production of wealth must mean that labor cannot be the sole producer of wealth; yet a little later, the writers still refer to "labor (the only source)." [10] Still later, they contradict themselves once again by saying that everyone depends for subsistence "upon the employment of his skill, his labor, or *his capital.*" [11] I add the italics to stress the fact that labor cannot be the only source of the wealth produced if some individuals can obtain their subsistence from the employment of their capital rather than their labor power.

The one long text discussed in the first seminar was the whole of an essay by William Graham Sumner, a professor of sociology at Yale University, entitled "The Challenge of Facts," taken from a book of his, *The Challenge of Facts and Other Essays,* published in 1914. The essay was written at the end of the nineteenth century.

I included this essay in the readings for the first seminar because I surmised that most of my participants would find themselves in agreement with it. I was correct in this anticipation. The essay is a forthright rejection of socialism. It begins with the words: "Socialism is no new thing." [12] Later in the essay are the following passages:

> . . . Socialists are filled with the enthusiasm of equality. Every scheme of theirs for securing equality has destroyed liberty.
>
> The student of political philosophy has the antagonism of equality and liberty constantly forced upon him. Equality of possession or of rights and equality before the law are diametrically opposed to each other. . . .
>
> The newest socialism is, in its method, political. The essential feature of its latest phases is the attempt to use the power of the state to realize its plans and to secure its objects. These objects are to do away with poverty and misery, and there are no socialistic schemes yet proposed, of any sort, which do not, upon analysis, turn out to be projects for curing poverty and misery by making those who have share with those who have not. [13]

I pointed out that many writers in the nineteenth century, John C. Calhoun and Alexis de Tocqueville, for example, had, like Sumner, thought liberty and equality to be incompatible; but Sumner, more explicitly than they, declares that

> . . . we cannot go outside of this alternative: liberty, inequality, survival of the fittest; not-liberty, equality, survival of the unfittest. The former carries society forward and favors all its best members; the latter carries society downward and favors all its worst members. [14]

Before going any further, I explained to the participants how to correct this great nineteenth-century error. When both liberty and equality are limited by the restraints of justice, they are not incompatible. The conflict is between libertarianism, which asks for unlimited liberty, and egalitarianism, which asks for complete equality and no inequality. It is never between limited liberty and equality combined with inequality.

The correct principles are: (a) No one should have more liberty than justice allows, which is to say, no more than individuals can use without injuring anyone else or the general welfare of society; and (b) No society should establish more equality than justice requires, combining that with as much inequality as justice also requires.

The core of Sumner's rejection of socialism, as he understood it, is his rejection of natural rights, as he understood them. Here are excerpts from the long passage in which that occurs.

> Another development of the same philosophy is the doctrine that men come into the world endowed with "natural rights," or as joint inheritors of the "rights of man," which have been "declared" times without number during the last century. . . .
>
> The notion of natural rights is destitute of sense, but it is captivating, and it is the more available on account of its vagueness. It lends itself

to the most vicious kind of social dogmatism, for if a man has natural
rights, then the reasoning is clear up to the finished socialistic doctrine
that a man has a natural right to whatever he needs and that the
measure of his claims is the wishes which he wants fulfilled. If, then, he
has a need, who is bound to satisfy it for him? Who holds the obligation
corresponding to his right? [15]

Sumner here reveals his misunderstanding of natural rights (which
are identical with the rights that were called "unalienable" in the Declaration of Independence and the rights that everyone now calls "human
rights"). It lies in his use of the words *needs* and *wishes* or *wants*, as if
their meaning were equivalent.

Needs are natural desires, the same in all human beings, for they
are inherent in human nature; and wants are acquired desires, differing from individual to individual as they are nurtured under different
conditions and are affected by different environmental circumstances.
We have a natural right only to those things that all human beings
naturally need in order to lead a decent human life. This includes not
only life and liberty but whatever else anyone needs in order to engage
in the pursuit of happiness, when happiness is understood not just as the
contentment one experiences when one's needs are satisfied but rather
as a morally good life as a whole. Such rights are accompanied by the
individual's obligation to make the effort to live well. The obligation to
secure these rights falls upon organized society as a whole, since a just
government should aim to secure all the natural rights of its citizens.

The first seminar came to end with almost everyone understanding
that natural rights derive from natural needs, among which is the need
for a decent livelihood without which no one can live a decent human
life. That raised a question about the different ways in which the right
to a decent livelihood might be secured, and also a question about
whether securing all natural rights—economic as well as political—
would lead to socialism as well as to democracy.

## 4. The Self-Destruction of Bourgeois Capitalism and Its Transformation into Socialized Private-Property Capitalism (Session II)

In the afternoon after the session is over, I reflect on the ground
covered in the morning and make notes of the main points that I wish
to remind the participants to carry over to the following day.

I need not repeat here the full summary presented. For our present
purposes only two things should be noted. One is the understanding
of democracy and socialism as the correlated political and economic
aspects of a justly constituted society.

With constitutional government, political liberty comes into being,
but usually only for some, not for all. The United States, for example,

was first established as a republic, with political liberty extended only to the small portion of the population that was then enfranchised as citizens. It remained in that condition until the twentieth century, at the beginning of which more than half the population was disfranchised— all the women, most of the blacks, and the poor in those states where there was a poll tax they could not pay. It slowly became a democracy with the Nineteenth and Twenty-Fourth Amendments, the latter in 1964 when the poll tax was abolished. But if in addition to establishing universal suffrage, a democracy should secure all human rights, then further constitutional or legislative enactments are needed to complete the progress toward the twin ideals of democracy and socialism.

That ideal is political equality, or the equal political liberty for all as required by justice—all with the equal political status and power of citizenship. Justice also requires the political inequality of citizens holding public office for a time, as compared with those not in office. To discharge the responsibilities of their offices, officials must exercise more political power and perform more functions than ordinary citizens. In short, a society is democratic if all, except the few who are justly disfranchised (infants, the mentally incompetent, and felons), are political *haves* as citizens, and some—those in public office—*have more* political power than those not in office.

In the economic order, socialism parallels democracy in the political order. It stands for the ideal of economic equality, as democracy stands for the ideal of political equality. As we recognized in yesterday's discussion of Sumner, among the natural, unalienable, and human rights is the economic right to a decent livelihood.

Postponing for a moment the consideration of the various means by which this right can be secured, the clearest way of stating the parallelism and correlation of democracy and socialism is to say that a society is socialistic to the extent that it achieves in the economic order the same kind of equality that justice requires in the political order and which democracy achieves: all *haves* (i.e., no *have-nots,* no persons *deprived* of a decent livelihood), but among the *haves,* some *having more* and some *having less* according to the degree to which they contribute to the economic welfare of society as a whole.

The second thing I stressed at the beginning of the second seminar was the sharp distinction between the meaning of the word *socialism* as here used and the meaning of the word *communism.* It is communism, not socialism, that is incompatible with democracy and with private-property capitalism.

I pointed out that the discussion of the texts assigned for the second seminar would soon make manifest that, in this century, the private-property, free-enterprise, and market economies of the United States, of the United Kingdom, and of Sweden were socialized. Another way of saying the same thing is to say that they all gradually became, in the twenties and thirties, "welfare states." The insights to be found in the *Manifesto* not only led to the Russian Revolution of 1917 and the establishment of totalitarian communism in the Soviet Union. It also contained insights that led to the overthrow of the bourgeois capitalism that dominated Western industrial societies in the nineteenth century and supplanted it by the welfare states or the socialized capitalisms of the societies that became democratic in the twentieth century.

The second seminar opened with a discussion of those pages in the *Manifesto* in which Marx explains his prediction that the then regnant bourgeois capitalism would sow the seeds of its own destruction. Bourgeois capitalism operated under the governance of Ferdinand Lassalle's and David Ricardo's iron law of wages. The capitalist owners of the factories and employers of labor should seek to maximize their profits by paying labor bare subsistence wages—just enough to keep the laborers alive and able to reproduce the next generation of workers.

Since the owners of capital were the few and the workers represented the great mass of the population with scant purchasing power, capitalism's increasing production of consumable goods for a domestic market on subsistence wages would lead to overproduction and underconsumption. Though periodically lifted by unmet demand, after temporary failures, capitalism would soon overproduce again, leading to cycles of boom and bust. The final bust would bring about the complete collapse or self-destruction of unreformed bourgeois capitalism.

There are many passages in which Marx describes the utter misery of the working class, those men, women, and children whom he calls the "wage slaves" of bourgeois capitalism. The children went into the factories at a tender age and the rest of their lives was totally consumed by grinding toil—usually twelve hours a day and seven days a week. But instead of quoting these passages, I am going to cite passages written by Tocqueville in 1835 and by the American educator Horace Mann around the middle of the century, in which the condition of the working class is vividly depicted by observers who are far from being Marxist communists. First, the passage in Tocqueville, taken from Volume 2, Book 2, Chapter 20, of his *Democracy in America,* entitled "How An Aristocracy May Be Created by Manufacturers."

> When a workman is unceasingly and exclusively engaged in the fabrication of one thing, he ultimately does his work with singular dexterity; but, at the same time, he loses the general faculty of applying his mind to the direction of the work. He every day becomes more adroit and less industrious; so that it may be said of him that, in proportion as the workman improves, the man is degraded. What can be expected of a man who has spent twenty years of his life in making heads for pins? and to what can that mighty human intelligence, which has so often stirred the world, be applied in him, except it be to investigate

the best method of making pins' heads? When a workman has spent a considerable portion of his existence in this manner, his thoughts are forever set upon the object of his daily toil; his body has contracted certain fixed habits, which it can never shake off: in a word, he no longer belongs to himself but to the calling which he has chosen. . . .

Not only are the rich not compactly united amongst themselves but there is no real bond between them and the poor. Their relative position is not a permanent one; they are constantly drawn together or separated by their interests. The workman is generally dependent on the master, but not on any particular master. These two men meet in the factory but know not each other elsewhere; and, whilst they come into contact on one point, they stand very wide apart on all others. The manufacturer asks nothing of the workman but his labor; the workman expects nothing from him but his wages. The one contracts no obligation to protect, nor the other to defend; and they are not permanently connected either by habit or duty. [16]

The following passage comes from an essay by Mann included in a book of his writings published in 1867.

. . . The British manufacturer or farmer prescribes the rate of wages he will give to his work people; he reduces these wages under whatever pretext he pleases; and they, too, have no alternative but submission or starvation. In some respects, indeed, the condition of the modern dependent is more forlorn than that of the corresponding serf class in former times. Some attributes of the patriarchal relation did spring up between the lord and his lieges to soften the harsh relations subsisting between them. Hence came some oversight of the condition of children, some relief in sickness, some protection and support in the decrepitude of age. But only in instances comparatively few have kindly offices smoothed the rugged relation between British capital and British labor. The children of the work people are abandoned to their fate; and notwithstanding the privations they suffer, and the dangers they threaten, no power in the realm has yet been able to secure them an education; and when the adult laborer is prostrated by sickness, or eventually worn out by toil and age, the poorhouse, which has all along been his destination, becomes his destiny. [17]

With these two passages before us, reinforcing everything Marx has to say about the misery of the working class under bourgeois capitalism, I asked the seminar whether anyone in the room, if he or she could have chosen otherwise, would have chosen to be a factory worker under the conditions that prevailed everywhere in the nineteenth century, in Europe and the United States. These conditions persisted relatively unchanged until the second and third decades of the twentieth century. The answer was a resounding and unanimous negative.

We found evidence of the persistence of these deplorable conditions in Theodore Roosevelt's platform for his Progressive Party in 1912. In it were planks that called for one day's rest in seven for every wage worker, for the prohibition of child labor, for minimum wage standards for working women, for the prohibition of night work for women, for an eight-hour day in continuous twenty-four-hour industries, and for "the protection of homelife against the hazards of sickness, irregular employment, and old age, through the adoption of a system of social insurance." [18]

Everyone recognized that many of the reforms proposed by Theodore Roosevelt were not legislatively enacted until Franklin D. Roosevelt's New Deal in the thirties. I pointed out that Big Steel in Pittsburgh was still operating the mills on two twelve-hour shifts as late as 1928 and that unemployment insurance, old age pensions, and social security entitlements came later than that.

We stayed a moment longer with Theodore Roosevelt, turning to his great New Nationalism address in Kansas in 1910. He began it by confessing that he would probably be "denounced as a Communist agitator" for talking about the rights of labor as well as the rights of capital and for proclaiming that "the object of government is the welfare of the people." To achieve this goal, Roosevelt insisted that human rights must take precedence over property rights.

> . . . We are face to face with new conceptions of the relations of property to human welfare, chiefly because certain advocates of the rights of property as against the rights of men have been pushing their claims too far. The man who wrongly holds that every human right is secondary to his profit must now give way to the advocate of human welfare, who rightly maintains that every man holds his property subject to the general right of the community to regulate its use to whatever degree the public welfare may require it. [19]

Following that, he pointed out a little later that the economic welfare of the citizens was indispensable to making democracy prosper, for without it most members of the working class were citizens in name only. "We keep countless men," he said, "from being good citizens by the conditions of life with which we surround them." [20]

We turned from Theodore Roosevelt's "socialistic" proposals (socialistic, not communistic) to Franklin D. Roosevelt's establishment in this country of a welfare state by transforming bourgeois capitalism, reeling from the Great Depression, into socialized capitalism. I called the seminar's attention to one other text that had a bearing on Franklin D. Roosevelt's "economic declaration of rights" in his Commonwealth Club Address of 1932, [21] and in his "Economic Bill of Rights," which he delivered in his address to Congress on the State of the Nation in 1944. [22]

That text was Monsignor John A. Ryan's treatise on The Right to a Living Wage (1906). [23] This followed in the footsteps of two great papal encyclicals demanding relief for the plight of the working class. Monsignor Ryan made clear that the inventory of natural or human rights was incomplete unless it included the right to a decent livelihood, secured either through earning a living wage or by other means. [24]

The socialization of private-property capitalism (in different ways and in different degrees) in the United States under Franklin D. Roosevelt, in the United Kingdom under Clement Attlee, and in Sweden (or, to put it in other terms, those societies becoming welfare states in the twenties, thirties, and forties of this century) went a long way toward alleviating the misery of the working class. It was clear to all of us that the alleviation or extirpation of that condition had been from the very start the controlling motivation in Marx's thought and program.

A careful reading of the *Manifesto* that he and Engels promulgated in 1848 revealed the steps they proposed for moving toward this objective before what they regarded as the final revolution would (by force, they thought) expropriate the expropriators, i.e., take from them the ownership of capital which they used to exploit labor. It also revealed that the economic reforms enacted in the United States, in the United Kingdom, and in Sweden involved the erosion of capitalist property rights called for in the closing pages of the *Manifesto*, by means of redistributive taxation, though the Western democracies did not adopt all of the ten measures set forth at the end of the *Manifesto*.

The first step in this direction, according to Marx and Engels, was a step toward democracy, by extending suffrage to the laboring masses. This occurred earlier in England than elsewhere, in the Second Reform Bill of 1867. "The first step in the revolution by the working class," the *Manifesto* declared, "is to raise the proletariat to the position of ruling class, to establish democracy." Then it goes on to say:

> The proletariat will use its political supremacy to wrest by degrees all capital from the bourgeoisie, to centralize all instruments of production in the hands of the state, i.e., of the proletariat organized as the ruling class, and to increase the total of productive forces as rapidly as possible.
>
> Of course, in the beginning this cannot be effected except by means of despotic inroads on the rights of property and on the conditions of bourgeois production; by means of measures, therefore, which appear economically insufficient and untenable, but which, in the course of the movement outstrip themselves, necessitate further inroads upon the old social order, and are unavoidable as a means of entirely revolutionizing the mode of production. (*GBWW*, Vol. 50, pp. 428d–29a.)

We noted the following points in the foregoing passage. First, Marx and Engels did not realize the significance of the fact that their advocacy of increasing "the total of productive forces as rapidly as possible"

(Above) East Germans pour through the Berlin Wall, symbol of the Cold War, as the Communist regime gave up the effort to maintain it. (Below) The happy work of knocking it down begins.

(Above) Germans greet each other joyfully at an opening in the Berlin Wall. (Below) Traffic passes through Checkpoint Charlie, which has since been removed.

contained implicitly an acknowledgment that labor was not the *only* productive force in the economy. They were not advocating an increase in the quantity of the labor force at work, but rather an increase in the capital instruments employed productively. Only by regarding these capital instruments as "congealed labour" could they avoid contradicting their labor theory of value—that labor and labor alone produces wealth.

The second point we noted was that they did not abandon their ultimate revolutionary goal. They still anticipated that the proletariat would "wrest all capital from the bourgeoisie" and would "centralize all instruments of production in the hands of the state." In other words, private-property capitalism would ultimately be destroyed and would be replaced by state capitalism.

The third point, and the one that bears on what actually did take place in the twenties and thirties in the United States, the United Kingdom, and Sweden, is the step described by Marx and Engels as "despotic inroads on the rights of property." I reminded the seminar that when Marx and Engels refer to "property" or "private property" they are never referring to the ownership of consumable goods, but always to the ownership of the means of production, the private ownership of capital, by individuals or by corporations, as contrasted with its ownership by the state.

Earlier in the *Manifesto,* they had written that the Communist revolution could be summed up in a single mandate: *Abolish private property!* But later they describe what has been called "creeping socialism" in terms of inroads on the rights of private property before the ultimate goal is reached by its abolition. While private property still exists in societies that are being socialized economically, that socialization, by means of inroads on the rights of property, involves the erosion of those property rights by legislation which was then prophetic, but with which we are now familiar (cf. *GBWW,* Vol. 50, p. 429a–b).

Such enactments as the inheritance tax, the graduated income tax, the ownership by the state instead of private corporations of certain economic agencies, the establishment of national banks and credit facilities, the establishment of free public schools, the abolition of child labor, and the other welfare entitlements by which the national income is redistributed—all these have moved private-property capitalist societies in the direction of socialism.

Creeping socialism as thus accomplished does not, of course, go far enough in the view of Marx and Engels. It is only a step in the right direction, alleviating the misery of the working class. Marx and Engels have another objective in mind, one that for them is of equal importance. That is the removal of class conflicts and the ultimate establishment of a truly classless society. We found this clearly stated in the last two paragraphs of this chapter of the *Manifesto.*

When in the course of development class distinctions have disappeared and all production has been concentrated in the hands of a vast association of the whole nation, the public power will lose its political character. Political power, properly so called, is merely the organized power of one class for oppressing another. If the proletariat during its contest with the bourgeoisie is compelled by the force of circumstances to organize itself as a class; if by means of a revolution it makes itself the ruling class and, as such, sweeps away by force the old conditions of production, then it will, along with these conditions, have swept away the conditions for the existence of class antagonisms and of classes generally, and will thereby have abolished its own supremacy as a class.

In place of the old bourgeois society, with its classes and class antagonisms, we shall have an association in which the free development of each is the condition for the free development of all. (*GBWW*, Vol. 50, p. 429b–c.)

I told the seminar that we would return later to these twin objectives of the Marxist revolutionary program: (1) the alleviation or, better, the elimination of the misery of the working class, and (2) the ending of all class conflicts by the establishment of a classless society. At the present stage of our discussion, we would be content to observe that the socialist or welfare measures adopted by various Western democracies, which remained private-property capitalist societies, have moved them toward the ideal of economic equality that is the end at which all the various forms of socialism aim. This ideal, I reminded the seminar, is approached to the degree that any society eliminates *have-nots*—those totally deprived of the essentials of subsistence, most certainly of a decent livelihood.

Before the second seminar closed, we looked at two more texts. One was Gus Tyler's article "On the Economic Divide" (1988), with special attention to the following paragraph.

The poorest tenth got 1.1 per cent of the national income in 1977. Tiny as that proportion was, it had shrunk by 1984 and has stayed down so that in 1988 the bottom decile is getting merely nine-tenths of 1 per cent of the national income. This represents a drop of 18 per cent in its share. [25]

In the last decade, the number of *have-nots,* the seriously deprived, has steadily increased in the United States. For 20% of our population, average family income is less than $8,000 per year—substantially below the so-called poverty line, under which people do not have what they need. [26] Not only does this nation now have less economic equality than justice requires, but it also has more inequality— a greater inequality between the *have-more* and the *have-less*—than justice also requires.

I also pointed out that the progress toward equality we have made since the turn of the century is more than phenomenal. It is like the crossing of a great divide. In the United States, as in all other societies before the twentieth century, the political and economic *haves* were everywhere the privileged few—those who were both citizens and owners of property. The deprived—the *have-nots*—were everywhere the many. For the first time in the twentieth century, the proportions of the total population have been strikingly reversed. In the societies that have moved toward democracy and socialism, we now have a privileged multitude. The *haves,* both politically and economically, are the many, and the *have-nots,* the seriously deprived, are the few.

The other text that we examined came from John Strachey's *The Challenge of Democracy,* posthumously published in *Encounter* in 1963 (*GIT* 1965, pp. 520–90). In it, Strachey points out that, while the standard of living of the workers in the Soviet Union has steadily gone down, the standard of living of the wage earners in the Western democracies has steadily increased. [27] His explanation of this is as follows.

> . . . Why is it that Marx's prophecy of ever increasing misery, which must have seemed thoroughly reasonable and sensible when he made it, turned out to be wrong? I have no hesitation in saying that the explanation is to be found in the increasingly effective use of their democratic institutions by the mass of the wage earners of the Western societies. It is democracy which has done it. The Western capitalist employers have not had a change of heart; they still work, and must work, their industries in order to make the maximum amount of profit. They do not like paying higher wages to their workers, or working these shorter hours. By and large they have been impelled to do these things by the wage earners themselves. It is the fact that the wage earners in the democracies have been able to organize themselves, both politically and industrially, that has done the trick. . . .
>
> . . . Slowly, but in the end inexorably, the pressure of the wage earners has driven the governments of the Western democracies to undertake a substantial redistribution of the national income by means of taxation. . . . (*GIT* 1965, pp. 540a, 540c.)

In concluding this report of the second seminar discussion, I must mention an illuminating intervention by my associate, James O'Toole, Professor of Management in the Graduate School of Business Administration at the University of Southern California. He pointed out the contribution made by Robert Owen in his effort to correct the mistake made by the bourgeois capitalists, in England in the nineteenth century, by their obstinately adhering to the iron law of wages in their treatment of their factory workers.

Owen was himself the owner of a factory in which he demonstrated the economic effectiveness of treating the labor he employed in a quite different manner, paying higher wages, improving the conditions of work in the factories, shortening the hours of work, and consulting the

workers about the conduct of the enterprise. All of his recommendations fell upon deaf ears and caused Owen to support the establishment
of trade unionism as the only way to bring about the reform of bourgeois capitalism, a reform that he deemed both desirable and necessary
for its survival as well as to rectify its injustice.

## 5. The Self-Destruction of Communist Socialism and Its Transformation into Privately Capitalized Socialism (Session III)

I started this session with Professor O'Toole's discussion of Owen's
attempt to reform bourgeois capitalism. Commenting on Owen's style
of industrial management, Professor O'Toole pointed out that today we
recognize Owen's New Lanark as an example of what we have come to
call the Japanese style of management. Professor O'Toole also said that
Marx was quite correct in dismissing Owen as a utopian socialist. Owen
was utopian in hoping that the bourgeois capitalists of his day would act
in terms of long-term enlightened self-interest instead of being solely
motivated by short-term gains in profit for themselves.

I then returned to a matter that had been postponed the day before
when we discussed Monsignor Ryan's argument for the natural right
to a decent livelihood, either obtained by a living wage or by other
means. The question that remained to be answered was: What are all
the various means by which this right can be secured?

In the first place, a decent livelihood is either earned or obtained
by other means. If it is an earned livelihood, it may be income in the
form of wages or salaries, income in the form of the earned dividends
from the ownership of productive capital, or it may involve, as we will
find Louis O. Kelso advocating in his theory of binary economies, an
income derived from the combination of wages and dividends.

In the second place, some portion of a decent livelihood may not
come from earned income but from welfare benefits or entitlements,
such as social security and Medicare. In addition to these welfare benefits for all, there may have to be special welfare benefits for some, for
those who have serious pathological disabilities and for those who, for a
time, may be unemployed through no fault of their own. The larger the
portion of a decent livelihood that comes from earned income, the less
need be provided by welfare benefits. The ideal is a decent livelihood
secured for all by means of earned income.

The uneasiness I detected on the faces of the participants caused
by these considerations prompted me to add one further point of
explanation concerning the difference between political and economic
rights. When a government tries to secure or safeguard natural rights
that are political in character, it adopts constitutional provisions or
legislative enactments that restrain it from invading, transgressing, or

violating these rights. For example, the first seven amendments to the Constitution of the United States *protect* the individual's natural and unalienable right to civil liberty and freedom of action *from governmental impediments or interference.* The italicized words indicate what the government *should not do.*

When we turn from liberty to a decent livelihood, we see at once the difference between a political and economic right. In the latter case, securing the right requires positive action and governmental intervention in the economy, not negative action or governmental restraint. That is why securing the right to a decent livelihood has so far involved and will continue to involve legislative enactments, such as minimum wage laws, rather than constitutional amendments of the sort we find in our eighteenth-century Bill of Rights (i.e., the first ten amendments).

These matters being somewhat clarified, the third session of the seminar began with a consideration of its title: the self-destruction of communist socialism and its capitalization. We saw at once the parallelism of this title with the title of the second session: the self-destruction of bourgeois capitalism and its socialization. The question this led us to ask ourselves was: What basic mistake was made by communist socialism that sowed the seeds of its self-destruction, comparable to the mistake made by bourgeois capitalism that sowed the seeds of its own destruction?

In other words (1) what mistake did Marx and Engels make that had the same destructive effect on communist socialism that the obstinate espousal of the "iron law of wages" had upon bourgeois capitalism? and (2) what is meant by the capitalization of communist socialism to correct this mistake, paralleling the socialization of private-property capitalism to correct the basic mistake made by the bourgeois capitalists?

Before we attempted to answer these two questions, I reminded the participants of certain points that had been covered in a lexicon of terms which I distributed. It is necessary to remember that the word *socialism* unmodified by any adjective signifies an ideal or goal to be sought— a society in which all are economic *haves* and there are no *have-nots.* As we have seen, socialized private-property capitalism is one means of moving toward this end. Communist socialism, which is identical with state capitalism, is the means that Marx and Engels proposed for moving toward the same end. Accordingly, the phrases "communist socialism," "Marxist communism," and "state capitalism" all refer to one and the same set of means, quite distinct from the set of means referred to by the phrase "socialized private-property capitalism."

To answer the first of the above questions, we went back to a section of the *Manifesto* that we had not examined before. Here it is.

> The distinguishing feature of Communism is not the abolition of property generally, but the abolition of bourgeois property. But modern bourgeois private property is the final and most complete expression

of the system of producing and appropriating products that is based on class antagonisms, on the exploitation of the many by the few.

In this sense the theory of the Communists may be summed up in the single sentence: abolition of private property.

We Communists have been reproached with the desire of abolishing the right of personally acquiring property as the fruit of a man's own labour, which property is alleged to be the groundwork of all personal freedom, activity and independence.

Hard-won, self-acquired, self-earned property! Do you mean the property of the petty artisan and of the small peasant, a form of property that preceded the bourgeois form? There is no need to abolish that; the development of industry has to a great extent already destroyed it and is still destroying it daily.

Or do you mean modern bourgeois private property?

But does wage labour create any property for the labourer? Not a bit. It creates capital, i.e., that kind of property which exploits wage labour and which cannot increase except upon condition of begetting a new supply of wage labour for fresh exploitation. Property in its present form is based on the antagonism of capital and wage labour. (*GBWW*, Vol. 50, pp. 425d–26a.)

The abolition of "bourgeois property" (the private ownership of capital, consisting in the means of production that have emerged since the beginning of the Industrial Revolution) leads necessarily to state capitalism. The capital instruments at work must be owned and operated. If not by private individuals and corporations, the only other alternative is collective ownership by the state.

What is the mistake that lies at the root of this radical transference of the ownership of capital to the state? It is the error that we discovered when we read and discussed Locke in our first session. It is the *labor theory of value,* the theory (1) that all wealth is produced by labor, living or congealed labor, (2) that the owners of capital are totally unproductive, and (3) that they exploit labor by taking from it an "unearned increment" or the "surplus value" that labor produces. The profits of the capitalists come from thus exploiting labor; therefore, profit is theft. The following text from the *Manifesto* says all this, though as we saw, it says it not too clearly.

To be a capitalist is to have not only a purely personal, but a social, *status* in production. Capital is a collective product, and only by the united action of many members—nay, in the last resort, only by the united action of all members of society—can it be set in motion.

Capital is, therefore, not a personal, it is a social, power.

When, therefore, capital is converted into common property, into the property of all members of society, personal property is not thereby transformed into social property. It is only the social character of the property that is changed. It loses its class character.

Let us now take wage labour.

The average price of wage labour is the minimum wage, i.e., that quantum of the means of subsistence which is absolutely requisite to keep the labourer in bare existence as a labourer. What, therefore, the wage labourer appropriates by means of his labour merely suffices to prolong and reproduce a bare existence. We by no means intend to abolish this personal appropriation of the products of labour, an appropriation that is made for the maintenance and reproduction of human life and that leaves no surplus wherewith to command the labour of others. All that we want to do away with is the miserable character of this appropriation, under which the labourer lives merely to increase capital, and is allowed to live only insofar as the interest of the ruling class requires it.

In bourgeois society living labour is but a means to increase accumulated labour. In Communist society accumulated labour is but a means to widen, to enrich, to promote the existence of the labourer. (*GBWW,* Vol. 50, p. 426a–b.)

What is meant here by "accumulated labour"? It is the machinery produced by labor that Marx in other places called "congealed labour." Only by thus calling machinery itself a form of labor can any sense be made of the statement that all wealth is produced by labor and also the statement that the capitalists are unproductive even when they put their capital to work productively.

We saw that the text just quoted contained another fundamental point, also a mistake that underlies the Marxist abolition of the private ownership of capital. The *Manifesto* maintains that capital is collectively produced and collectively operated and, therefore, must be collectively, not privately, owned. What can this mean?

To answer that question, we turned to an essay by Charles Vail, an American socialist, who wrote a pamphlet entitled *The Socialist Movement,* published in 1902. We examined the following passage.

> . . . In the days of individual production private ownership of the tools was necessary to secure to the laborer his freedom and the full product of his toil. But when the method of production was revolutionized and the tools were transformed into social instruments, they were not capable of individual ownership on the part of the laborers. The principle of private ownership, which had hitherto been the means of securing to the laborer his full product, became now the means of his servitude and exploitation. The changed conditions rendered what was once right a decided wrong. [28]

The hand tools that the laborer produces for his own use are privately produced and privately operated and therefore it is right that they should be privately owned. But the industrial machinery the capitalist owns involves many gadgets and elements that have been collectively produced by human society as a whole in the course of its long history;

as, for example, wheels, levers, fulcrums, pulleys, screws, nails, leather, rope, and many other technological devices that are embodied in the industrial machinery. They have been collectively produced. The bourgeois capitalist has not paid for them, and, therefore, he has no right to own them. In short, modern industrial machinery cannot rightfully be a private possession.

Just as the mistake made by the labor theory of value in declaring the capitalist unproductive was exposed in our discussion of Locke, so the mistake of saying that industrial machinery cannot rightfully be private property can be corrected by remembering Locke's point that whatever is in the sphere of the common, or in the public domain, can be privately appropriated. Such private appropriations are protected by patent laws and regulations that usually have time limitations. When the time limit expires, whatever has been protected by patents returns to the public domain and is once again subject to private appropriation.

I presented the following concrete example to the seminar. Jones, a capitalist, is approached by White, an inventor, who offers him the design and blueprints of a new machine that incorporates many things that have long been in the public domain and that, therefore, can be appropriated by him. Jones thinks well of the new machine and offers to pay the inventor a fee for his device and also an annual royalty for a term of years. Jones then hires laborers to produce the machine whose design and blueprints he has bought from the inventor. He pays the laborers off each week for the work they do in building the machine. When they have completed their work, he owns the machine and can put it into productive operation by paying other laborers to operate it.

If there is any injustice in this whole series of transactions, it must be that Jones has not paid the inventor adequately and has not paid the workers fairly. It cannot lie in the fact that what he has paid for is privately rather than collectively owned. It cannot be that it must be collectively owned because it is collectively produced by all the work done by society in the past and must now be collectively operated.

There was one more text in the *Manifesto* to which I called attention. It follows closely on the texts already quoted. It is as follows.

> You are horrified at our intending to do away with private property. But in your existing society private property is already done away with for nine-tenths of the population; its existence for the few is solely due to its non-existence in the hands of those nine-tenths. You reproach us, therefore, with intending to do away with a form of property, the necessary condition for whose existence is the non-existence of any property for the immense majority of society.
>
> In a word, you reproach us with intending to do away with your property. Precisely so; that is just what we intend. (*GBWW*, Vol. 50, p. 426d.)

Soviet President Mikhail Gorbachev manages a smile during 1990 May Day celebrations when antigovernment protesters, some carrying banners and calling for his resignation, were allowed in the streets of Moscow.

The importance of this text, I pointed out to the participants, is that it implies a third remedy, not found in the *Manifesto*, but consistent with its stated objective of alleviating or curing the misery of the working class.

The first of the remedies actually proposed by Marx we discussed in the previous session—inroads on the rights of capital, or the erosion of private property rights by the ten measures that the *Manifesto* enumerates in its closing pages.

Marx's second remedy is more drastic. It is the one that we considered earlier in this session—the abolition of the private ownership of the means of production, not just the erosion of the rights of the own-

In Moscow's 1990 May Day parade, ethnic flags appear along with a photo, carried like an icon, of physicist Andrey Sakharov, a symbol of resistance to Communist authority who enjoyed serving as an elected gadfly of the government before his death in 1989.

ers. While the first remedy may only alleviate the misery of the working class, the second, in Marx's judgment, goes much further. It eliminates it, by eliminating the capitalist's exploitation of labor. That is why Marx chose it as the radical remedy for the misery of the working class.

Now here, in the text just quoted, we can see the opportunity for a third and quite distinct remedy, not recognized by Marx, but equally appropriate to his purpose—that is, neither the erosion of private property rights, nor the abolition of private property itself, but the extension of the ownership of capital from the few to the many.

If the cause of the misery of the working class is the private ownership of capital instruments, then the abolition of that is the cure.

But, if the cause of the misery of the working class is the uneroded property rights of the capitalist who, under completely laissez-faire conditions, pays the labor employed a bare subsistence wage, then just as obviously the remedy is to erode those rights, not abolish them.

If the cause of the misery of the working class is that all or most of the capital available to a society is privately owned by less than one-tenth of the population, then the remedy which fits that cause is promoting the ownership of capital by a much larger proportion of the population.

The open letter written by Louis O. and Patricia Hetter Kelso to Gorbachev, included in the readings for the fourth session of the seminar, recommends that he use the third remedy to achieve the reforms for which he is striving.

I told the seminar that we would discover the variety of ways in which the Kelsos think that all capital-intensive economies, that of the United States as well as that of the Soviet Union, can widely diffuse the ownership of capital equities and thus give to many members of society a double income (i.e., from earned wages or salaries combined with the earned dividends of capital profits). This is what "binary economics" recommends. A decent livelihood will thus become largely an earned livelihood; it will become less dependent on welfare benefits and entitlements.

One more thing remained to be done in this third session. I had assigned for the second session the passage from Tocqueville that described the misery of the working class as he observed it in America in 1831–32. But I had failed to assign the chapters in *Democracy in America* that were most relevant to the undesirable results of state capitalism under the dictatorship of the proletariat (i.e., the Communist party), results that Gorbachev's *perestroika* was trying to undo. To make amends for this omission, I concluded the third session and prepared for the fourth by calling attention to the great, almost indispensable, contribution that Tocqueville had made to the solution of the problem with which the seminar began.

The stage is set by one paragraph in which Tocqueville refers to a new kind of oppression—tyranny or despotism—that he fears will develop in any nation that tends toward democracy, which for him means any nation that tries to establish an equality of conditions, especially economic conditions. Here is that paragraph.

> I think, then, that the species of oppression by which democratic
> nations are menaced is unlike anything which ever before existed in the
> world; our contemporaries will find no prototype of it in their memories.
> I seek in vain for an expression which will accurately convey the
> whole of the idea I have formed of it; the old words "despotism" and
> "tyranny" are inappropriate. The thing itself is new, and, since I cannot
> name, I must attempt to define it. [29]

The word that Tocqueville was looking for and could not find became current almost a hundred years later after the Russian Revolution eventuated in the state capitalism of the Soviet Union. It is *totalitarianism.* State capitalism or Marxist socialism is totalitarian communism. Totalitarianism comes into existence when all the governing and managing power of a society, both its political and its economic power, is concentrated in the centralized bureaucracy of the state, the apparatchiks of the Communist party.

What word names the diametrical opposite of monolithic totalitarianism? It is *pluralism,* the kind of political and economic pluralism that preserves the liberties that democratic societies seek to maximize, even as they also aim to maximize, as far as justice requires, an equality of economic conditions.

Tocqueville refers back to the kind of pluralism that existed in what he calls the ancient regime: the aristocratic, feudal society of his own French past. In this feudal society, the many lords, barons, earls, marquises, and dukes were each secondary agencies of government, each with its own domain. The monarch was the sole ruler of the whole country, but his authority and power were checked and diluted by the nobles who were not only his vassals but also the lords of their own domains.

Tocqueville draws from this historic example of feudal pluralism the lesson to be learned by the democracies of the present. Private associations of all sorts, profit and nonprofit corporations, private business organizations, labor unions, and competing political parties, must play the role that the feudal lords played in the ancient regime. They must function as secondary agencies of government, lessening the concentration of power in the central government. The multiplicity of private associations is the cornerstone of a pluralistic society in which the decentralization of power and authority operates in the balance against its centralized concentration. Abraham Lincoln aptly summarized the pluralistic principle when he said that the government should do for the people only that which the people, individually or collectively (i.e., in private associations), cannot do for themselves.

The principle of totalitarianism is exactly the opposite. Everything, except perhaps the private association of the family, is a creature of the state. There is only one political party; there are no private labor unions; there are no private universities or hospitals; there are no private businesses or industrial corporations.

Can private associations exist and operate effectively in the economic sphere without the private ownership and management of capital? Can there be free enterprise and a free market economy without the operation of a plurality of private associations? Can Gorbachev achieve a higher standard of living, especially an abundance of consumer goods, for the people of the Soviet Union without the market

257

economy and the free enterprise that require a plurality of private associations? In short, can Gorbachev achieve the results at which he and his fellow reformers aim without replacing totalitarianism with pluralism and without introducing private-property capitalism to replace state capitalism? [30]

With these questions to be answered the following day, the third session closed.

## 6. The Ideal of the Classless Society:
## Political and Economic Equality (Session IV)

In the previous session we saw how Joseph Schumpeter in his classic treatment of Marxism, *Capitalism, Socialism and Democracy* (1942), [31] provides us with further critical comments on Marxist errors, in addition to the two basic mistakes made by Marx, the errors we learned from our study of Locke's chapter on property. [32] In Schumpeter's judgment, Marxist communism is doomed to fail (1) because it is conceived in terms of a static, not dynamic, economy; and (2) because it is mainly managerial rather than entrepreneurial. It should be added here that Schumpeter also directs the second of these criticisms against Western private-property capitalism. That has become increasingly subject to the second criticism since Schumpeter's book was published, not to mention leveraged buyouts and junk-bond sales.

Some of the participants had already read the dialogue between John Kenneth Galbraith and Stanislav Menshikov (*Capitalism, Communism and Coexistence*, 1988), [33] which had been assigned for the sixth session of the seminar. In this dialogue Galbraith argued, on the one hand, that to achieve the minimal conditions of economic equality in the United States (all *haves*, no *have-nots*), private-property capitalism would have to move further in the direction of socialism. Menshikov, on the other hand, expressed the opinion that Gorbachev's reforms could achieve, to some degree, free enterprise and a free market economy, accompanied by a modicum of decentralization, while still remaining what the seminar would recognize as a totalitarian regime, with private ownership of the means of production abolished and with the state the sole owner of capital. It was in these terms that Galbraith and Menshikov agreed in their closing chapters on the future coexistence of the United States and the Soviet Union.

Some of the participants asked why I thought that the position Menshikov advanced was not a feasible one—that achieving free enterprise and a market economy was simply not possible as long as the Soviet Union remained a totalitarian state, as it had to remain as long as its socialistic goals were to be accomplished by state capitalism. I went to the blackboard and put on it the following diagram.

| Pluralistic Society with Competing Political Parties | Totalitarian State with One-Party Rule |
|---|---|
| Decentralized Private-Property Capitalism | Centralized State Capitalism |
| Private Economic Associations | *No* Private Economic Associations |
| Free Enterprise | *No* Free Enterprise |
| Market Economy | *No* Market Economy |

I argued that there was no middle ground here—no mixture of free enterprise and a market economy with the nonexistence of private economy associations and the nonexistence of the private ownership of capital. I also predicted a different future from that predicted by Menshikov—not coexistence, but convergence toward a middle ground of the socialist economies of the Soviet Union and the United States. This called for more than minor reforms of the government and economy of the Soviet Union. It required the replacement of a totalitarian state by a pluralistic society, and of state capitalism by private-property capitalism. [34]

As a preamble to the new turn in the seminar that had been planned for this fourth session, I thought it helpful briefly to recapitulate the ground we had covered in the two preceding sessions.

In the second and third sessions, we had concentrated on only one of the two chief motivations of the Marxist revolutionary program. That was Marx's deep and passionate desire to alleviate or eliminate the misery of the working class under the reign of bourgeois capitalism in England, the United States, and other Western nations.

In the second session, we saw how the alleviation of this misery, if not its elimination, was accomplished in the Western nations by the socialization of their economies, adopting in various ways and in different degrees measures for the erosion, not the abolition, of the rights of private property (i.e., inroads on capitalistic profits in order to secure a better standard of living for the working class).

In the third session, we saw how the attempt to eliminate the misery of the working class by abolishing private property and by establishing the dictatorship of the proletariat (i.e., the totalitarian state with all political and economic control in the hands of the Communist party) had been unsuccessful. It had failed to provide sufficient consumer goods in the marketplace and a decent standard of living for the working class. The fact that their misery had not so far been eliminated or even greatly alleviated was the prime motivating cause of Gorbachev's *perestroika*.

What I referred to above as a "new turn in the seminar" consisted in turning now, in this fourth session, to the second of the two motivations of the Marxist revolutionary program. For Marx and Engels as well as for Lenin, class warfare or conflict in all the societies of the past was a historic social evil that had to be remedied. The only remedy for that evil was the establishment of a truly classless society.

To begin the discussion of this matter, I called attention to the following text in Strachey's *The Challenge of Democracy.*

> The first thing to realize is that for Lenin, as for Marx, the division of society into social classes is everything. And when I say "everything," I mean that phrase almost literally. For the Leninist, even more than for the Marxist, nothing in human life really counts compared with this division into social classes. Politics is the struggle for power between these social classes, and power is the power of the state. The state is simply an engine of coercion by the use of which any class which is at the moment in power controls by physical force the class or classes which are not in power. This whole conception derives directly, of course, from Marx's and Engels' formulation of the matter in the *Communist Manifesto* where they wrote that the state is "the executive committee of the ruling class." (*GIT* 1965, p. 549a–c.)

The correctness of the Marxist and Leninist assertion that class warfare or conflict has plagued civilized societies from the beginning is amply confirmed by the facts of history. In antiquity, Plato, in his *Republic,* remarked that there have always been two cities, not one, the city of the rich and the city of the poor, and they are forever at war with one another. In the nineteenth century an American reformer, Orestes Brownson (in an essay on "The Laboring Classes" written in 1840 [35]), anticipated by eight years the depiction of class conflict in the *Manifesto.* In our own century, Arnold J. Toynbee, in his twelve-volume *A Study of History,* singled out two causes for the decline of all historic civilizations: war and class. These are two forms of the same root evil: external conflicts between societies and internal conflicts within each society by virtue of its division into antagonistic classes.

The history of the West records a succession of class conflicts, changing with changes in the economy: chattel slaves vs. masters, dispossessed agrarian workers vs. landlord magnates, plebeians vs. patricians, feudal peons or serfs vs. feudal lords, the industrial proletariat vs. the bourgeois capitalists—in general, the *have-nots* vs. the *haves.*

At this point, I found it necessary to digress, reminding the participants of one point that had great relevance to the Marxist-Leninist ideal of a completely classless society. We had agreed earlier that justice calls for the establishment of a society in which all are political *haves,* all have the status and power of suffrage; economically, all have the right to a decent livelihood secured. But we also agreed that, in both the political and the economic order, justice also requires that some *have more* and some *have less* (based in the political order on the greater political status and power of citizens in public office; and based in the economic order on different degrees of contribution to the economic welfare of society as a whole). The ideal, in short, is a nonegalitarian socialism.

To try to eliminate such inequality between the *have-mores* and the *have-lesses* would be an act of injustice. [36] Hence in a justly constituted society, one class distinction must remain. It would not be a perfectly classless society, for while all would be *haves,* some would have more than others. Whether this irremovable class distinction engenders a class conflict in society as grievous and bitter as the age-old class conflict between the *haves* and *have-nots* was a difficult question. There were differences of opinion that our discussion left unresolved. In any case, we did agree that the ideal to be attained could not be a completely classless society but rather one that was only relatively classless, with the distinction between the *have-mores* and the *have-lesses* remaining as a matter of distributive justice. [37]

After this digression, I called attention to a few other texts that clearly embraced classlessness as an ideal. One was a single sentence in the essay by Mann that we had discussed earlier. Using the word *property* to signify the ownership of capital, Mann declared: "Property and labor in different classes are essentially antagonistic; but property and labor in the same class are essentially fraternal." [38] I have often used this statement by Mann as an endorsement of Kelso's binary economics: that as many persons as possible should become economic *haves* through two sources of earned income: wages or salaries, on the one hand; dividends derived from the profits of capital, on the other hand. Labor and property should be in the same hands. Society should not be divided into nonlaboring owners of capital and nonowning laborers.

Exactly the same point is made in the following passage from Strachey.

> What, then, will be the future of the Communist countries? Will they in fact develop into the "classless societies" which their spokesmen hold before them as the goal to be aimed at? I myself believe in the goal of a classless society as strongly as ever I did. It still seems to me that the organization of an economic and social system which does not result in men being separated from each other by the barriers of class— peasants from landlords, wage earners from the owners of the means of production, educated from uneducated, rich from poor—would be the greatest step forward that humanity could take. That is why I am and remain a socialist. (*GIT* 1965, p. 571b–c.)

In the planning that I did to prepare for the seminar, I chose Lenin's Chapter 5 of *The State and Revolution* [39] as the central text for the fourth session. Its analysis and argument was both inspired by and based on Marx's *Critique of the Gotha Program.* Taken together, these two documents constitute an essential component of Marxist-Leninist doctrine.

As the *Manifesto* and *Capital* deal with the economic objectives of the revolution that Marx and Lenin spent their lives promoting, so these two documents deal with its political objectives. As the one aims at eliminating the misery of the working class by establishing state capitalism, so the other aims at removing class conflict and at establishing the classless society.

As the abolition of the private ownership of the means of production is the crux of the revolution in the economic sphere, so in the political sphere the crux of the revolution is the withering away of the state.

To explain why I thought these two Marxist-Leninist documents were so important for Gorbachev to interpret correctly in his concern with the future of the Soviet state in relation to its origins in the second decade of this century, and to also explain the significance of these two documents for me, I decided to summarize, as briefly as possible, the main points that deserved our close attention.

To this end, the first thing I did was to call attention to their dates. Marx's *Critique of the Gotha Program* was written in 1875 and was first published in 1891, at a time when Marx was acquainted with the civil societies of the two most advanced industrial nations, England and Germany, and when he thought of his projected revolution occurring there and not in a backward industrial country such as czarist Russia. Lenin's *The State and Revolution* was written early in 1917 while Lenin was still resident in Switzerland, six months before the October Revolution that put him and Leon Trotsky in power.

Keeping these dates in mind, we are compelled to ask what vision of the state did Marx and Lenin have at the time they were writing. It could not have been the totalitarian state that came into existence with the dictatorship of the proletariat after October 1917. In the immediately succeeding years, the fledgling Communist party then in power was engaged in two struggles—one against the White Armies of the West who were attempting to undo the revolution, the other the forceful effort to wrest the ownership of the land and of other capital instruments from private capitalists, the so-called expropriators, and put them into the possession of the state. It, therefore, had to be the English and German constitutional monarchies, which at that time were oligarchies, not democracies, and in which the ruling class were the bourgeois capitalists of that day. In the populations of these two nations, the ruling few controlled the government, justifying Marx's epithet that the government was nothing but "the executive committee of the ruling class."

In these two nations, as in czarist Russia, class warfare did, indeed, exist. The state or its government, controlled by the ruling class, did use coercive force at its disposal to crush the opposition of the disfranchised many—to put down riots and demonstrations, to suppress revolutionary movements, to prevent bomb-throwings and assassinations and to punish those who attempted such extreme measures. Against this background, the following points became clear.

(1) Lenin distinguished between a first and lower stage of the Communist revolution and a second and higher phase. Since for him in the spring of 1917 the revolution was most likely to occur initially in czarist Russia, not in England or Germany, Lenin described the first phase as a dictatorship of the proletariat (i.e., despotic rule by the Communist party in the name of the proletariat) to serve the two purposes already mentioned: (a) to wage war against the capitalist, imperialist nations of the West that would try to counteract the revolution; and (b) to seize by force the private property of the Russian capitalistic class—the landowning boyars and the industrial magnates—and to turn over to the Soviet state their capital holdings.

(2) This, in Lenin's view, as it had also been the earlier view of Marx, was only a temporary measure, justified by its pragmatic expediency. While the government of the state was in the hands of the few, and coercive force had to be employed by the government to serve its purposes, the dictatorship of the proletariat could not be regarded as the classless society that was the ultimate objective of both Marx and Lenin. Putting the possession of all capital into the hands of the state and all political power into the hands of the Communist party created a totalitarian regime, not the socialistic democracy that Marx and Lenin envisioned.

(3) But this totalitarian regime, they thought, would be only a temporary measure, necessitated by the circumstances that existed in the early years of the revolution. Both Marx and Lenin thought this first and lower phase of the Communist revolution would be succeeded by a second and higher phase. This they described as the classless society that would come into existence when the state withered away—dwindled and disappeared.

(4) In their use of the phrase "the withering away of the state," it is difficult to give a precise denotative reference to the word *state*. For Marx, it certainly had to be the bourgeois oligarchies of England and Germany, in which the oppressors were the few capitalists and the oppressed many were the working masses. For Lenin, the reference could also have been the totalitarian state that came into existence with the first stage of the Communist revolution. The totalitarian state in Russia in the third decade of this century resembled the bourgeois oligarchies that Marx had in mind. The class divisions and the class conflicts were the same: between the few who were the oppressors and the many who were the oppressed; the few who used the coercive force of the state to impose their will upon the many.

(5) Both Marx and Lenin disclaim the notion that the withering away of the state substitutes anarchy for a government exercising coercive force. But their disclaimers have almost no foundation in their vision

of the classless society that will come into existence with the withering away of the state. As they conceive the classless society, the state as such will cease to exist; there will be no government that exercises coercive force to impose its will upon those subject to its power. In any tenable view of the meaning of anarchy, that is anarchy. [40]

(6) The espousal of anarchy is one of two basic mistakes in the Marxist-Leninist doctrine concerning the withering away of the state. They commit a second basic error. That is the extreme egalitarianism in which they clothe the classless society that will come into existence when the state has withered away.

Though they both acknowledge the individual inequalities that exist in any human population, inequalities in endowment and in performance, they do not acknowledge that in a classless society, in which all are *haves* and there are no *have-nots,* there will still be a justifiable distinction between those who deserve to *have more* and those who deserve to *have less.* They did not anticipate Khrushchev's amendment of the maxim "from each according to his ability, to each according to his needs," by adding the principle of distributive justice that is expressed in the maxim "to each according to his contribution." [41]

(7) Lenin carefully cautions his readers that he cannot assign a definite time for the transition from the first to the second stage of the revolution—the date when the totalitarian state can be expected to wither away and be replaced by the classless society. His description of that classless society as a society that has no "political state" but in which only administrative functions are performed by the people is contained in the closing paragraphs of Chapter 5 of *The State and Revolution.* I quote them below. Readers should note that by the words "Communist society," Lenin means the classless society that comes into existence when the class-divided state withers away (whether that be the constitutional monarchies governed by a bourgeois oligarchy or the totalitarian state governed by the dictatorship of the proletariat).

> Accounting and control—these are the *chief* things necessary for the organising and correct functioning of the *first phase* of Communist society. *All* citizens are here transformed into hired employees of the state, which is made up of the armed workers. *All* citizens become employees and workers of *one* national state "syndicate." All that is required is that they should work equally, should regularly do their share of work, and should receive equal pay. The accounting and control necessary for this have been *simplified* by capitalism to the utmost, till they have become the extraordinarily simple operations of watching, recording and issuing receipts, within the reach of anybody who can read and write and knows the first four rules of arithmetic. . . .
>
> From the moment when all members of society, or even only the overwhelming majority, have learned how to govern the state *themselves,* have taken this business into their own hands, have "established"

control over the insignificant minority of capitalists, over the gentry with capitalist leanings, and the workers thoroughly demoralised by capitalism—from this moment the need for any government begins to disappear. The more complete the democracy, the nearer the moment when it begins to be unnecessary. The more democratic the "state" consisting of armed workers, which is "no longer a state in the proper sense of the word," the more rapidly does *every* state begin to wither away.

For when *all* have learned to manage, and independently are actually managing by themselves social production, keeping accounts, controlling the idlers, the gentlefolk, the swindlers and similar "guardians of capitalist traditions," then the escape from this national accounting and control will inevitably become so increasingly difficult, such a rare exception, and will probably be accompanied by such swift and severe punishment (for the armed workers are men of practical life, not sentimental intellectuals, and they will scarcely allow any one to trifle with them), that very soon the *necessity* of observing the simple, fundamental rules of every-day social life in common will have become a *habit*.

The door will then be wide open for the transition from the first phase of Communist society to its higher phase, and along with it to the complete withering away of the state. [42]

(8) Lenin did not live to see how the totalitarian state developed under the despotic rule of the Communist party when first Joseph Stalin and then Leonid Brezhnev became its chairman. The pragmatic necessity for the dictatorship of the proletariat, to expropriate the capitalists and to safeguard the Soviet state against the White Armies, had disappeared. Like any other nation, the Soviet Union needed a large military installation for its national security, but that could have been managed without resorting to totalitarianism in the organization of the state or despotism in the operation of its government.

It is reasonable to ask whether Lenin would have regarded the totalitarian state as it developed after his death, together with its despotic control by the Communist party, as a class-divided society that should wither away, to be replaced by the classless society that, for Marx and for him, was an ultimate objective of the Communist revolution.

Would he not have recognized that the bureaucrats of the Communist party had become what the Yugoslav writer Milovan Djilas called "the new class," a class that oppressed the working class, the disfranchised masses, as grievously as the bourgeois capitalists had oppressed the proletariat at an earlier time? If the answer to these questions is affirmative, then we must conclude that Lenin would have called for an end to the prolonged first phase of the Communist revolution.

(9) What should replace the despotic rule of the Communist party? Certainly not a government that eschews the use of coercive force to enforce its laws. Even in a classless society, there will always remain a

criminal element against whom the government must exercise coercive force. The notion that in a classless society the criminal element in the population will disappear is contrary to all recorded facts. In the Western societies that have approached, but not yet fully realized, classlessness, a criminal class still remains.

The notion that when the Communist revolution reaches its second and higher stage a new type of man will emerge, and there will be a whole population without any criminal class, is a utopian fantasy of the most extreme sort.

That being so, whatever society and government emerges in the Soviet Union to replace the totalitarian state and despotic rule by the Communist party, that state and government will have to exercise coercive force against criminals. It can do so without any loss of liberty, the view of Marx and Lenin to the contrary notwithstanding.

(10) The replacement of the totalitarian state by a socialistic democracy that is pluralistic in its economic and political structure depends upon more than the foregoing correction of the errors made by Marx and Lenin in their theory of the first and second phases of the Communist revolution, leading to the ultimate establishment of a classless society. As we agreed earlier, state capitalism must be superseded by privately capitalized socialism; for without privately owned capital, the private associations indispensable for free enterprise, a free market economy, and competing political parties cannot exist or operate.

When I finished this detailed commentary on Lenin's *The State and Revolution,* the fourth session of the seminar concluded with the consideration of an interesting point made by Strachey in his *Challenge of Democracy.* He asked about the role of political parties in a relatively classless society and observed that in the divided societies of the past, opposing parties represented the opposed interests of conflicting classes. The conflicting classes had different political and economic ends in view, and so the opposition of the political parties that represented their interests was about conflicting ends. But in a society without class conflicts, there can be no opposition about ends, but only about the means by which the ends agreed upon by all should be achieved. In Strachey's words, the issues will be over

> . . . such things as these: how much education are our children to
> have, and what is to be its character—predominantly humanistic or
> predominantly scientific, or in practice, of course, what blend of the two?
> Or again: what is to be the attitude of the state to organized religion,
> favorable, hostile, or neutral? Is complete national independence and
> sovereignty to be maintained at all costs or should there be federations
> and mergers with other suitable nation-states? Or finally, how much
> control from a world organization can be accepted? The moment one
> thinks of it, one sees that there will be plenty for rival parties to dispute
> about in classless societies. (*GIT* 1965, pp. 574d–75c.)

## 7. Conclusion: The solution of the problem

Sections 3–6 have not given an exhaustive account of all the turns and twists in the seminar. What has been selected for presentation in this report has been controlled by the central focus of this article: the problem posed by Pfaff with which the article began and which instigated the plan of the seminar in the first place. In my judgment, we have now either reached or closely approximated a solution to that problem.

Before I restate the problem and propose what I think is its solution, I wish to call attention to the essay by Professor O'Toole which was the centerpiece of the fifth session of the seminar. I have already commented on the book by Galbraith and Menshikov that had been assigned for the sixth session. I have given our reasons for maintaining that the future of private-property capitalism in the West and state capitalism in the Soviet Union lies not in their coexistence but in their convergence toward a common set of economic arrangements.

What I now wish to report is the culmination of the discussion in the fifth session of Professor O'Toole's essay, entitled "From Marx to Madison: Socialism's Cultural Contradictions." [43] That is best summarized in the following closing paragraphs of Professor O'Toole's essay.

> ... Pluralism thus becomes the only effective mechanism for reconciling the adversarial issues found in a modern society—conflicts between those who seek greater political and market freedom and those who seek equality and economic security, between those who want greater industrial efficiency and economic growth and those who desire a higher quality of life.
>
> All the great domestic political and economic issues facing any advanced nation—including the Soviet Union—can be mapped as conflicts between groups with these different values and goals. The genius of Western democracies is that they have arrived at ways of getting as much of all of these values as possible. A pluralistic society attempts to satisfy *all* competing interests. Because no system is perfect, all the various constituents in a democratic society will never be fully satisfied. Yet, because the system treats the values of all the constituents as legitimate, democracy is the only condition that modern men and women accept as just. . . .
>
> ... But the only way to find the centre is through the turbulent, conflict-ridden pluralistic process. The citizens of Western nations have learned to pay the price of political turbulence, flux, and tumult in order to achieve the continual economic renewal, social justice, and institutional legitimacy that emerge from Madison's miraculous process. Now the question is whether the entrenched leaders of the Marxist states will accept the unpredictability and uncontrollability of democracy in order to overcome the technological stasis, social injustices, and institutional illegitimacy of their societies. They will not *want* to do so—

that is certain—but, ultimately, they may be *forced* to accept democracy
as the international cultural revolution creates irresistible pressures
for change. [44]

To proceed now with the solution of the problem that initiated the
seminar, let me paraphrase the summary statement of it given in Section
1: "In what limited respect should the [Communist] party be retained
and continue to function in the Soviet Union; and what principles or
propositions in Marxist-Leninist doctrine should be retained while others should be rejected?"

The answer to the first interrogative clause is immediate and obvious. If political pluralism is to be achieved as the needed replacement
for monolithic totalitarianism, the Communist party, if it remains at
all, must become merely one of several competing and opposing factions in the political arena. This has now been decreed, and seems
likely to happen.

The second interrogative clause also has a quick answer, one that
was also implied in Section 1: "The solution of the problem cannot be
found in terms of All or None, but rather in terms of partial retention
and partial rejection. The Marxist-Leninist doctrine is not wholly true
and sound, but neither is it wholly false and unsound."

That quick answer now needs to be spelled out in some detail. What
are the correct and sound elements in the Marxist-Leninist doctrine
that Gorbachev should retain and to which he should appeal in his
effort to persuade the people of the Soviet Union to adopt the policies
of *perestroika?* What is fallacious and unsound in the Marxist-Leninist
doctrine that Gorbachev should unhesitatingly reject and be able to
give clear reasons for rejecting?

The preceding sessions of the seminar succeeded, I think, in putting
a finger on the points that have to be rejected by Gorbachev if he is
to succeed in raising the standard of living of the great mass of the
Soviet people by filling the marketplace with a more plentiful supply of
consumer goods; and also if he is to succeed in giving the Soviet people
the political liberty that is in increasing demand throughout the world
and has already produced radical changes in Hungary, Poland, East
Germany, Romania, and Czechoslovakia. Gorbachev's success in these
efforts still leaves him with a problem that may cause his downfall—the
problem of the growing ethnic nationalism and demands for independence in the Baltic provinces, in the Ukraine, Georgia, Armenia, and so
on. But the remarkable succession of events that occurred with startling
rapidity in the summer of 1989 plainly show that when the power of the
Communist party is drastically reduced or completely overthrown, as it
was in these four satellites of the Soviet Union, socialist democracies
tend to emerge in place of totalitarian despotism.

In all but the recent decade of the last seventy years, the world has seen, in the Soviet Union and in the United States, a dogmatic, quasi-religious devotion to doctrinal extremism. The extreme right wing of the Communist party in the Soviet Union, the faithful zealots of the party line, swear their allegiance to a literal interpretation of the words of Marx and Lenin as if they spoke the truth in every respect. The zealots treat the writings of Marx and Lenin, all composed before the advent of the Russian Revolution, as if they were sacred scripture, in the same way that fundamentalist Christians quote the Bible. There is the unvarnished literal truth, infallible, incorrigible, and final.

The extreme right wing of the large conservative faction in the United States, the fanatical anti-Communists of the McCarthy era and ever since, reject Marx and Lenin as wholly wrong, mistaken in every respect. There is no truth at all to be found in their writings. The fact that they have not read the basic Marxist and Leninist documents, the fact that the constituents of this faction could not give anything like an accurate account of their content, does not deter them from rejecting the caricature of what communism stands for, which they suppose these documents to contain. They simply do not know what motivated Marx and Engels to propose revolutionary measures in the first place, nor do they recognize that we in the United States have adopted many of these measures in making the economic improvements that have occurred in this country.

In between these two extremes is a middle ground to be occupied by those, in the United States and in the Soviet Union, who are or can be persuaded that political and economic problems are never likely to be solved by proposals that are either wholly true or wholly false.

In my long experience of conducting Aspen seminars, in which the *Communist Manifesto* is read and discussed, I have always begun by saying that Marx is more right than wrong, but that his correctable errors are of the first importance in our effort to get at the truth. I have had no difficulty in persuading the participants to read and discuss the *Manifesto* with that in mind.

From the evidence of what has happened in Hungary, in Poland, in East Germany, in Romania, and in Czechoslovakia, it can be fairly assumed that a large portion of the people of the Soviet Union are similarly persuadable. The unpersuadable zealots in the Communist party, who adhere to the party line with religious fervor, are likely to remain a problem that Gorbachev must deal with. He must choose between scuttling them or being himself scuttled by a popular uprising against them.

What is the retainable validity in the Marxist-Leninist doctrine, its unrejectable insights and proposals?

The first things to be mentioned are the two prime motivations of the revolutionary proposals by Marx and Lenin. Can anyone deny truth in the insight that the misery of the working class in the nineteenth

century and the mistreatment of proletariat labor by the bourgeois capitalists of that era and in the first decades of this century was a problem
that justice required mankind to solve? Can anyone deny truth in the
insight that class divisions, class conflicts and warfare, which have been
going on in civilized societies from their beginning, are a social evil
that prudence required mankind to remedy? Must not everyone who
answers these questions affirmatively also acknowledge their indebtedness to Marx and Lenin for devoting all their efforts to putting these
matters at the top of mankind's agenda, as well as indebtedness to them
for whatever is sound in their proposals for dealing with them?

That Marx was right in predicting the self-destruction of bourgeois
capitalism by its adherence to the iron law of wages is a matter of
historical record.

That he was also right in his proposals of two measures for the
alleviation of the misery of the working class (by inroads on or the
erosion of the unregulated rights of the private owners of capital and
by the widest possible diffusion of the private ownership of capital) is
also attested by the successful adoption of these two measures in the
economic reforms which have occurred in this century in the United
States, in the United Kingdom, and in Sweden.

These reforms have not yet gone far enough to create the economic
equality that is the goal of socialism, a society in which all are economic
*haves* and there are no economic *have-nots*. They have been accomplished in different ways and in different degrees in all the democratic
societies in which all (with justifiable exceptions) are political *haves* and
there are no political *have-nots*. But in these societies, the apparent
motion is toward the realization of the Marxist-Leninist ideal of a
classless society.

These are the points that Gorbachev can certainly stress in claiming
that *perestroika* is faithful to the teachings of Marx and Lenin. They
are also the points with respect to which he should be able to win the
support of the Western societies that have reformed private-property
capitalism and have established welfare states.

What, then, in Marxist-Leninist doctrine must be rejected as mistakes
to be corrected if *perestroika* is to serve the ends Gorbachev has in mind
for it? We have discovered all of them in the course of the preceding
sessions of the seminar. Let me list them in the order in which we
discovered them.

(1) Marx's labor theory of value, the theory that labor, living labor
or the labor congealed in machinery, produces all the wealth a society
consumes and uses; and that the private owners of capital who derive
income without working for it are totally unproductive.

(2) Marx's assertion that capital instruments cannot rightfully be
owned and operated by private individuals or corporations and, therefore, that capital must be owned and operated by the state.

(3) As an inexorable consequence of the state capitalism that Marx advocated, the establishment of a totalitarian state, in which all political and economic power is concentrated in the central government, called by Marx "the dictatorship of the proletariat," as carried on by the despotic regime of the Communist party.

(4) The Leninist doctrine of the withering away of the state (either the bourgeois oligarchy in the West or the dictatorship of the proletariat in the Soviet Union) on the march to the establishment of a classless society. This has not yet occurred in Russia and is not likely to occur there or elsewhere except by steps in the direction of political and economic justice that eliminate political subjugation and economic deprivation and that institute pluralistic societies that are both democratic and socialistic.

(5) The utopian fantasy of a society existing without any government at all, one that exercises coercive force to maintain peace and harmony and to prevent and punish criminal conduct; in short, the espousal of philosophical anarchy implicit in Lenin's doctrine of the withering away of the state.

(6) Finally, the Marxist-Leninist misunderstanding of what justice requires with regard to equality and inequality, political and economic. Not only does it require that all should be *haves,* but it also requires that some should deservedly *have more* and some *have less.*

When the six mistakes in Marxist-Leninist doctrine are corrected, what is the positive picture that emerges?

The verdict of history, looking back at the rise and fall of communism in the twentieth century, will be that communism chose the wrong means to establish socialism as a desirable goal. This will be seen as the reason for its miserable failure and its total rejection.

When a relatively classless society and a nonegalitarian socialism has come into existence, both East and West, it will not be thought that communism projected a wrong goal for the social revolution it initiated—socialism conceived as a society in which the right to a decent livelihood is secured for all and all economic *have-nots* have been eliminated. It will be recognized that socialism as a desirable end could not be achieved by communist means—the abolition of the private ownership of capital, replaced by the totalitarianism of state capital.

The positive side of the picture can be further stated as follows. Human beings have natural needs that should be fulfilled; and they have innocuous wants that also deserve fulfillment. A society that aims at nonegalitarian socialism serves basic human needs by securing the right to a decent livelihood for all. Private-property capitalism, not state capitalism, is the effective means for producing enough consumable wealth and providing a decent standard of living to satisfy all the reasonable wants of its members.

In conclusion, one question that may arise in the minds of readers deserves an answer. If it is true that the recorded history of civilizations is a history of class conflicts and class warfare, is not the forthcoming desirable establishment of classless societies the end of history? [45]

To answer that question, let us assume that all the present threats to the viability of this planet are removed by drastic measures for protecting the environment from irreversible lethal changes. Let us assume that mankind has centuries of time ahead for the continuance of life on earth.

On that assumption, here is the answer. With the establishment of classless societies the first great epoch in human history will come to an end—the epoch that began with the rise of cities and the emergence of civilized life, enduring from 6,000 years ago to the present. The second great epoch of civilized life on earth will then begin when the first classless societies are established in the next century or two.

## Appendix: The Reading List

### Session I
### Labor and Capital as Forces in Production

**John Locke:** *Second Treatise Concerning Civil Government*
*Preamble of the Mechanics' Union of Trade Associations*
**Alexander Hamilton:** *Report on Manufactures*
**William Graham Sumner:** *The Challenge of Facts*
**Mortimer J. Adler:** *A Vision of the Future*

### Session II
### The Self-Destruction of Bourgeois Capitalism and Its Socialization

**Karl Marx &**
  **Friedrich Engels:** *Manifesto of the Communist Party*
**John A. Ryan:** *A Living Wage*
**Theodore Roosevelt:** *The New Nationalism;*
  *The Progressive Party Platform of 1912*

**Alexis de Tocqueville:** *Democracy in America*
**Charles H. Vail:** *The Socialist Movement*
**Franklin D. Roosevelt:** *The Commonwealth Club Address*
**Henry A. Wallace:** *An Economic Bill of Rights*
**Gus Tyler:** *On the Economic Divide*
**John Strachey:** *The Challenge of Democracy*

### Session III
### The Self-Destruction of Communist Socialism and Its Capitalization

**Joseph A. Schumpeter:** *Capitalism, Socialism and Democracy*

Karl Marx &
  Friedrich Engels:    *Manifesto of the Communist Party*
John Strachey:    *The Challenge of Democracy*

### Session IV
## The Ideal of the Classless Society: Political and Economic Equality

Horace Mann:    *The Importance of Universal,*
              *Free, Public Education*
John Strachey:    *The Challenge of Democracy*
Mortimer J. Adler:    *A Vision of the Future*
              *Six Great Ideas*
V. I. Lenin:    *The State and Revolution*
Louis O. Kelso &
  Patricia Hetter Kelso:    *Open Letter to Mikhail Gorbachev*

### Session V
## The Emergence of a Homogeneous World Economy

James O'Toole:    *From Marx to Madison:*
              *Socialism's Cultural Contradictions*
Gus Tyler:    *The Rise and Fall of the Great Powers*

### Session VI
## Conclusion: Coexistence or Union?

John Kenneth Galbraith
  & Stanislav Menshikov:    *Capitalism, Communism and Coexistence*

---

1. *The New Yorker*, Aug. 1, 1988, pp. 60–62.

2. Ibid., p. 63.

3. Ibid., p. 65.

4. *The Annals of America* (Chicago: Encyclopædia Britannica, 1968), Vol. 3, p. 465.

5. Ibid.

6. The equivalent of the addition of machinery to an increase of hands has another profound significance. When I asked the participants whether the addition of power-driven machinery to the productive forces at work resulted in (a) making the economy more productive, or (b) making the laborers that worked with the machinery more productive, or (c) both in differing degrees, they argued for some time about these three alternatives. I then pointed out that if an addition of machinery was equivalent to an increase of hands, then the correct answer must be (a), not (b) or (c), because one laborer's productiveness added to the productiveness of another laborer does not result in the latter's becoming more productive.

7. *Annals*, Vol. 5, pp. 227–28.

8. Ibid., p. 228.

9. Ibid.

10. Ibid.

11. Ibid., p. 229.

12. *Annals*, Vol. 10, p. 537.

13. Ibid., pp. 544, 546.

14. Ibid., p. 540.

15. Ibid., pp. 542, 543.

16. *The People Shall Judge* (Chicago: The University of Chicago Press, 1949), Vol. I, pp. 548, 549.

17. "The Importance of Universal, Free, Public Education," *The People Shall Judge,* ibid., pp. 591–92.

18. *Annals,* Vol. 13, pp. 348–49.

19. Ibid., pp. 252–53.

20. Ibid., p. 253.

21. *Annals,* Vol. 15, pp. 158–66.

22. *Annals,* Vol. 16, pp. 211–14.

23. *Annals,* Vol. 13, pp. 76–84.

24. Here are the economic components of a decent livelihood, obtained by a living wage together with other sources of income, including welfare benefits: ". . . a decent supply of the means of subsistence; living and working conditions conducive to health; medical care; opportunities for access to the pleasures of sense, the pleasures of play, and aesthetic pleasures; opportunities for access to the goods of the mind through educational facilities in youth and adult life; and enough free time from subsistence-work, both in youth and in adult life, to take full advantage of these opportunities." Adler, *The Common Sense of Politics* (New York: Holt, Rinehart and Winston, 1971), p. 25.

25. From *The New Leader,* July 11, 1988, p. 12.

26. Ibid., p. 13.

27. Strachey makes the following comparison of the condition of workers in Western democracies and of workers in the Soviet Union:

> Compare the position of a wage earner in a factory which is owned by a Western-type, private, profit-making, joint-stock company, but who possesses full democratic voting and trade-union rights, with the position of a wage earner in a Communist-type state-owned factory, without the right to choose either the kind of government which he prefers or to organize a political party of his choice, or to form his own trade union, or to strike for better pay if he thinks he can get it. Which of the two men has the better chance of getting for his own consumption a high proportion of the values which he produces? I have no doubt that experience has now shown that the wage earner with democratic rights, even if he works in a privately owned factory operated for profit, has the better chance. (*GIT* 1965, p. 573a.)

Readers should be informed that Strachey was at one time the leader of the Communist party in Great Britain. *The Challenge of Democracy* is, in a sense, a retraction of Strachey's pro-communist *apologia* in an earlier book, *The Coming Struggle for Power* (1932), in which he predicted the triumph of Soviet communism throughout the world.

28. *The People Shall Judge,* Vol. 2, p. 121.

29. *The People Shall Judge,* Vol. 1, p. 560.

30. At the beginning of Section 5, we asked what is meant by a phrase implied in the title of the third seminar: "the capitalization of communist socialism." We now have the answer. The capitalization of socialism results by replacing state capitalism with private-property capitalism. The socialization of private-property capitalism and the private-property capitalization of socialism are two faces of the same movement toward an economy that is both just and expedient, i.e., effective in the production of a decent standard of living for all.

31. New York: Harper & Row, Publishers/Torchbooks, 1975.

32. The two basic mistakes are: the labor theory of value and the notion that modern industrial capital cannot rightfully be a private possession.

33. Boston: Houghton Mifflin Company.

34. Even as we talked, Hungary and Poland were moving in that direction during the summer of 1989; and now, as I write these words in the autumn of 1989, the mass protests in East Germany, and the mass exodus to the West, betoken the same direction of change there.

35. *Annals,* Vol. 6, pp. 534–43.

36. At this point, I digressed to report Nikita Khrushchev's amendment of the Marxist slogan "From each according to his ability, and from each according to his needs." That the common needs of each should be served is certainly a principle of justice, for natural

rights have their basis in inherent natural human needs. But Khrushchev went a step further. He added a second principle of justice: "To each according to his contribution." Applying this principle would obviously create a class distinction between the *have-mores* and the *have-lesses*.

37. I should record here, but cannot report in detail, a fairly extended discussion of the ways in which class conflicts arising from this one remaining class distinction might be ameliorated; as, for example, by reducing the gap or chasm that exists between those who have more and those who have less, especially in the economic dimension. This holds true for the Soviet Union as well as for the United States.

38. *The People Shall Judge,* Vol. 1, p. 592.

39. New York: International Publishers, 1932.

40. In *The Common Sense of Politics,* Chapter 8 deals with "the anti-political philosophers," in whose number are Marx and Lenin as well as such self-confessed anarchists as Peter Kropotkin and Mikhail Bakunin. One section of that chapter argues, successfully I think, against the utopian fantasy that a peaceful and harmonious society can exist without government, one which, if it is constitutional government, must exercise, in the words of the great German jurist Hans Kelsen, a monopoly of authorized force.

41. This error of extreme egalitarianism is the fatal flaw in the doctrine that Chairman Mao thought was based on the teaching of Marx and Lenin. It was what led to the cultural revolution that China, after ten years of unspeakable horrors and disasters, finally abandoned.

42. New York: International Publishers, 1932, pp. 83, 84–85.

43. The essay was published as a feature piece in Encyclopædia Britannica's *Book of the Year* 1989 (pp. 5–14). I disagree with Professor O'Toole on only one point. I think that Tocqueville is a much better, more penetrating exponent of democratic pluralism than James Madison. As any reader of Federalist No. 10 can find out for himself, Madison, like many others of the Founding Fathers, was no democrat. They were proponents of liberty, *not* equality. (On this point *see* Part 4 of my commentary on the Constitution, *We Hold These Truths* [New York: Macmillan Publishing Company, 1988], which is entitled "The Emergent Ideal of Democracy.")

Madison regarded the plurality of factions in society as the cause of many mischiefs, but as long as liberty is preserved, factions cannot be eliminated. However, their effects can be controlled. In Federalist No. 10 Madison argues for those measures in the Constitution that he thinks will serve to control the worse effects of factions. They are the constitutional provisions which place dominant political power in the hands of the landowners and manufacturers. These provisions made our eighteenth-century constitution antidemocratic; they have since been amended as, in the course of time, our constitution gradually became democratic. In my judgment, Professor O'Toole's essay would be more accurate by dropping Madison out of the picture, even at the expense of abandoning its catchy alliterative title.

44. *BBOY* 1989, p. 14.

45. The phrase "the end of history" is the phrase used by Francis Fukuyama (the deputy director of the policy planning staff of the U.S. State Department) as a title for a mistitled, misguided article that was published in *The National Interest* (Summer 1989) and excerpted in the *New York Times* (Aug. 27, 1989, IV, p. 5). It caused a flurry of discussion that it did not deserve, discussion that was as misguided as the article itself.

# Determinism and Reality

## Stanley L. Jaki

Stanley L. Jaki is a physicist as well as a Catholic priest of the Benedictine order. Born and raised in Hungary, he did his graduate work at Rome in theology. In the early 1950s he came to the United States and taught systematic theology while taking his bachelor of science degree. He received his doctorate in physics from Fordham University and has been on the faculty of Seton Hall University, where he is now a distinguished university professor, since 1965.

Professor Jaki is the author of numerous books on the history and philosophy of science and on theology, as well as translations of works by Giordano Bruno and Immanuel Kant. Among the works he has published is *The Road of Science and the Ways to God* (1978), based on his Gifford Lectures at the University of Edinburgh in 1974–76. More recent titles are *God and the Cosmologists* (1989), *Miracles and Physics* (1989), and *The Only Chaos and Other Essays* (1990).

## The old determinism

In its broadest sense *determinism* means that not only purely physical events but conscious human choices, too, are the inevitable consequences of their antecedent conditions. In modern times, champions of this universal determinism banked heavily on mechanistic or Newtonian physics. Its spectacular successes were taken for a proof that mental and volitional acts follow one another in the same ironclad sequence which, according to that physics, regulates the material world.

Those who endowed mechanistic causation with this kind of universal validity did not engage in an enterprise free of perplexities. Doubts that were bravely suppressed by Hobbes, Spinoza, and the eighteenth-century French philosophers Pierre Bayle, Julien de La Mettrie (*GIT* 1982, pp. 380–411), Claude-Adrien Helvétius, and Paul-Henri d'Holbach surfaced now and then in the writings of Voltaire and Denis Diderot. Subtly worrisome was Voltaire's witticism as he wondered why puny man should have a quality—freedom—which huge celestial bodies did not possess. Diderot felt tormented by the possibility that his love for Mme de Maux might be as blind as a comet's submission to the law of gravitation: "It makes me wild," he wrote to her, "to be entangled in a devil of philosophy that my mind cannot deny and my heart gives the lie to." [1]

No such perplexities are noticeable in the celebrated testimonial to universal determinism which Laplace offered in 1814 in his *Philosophical Essay on Probabilities*. Not for a moment did it dawn on Laplace that the *Essay* lacked that elementary philosophical ingredient which is attention to the inexorable force whereby logic takes its due. The force in question finds the smallest loopholes in reasoning and works on it like water does on a ship that springs a leak, big or small.

Laplace's reasoning could hardly appear watertight to anyone attentive to his ambiguous and inconsistent use of words. He failed to make it clear whether all truths rested on probability considerations or whether what he called "eternal truths" formed an exception. He leaned toward granting universal validity to mechanistic causation, which he seemed to equate with sufficient reason. As he turned free acts into the effects of one's motivations he did not care to consider whether he had written his book freely, in spite of his obviously strong motivations for writing it.

277

The phrase that in the crucial second chapter of the book could appear least objectionable to a contemporary reader is related to chance. By endorsing the notion of chance as "merely the expression of ignorance of true causes," Laplace was forced to say that

> Given for one instant an intelligence which could comprehend all the forces by which nature is animated and the respective situation of the beings who compose it—an intelligence sufficiently vast to submit these data to analysis—it would embrace in the same formula the movements of the greatest bodies of the universe and those of the lightest atom; for it, nothing would be uncertain and the future, as the past, would be present to its eyes. [2]

To this Laplace added that for all its advances in the sciences, actual and future, the human mind would forever remain "infinitely removed" from that superior intelligence. This, however, was not to be taken for a concession that shortcomings in man's scientific knowledge could ever weaken strict determinism in the physical world: "The curve described by a simple molecule of air or vapor is regulated in a manner just as certain as the planetary orbits; the only difference between them is that which comes from our ignorance."

Laplace's reference to the trajectory of vapor molecules reappeared in the reminiscences which Thomas H. Huxley wrote in 1885, at the request of Francis Darwin (Charles Darwin's son), about the first reactions to *The Origin of Species* (*GBWW*, Vol. 49, pp. 1–252). Among them was a response to the charge that Darwin attributed evolution to chance, which implied the absence of causes. To dispose of this "misinterpretation" of Darwin's thinking Huxley resorted to the tactic that attack was the best defense. He asked Darwin's critics what they meant by chance, as if they and not Darwin had set such great store by it. "Do they believe that anything in this universe happens without reason or without a cause?" To that rhetorical question Huxley was ready with an answer full of rhetoric: "If they do, it is they who are the inheritors of antique superstitions and ignorance." And if they were to convert to science, they would have first to subscribe to the creed of science with only one article of faith in it, namely, "the absolute validity in all times and under all circumstances of the law of causation." [3]

Laplace's reference to the trajectory of vapor molecules may have directly inspired Huxley's further elaboration of the topic. He invited Darwin's critics for a stroll along the seaside. There they were to be coaxed into taking the view that the apparently irregular splashing of the waves against the rocks, the play of colors on the myriads of bubbles, and "the roar and scream of the shingle as it is cast up and torn down the beach" were so many chance events. Then Huxley would let Darwin's critics perceive some deity in the gaps of causality where chance is supposed to operate without doing anything. Such perception,

Huxley warned, radically differed from the perspective of the "man of science" who

> knows that here, as everywhere, perfect order is manifested; that there is not a curve of the waves, not a note in the howling chorus, not a rainbow-glint on a bubble, which is other than a necessary consequence of the ascertained laws of nature; and that with a sufficient knowledge of the conditions, competent physico-mathematical skill could account for, and indeed predict, every one of these "chance" events.

Although he spoke of purely physical entities and events as subject to strict causation, Laplace did not wish to make exceptions to acts of free will. Whatever philosophical loopholes he wanted to secure by coining the word *agnosticism,* he certainly did not want to weaken thereby faith in universal determinism. When presented, on the occasion of the death of his seven-year-old son, with the prospect of the soul's immortality, he referred to the inverse-square law of gravitation as the only reliable truth to have faith in.

Such a faith is insensitive to its blindness. Led by that faith, Huxley did not see that if universal determinism were true, scientific faith had to be blindly predetermined. It remains impervious to arguments, however concise, such as the one formulated by Poincaré, certainly a "man of science." Poincaré's phrase, "c'est librement qu'on est déterministe" ["it is freely that one is a determinist"], [4] dating from 1902, shows how easy it is to turn the tables on a universal determinist, provided he has some respect for logic.

## The new indeterminism

At that time such a determinist would not have as much as suspected that science might soon deprive him even of ordinary objects, such as tables. Determinists could still be confident that no objections would come from science, even to strict determinism in the interaction of material objects. Yet the eventual acceptance of those objections gave credence in the long run to a radically new form of indeterminism. In the latter, the ultimate bone of contention is neither the status of free will nor the precision of material interactions. What is truly at issue touches on that fundamental or ontological aspect of determinism whereby a thing is unequivocally distinct from mere nothing. In that new indeterminism, not only tables may lose their reality; the same fate is in store for that supreme totality of objects which is the universe.

Around 1900 or so, few physicists took seriously the claims of Poincaré and Ernst Mach about scientific laws as purely conceptual tools to facilitate the economy of thought. Their claims followed, of course, from their rejection of ontology, i.e., any theory as to the reality of being, which meant a rejection of mechanistic causation as well. Most physicists would have agreed with Marie-Alfred Cornu, of physical optics fame, who declared at the 1900 meeting of the International Congress of Physics in Paris: "The more we penetrate into the knowledge of natural phenomena, the more developed and precise is the audacious Cartesian conception of the mechanism of the universe." [5]

Cornu's words did not seem to take into account that statistical theories as applied to physical problems, molecular gas theory in particular, began to be taken for a proof of indeterminism. In 1905 the Irish physicist Joseph Larmor had those theories in mind as he warned "mental philosophers" (speculative philosophers, as distinct from natural philosophers or physicists) that determinism "is not a conception universally entertained in physical science." [6] Philosophers, bent not so much on speculations as on facts and logic, could have easily replied that the statistical gas theory was indeterminist only in appearance. It started with the assumption that molecules were strictly defined entities with exact physical properties, and so were their individual interactions.

It was a signal failure in elementary logic to forget that starting point and take average values of probabilities for an absence of strict precision in individual interactions. Even more illogical was to present highly improbable events as being acausal. Yet it was in this vein that the nineteenth-century Scottish physicist William Rankine spoke of the chance reconcentration of light into massive stars as a means for the universe to reconstitute itself. The same is true of Ludwig Boltzmann's suggestion that a table might suddenly rise from the floor whenever all atoms in it happened to move in the same upward direction.

Once given room, however narrow, disregard for logic could but claim ever more spacious accommodations. No major physicist protested when in the late 1920s Arthur Eddington claimed that the table in front of him was more real as a bundle of wave functions than as an object of plain sensory perception (*GIT* 1990, pp. 307–310). Two generations later, no prominent protest was heard when Professor Alan H. Guth of MIT claimed that he could create universes literally out of nothing, a claim that made the headlines in the *New York Times* (April 14, 1987).

It made no headlines that soon physicists were busy turning those "universes" into a single, well-determined universe. Their reawakening to the fact that only such a universe gives meaning to science illustrates an elementary lesson. A restitution is in order not only when bank robberies come to light but also when "scientific" sleights of hand obviously get out of hand.

Compared with a sleight of hand that pretends to have the very universe for its object, the great train robbery of the 1960s should appear a puny matter. Since only the latter touched on a well-determined reality, the sum of five million pounds sterling, the gist of the comparison relates not to the object but to the skill underlying the two actions. Those who performed that robbery had to precondition themselves through petty thefts and minor robberies over a few years, at least. It took the relentless immersion of two generations of physicists in the Copenhagen philosophy of quantum mechanics to let the claim be hatched that physicists can conveniently rob the "nothing" and literally create thereby a universe. Were that claim justified, it would make senseless any talk about determinism, and certainly about its deepest, ontological kind.

## Physical theory as mental conditioning

The seeds of that claim have blossomed so as to appear the purest and best science. At least, it would indeed be difficult to think of a context more purely scientific than the pages of the *Zeitschrift für Physik,* which carried in its issue of April 1927 a paper by Werner Heisenberg, "On the visualizable content of quantum-mechanical kinetics and mechanism." The cunningly philosophical title of the paper should have served warning to its physicist readers that physics was not its real subject. The very end of the paper made this all too clear. There, in a stylistically overloaded sentence, Heisenberg drove home what in his eyes was the all-important point, a point essentially philosophical. The definitive truth of the point rested, according to him, with the uncertainty relation he had just derived and referred to as equation (1):

> One can characterize the [paper's] real content [*wahren Sachverhalt*] [as follows]: Because all experiments are subject to quantum mechanics and therefore to equation (1), the invalidity of the law of causality will thereby definitively be established by quantum mechanics.

A little-noted though most revealing part of this declaration was Heisenberg's reference to the *definitive* disproof of causality by quantum mechanics. He may have thought that he had said enough about what had preceded that definitive proof by referring to the bearing of statistical theories on the status of causality. They, he noted, bore only on a weak form of causality, namely, that "from exact data only statistical conclusions can be inferred." What he called the "strong formulation of causality" had a distinctly Laplacian touch to it: "If we know exactly the present, we can predict the future." It is this kind of causality that was definitively disproved by quantum mechanics, or rather by the uncertainty principle, because "we *cannot* know, as a matter of principle, the present in all its details."

The uncertainty principle proved, in Heisenberg's words, "the imprecision of all perception," and therefore it was futile to look for a "hidden 'real' world ruled by causality." What later became known as "hidden variable theories" formed the target of Heisenberg's next declaration: "Such speculations seem to us—and this we stress with emphasis—useless and meaningless." There followed a phrase, laden with philosophy, but not for Heisenberg, who noted in a matter-of-fact way that "physics has to confine itself to the formal description among perceptions." Perhaps Heisenberg felt that he had gone deeply enough into the philosophy of perception when he stated: "All true perception is a choice out of a wealth of possibilities and a limitation of the possible future [perception]." [7]

The philosophical instructiveness of these phrases, replete with non sequiturs, cannot be emphasized enough. They contain much more than a blunt declaration as to a new indeterminism, one far more treacherous than that implied in the accidental swerving of atoms postulated by Epicurus. They also vitiate the enterprise of the quantum physicist. First, if physics is but a formal or quantitative description of relations among perceptions, it justifies no statement about causality and not even a statement about the objective real world. The physicist who subscribes to Heisenberg's definition of the aim and method of physical theory cannot consistently communicate his own construction of it to other physicists, if these are but mere bundles of his own perceptions. Similarly inconsistent should appear the same physicist's reliance on laboratory instruments which would not cost hundreds of millions of dollars of taxpayers' money if they *were* but *his* perceptions.

## The Copenhagen philosophy and its roots

This formalistic and self-defeating view of physical theory is a mainstay of the Copenhagen interpretation of quantum mechanics as worked out by Niels Bohr. It entails a denial of causality regardless of quantum mechanics. Three years before Heisenberg formulated the uncertainty principle, Bohr implicitly denied causality by postulating a wide departure from the principle of the conservation of energy in the interaction of X rays with atoms. His theory, proposed together with Hendrik Kramers and J. C. Slater, quickly turned out to clash with observational results.

There is much more to the Copenhagen philosophy of quantum mechanics than its customary image. The latter is similar to a naive account of an iceberg as its visible part or peak. The culminating or widely perceived point of Bohr's interpretation consists in the assertion that causality operates only partially on the atomic level and that atoms have complementary aspects (waves and particles).

The second part of this claim may, when compared with the first, seem a very innocent affair, but not when taken in its full philosophical consequences. In working with atoms, the physicist registers sensory evidence, some of which is best interpreted as the result of actions by waves, some as the action of corpuscles. Patterns of X-ray diffraction are illustrations of the former case, while the latter is indicated by sparks produced by alpha rays on a scintillation screen. If these two forms had ever been observed simultaneously, there would be some justification for the inference that one and the same material entity has mutually irreducible characteristics.

Irreducibilities are never to the liking of physicists, whose immediate aim is to turn their sensory findings into quantitative data transformable into one another. Notes of despondency are struck when such a transformation appears to be impossible. No physicist in modern times has, of course, imitated the Pythagorean of old who threw himself into the sea on encountering an irreducibility in the relation of the hypotenuse of a right-angled triangle to its unit sides. Later, the fact that one cannot reduce by geometric means the area of a circle to that of a square became a source of despondency to many. The frustratingly unsuccessful attempts to quantize Einstein's gravitational equations are a recent phase in that story of which, in this century, the mutual irreducibility of waves and particles represents a major chapter.

The measure of a physicist's insensitivity or hostility to philosophical questions about the real as such is his unwillingness to blame the limitations or shortcomings of the physics at his disposal when he encounters this or that kind of irreducibility. He is likely to blame reality itself for being more subtle than are his conceptual and experimental tools. He then may try to take revenge on reality by sublimating it into high-sounding words and, in fact, may try to abolish it altogether by not talking about it. He will then present his discourse about the irreducible aspects of reality as the last word in philosophy and science.

The philosophical heritage on which Bohr grew up (and of which more shortly) certainly predisposed him to such a revengeful posture vis-à-vis reality. It revealed itself in his systematic avoidance of ontological questions, as noted in a major analysis of his thought. [8] He seemed to be unconcerned about the fact that his theory of complementarity was as severed from reality as are two cheeks that can have no claim to a head. Such is the gist of the horns of complementarity on which he had impaled himself. [9] The complementarity of Bohr is a doctrine of indeterminism in that deepest sense in which the real itself loses a determinate meaning because it ceases to be the ground and supportive ontological matrix for what are mere aspects of reality.

The threat to reality should appear more immediate in connection with the denial of strict causality on the atomic level. About that threat, which is essentially philosophical, the first thing to realize is that it has no scientific merit, whatever its alleged connection with Heisenberg's uncertainty principle. The reason for this is that there can be no scientific method of measuring, either on the atomic or on the ordinary level, the process known as causality. The latter is a philosophical and, indeed, a thoroughly metaphysical inference, however spontaneous. Its validity rests on one's view of external reality.

Here the options are essentially two. One can take external reality as the very factor that activates, in the first place, man's ability to know, which is more than a matter of sensory impressions. This view, which is the classical realist position in epistemology (as distinct from mere empiricism), is recommended for various reasons. One is that it corresponds to common or good sense, a commodity not at all coterminous with commonly held opinions. Another is that it finds support in the best modern studies of early intellectual development in children. Still another is that, by holding to that view, one is spared the inconveniences of the other option. Among these is the dreadful necessity of turning external reality into a function of one's thought.

This necessity became evident in the development of philosophy from Kant through Fichte and Schelling to Hegel. While the Hegelian Left tried to rescue real matter from evanescing into mere ideas, it rescued only the mechanistic properties of matter. Throughout its checkered history, Marxist philosophy remained stuck with mechanistic causality in its effort to become genuinely realist. The Hegelian Right tried to thrive in the rarefied atmosphere of disembodied ideas, from which others hoped to escape by calling for a return to Kant. They merely endorsed as remedy a virus that had already infected epistemology.

In the closing decades of the nineteenth century, despair about man's ability to account intellectually for the real as such prompted the rise of philosophies such as Mach's sensationism, Poincaré's commodism, the pragmatism of William James and Harald Höffding, Nietzsche's apotheosis of the will, and the intellectually even less respectable Lebensphilosophies. Early in his university studies Heisenberg felt torn as to whether to specialize in Lebensphilosophie or in physics. [10] Part of the Lebensphilosophie he so enthusiastically subscribed to consisted of denouncing mechanistic causality as a threat to human initiatives and creativity. Sometime before he had written his historic paper, Heisenberg explicitly denied causality and knew that not a few prominent German physicists were doing the same. [11] There is much more than meets the eye in his claim that his uncertainty relation has *definitively* proved the invalidity of causality. As so often before and after him, a grave philosophical error took on the glamour of indisputable verity once it was tied to good physics.

As one who was unable to see that mechanism offered merely a surface view of causality, Heisenberg could hardly suspect that once ontology was disregarded, a road opened up with solipsism as its logical dead end. This possible outcome was protested by Bohr, certainly. While rejecting ontology, he also claimed that complementarity was the only realist philosophy! Recognition of the connection between complementarity (that is, the knowledge of things through their correspondence) and solipsism is still widely resisted by the champions of the Copenhagen interpretation of quantum mechanics, although solipsism comes into view when the ultimate implications of that interpretation are faced. A telling illustration of this is the multi-world theory, developed in the early 1970s, according to which there are as many universes as there are observers. One wonders how the universe could be turned any more effectively into an undetermined and undeterminable entity.

## Ineffective criticisms

That the Copenhagen philosophy of quantum mechanics logically leads to solipsism has been repeatedly noted. The ineffectiveness of its leading critics derives from the fact that, with respect to Heisenberg's claim that it is useless to speculate about a hidden real world ruled by causality, they endorse an elementary equivocation. What they look for in theories of hidden variables is a causality which they can turn into a function of exact measurability. This is precisely the idea which Heisenberg in his historic paper called "the strong formulation of the causal law," although it should appear such only to one weak in a respect for ontology and logic. No wonder he dismissed that apparently strong but in fact very weak form of causality on the basis of the fallacious inference: since we cannot know (that is, measure, a purely operational procedure) the present exactly, we cannot predict the future as it takes place exactly (an ontological process, independent of the question of measurement).

This was not only bad logic but also defective thinking about physical theory. Being essentially nondefinitive and revisable, physical theory cannot justify definitive conclusions even within its own realm, let alone within other realms such as philosophy. Among leading proponents of quantum theory there has not been, for over half a century now, a single one who realized the bearing on it of Kurt Gödel's incompleteness theorem first proposed in 1930.* This is especially startling in the case of John von Neumann, who for many years was a colleague of Gödel at the Institute for Advanced Study in Princeton. In spite of that, von Neumann did not develop second thoughts on the "definitive" truth of quantum theory he proposed in 1932, and on the basis of which he celebrated the final overthrow of causality. [12]

But there is no evidence either that Gödel's theorem prompted Paul Dirac when, at the Einstein-centenary conference at Jerusalem in 1979, he predicted a new form of quantum mechanics which "will have de-

---

*Often called "Gödel's Proof," this theorem states that a nontrivial set of arithmetical propositions cannot have its proof of consistency within itself. Therefore, unless a firm starting point is accepted in reasoning, such as that these are arithmetical propositions, Gödel's proof cannot be proven and much less can it be communicated as being valid.

terminism in the way that Einstein wanted." In doing so, Dirac did not refrain from chastising the mental inertia prevailing among quantum physicists. Determinism, he said, will be introduced in quantum mechanics "only at the expense of abandoning some of the preconceptions which physicists now hold, and which it is not possible to try to get at now; . . . for the time being physicists have to accept Bohr's probability interpretation—especially if they have examinations in front of them." [13]

Although the context of these remarks of Dirac, and their biting tone, should have guaranteed them wide publicity, they produced hardly a ripple. At any rate, most prominent physicist-critics of the Copenhagen philosophy remained caught in the misleading tracks which Max Planck had charted in his defense of causality and determinism. [14] Einstein merely followed Planck in propagating the fallacy that only the possibility of perfectly accurate measurement and prediction can give solid basis to determinism and realism, in that order. As will be seen shortly, Einstein failed to see that realism came first, with determinism only a distant second step, insofar as it could be useful for the physicist at all.

Failure to see this sequence meant a shift on the part of the physicist from the ground of very good physics, whatever its essentially revisable character, to the ground of plain non sequiturs. A road was thereby opened to the land of pseudo-metaphysics, where irresponsible games could be played with the real. The farce on philosophy amounted to leaving the ledgers of physics unbalanced. For the uncertainty principle, when taken for incomplete causality in the interaction between two atoms, implied an ontological imbalance, or more bluntly, a plain "cheating" with real matter.

## Cheating with real matter

This point should have been surmised by Heisenberg in 1927, as nothing is more natural than to think about the interaction of two subatomic particles (say, an electron and a photon) in connection with the form of the uncertainty principle. As given by him, this is expressed as $\Delta x \cdot \Delta mv \geqq \hbar$, where $\Delta x$ is the uncertainty (margin of error) in measuring the position $x$ of the electron and $\Delta mv$ is the uncertainty (margin of error) in measuring the momentum $mv$, which is a product of mass $m$ and velocity $v$. By itself the formula states no more than that the product of those uncertainties, as measured by the physicist, cannot be smaller than $\hbar$ (Dirac's $\hbar$, which equals Planck's constant divided by $2\pi$). By taking that very small operational inexactitude for an inexactitude in causality, Heisenberg implied an inexactitude on the ontological level, namely, a defect $\Delta$ touching not only on $v$ but also on $m$. This consequence, which curiously he overlooked, was equally overlooked by countless others after him.

The reason may lie in the perception, derived from relativity theory, that the reality of velocity is a mere relation. Thus, in considering the defect when measuring the momentum $\Delta mv$, the physicist could be tempted to tack it onto $v$ instead of onto $m$. There is no such easy escape from real matter and therefore from ontology should the physicist consider an alternate form of the uncertainty principle, $\Delta E \cdot \Delta t \geqq h$, a form postdating Heisenberg's historic paper. Like the form given by Heisenberg, this form involves two *conjugate* variables, energy $E$ and time $t$. Just like position $x$ and momentum $mv$, these two parameters are also conjugate variables, because one cannot be measured without influencing the other. Theirs is the physically most inseparable "conjugal" connection.

In order to bring out the ontological relevance of this second form of the uncertainty principle, it should be rewritten, with the help of the famous Einsteinian formula $E = mc^2$, as $\Delta mc^2 \cdot \Delta t \geqq h$. If further rewritten as $\Delta mc^2 \geqq h/\Delta t$, the inequality shows that, if the time of the action is measured with perfect accuracy, that is, if $\Delta t = 0$, then the uncertainty of measuring the energy becomes $\Delta mc^2 \geqq h/0$ or $\infty$. This uncertainty can, however, affect only the mass $m$, because $c$ (the speed of light) is an invariable constant.

The presence of an infinity sign in an equation which relates to an actual physical situation makes it meaningless for the physicist. He reaches a dead end whenever his equations conjure up what is usually called the infinity catastrophe. This should make plain the irrelevance of references, first made by Heisenberg himself and then greatly emphasized more recently by Karl Popper, that the uncertainty principle leaves intact the possibility of measuring with perfect accuracy one of the conjugate parameters. [15] Both have overlooked the fact that any perfectly exact evaluation of only one of two conjugate variables is based on data that are themselves the result of an actual measurement. Such a measurement always involves an interaction between photons and the object, be it the marking on any ruler or scale, or the position of spectral lines, and therefore *is* subject to the uncertainty relation. Moreover, the evaluation, however exact, of one of two conjugate parameters can have no bearing on causality. Causality is not a mere position in place, nor is it an action that takes place outside space or time, or with no energy transfer involved. Causality is a *real* action in the broadest and deepest sense of that word.

No less real is that constant of physics, usually called Planck's constant, but appropriately called by Planck himself the quantum of action. Of course, this quantum of action, the minimum of uncertainty involved in actual measurements, is so small a quantity that a physicist might be tempted to write it off. The temptation may not seem to matter if he

287

thinks of the ontologically real as something "determined" insofar as he can measure it with complete precision. But for one respectful of the real in the sense of simply being, the incredibly small quantity of Planck's quantum of action stands, if taken as a minimum of inexactitude, for the infinite distance that separates being from nonbeing. It is the distance between being and not being, a distance significant to Hamlet, though ignored by most prominent physicists of our times.

An ontologically sensitive thinker, physicist or not, must take reality for something really real, and not for a mere construct of his intellect. Such a reality cannot have for its contours a grayish margin of transition between being and nonbeing. To assume the existence of a margin would land one in the most pathetic part of Alice's wonderland, where the queen claims for herself the right to graft any meaning she wants on any word. But even that gruesome lady stops short of engaging in what has become a favorite game where thinking is governed by the Copenhagen philosophy. There the word *nothing* may denote some real thing, and some real thing may be taken for nothing, whenever this dubious transaction can be used as a mental barbiturate for desensitizing one to basic philosophical questions.

## From petty thefts to cosmic robbery

When Heisenberg in 1927 proposed the uncertainty principle, positivist physicists could no longer slight atoms as pure fictions of mind. Then the problem for physicists related to various operations of atoms, such as their radioactive emission. Most extensively investigated among such emission was the alpha radiation, or the escape of helium nuclei (two protons and two neutrons) from the nuclei of radium atoms. Quantum mechanics came to the rescue in George Gamow's famous theory of alpha tunneling. It was meant to resolve the question of how alpha particles, whose average energy as measured in cloud chambers fell far short of the height of the energy barrier posed by the force keeping the nucleus together, nevertheless manage to cope with that barrier.

In Gamow's theory the alpha particles "tunneled" through the potential barrier, though at a price. During the time they were in that tunnel (a wholly fictitious entity), they too were fictitious, that is, unobservable. The time corresponded to $\Delta t$ as set by the uncertainty principle. Gamow and countless others, who had by then been conditioned by relativity theory to take time for a purely mathematical relation, could be forgiven for enjoying their triumph which, being statistical in character, had only fictitious ties with physical reality.

Their attitude would seem cavalier with respect to a problem that represented the other side of the coin, namely, the mass defect $\Delta m$ corresponding to the uncertainty in time $\Delta t$. For if the uncertainty principle meant a defect in ontological causality, the mass defect $\Delta m$ stood for something physically real and wholly unaccounted for by physics. Gamow could easily have estimated the average amount of that unaccounted mass, or $\Delta m$, by taking the average amount of energy of alpha particles. The amount would have been of the order of the millionth of the mass of an alpha particle, in itself an exceedingly small bit of matter, though very real matter. Neither Gamow nor his many colleagues, who hailed his explanation, cared to calculate the missing amount in order to set the balance straight. They may have realized that in doing so they would have revealed the involvement of the Copenhagen interpreters of quantum mechanics in systematic petty thefts of real matter.

They looked the other way, and in doing so they fostered a mental attitude that was soon to turn into a climate of thought. Already in 1931, some cosmologists talked about the emergence of matter out of nothing and met with no rebuke on the part of fellow physicists. The latter suddenly became oblivious to the enormous and indispensable service which the principle of the conservation of matter and energy had given them for three hundred years or so. This could only embolden the steady state theorists when in 1947 they claimed that, without a Creator, hydrogen atoms were popping up at a steady rate out of nothing everywhere in cosmic spaces. Had they summed up the total mass coming in this way into existence every second, the result would have shown a new matter equivalent to the mass of several stars. Such was the apparently insensible, but actually massive "mechanism" whereby they tried to dispose of the temporality of the universe, so strongly evoked by its expansion.

None of the steady state theorists thought it necessary to justify their claim that such an emergence was within the ken of reason in general and of science in particular. Nor did their scientific critics call attention to the fact that such a "mechanism" struck at the very root of determinism, insofar as there is a difference between something and nothing. Rather, scientific criticism centered on the detection of an extra amount of radiation at 21-centimeter wavelength, natural to free hydrogen. No physicist dared to suggest that such an observation could not conceivably prove that atoms had just emerged out of nothing. Such an emergence, a philosophical inference, is infinitely beyond the competence of physics, which by definition can deal only with things already existing.

Lack of philosophical sensitivity encouraged further furtive actions with reality, that is, with real matter. The claim that our universe might just as well have been "created" out of nothing from a basement laboratory in another universe [16] is but the latest phase in a most dubious and extremely dangerous intellectual process. Although it parades in the garb of the finest science, that is, quantum mechanics, it is really cavorting in philosophical fallacies. The danger of the process will be apparent only to those aware of an invariable connection: Presentations of moral principles as mere transient patterns of thought have always sought support in ontological indeterminism, which means that nothing is really real.

## Some moral perspectives

A recent case of this connection is Popper's advocacy of an "open society" ruled by what he called "Democritean ethics." [17] He also argues at length the merits of an "open universe" as the supreme embodiment of indeterminism. [18] Where Popper is most inconsistent is in his determination to appear as a realist philosopher. He has resolutely opposed the Copenhagen interpretation of quantum mechanics. What he fails to see, or perhaps wants not to see, is that the basic issue with that interpretation is a question of ontology, and not whether exact measurements of physical interactions are feasible or not on the basis of the latest in physics. His aversion to ontology [19] indeed may have led him into the erroneous claim that it is possible to measure one conjugate variable independently of the other.

The realism of a philosopher who champions a universe as the supreme entity in which everything can happen and will ultimately happen should seem highly suspect. Popper based his idea of an ever novel universe on probability reasonings which offer a purely pragmatic or practical way around the actually and individually real existent. He seems anxious to keep out of sight that ground of all existence whose best philosophical name was given as HE WHO IS. This ground alone guarantees the truth of realism which G. K. Chesterton put in an inimitably short but grave phrase, "There *is* an Is." [20] Compared with such an elemental dictum, all philosophical discourse pales into relative insignificance.

Only within such realism can both freedom and complete ontological determinism be upheld with consistency, because both will be seen as creation by the One who, alone in his ontological infinity, can call forth ontologically finite entities into existence. Such a call is an act of creating something out of nothing. Further, because the most determinate difference is between something and nothing, any material reality must have strictly determined quantitative contours insofar as quantity denotes something real. Whether with the actual tools, conceptual and experimental, of physics a completely precise measurement of those contours is possible or not is a secondary or operational question. At any rate, the realism set forth in this paragraph certainly implies that such a measurement may intrinsically be possible.

Within that realism, biblical in its deepest roots, there follows naturally the truth of the biblical phrase that "God arranged everything according to measure, number, and weight" (New American Bible, Wisdom 11:20). Within that realism, so intent on the ontologically first step, there is no temptation to start an intellectual argument with the second or third steps. Within that realism there is no occasion to explain such firsts as reality, intellect, and freedom of the will in terms of secondary and derivative notions, such as quantities, seductively easy and sweeping as their handling may appear. Within that realism, and in it alone, it is possible to uphold the vision of a superior intelligence to which all past, present, and future are fully known. It may be doubted that in speaking of such an intellect Laplace had not subconsciously given a feeble deistic twist to an ontologically vibrant biblical passage about determinism that leaves intact human freedom and responsibility:

> The works of God are all of them good . . .
> He has to command and his will is done;
> nothing can limit his achievement.
> The works of all mankind are present to him;
> not a thing escapes his eye.
> His gaze spans all the ages;
> to him there is nothing unexpected (Sirach 39:16–20)

It would be tempting to go on quoting. The next phrase, "No cause then to say: What is the purpose of this?" offers the very commodity, existential confidence with a firm sense of purpose, of which our boasted scientific culture stands in far greater need than of science, enormous as may be its scientific needs. Physicists and philosophers of science will take the realism set forth in these last two paragraphs for a brazen intrusion of religion, or at least of a philosophy which Étienne Gilson aptly called "methodical realism." [21] Had they pondered its merits, they might have spared themselves being entangled in the most notorious paradox of the last half century.

## A misplaced paradox

The paradox saw formulation in a paper which Einstein published in 1935, with Boris Podolsky and Nathan Rosen in *Physical Review,* under the title, "Can quantum-mechanical description of reality be considered complete?" [22] Here too, as in the case of Heisenberg's paper, one is faced with an essay having a markedly philosophical title in a leading journal of physics. Here too a philosophical question was discussed as if it could be decided by the methods of physics. Indeed, the question touched on that chief task of philosophy, which is to determine reality, or rather to take reality as being determined in the radical sense of differing from nonreality. For such is the ultimate target of what later became known as the Einstein-Podolsky-Rosen (EPR) paradox. Today it is considered experimentally resolved against its original proponents in particular and philosophical realism in general.

The physics in the EPR paper is a thought-experiment in which the simultaneous measurement of position $P$ and momentum $Q$ in one system affects the same measurement in another system not in physical connection with the former. The upshot was that if one denied "that two or more physical quantities can be regarded as simultaneous elements of reality *only when they can be simultaneously measured or predicted*" one would arrive at a conclusion which "no reasonable definition of reality could be expected to permit." The conclusion stated nothing less than that the Copenhagen interpretation of quantum mechanics "makes the reality of $P$ and $Q$ depend upon the process of measurement carried out on the first system, which does not disturb the second system in any way."

The philosophy evident in this argument about physical reality and the method of physics was vintage Einstein. The very first sentence of the paper emphasized the distinction between "the objective reality which is independent of any theory and the physical concepts with which it operates." This could but remind the readers of the EPR paper of Einstein's ringing declaration, made four years earlier, that "belief in an external world independent of the perceiving subject is the basis of all natural science." [23] One wonders how many of them recalled Einstein's halfhearted acknowledgment, made in his Herbert Spencer memorial lecture in 1933, that the physicist should "leave all questions of the structure of theoretical science to the epistemologist." [24] In his defense Einstein could, of course, have pointed out that epistemologists notoriously disagreed with one another on almost every point, not least points of fundamental importance. This, however, did not dispose of the philosophical nature of an epistemological question. Much less did it dispose of the logic whereby one's starting point in defining reality would unfold its consequences in a remorseless way.

Indeed, Einstein (and his colleagues) made it rather easy for any moderately careful reader of their essay to spot the point from which logic would start exacting its due. Such a reader could, by giving the benefit of doubt, assign an unobjectionable sense to Einstein's opening distinction between a "comprehensive definition of reality" and a definition sufficient for physics, namely, that "every element of physical reality must have a counterpart in the physical theory." The same reader could assume that Einstein reserved for physics only the right to deal with the quantitative aspects of reality when he declared that human experience, "which alone enables us to make inferences about reality, in *physics* takes the form of experiment and *measurement*." (Italics added.)

If such was the case, the physicist could declare, as Einstein did, that a "comprehensive definition of reality" was not "necessary" for his purposes. But Einstein's very next phrase was too sweepingly clear to allow a benevolent interpretation: "We shall be satisfied with the following criterion, which we regard as reasonable. *If, without in any way disturbing a system, we can predict with certainty (i. e. with probability equal to unity) the value of a physical quantity, then there exists an element of physical reality corresponding to this physical quantity.*" To prevent any misunderstanding, Einstein and his colleagues let the passage appear in italics.

The criterion offered by them about reality was most unreasonable, and certainly contradicted Einstein's ringing endorsement of an objective physical reality existing independently of the perceiving subject, whether he had measuring instruments in his hands or not. For the criterion meant that unless a physical quantity was measured with a probability equal to unity, that is, with complete quantitative exactness, that physical quantity could not be considered to exist unambiguously. In other words, Einstein, without being aware of it, espoused the very basis of Heisenberg's denial of causality, or the fallacious inference that an interaction that cannot be measured exactly, cannot take place exactly. Worse, Einstein went much farther than did Heisenberg, who stopped short with a denial of causality. By proposing the foregoing criterion, Einstein made the existence of all physical reality dependent on whether the physicist can measure it exactly or not.

That this is the point where Einstein gave away the game of realism is yet to be perceived by interpreters of the EPR paradox, although their number is legion. The point was not, of course, taken up by Bohr, the first to respond to the EPR paper. Bohr was careful not to be dragged into questions of ontology. He merely insisted that a complete theory had to do but with the aspects of reality and never with reality as such. In defense of this contention he rehashed his ideas on complementarity as a "new feature of natural philosophy" and its ultimate scientific support, Heisenberg's uncertainty principle. Bohr was far from ready to unfold in full the consequences of that new feature. Nor did he seem to be aware of all the dire consequences when he stated that this new feature "means a radical revision of our attitude as regards physical reality, which may be paralleled with the fundamental modification of all ideas regarding the absolute character of physical phenomena, brought about by the general theory of relativity." [25] Once more, the word *radical* failed to evoke its true etymological trust, which is to touch on the root of a question or thing, with the distinct possibility of uprooting it completely.

## A passionate universe

If Bohr was right, the only absolute truth that remained was that everything was relative, even reality itself, and in a subjectivist sense which was more sinister than Bohr might have suspected. It took twelve years for Einstein to voice, in a letter of 1947 to Max Born, his forebodings that "spooky actions at a distance" were to invade physics once Bohr's ideas about complete physical theory had been taken for the last word on the subject. Even when that letter was published, in 1971, [26] Einstein's conjuring up of such spooky actions could appear but a morbid concern about the abstract consequences of a purely theoretical matter. Physicists were still to devise experiments that tested the EPR paradox, as further elaborated by David Bohm in 1951 and given a very specific form by John S. Bell in 1964. It was only after Alain Aspect and his co-workers in 1981 successfully tested the quantitative prediction specified by Bell that physicists began to face up to its deepest challenge. Even then, they failed to realize that the challenge was posed by their own thinking about some facts of physics rather than by physical facts themselves.

Aspect's famous experiment consists in a count of photons (emitted from a common source in two opposite directions and screened through identical polarizers) whenever they simultaneously hit their corresponding targets. These are photosensitive detectors that can be rotated at different angles. The number of coincidences is not the same when predicted respectively on the basis of quantum theory and of a theory that, in principle, allows exact measurements of individual atomic interactions. The number registered is in clear support of the quantum theoretical prediction.

Such are the bare facts. Beyond that, every step becomes more and more theory-laden and revisable in proportion. As to the experimental apparatus, the observations of its operation, regardless of its sensitivity and precision, remain subject to the uncertainty principle. In other words, no measurement of coincidences, however accurate, can be fully exact. The physicist who subscribes to the Copenhagen fallacy that a physical interaction he cannot measure exactly cannot take place exactly is forced to deny that plain matter can be the carrier of those coincidences. Since as a physicist he cannot live without a universe which is coherent, he will have to look for its cause in a nonphysical factor.

Most likely he will take the view that it is neither reasonable nor fashionable to rehash the occasionalism of old. As worked out independently and at very different times by al-Ashari, William of Ockham, and Nicolas Malebranche, occasionalism leaves to God the task of making every moment and event coherent. Since the Copenhagen philosophy does not permit the physicist to credit matter with coherence, he will have no choice but to fall back on some kind of "soul." For this is what the physicist does when he credits the coherence of those photons to some "passion" operating in them, whereby they can communicate with one another at any distance. [27] But then why not attribute a "soul" to all matter, nay to the universe itself? After all, it is now becoming fashionable to look at the earth as some semiconscious "Gaia."

This is not to suggest that physicists, who seem to attribute such passion to photons, speak of the soul of the universe. Nor do they list the three main objects of metaphysics—the universe, the soul, God—while, having no use for God, and having bartered away the objective material universe, they attribute some passion, if not "soul," to things to make them coherent. In their customary philosophical amateurism they grope their way among the only possible choices, being aware more or less of the restrictions imposed on them by the Copenhagen philosophy and the fashions of the day. That is, if they bother to grope at all. Of course, most physicists just do their good quantum mechanics and ignore philosophy, including its Copenhagen version.

Physicists who care for the Copenhagen philosophy to the point of conjuring up passions at a distance would do well to take stock of their procedure's immediate and remote antecedents. The remote kind relates to the most monumental stillbirth which science suffered in the great ancient cultures, in classical Greece of all places. [28] There the attribution, within the Socratic tradition, of a striving to all bodies nipped in the bud any promising move toward an anticipation of Newton's first law, or the law of rectilinear inertial motion. As to the immediate antecedents, a quick look at them may illustrate the point that a diffuse climate of thought must for some time be on hand before its raw nature can suddenly reveal itself. Passions at a distance, that for a physicist should seem far more disreputable than actions at a distance, relate to the realm of will, a realm far removed from and potentially most hostile to the subject matter of physics. Yet, no sooner had the uncertainty principle crowned the young edifice of quantum mechanics than "will" and "psyche" were invoked as factors of coherence in physical interactions.

The scene that first witnessed this act was the famed Solvay Conference on physics held in Brussels in late 1927 with Heisenberg and Dirac as its youngest participants. Dirac was still to make his famous postulation of the existence of antimatter and publish his classic axiomatization of quantum mechanics. In retrospect he would seem to have displayed penetrating insight when, at that conference, he challenged Heisenberg to account for the coherence of ionization tracks produced by alpha particles in cloud chambers. The distinguished participants of the conference must have taken for a joke Dirac's remark that, in view of the inability of quantum mechanics to account for that coherence, the individual droplets of condensation somehow know how to cohere into a single track and wish to do so. [29] The joke was an ominous straw in the wind.

A few years later, in 1930, George P. Thomson, a future Nobel laureate, published a smallish book, *The Atom*, which in thirty years went through six editions and saw wide circulation as a title in the Home University Library series. There Thomson spoke of the electron's wave

function, whose intensity at a particular point is a measure of the probability of the electron's being there, and added: "This introduction of
probability as a factor in the expression of a fundamental law is very
characteristic of the recent trend of physics, which is moving away from
the rigid determinism of the older materialism into something vaguely
approaching a conception of free will." [30]

Such was the loose talk about free will on the part of a prominent
cultivator of the most exact form of empirical investigations, physics. It
should have been the target of immediate and unsparing criticism on
the part of physicists. Instead, far from seeing anything wrong in it,
they for the most part quickly followed suit, with Einstein being here
too a most noteworthy exception. [31] Philosophers were almost as
guilty of connivance, if not by action at least by omission. This was true
even of John E. Turner, a philosopher at the University of Liverpool,
who quickly and unanswerably made short shrift of Thomson's assertion of indeterminism. Although Turner's concise remarks appeared in
*Nature,* its physicist readers worldwide failed to take notice. They went
on celebrating "indeterminism" in spite of the logical fallacy which he
put tersely, though not in a language easily recognizable by physicists:
"Every argument that, since some change cannot be 'determined' in the
sense of 'ascertained,' it is therefore not 'determined' in the absolutely
different sense of 'caused,' is a fallacy of equivocation." [32]

Turner, who should have used the word *measured* instead of *ascertained,* made his real omission by failing to excoriate Thomson's injec-
tion into physics "of something vaguely approaching the conception of
free will." He might in fact have felt some sympathy with Thomson on
that score. Will, in the form of *nisus,* was the driving force of nature
in Samuel Alexander's philosophy, to which Turner wanted to give a
more realistic character. Turner, who even hoped to cast into a realist
frame the idealism of the British philosopher John McTaggart, was not
enough of a realist to see that the real problem with the "new" physics
touched on that deepest layer of realism which is ontology. No wonder
that he confused realism with mechanistic causation, which he tried, in
a different context, to defend with an eye on sufficient reason. [33]

Before long the effort to save free will on the basis of quantum
mechanics had formed the ground on which prominent physicists could
assure laymen about their deliverance from the shackles of determinism. A series of lectures given in 1934 by Arthur H. Compton, who
with C. T. R. Wilson had received the Nobel Prize in physics in 1927,
is worth recalling for two reasons. As the Terry Lectures given at Yale,
they received wide publicity, and they also contained a classic case of a
great mistake made by a great physicist in philosophical reasoning. The
error consisted in Compton's asserting and abandoning in the same
breath the only possible defense of free will. He did so in his reference
to the determinism of classical or Newtonian physics:

. . . It seems unfortunate that some modern philosopher has not forcibly called attention to the fact that one's ability to move his hand at will is much more directly and certainly known than are even the well-tested laws of Newton, and that if these laws deny one's ability to move his hand at will the preferable conclusion is that Newton's laws require modification. Yet I suppose such an argument would have been scorned by the physicist, who has found it necessary to show in his own way the inadequacy of Newton's laws. [34]

Compton's first remark was genuine gold, and he immediately bartered it away for a piece of fool's gold. There has not been and never shall be a better and more inescapable proof of free will than one's immediate experience of it, which is applicable even to the determinist's arguing against it. The physicist therefore traps himself in a vicious circle when he tries to prove "in his own way," that is, in terms of his physics, the "inadequacy of Newton's laws." By that "inadequacy" Compton could, in that context, mean only the irrelevance of those laws to the question of free will versus determinism.

Compton immediately forgot about that irrelevance in turning the discussion, a page or two later, to Heisenberg's uncertainty principle. Less than twenty years afterward, no less a physicist than Henry Margenau disapproved of the orgy of endless references to "violation of causal reasoning" on the basis of quantum mechanics. [35] Yet Margenau contributed to the further flourishing of that intellectual orgy when years later he claimed that the physicist's *psi* (Margenau had in mind Erwin Schrödinger's wave function), "has a certain abstractness and vagueness of interpretation in common with the parapsychologist's *psi*." [36]

Less shocking, though intellectually just as treacherous, was Heisenberg's mature interpretation of quantum mechanics. In the 1950s he saw in its probabilistic character something akin to the tendency of the Aristotelian potency toward its fulfillment in act. [37] By then Bohr had devised his own coat of arms with the yin-yang as its chief feature. Self-confessed amateurs clearly felt they had obtained the highest license for casting modern physics into the categories of Tao philosophy and the steps of dancing Wu Li masters. The climate was ripe for the introduction of passions at a distance into physics to save the coherence and unity of the physical universe, a coherence lost on the basis of an elementary fallacy in reasoning.

## The logic of demoralization

The potentially most destructive aspect of that climate can be best seen in a remark of Wolfgang Pauli, who received the Nobel Prize in physics in 1945 for his formulation of the exclusion principle. When two years earlier Max Born wrote to him about his repeated failures over many years to convert Einstein to the Copenhagen interpretation, Pauli, in his reply, put his finger at the heart of the matter and ridiculed it at the same time. He did so by specifying the crux of the difference between Born and Einstein not as something relating to physics but to philosophy. Einstein's concern for reality belonged, Pauli wrote, with the medievals' preoccupation over the number of angels that could be put on a pinhead. [38]

Such a slighting of concern for reality, over which no revulsion is felt among physicists, bespeaks a thick climate of thought in which one cannot see beyond one's very nose. Pauli failed to note that those who cared about angels did not despair of the reality of pinheads even if they could not measure exactly their dimensions. More important, they did not turn into those eggheads who cherish doubts about their own heads as reliable instruments of knowing a reality that exists independently of their thinking it.

Nor did Pauli see something crucial to his own predicament. Although victimized by a totalitarian regime that swore by the will of the race, Pauli did not seem to look deep into the roots of that will. He might have found enlightenment in a survey which Heinrich Heine published in 1837 on the history of religion and philosophy in Germany. Heine asked the French to keep their arms while watching German Idealism produce, by its own logic, Kantians "with sword and axe" who "would mercilessly rummage around in the soil of our European culture in order to eradicate the last roots of the past," a Christian past to be sure. Heine, in fact, foresaw that in the process the Cross, "this last restraining talisman," would be broken to pieces. [39] That Cross was and still is the best reminder of reality in more than one sense of the term.

It may seem unjust to use Heine's dire prophecy as a warning about long-term consequences of the prevailing interpretations of experimental verifications of Bell's theorem. Unfortunately, these verifications are taken for conclusive proof that everything in the world is enveloped in "mysteries," or at least in passions that always border on the mysterious. Yet, those "mysteries" are but the by-products of a fallacy in logic that supports the entire edifice of the Copenhagen interpretation of quantum mechanics. One is faced here with a form of mystery-mongering all the more dangerous because it parades in the paraphernalia of a truly marvelous science. As such it contributes to the ultimate demoralization, which is what we have when we condone irrationality, conceptual and behavioral.

That counsels of "irrationality" readily seek their justification in the uncertainty principle could be seen in a *New York Times* editorial, toward the end of 1989, when Samuel Beckett's death was still fresh in memory and his chief disciples were widely commemorated. One of them, the Czech playwright Vaclav Havel, gained further fame by becoming the interim president of Czechoslovakia. His unforeseeable rise to political prominence was taken in that editorial as an illustration of the lesson contained in Beckett's *Waiting for Godot* in which Godot never knows what he waits for: "The uncertainty principle in physics found its counterpart in his [Beckett's] plays and novels, allegories in randomness . . . "Godot" seems a surer guide to an unknowable world than all the effusions of the experts." [40]

Political experts have proved wrong more than once. The wrong done by them, or by anyone else, will, however, grow exponentially if "allegories in randomness" are to be taken for guides in real life. There, time and again, one must act now and with a clear goal in mind, because the next moment may be too late to achieve any goal. Such was the argument which a president of the United States used twenty-five years ago before a distinguished gathering of academics in defense of some agonizing decisions he had to make. He, of course, wished that his had been the luxury available for academics, who can indefinitely go on considering two sides of a coin without ever using it. In the real world, he warned, a coin must be used before it loses its value.

Within the Copenhagen view, two sides of a coin do exist, but not the coin itself; and similarly with other things. This essay is in a sense a survey of the genesis of that very arbitrary view of reality, indicating as well the long-range demoralization to which it has led. No sympathy has been offered for that view and no apologies either for rejecting it without reservation. No more is asked from an unsympathetic reader than to stop and ponder, however briefly, the consequences of a fatal first step in reasoning, infinitesimal as it may appear from the scientific or quantitative viewpoint. An error which is infinitesimal in science can become infinite in logic, though in a different sense, of course.

If the same reader wonders whether so many brilliant physicists could be so wrong in so elementary a matter of logic, he should recall the conclusion of a once famous article on the ether. It was contributed by no less a physicist than Maxwell, around 1873, to the famed 9th edition of the *Encyclopædia Britannica*. "There can be no doubt," Maxwell declared, "that the interplanetary and interstellar spaces are not empty, but are occupied by a material substance or body, which is certainly the largest, and probably the most uniform body of which we have any knowledge." [41] He merely voiced the unanimous conviction of the body of physicists.

Within a generation or so, physicists began to be tight-lipped about the ether and soon afterward celebrated its final demise. In doing so they grew doubtful of the reasoning—if there is undulation, there ought to be something that undulates, an inference which was the sole support of their former belief in the existence of the ether. Yet that support, however shaky, should seem rationality incarnate when compared with the fallacy of saying that an interaction which cannot be measured exactly cannot take place exactly.

This fallacy forms the stage on which not a few prominent physicists have now for over two generations been turning their noble art into a glamorous farce. They claim that their physics can perform fantastic feats, both conceptual and factual. According to them, the quantum mechanical vacuum is *almost* nothing, as if such a nothing would make any sense. They are busy indoctrinating their students into believing that the nothing is also something. They conjure up universes out of nothing like so many rabbits from under a hat. To keep fundamental particles coherent, they prescribe passions at a distance as glue. They hold high randomness as the fundamental feature of reality, without giving a truly random or chaotic definition of it. In the name of indeterminacy, they ask the layman to take the wonderful science of physics for a mere game, provided it has its rules, always to be determined by them alone.

They speak of quantum mechanical models of consciousness as if the very gist of consciousness, the sense of *now*, could be caught in the net of physics, even quantum mechanics. They pretend to know and not to know at the same time as to what they really know, as if this were a sign of profundity. They claim that their mere thinking about "state-functions" makes these "collapse" into tangible reality, as if that were not a collapse of one's stance vis-à-vis reality. They assert ownership over all reality and in return they offer a fallacy that leaves nothing determined. The bargain they drive should seem infinitely more disreputable than the one in which an entire orchard must be bartered away for a single apple. To crown the comedy, they remain firmly determined to treat their lay listeners with condescending glee, leaving them on a road that leads from mere bewilderment to total demoralization. If one is not to be swept off one's feet by the "liberating" tidal wave of the new indeterminism, one must, in addition to having a clear head, be determined, in a genuinely moral sense, to keep one's feet firmly planted in good old reality.

---

1. Arthur M. Wilson, *Diderot* (New York: Oxford University Press, 1972), p. 577.

2. For this and the subsequent quotations from Laplace, *see* his *A Philosophical Essay on Probabilities*, trans. Frederick W. Truscott and Frederick L. Emory (New York: Dover, 1951), pp. 4, 6.

3. For this and the next quotation, *see* Francis Darwin, *The Life and Letters of Charles Darwin* (New York: Basic Books, 1959), pp. 553–54.

4. Poincaré, "Sur la valeur objective des theories physiques," *Revue de métaphysique et de morale* 10 (1902), p. 288.

5. *Travaux du Congrès International de Physique 1900*, ed. C. E. Guillame and Lucien Poincaré, Vol. 4 (Paris: Gauthier-Villars, 1901), p. 7.

6. Larmor did so in his introduction to Poincaré's *Science and Hypothesis* (London: The Walter Scott Publishing Co., 1905), p. xiv.

7. Heisenberg, "Über den anschaulichen Inhalt der quantentheoretischen Kinematik und Mechanik," *Zeitschrift für Physik* 43 (1927), p. 197 (my own translation).

8. C. A. Hooker, "The Nature of Quantum Mechanical Reality: Einstein versus Bohr," in Robert G. Colodny, ed., *Paradigms and Paradoxes: The Philosophical Challenge of the Quantum Domain* (Pittsburgh: University of Pittsburgh Press, 1972), p. 208.

9. A theme further developed in chap. 13, "The Horns of Complementarity," in my Gifford Lectures, *The Road of Science and the Ways to God* (Chicago: University of Chicago Press, 1978).

10. Heisenberg, *Physics and Beyond: Encounters and Conversations,* trans. Arnold J. Pomerans (New York: Harper and Row, 1971), p. 27. More and important light is shed on this point by Paul Forman, "Weimar Culture, Causality and Quantum Theory 1918–1927," in *Historical Studies in Physical Science* 3 (1971), pp. 105–6.

11. Ibid., pp. 80–87.

12. von Neumann, *Mathematical Foundations of Quantum Mechanics,* trans. Robert T. Breyer (Princeton, N.J.: Princeton University Press, 1955), p. 327.

13. Reported by Robert Resnick, "Misconceptions about Einstein: His Work and His Views," *Journal of Chemical Education* 52 (1980), p. 860.

14. For a detailed discussion, *see* my essay, "The Impasse of Planck's Epistemology" (1985); reprinted in my *The Absolute beneath the Relative and Other Essays* (Lanham, Md.: The University Press of America, 1988), pp. 18–42.

15. Popper, *Quantum Theory and the Schism in Physics* (London: Unwin Hyman, 1982), pp. 54–60. As to the hope that physicists might be more tuned to ontological causality if "exact" measurements of conjugate variables (let alone of just one in a pair of them) were to be proven possible, it is difficult to reconcile with the chronic dislike or miscomprehension of ontology evident, now for almost a century, in their dicta on the subject.

16. *See* Malcolm W. Browne, "Physicist Aims to Create a Universe, Literally," *New York Times,* April 14, 1987, pp. C1, 4.

17. Popper, *The Open Society and Its Enemies* (Princeton, N.J.: Princeton University Press, 1950), pp. 222 and 641. Revealingly, Popper connects that ethics with the one proposed by Epicurus!

18. Popper, *The Open Universe: An Argument for Indeterminism* (Totowa, N.J.: Rowman and Littlefield, 1982), p. 130.

19. Ibid., p. 7.

20. Chesterton, *St. Thomas Aquinas* (*GIT* 1974, p. 338d).

21. A collection of five essays, written between 1932 and 1936, first published in 1937, now available in English translation, *Methodical Realism,* trans. Philip Trower, with an introduction by me (Front Royal, Va.: Christendom Press, 1990).

22. *Physical Review* 47 (1935), pp. 777–80.

23. Einstein, *The World as I See It* (New York: Covici-Friede, 1934), p. 60.

24. Ibid., p. 30.

25. Niels Bohr, "Can Quantum-Mechanical Description of Physical Reality Be Considered Complete?" *Physical Review* 48 (1935), p. 702.

26. March 3, 1947; see *The Born-Einstein Letters,* with commentaries by Max Born, trans. Irene Born (New York: Walker and Company, 1971), p. 158.

27. An expression of Abner Shimony of Boston University; *see* Malcolm W. Browne, "Quantum Theory: Disturbing Questions Remain Unsolved," *New York Times,* Feb. 11, 1986, p. C3.

28. For a detailed discussion, *see* chap. 6 in my *Science and Creation: From Eternal Cycles to an Oscillating Universe* (1974; new rev. ed., Edinburgh: Scottish Academic Press, 1986; Lanham, Md.: The University Press of America, 1990).

29. *Electrons et photons: Rapports et discussions du Cinquième Conseil de Physique tenu à Bruxelles du 24 au 29 Octobre 1927 sous les auspices de l'Institut International de Physique Solvay* (Paris: Gauthier-Villars, 1928), p. 264.

30. London: Thornton Butterworth, 1930, p. 190.

31. Einstein's was here too a rather lonely voice as he decried, about the same time, that the fashion of ascribing a sort of free will to inorganic matter was not merely a

"nonsense but an objectionable nonsense." *See* "Epilogue: A Socratic Dialogue. Planck-Einstein-Murphy" in Max Planck, *Where Is Science Going?* trans. James G. Murphy (New York: Norton, 1932), p. 201.

32. *Nature,* Dec. 27, 1930, p. 995.

33. Turner, *Essentials in the Development of Religion: A Philosophic and Psychological Study* (London: G. Allen & Unwin, 1934), pp. 224–26.

34. *The Freedom of Man* (New Haven: Yale University Press, 1935), p. 26.

35. *The Nature of Physical Reality* (New York: McGraw Hill, 1950), p. 418.

36. "ESP in the Framework of Modern Science," in *Science and the E.S.P.,* ed. John R. Smythies (London: Routledge and K. Paul, 1967), p. 209.

37. Heisenberg, "Development of the Interpretation of Quantum Theory," in *Niels Bohr and the Development of Physics,* ed. Wolfgang Pauli (New York: McGraw-Hill, 1955), pp. 12–29.

38. Pauli to Born, March 31, 1954; *The Born-Einstein Letters,* p. 223. There Pauli credits another Nobel laureate, Otto Stern, with that disparaging comment on concern for reality.

39. *Selected Works,* trans. and ed. Helen M. Mustard (New York: Random House, 1973), pp. 417–18.

40. "What 'Godot' Hath Wrought," *New York Times,* Dec. 28, 1989, p. A20.

41. *The Scientific Papers of James Clerk Maxwell,* ed. W. D. Niven (Cambridge: University Press, 1890), vol. 2, p. 775.

# PART FOUR

# Additions
# to the
# Great Books Library

# How Things Seem and What They Are: A Philosophical-Scientific Discussion

Sir Arthur S. Eddington (1882–1944), author of *The Nature of the Physical World*.

## Editor's Introduction

Few scientists have shown such youthful promise as Arthur Stanley Eddington (1882–1944); fewer still have so abundantly lived up to it; and hardly any of them, in modern times, have shown an ability, as he did, to explain the great scientific discoveries of their age, so far as possible, to the layman.

His genius was first mathematical. The son of an English schoolmaster, himself both gifted and learned, who died two years after the boy was born, Eddington was raised by his mother in a small seaside English town, from which in 1898 he went to Owens College, Manchester, and in 1902, when he was twenty, to Trinity College, Cambridge. There he was senior wrangler (1904), which is to say that he placed first in probably the longest and most difficult mathematics examinations of their kind in the world at the time (five and a half hours for eight consecutive days), and also won Smith's prize, next in distinction, as well as, in due course (1907), a fellowship at Trinity.

From 1906 to 1913 Eddington served as chief assistant at the Royal Observatory at Greenwich, where he pursued an interest in astronomy. By the end of this time he had made a number of significant observations and had arrived at important theories, among them the one he published in *Stellar Movements and the Structure of the Universe* (1914), where he argued that spiral nebulae, seen only as cloudy structures in a telescope, were in fact galaxies like the Milky Way.

He was made Plumian professor of astronomy at Cambridge in 1913 (at the age of thirty-one), succeeding Sir George Darwin, the son of Charles, and the next year was put in charge of the university observatory. It was from this position that in 1919 he led the expedition to West Africa that confirmed Einstein's theory of relativity—specifically, that gravity bends the path of light when it passes near a star—as noted during a total eclipse of the sun (information which is said to have inspired, in Einstein, the comment that, had it come out otherwise, the sun would have been wrong). In the same period Eddington wrote entire books on Einstein's theory, including *Space, Time and Gravitation* (1920) and *The Mathematical Theory of Relativity* (1923), perhaps his greatest work and the one that Einstein himself considered the best presentation of the subject in any language.

*The Nature of the Physical World,* Eddington's best-known book, appeared in 1928 and was followed in 1933 by *The Expanding Universe.* Both of these works were directed to the general public and did more than any other writings of their time to explain physics and astronomy in layman's terms. Eddington also lectured frequently in these years on relativity, and he did it so well that J. J. Thomson, the leading English physicist of the day, credited him with having convinced the world that it knew what the theory meant.

Knighted in 1930 and awarded the Order of Merit in 1938, Eddington by then had contributed much to his chosen field of astrophysics. Though he took the position that most physical theories could be derived through mathematics and was all but uniquely capable of doing it, he believed, as had Newton before him, that the ultimate reality of things was spiritual. Of his students, perhaps the most distinguished was S. Chandrasekhar (see *GIT* 1980), who became a great astrophysicist in his own right at the University of Chicago and was a Nobel Prize winner in 1983.

What we here reprint is only the Introduction to *The Nature of the Physical World,* a work still worth reading in its entirety, though of course dated in many respects. The Introduction is offered as having inspired two responses, one of them some years ago by Mortimer J. Adler, our editor in chief, in his *Ten Philosophical Mistakes* (1985), and the other, more recent, by A. Brian Pippard, whose further essay, "The Invincible Ignorance of Science," appears following. Both Dr. Adler and Professor Pippard, himself a distinguished scientist of our own day, are concerned to say what each of them can say—the one a philosopher, the other a physicist—about the nature of reality, this being the question that Eddington raised with the account of his two hypothetical tables. Which of those tables is real, whether both are, or whether the most real of tables is not something else yet again, is what all three commentators are trying to decide. The result is a brief disputation of an interesting kind on this fundamental question—interesting for the reason, among others, that it is seldom that we find three persons of comparable stature talking to each other, as it were, about a common problem, the problem in this case being one as to which science and philosophy nowadays offer different solutions.

Readers will note that this discussion is very closely related to the essay by Professor Jaki on "Determinism and Reality," which appears in Part Three of this issue of *The Great Ideas Today.* It is related also, in its questioning of the way we look at things, to matters that Evelyn Fox Keller takes up in "Gender and Science: 1990," which will be found in Part One.

# The Nature of the Physical World (Introduction)

## Sir Arthur S. Eddington

I have settled down to the task of writing these lectures and have drawn up my chairs to my two tables. Two tables! Yes; there are duplicates of every object about me—two tables, two chairs, two pens.

This is not a very profound beginning to a course which ought to reach transcendent levels of scientific philosophy. But we cannot touch bedrock immediately; we must scratch a bit at the surface of things first. And whenever I begin to scratch the first thing I strike is—my two tables.

One of them has been familiar to me from earliest years. It is a commonplace object of that environment which I call the world. How shall I describe it? It has extension; it is comparatively permanent; it is coloured; above all it is *substantial*. By substantial I do not merely mean that it does not collapse when I lean upon it; I mean that it is constituted of "substance" and by that word I am trying to convey to you some conception of its intrinsic nature. It is a *thing;* not like space, which is a mere negation; nor like time, which is—Heaven knows what! But that will not help you to my meaning because it is the distinctive characteristic of a "thing" to have this substantiality, and I do not think substantiality can be described better than by saying that it is the kind of nature exemplified by an ordinary table. And so we go round in circles. After all if you are a plain commonsense man, not too much worried with scientific scruples, you will be confident that you understand the nature of an ordinary table. I have even heard of plain men who had the idea that they could better understand the mystery of their own nature if scientists would discover a way of explaining it in terms of the easily comprehensible nature of a table.

Table No. 2 is my scientific table. It is a more recent acquaintance and I do not feel so familiar with it. It does not belong to the world previously mentioned— that world which spontaneously appears around me when I open my eyes, though how much of it is objective and how much subjective I do not here consider. It is part of a world which in more devious ways has forced itself on my attention. My scientific table is mostly emptiness. Sparsely scattered in that emptiness are numerous electric charges rushing about with great speed; but their combined bulk amounts to less than a billionth of the bulk of the table itself. Notwithstanding its strange construction it turns out to be an entirely efficient table. It supports my writing paper as satisfactorily as table No. 1; for when I lay the paper on it the little electric particles with their headlong speed keep on hitting the underside, so that the paper is maintained in shuttlecock fashion at a nearly steady level. If I lean upon this table I shall not go through; or, to be strictly accurate, the chance of my scientific elbow going through my scientific table is so excessively small that it can be neglected in practical life. Reviewing their properties one by one, there seems to be nothing

to choose between the two tables for ordinary purposes; but when abnormal circumstances befall, then my scientific table
shows to advantage. If the house catches
fire my scientific table will dissolve quite
naturally into scientific smoke, whereas my
familiar table undergoes a metamorphosis
of its substantial nature which I can only
regard as miraculous.

There is nothing *substantial* about my
second table. It is nearly all empty space—
space pervaded, it is true, by fields of force,
but these are assigned to the category of
"influences," not of "things." Even in the
minute part which is not empty we must
not transfer the old notion of substance.
In dissecting matter into electric charges
we have travelled far from that picture of
it which first gave rise to the conception
of substance, and the meaning of that conception—if it ever had any—has been lost
by the way. The whole trend of modern
scientific views is to break down the separate categories of "things," "influences,"
"forms," etc., and to substitute a common
background of all experience. Whether we
are studying a material object, a magnetic
field, a geometrical figure, or a duration of time, our scientific information is
summed up in measures; neither the apparatus of measurement nor the mode of
using it suggests that there is anything essentially different in these problems. The
measures themselves afford no ground for
a classification by categories. We feel it
necessary to concede some background to
the measures—an external world; but the
attributes of this world, except insofar as
they are reflected in the measures, are outside scientific scrutiny. Science has at last
revolted against attaching the exact knowledge contained in these measurements to
a traditional picture gallery of conceptions
which convey no authentic information of
the background and obtrude irrelevancies
into the scheme of knowledge.

I will not here stress further the nonsub-
stantiality of electrons, since it is scarcely
necessary to the present line of thought.

Conceive them as substantially as you will,
there is a vast difference between my scientific table with its substance (if any) thinly
scattered in specks in a region mostly empty
and the table of everyday conception which
we regard as the type of solid reality—an
incarnate protest against Berkeleian sub-
jectivism. It makes all the difference in
the world whether the paper before me is
poised as it were on a swarm of flies and
sustained in shuttlecock fashion by a series
of tiny blows from the swarm underneath,
or whether it is supported because there
is substance below it, it being the intrinsic nature of substance to occupy space to
the exclusion of other substance; all the
difference in conception at least, but no
difference to my practical task of writing
on the paper.

I need not tell you that modern physics
has by delicate test and remorseless logic
assured me that my second scientific table
is the only one which is really there—wherever "there" may be. On the other hand
I need not tell you that modern physics
will never succeed in exorcising that first
table—strange compound of external nature, mental imagery, and inherited prejudice—which lies visible to my eyes and
tangible to my grasp. We must bid good-
bye to it for the present for we are about to
turn from the familiar world to the scientific world revealed by physics. This is, or
is intended to be, a wholly external world.

"You speak paradoxically of two worlds.
Are they not really two aspects or two interpretations of one and the same world?"

Yes, no doubt they are ultimately to be
identified after some fashion. But the process by which the external world of physics
is transformed into a world of familiar acquaintance in human consciousness is outside the scope of physics. And so the world
studied according to the methods of physics
remains detached from the world familiar
to consciousness, until after the physicist
has finished his labours upon it. Provision-
ally, therefore, we regard the table which
is the subject of physical research as al-

together separate from the familiar table, without prejudging the question of their ultimate identification. It is true that the whole scientific inquiry starts from the familiar world and in the end it must return to the familiar world; but the part of the journey over which the physicist has charge is in foreign territory.

Until recently there was a much closer linkage; the physicist used to borrow the raw material of his world from the familiar world, but he does so no longer. His raw materials are aether, electrons, quanta, potentials, Hamiltonian functions, etc., and he is nowadays scrupulously careful to guard these from contamination by conceptions borrowed from the other world. There is a familiar table parallel to the scientific table, but there is no familiar electron, quantum, or potential parallel to the scientific electron, quantum, or potential. We do not even desire to manufacture a familiar counterpart to these things or, as we should commonly say, to "explain" the electron. After the physicist has quite finished his world-building a linkage or identification is allowed; but premature attempts at linkage have been found to be entirely mischievous.

Science aims at constructing a world which shall be symbolic of the world of commonplace experience. It is not at all necessary that every individual symbol that is used should represent something in common experience or even something explicable in terms of common experience. The man in the street is always making this demand for concrete explanation of the things referred to in science; but of necessity he must be disappointed. It is like our experience in learning to read. That which is written in a book is symbolic of a story in real life. The whole intention of the book is that ultimately a reader will identify some symbol, say BREAD, with one of the conceptions of familiar life. But it is mischievous to attempt such identifications prematurely, before the letters are strung into words and the words into sentences.

The symbol *A* is not the counterpart of anything in familiar life. To the child the letter *A* would seem horribly abstract; so we give him a familiar conception along with it. "*A* was an Archer who shot at a frog." This tides over his immediate difficulty; but he cannot make serious progress with word-building so long as Archers, Butchers, Captains, dance round the letters. The letters are abstract, and sooner or later he has to realise it. In physics we have outgrown archer and apple-pie definitions of the fundamental symbols. To a request to explain what an electron really is supposed to be we can only answer, "It is part of the A B C of physics."

The external world of physics has thus become a world of shadows. In removing our illusions we have removed the substance, for indeed we have seen that substance is one of the greatest of our illusions. Later perhaps we may inquire whether in our zeal to cut out all that is unreal we may not have used the knife too ruthlessly. Perhaps, indeed, reality is a child which cannot survive without its nurse illusion. But if so, that is of little concern to the scientist, who has good and sufficient reasons for pursuing his investigations in the world of shadows and is content to leave to the philosopher the determination of its exact status in regard to reality. In the world of physics we watch a shadowgraph performance of the drama of familiar life. The shadow of my elbow rests on the shadow table as the shadow ink flows over the shadow paper. It is all symbolic, and as a symbol the physicist leaves it. Then comes the alchemist Mind who transmutes the symbols. The sparsely spread nuclei of electric force become a tangible solid; their restless agitation becomes the warmth of summer; the octave of aethereal vibrations becomes a gorgeous rainbow. Nor does the alchemy stop here. In the transmuted world new significances arise which are scarcely to be traced in the world of symbols; so that it becomes a world of beauty and purpose—and, alas, suffering and evil.

The frank realisation that physical science is concerned with a world of shadows is one of the most significant of recent advances. I do not mean that physicists are to any extent preoccupied with the philosophical implications of this. From their point of view it is not so much a withdrawal of untenable claims as an assertion of freedom for autonomous development. At the moment I am not insisting on the shadowy and symbolic character of the world of physics because of its bearing on philosophy, but because the aloofness from familiar conceptions will be apparent in the scientific theories I have to describe. If you are not prepared for this aloofness you are likely to be out of sympathy with modern scientific theories, and may even think them ridiculous—as, I daresay, many people do.

It is difficult to school ourselves to treat the physical world as purely symbolic. We are always relapsing and mixing with the symbols incongruous conceptions taken from the world of consciousness. Untaught by long experience we stretch a hand to grasp the shadow, instead of accepting its shadowy nature. Indeed, unless we confine ourselves altogether to mathematical symbolism it is hard to avoid·dressing our symbols in deceitful clothing. When I think of an electron there rises to my mind a hard, red, tiny ball; the proton similarly is neutral grey. Of course the colour is absurd—perhaps not more absurd than the rest of the conception—but I am incorrigible. I can well understand that the younger minds are finding these pictures too concrete and are striving to construct the world out of Hamiltonian functions and symbols so far removed from human preconception that they do not even obey the laws of ortho-dox arithmetic. For myself I find some difficulty in rising to that plane of thought; but I am convinced that it has got to come.

In these lectures I propose to discuss some of the results of modern study of the physical world which give most food for philosophic thought. This will include new conceptions in science and also new knowledge. In both respects we are led to think of the material universe in a way very different from that prevailing at the end of the last century. I shall not leave out of sight the ulterior object which must be in the mind of a Gifford Lecturer, the problem of relating these purely physical discoveries to the wider aspects and interests of our human nature. These relations cannot but have undergone change, since our whole conception of the physical world has radically changed. I am convinced that a just appreciation of the physical world as it is understood to-day carries with it a feeling of open-mindedness toward a wider significance transcending scientific measurement, which might have seemed illogical a generation ago; and in the later lectures I shall try to focus that feeling and make inexpert efforts to find where it leads. But I should be untrue to science if I did not insist that its study is an end in itself. The path of science must be pursued for its own sake, irrespective of the views it may afford of a wider landscape; in this spirit we must follow the path whether it leads to the hill of vision or the tunnel of obscurity. Therefore till the last stage of the course is reached you must be content to follow with me the beaten track of science, nor scold me too severely for loitering among its wayside flowers. That is to be the understanding between us. Shall we set forth?

# Eddington's Two Tables

## A. Brian Pippard

Why only two? Surely there are at least three tables, and probably more. Let us define them before discussing how they relate to each other.

*Table 1 ($T_1$)* is the table which we say we see and talk about with others, confident that they will understand. It is the table of the marketplace whose existence is taken for granted in the ordinary course of life. We do not doubt it continues to exist when we are not present, for others who remain describe it in the same terms as we ourselves employ. To the naive realist (who has a place in the minds of us all) it is the real table, and there's no more to be said.

*Table 2 ($T_2$)* is my mental picture (or model) of a particular table, whether in view or remembered, or even imagined in a form unlike any I have ever seen. [1] It is my personal table, in the sense that no one else can get into my mind to know it as I know it; and I cannot know your mental picture either. Yet when you try to describe it I recognise that your picture and mine are not dissimilar; that is why we agree about the real existence of $T_1$, being something apart from ourselves which we each perceive and interpret in similar ways. It is easy to conclude that $T_2$ is little more than a photographic image of $T_1$, but this is an error, if for no other reason than that the mental picture has a three-dimensional quality absent from its source material, the two-dimensional optical images thrown on the retina. Indeed, what persists in my memory is so clearly a three-dimensional table that if I walk into the room at night I can visualise its form and position well enough to stretch out my hand without hesitation to touch it.

That this mental picture is something I have constructed with marvellous, if unconscious, cunning is brought home by the experience of handling a previously unseen object in a dark room. Out of the complex sequence of pressure-sensations conveyed to my brain emerges a visual image—though until now I have never seen the object, yet I recognise it as a three-dimensional object as soon as the light is switched on.

Table 2 is the table most immediately known to me, the existence of $T_1$ being an inference. When a physical scientist talks about a table he is, at least initially, referring to $T_1$, for he is himself a creature of the marketplace, concerned only with matters he can discuss with others. He regards himself as an observer, aloof from the object of his observation, having found by experience that its behaviour is not affected by what he thinks of it.

*Table 3 ($T_3$)* is what the physicist makes of $T_1$ after prolonged experimentation and analysis—the table that Eddington as a physicist describes in terms of empty space and rapidly moving particles, none of which he perceives by means of sight or touch. Just as Eddington, as an ordinary man, can assert that the table he sees, touches, and is even leaning on when he delivers his lecture is a really existent table, not a fantasy of the mind, so Eddington, the theoretical physicist, has scientific grounds for asserting that the table of which he gives a scientific description also exists in reality in the same place that is occupied by the table of his perceptual experience, the table of the marketplace.

*Table 4 ($T_4$)* is something we are not ready for at present, but if it exists at all it is the table-as-it-is-in-itself, when it is neither perceived by us, nor remembered by us, nor thought about scientifically by us—the table that somehow underlies all the others. We are conscious of Tables 1, 2, and 3 in different ways—by sense perception, by memory or imagination, and by scientific thought—but, of these three tables, one, $T_2$, exists *only* in our minds. To $T_1$, $T_3$, and $T_4$ we attribute existence in reality, and we are compelled to wonder whether the table-in-itself ($T_4$) has the same character as the table we perceive ($T_1$) or the table scientifically described ($T_3$). Or is it something quite other, outside the range of our thought?

I shall be talking about more things than tables and shall use the symbol T to refer, as convenient, to a table or a lump of tungsten or anything else of a material nature that enters the argument. I am not sure that I understand what Eddington means by his first table, but it is $T_1$ alone or a combination of $T_1$ and $T_2$; his second table is $T_3$. My argument leads off with $T_1$ and $T_3$, the object we all recognise and what the physicist says it's made of.

It might be thought $T_3$ is no more than a microscopic view of $T_1$. For example, when a crystal of tungsten is examined by X rays, their reflection into various directions is exactly what would be expected from something composed of an orderly arrangement of identical tungsten atoms. And when we magnify the bumps on its surface a hundred million times in a field-ion microscope, the pattern we see reproduces the same arrangement of atoms. There are many other analytical tools, and the information they give dovetails so beautifully

that no physicist doubts the atoms are as real as the object they constitute.

Of course, the physicist is not bound to keep in mind, at all times, this atomic picture of matter. Long before the existence of atoms was generally accepted physicists were saying useful things about matter, treating it as a $T_1$ rather than a $T_3$. A lump of tungsten is heavy, and that may be all we need to know about it; and it is hard, but we may not care how this arises from the strong preference of the atoms to pack in a particular way. The atomic theorist explains how Eddington's empty space, with a good few particles running around, gives rise to the rigid structure, but the engineer making tungsten wire for a light bulb has little concern for any but the gross (or macroscopic) properties, the subject matter of classical, pre-atomic physics. Even when it becomes necessary to consider atomic constitution it is surprising how often the chemist's and crystallographer's model kit of balls and rods provides as much as is needed.

If only we had been able to halt scientific advance at this point we might have continued to accept the naive realism that controls our daily lives—a table may indeed be composed of atoms like little hard spheres, but what we see standing there, and remember in our mind's eye, is the real table, no more and no less. Eddington wrote his Gifford Lectures less than a year after the revolutionary theories of Werner Heisenberg and Erwin Schrödinger had put paid to this illusion, and one must marvel at his assimilation of the implications for physics and philosophy. In brief, we are now aware that protons and electrons, and other atomic constituents, are not a bit like little bullets. When they come together in an atom, and atoms come together in molecules or larger aggregates, the individual peculiarities tend to be ironed out. But they are still there, ready to reveal themselves in the right circumstances; the operation of lasers, and the strange properties of superconductors and superfluid helium, cannot be understood without accepting that the rules governing microscopic objects also apply to systems of macroscopic scale, the scale of everyday perception. The paradoxes of subatomic physics refuse to be confined to their microscopic bounds. It is odd, to be sure, that one can never discover the path by which an electron got from A to B, and that when one knows it has left A one cannot say whether it will or will not arrive at B, only how likely that event is. But it is more than odd, it is distinctly disquieting to be told that a similar indeterminacy afflicts objects and events that we are accustomed to think are inexorably regulated by natural law. At this point the reader may be tempted to emulate Dr. Johnson, [2] and I must therefore present some simple arguments that reveal the logical difficulties besetting a latter-day Johnsonian realist.

In my Eddington memorial lecture (*GIT* 1990, pp. 324–37) I indicated how difficult it is to reconcile the wave and the particle theories of light; when the probability that a photon will enter an eye, and be observed as a flash of light, is governed by a wave, how is it that once the photon has actually been seen, the wave falling on other eyes is never permitted to lead the photon there as well? The comfortable solution, which I asserted without further explanation could not be maintained, is that the photon is really moving on a well-defined path even though we are unable to devise ways to catch it as it goes. And since the behaviour of particles follows a similar pattern, with waves to control their motion in Schrödinger's formulation, we might be tempted to adopt a similar interpretation for them. The objection to this resolution of the problem only becomes insistent, as I stressed, when more than one particle is involved, for then a single wave, expressed mathematically as a function of many variables, controls all the particles at once. One might be able to persuade oneself to believe in the real existence of a single particle and its guiding wave, but the many-particle wave function is too tall an order, demanding the abandonment of our instinctive perception of space. In trying to explain away the extraordinary goings-on of the microscopic world, one must not invoke a still more extraordinary model. It should not be necessary to point this out, yet all too many of the physicists who have proposed various ways out of the difficulty have ignored that simple principle.

To most physicists and philosophers, however, indeterminacy is a still greater obstacle than the many-particle problem. It worried Isaac Newton when he saw light, on striking a glass surface, being partially reflected and partially transmitted. He believed that light was composed of particles, but why should some bounce while others went through? His suggestion of "fits" of easy reflection and easy transmission was never very convincing, even to himself. On the other hand, the phenomenon is perfectly normal with waves, and partial reflection ceased to be a problem once the wave theory of light gained general acceptance. With Albert Einstein's photons, however, it reappeared in the same form that disturbed Newton, but with the significant difference that enough was now known about the nature of light to dispose of the idea that a rational cause for the fits could be devised without throwing received notions into desperate confusion. It seemed, and still seems, to be necessary to admit that the partition of wave energy into reflected and transmitted fractions decides the average numbers of photons that take the alternative paths; but there is nothing to tell which course will be followed by any given photon. The existence of alternatives, without any mechanism to determine the outcome in each particular case, is the fundamental indeterminacy of quantum mechanics. Many of the founding fathers of quantum physics, Albert Einstein, Louis de Broglie, and Erwin Schrödinger among them, refused to abandon their belief that at the deepest level determinacy still held sway ("God does not play dice," said Einstein; and Niels Bohr retorted, "Albert, don't tell God what he can do"). But neither they nor, in my opinion, any others have produced a model that does not involve believing six impossible things before breakfast. [3]

Let us return to the problem with which we started this discussion, the arrival of a photon at the eye. The conventional view of how to calculate what may happen is that one begins with a known situation, in this case perhaps that there is an atom in an excited state which will emit a photon on reverting to its unexcited ground state. By means of the wave equation one calculates the probability that during some specified interval the photon will enter the eye, and that is as far as we can go; we can only wait and see (or not). But if a flash of light is seen, this contributes a new observational fact which must be included in any subsequent calculation.

The worrying question that this procedure raises is that conscious observation plays an essential role in how a calculation is to be set up. A full treatment that reveals the paradoxes lying in wait, for anyone seeking a resolution in purely material terms, is out of the question here, since there is a vast literature devoted to what is technically called the quantum theory of measurement. And those who cheerfully enter the fray are only too likely to retire hurt, with nothing to show for their efforts except an intensified puzzlement. This is, I confess, my own position and I have great sympathy for the majority of physicists who, having given a little thought to the matter, thereafter relegate it to the category of metaphysical speculations that are irrelevant to their normal work. After all, the rules for applying quantum mechanics to physical problems are well established and have had astonishing success. It is a pity if one cannot picture what they mean beyond that, but no more relevant than are the mysteries of thermodynamics to an engine-driver.

To the man in the street, indeterminacy and its paradoxes are even less relevant, for it is normally made imperceptible by the smoothing out of a multitude of uncertainties into an apparently well-behaved average. The averaging process occurs to a considerable degree even with systems that we regard as, humanly speaking, microscopic. A photon entering the eye initiates the perception process by exciting a single molecule of rhodopsin, which breaks up and sets in train an avalanche of chemical processes. Eventually, by stages which are not yet fully understood, an electrical signal is sent along the optic nerve into the brain. Once the initial process is set going the outcome is virtually determined, so that one may state with little error that the electrical nerve signal is uniquely correlated with the breakdown of a single rhodopsin molecule. We may therefore, if we like, confine the indeterminacy to the relatively simple primary interaction between an excited atom and a rhodopsin molecule, by way of radiated light. That is the usual device adopted in quantum calculations, breaking the problem into manageable chunks—in this case a first stage of quantum mechanics applied to a rhodopsin molecule, and then some biochemistry and electrochemistry (which can be described pictorially, without invoking indeterminacy) to get from broken-down rhodopsin to a nerve-impulse. However, it is just this dissection which offends the severe philosopher, for it implies that at a certain moment we know a molecule of rhodopsin decomposed, having been struck by a photon; but that knowledge is unavailable until the nerve-impulse has entered the brain and been converted by some wholly mysterious alchemy into a conscious perception. To the innocent physicist this sort of reductionism seems harmless, and indeed it is harmless in his hands, for he knows how to apply it safely. But quantum mechanics, rigorously applied, allows no separation of systems that have once been joined until an observation changes what is known and, for example, provides separate information about different parts, so that henceforth they may be analysed independently.

The conclusion is that if we are to obey the rules strictly, the indeterminacy cannot be confined to atomic processes but in the present example must encompass everything, including the optic nerve. In principle we can calculate the probability of observing, with some suitable detector, a signal on the nerve, but it is the conscious mind of the owner of the eye, or of the one who watches the detector, that converts probability into certainty. Bishop Berkeley might well have told Dr. Johnson that the large stone only truly existed when he became aware of having kicked it. And the modern physicist agrees with James Boswell that he is satisfied Berkeley's doctrine is not true, though he cannot prove it.

What does a modern physicist believe, then? I cannot give a single comprehensive answer, for there is no unanimity of belief, except that the laws of physics work; but among those who are prepared to contemplate the problem the most frequent attitude is a vague compromise between Cartesian dualism and plain materialism, or naive realism. Realism involves unquestioning commitment to the real existence of photons, electrons, etc., albeit they have rather strange properties which need quantum mechanics to cope with them. The dualistic side is the recognition that the operations of the conscious mind are mysterious, but since they do not have an influence on the behaviour of matter they can be ignored. On the other hand, physics has been immensely successful in developing a unified derivation of material phenomena from a few basic principles, and it is a sort of treason to allow oneself to suspect that the phenomena of mind will not in due course be assimilated into the materialistic world-picture.

It is perhaps a caricature, though not grossly unfair, to portray the typical scientist as a philosophical simpleton. But among simpletons there is a world of dif-

ference between the opinionated (among whom some distinguished scientists are to be found) and the frankly puzzled, for it is from among the latter that enlightenment is more likely to emerge, when subtle and complex logic has apparently led to an impasse. The most enduring truths, in life and science, are those whose simplicity allows them eventually to be taken as almost self-evident; this cannot be said of the present state of theoretical physics, whose convoluted procedures have progressively distanced themselves from comprehension by any but initiates. I see no reason to expect that further digging away at the foundations will open up a vista of the heavens in all their glory. And it is this that is lacking from science and will elude us as long as the dualism of matter and mind remains unresolved.

A few scientists, including Schrödinger, have been attracted to Eastern mystical religion, and some (not Schrödinger) have even sensed a kinship between the writings of mystics and modern physicists. To expect to make progress in this direction is to attach too much importance to accidental parallels of metaphor used by entirely different kinds of thinker, in their popular accounts of ideas for which the language of the marketplace provides no adequate terms. Insofar as Eastern mysticism dismisses the material world as an irrelevance, and Western science washes its hands of the spiritual world, they can find no common ground on which to start building a synthesis. Each is corrupted (though they would concur in deploring the word) by exclusive devotion to a partial truth.

Is there, then, a way forward which might lead in the direction of the ultimately unknowable thing-in-itself, the $T_4$ of my introduction which is neither the naive realist's table ($T_1$) nor the table in my mind's eye ($T_2$), nor yet the physicist's table ($T_3$), but an entity, totally different in kind, which generates each of these limited, contrary, and distorted versions of itself? It is tempting to give way to despair at what appears a hopeless enterprise, and certainly it is not one to be tackled head-on. Yet although a scientist cannot say anything positive about the nature of the fundamental reality, beyond asserting that there must be something real underpinning the astonishing coherence of his physical world, the very existence of a coherent world allows him to eliminate various conceptions that have at times gained currency. The method of exhaustion, a favourite of Sherlock Holmes, [4] is a poor instrument of extremely limited application, but it at least removes from consideration all those cosmologies that lack any germ from which the strange laws of physics might spring. Nor is the scientist tempted to believe that all things are at the mercy of divine caprice.

This is not great progress, and perhaps for the scientist the most promising line is to try to discern in his own theories those parts which may have suffered least loss of identity in the transition from reality to appearance. A remark of the mathematician Leopold Kronecker may provide a hint: "The integers were made by God; all else is the work of man." Integers, by their very nature, are incapable of being gradually manipulated into other integers and can survive when the framework in which they are embedded is grossly distorted. For example, all mammals possess two eyes; through all the evolutionary changes from the most primitive to those of the present day, two-ness of eyes has survived unchanged. It is not impossible to violate this principle, as when bifurcation doubles a number—looking in the distorting mirror of a fairground you may find you have four eyes and two noses. Nevertheless, countable entities, especially those that are seen to be conserved through changes taking place around them, are candidates for inclusion in the catalogue of constituents of the real world, even if their countability is the only property that can be recognised as being transferred. We are aware, for

example, of three dimensions of space and one of time. They have not maintained their independence in the special theory of relativity, while in Einstein's general theory the four-dimensional space-time abandons Euclidean geometry and acquires strange properties that defeat normal imagination. Through all this, however, the dimensionality remains fourfold—it requires four numbers to define the occurrence of an isolated event—for each observer both the place (three numbers) and the time. One might expect, then, that whatever it is that constitutes an isolated event in the fundamental reality, it will have a fourfold character that presents itself to us in the guise of dimensionality.

And one may proceed, with hesitant steps, to add other conserved quantities—the number of protons and electrons, as well as such things as mass (or energy) which, though not countable, are very strongly conserved through all manner of physical change.

Eddington, in his last years, tortured himself with fancies like this, only much more penetrating, in the belief that he could develop a model from which the known laws of physics would arise as logical consequences. Of all his contemporaries he was perhaps the most powerfully endowed for this task, both in physics and mathematics but also through his sensitivity to man's spiritual nature; nevertheless, in spite of incidental ideas of great interest and ingenuity, his heroic onslaught is generally regarded as a failure. This does not mean, of course, that the enterprise is doomed, but that advances will at best be slow and fragmentary.

And what of his tables? Whatever view we take of true reality—the immaterial timeless, spaceless, and mindless from which we derive our time and space, matter and mind, we must never forget that the one certainty we have is of our own existence. Come what may, it is $T_2$, the table in the mind of each of us, to which all else we believe in must conform. $T_1$ is a commonplace invention, $T_3$ a clever invention, but they are inventions to enable us to live and discourse with others. What their relation is to $T_2$ and to the true table-in-itself, $T_4$, is a question that is likely to elude attempts to answer it for a very long time, if not forever.

I am greatly indebted to Mortimer Adler for encouraging me to venture into a philosophical arena in which, as a physicist, I have little experience or skill. If, as I suspect, his helpful criticisms have not eradicated all the confusions of the first draft, the fault is mine alone.

---

1. For my argument I do not need to distinguish between the mental pictures of an object in sight and of the same object remembered. It is enough that neither is $T_1$.

2. When James Boswell said of Bishop Berkeley's "ingenious sophistry to prove the nonexistence of matter" that though we are satisfied his doctrine is not true, it is impossible to refute it, "Johnson answered, striking his foot with mighty force against a large stone, till he rebounded from it, 'I refute it thus.' " "Life of Samuel Johnson," *GBWW*, Vol. 44, p. 134.

3. Lewis Carroll, *Through the Looking-Glass*, chapter 5.

4. "How often have I said to you that when you have eliminated the impossible, whatever remains, *however improbable,* must be the truth?" Arthur Conan Doyle, *The Sign of Four,* chapter 6.

# Reality and Appearances

## Mortimer J. Adler

### 1

The commonsense picture of the world in which we live would appear to be shattered by what we are told by the physical scientists of our own day.

I will never forget my shock when, more than fifty years ago, I read Sir Arthur Eddington's Gifford Lectures, *The Nature of the Physical World.* In his opening remarks, Sir Arthur told his audience that the table in front of which he was standing, the table which seemed so solid to them that they would bruise their fists if they tried to punch through it, was in reality an area of largely empty space in which tiny invisible bodies were moving about at great speeds, interacting with one another in a variety of ways, and making the table appear to us to be solid, of a certain size, shape, and weight, and having certain other sensible qualities, such as its color, its smoothness, and so on.

*Appearance and reality!* As Sir Arthur spoke, there seemed to be no doubt in his mind which was which. The table the lecturer and his audience perceived through their eyes and could touch with their hands might appear to them to be an individual thing that had an enduring identifiable identity which could undergo change while remaining one and the same thing. That was the appearance, an appearance that might even be called illusory in comparison to the invisible and untouchable reality of the atomic particles in motion that filled the space occupied by the visible table, a space largely empty even though impenetrable by us.

My initial shock increased when I passed from thinking about the table to thinking about myself and other human beings. We were not different from the table. We, too, were individual physical things. We might appear to ourselves and to each other to be as solid as the table, perhaps somewhat softer to the touch, but just as impenetrable to a probing finger. But, in reality, the space our apparently solid bodies occupied was just as empty as that of the table. Whatever attributes or characteristics our bodies appear to have as we perceive them through our senses, they have as a result of the motions and interactions of particles that themselves had none of these sensible characteristics.

(According to this view, the imperceptible particles that compose all the objects of our ordinary perceptual experience possess only quantitative properties, no sensible qualities at all. The latter, it is maintained, exist only in our consciousness of the objects we perceive, not in the objects themselves. They have no status in reality. Thus arises the riddle about what came to be called "secondary qualities," a puzzlement that always accompanies the reductionist fallacy to which atomists are prone.)

What becomes of my personal identity, or yours, and with it moral responsibility for our actions, if each of us ceases to be one individual thing, but becomes instead a congeries of physical particles that do not remain the same particles during the span of our lifetime?

To face the problem that here is raised, let us eliminate at once an easy way out of the difficulty. That easy way out is to regard both pictures—the one we have as a matter of common sense and common experience and the one we are given by atomic physicists—as convenient and useful fictions. The first of these serves all the practical exigencies of our daily lives. The second, applied through technological innovations, gives us extraordinary mastery and control over the physical world in which we live.

Approached this way, there is no conflict between the two views of the world in which we live and of ourselves as living organisms existing in it. We need not ask which is the reality and which is the mere appearance or illusion.

Before the middle of the last century, the theory of the atomists was regarded as positing a useful scientific fiction, and so it posed no challenge to the reality of the commonsense view that a sound philosophy endorsed. Until then, beginning with Democritus in the ancient world and coming down to Newton and Dalton in the modern world, the atom was conceived as the absolutely indivisible unit of matter. In the words of Lucretius, it was a unit of "solid singleness," with no void within it, as there must be a void in any composite and, therefore, divisible body having atoms as its component parts.

We know that in the late nineteenth century, and in our own day, all this has been radically changed. There is no longer any doubt about the real existence of atoms, which are now known to be divisible and to be as much filled microscopically with void or empty space as the solar system is filled macroscopically. In that empty space move the elementary particles that have now been discovered by the most ingenious detecting devices, the real existence of which is supposedly verified by inferences from the observed phenomena, phenomena that cannot be explained except by positing the real existence of these unobservable particles.

Let me make sure that the last point is fully clear. The elementary particles, which are the moving components of the divisible atom, are intrinsically imperceptible to our senses. As a contemporary writer puts it, they are essentially unpicturable—"unpicturable-in-principle." They and the atoms they constitute do not have any of the sensible qualities possessed by the perceptible physical things of common experience. Nor do the elementary particles even have the quantitative properties possessed by atoms and molecules, such as size, weight, shape, or configuration.

Werner Heisenberg's statement of the matter confirms how radical, indeed, is the unpicturability of the elementary particles. He writes as follows:

*. . . The indivisible elementary particle of modern physics possesses the quality of taking up space in no higher measure than other properties, say color and strength of material. [They] are no longer material bodies in the proper sense of the word.* [1]

Heisenberg goes on to say that they are units of matter only in the sense in which mass and energy are interchangeable. This fundamental stuff, according to him, "is capable of existence in different forms," but "always appears in definite quanta." [2] These quanta of mass/energy cannot even be exclusively described as particles, for they are as much waves or wave packets.

Speaking of atoms and molecules, are we not called upon to say of them what we seem to be called upon to say of ourselves and the other perceptible things of common experience? They, too, are divisible wholes made up of moving and changing components. What about their reality as compared with that of the elementary particles that constitute them? If we could perceive with our naked eyes an atom or a molecule, would we not be compelled to say that it only appeared to be what it was perceived as—a solid, indivisible body—but that in reality what we perceived was only an illusion?

What we are confronted with here is the fallacy of reductionism, a mistake that has become most prevalent in our own day, not only among scientists but also among contemporary philosophers. It consists in regarding the ultimate constituents of the physical world as more real than the composite bodies these elementary components constitute. Reductionism may go even further and declare these ultimate constituents to be the only reality, relegating everything else to the status of mere appearance or illusion.

## 2

How is this fallacy of reductionism, this philosophical mistake, to be corrected, as it must be if our commonsense view of things and if a philosophy of nature that accords with it is to be validated?

Before I attempt to suggest a solution, let me make sure that the conflict between the scientific and the commonsense view is clear. The chair on which I am now sitting fills a certain area of space. To say, on the one hand, that that space envelope is filled with the single, solid body that we experience as the perceived chair contradicts saying, on the other hand, that that space envelope is largely a void filled by moving and interacting imperceptible particles.

The conflict or contradiction here is not simply between filled and empty space. It involves a contradiction between the one and the many. The chair of our common experience, the reality of which a philosophy based on common sense defends, is not only a solid body, but even more fundamentally it is a single being. The chair of physical theory consists of an irreducible multiplicity of discrete units, each having its own individual existence.

If the unitary being which is the solid chair, with all its sensible qualities, is dismissed as an illusion foisted on us by our sense-experience, then no conflict remains. Or if the physicist's atoms, elementary particles, wave packets, or quanta of mass and quanta of energy are merely theoretical entities to which no real existence is attributed (that is, if they are merely mathematical forms which have no physical reality), then their being posited for theoretical purposes as useful fictions does not challenge the view that what really exists out there is the solid chair of our experience.

If, however, real existence *of the same kind* is attributed to the entities described by the commonsense view and by the scientific view, then we cannot avoid a conflict that must be resolved.

A clue or hint that leads to the solution is contained in the italicized words in the preceding statement: "of the same kind." Both the solid chair and the imperceptible particles have real existence, but their reality is not of the same kind, not of the same order or degree. By virtue of that fact, the conflict can be resolved. The contradiction is then seen to be only apparent.

The problem would be insoluble if the two assertions to be reconciled stood in relation to one another in the same way that the statement that Jones is sitting in a particular chair at a particular time stands to the statement that Smith is sitting in the same chair at the same time, and is not sitting on top of Jones or on the arm of the chair, but exactly where Jones is sitting. The statements about Jones and Smith cannot both be true. They cannot be reconciled.

The assertion about the nuclear particles as the imperceptible constituents of the chair and the assertion about the perceptible solid chair as an individual thing, both occupying the same space, can be reconciled on condition that we recognize different grades or degrees of reality.

Werner Heisenberg used the term *potentia*—potentialities for being—to describe the very low, perhaps even the least, degree of reality that can be possessed by elementary particles. He wrote:

*. . . In the experiments about atomic events we have to do with things and facts, with phenomena that are just as real as any phenomena in daily life. But the atoms or the elementary particles themselves are* not *as real; they form a world of potentialities or possibilities rather than one of things or facts.* [3]

Heisenberg, in saying that the elementary particles are *not as real* as the perceptible individual things of daily life, does not deny that they still have some reality.

The merely possible, that which has no actual existence at all, has no reality. That which has some potentiality for existence and tends toward existence has some, perhaps the least, degree of reality. It is barely more than merely possible.

Let me now summarize the solution of the problem, which corrects the philosophical mistake that arises from the fallacy of reductionism. It involves two steps.

(1) The reality of the elementary particles of nuclear physics cannot be reconciled with the reality of the chair as an individual sensible substance if both the particles and the chair are asserted to have the same mode of existence or grade of being. The same thing can also be said about the nuclear particles and the atoms of which they are component parts. The particles are less real than the atoms; that is, they have less actuality. This, I take it, is the meaning of Heisenberg's statement that the particles are in a state of *potentia*—"possibilities for being or tendencies for being."

(2) The mode of being of the material constituents of a physical body cannot be the same when those constituents exist in isolation and when they enter into the constitution of an actual body. Thus, when the chair exists actually as one body, the multitude of atoms and elementary particles which constitute it exist only virtually. Since their existence is only virtual, so is

their multiplicity; and their virtual multiplicity is not incompatible with the actual unity of the chair. Again, the same thing can also be said about a single atom and the nuclear particles which constitute it; or about a single molecule and the various atoms which constitute it. When an atom or a molecule actually exists as a unit of matter, its material constituents have only virtual existence and, consequently, their multiplicity is also only virtual.

What exists virtually has more reality than the merely potential and less than the fully actual. The virtually existing components of any composite whole become fully actual only when that composite decomposes or breaks up into its constituent parts.

The virtual existence and multiplicity of the material constituents do not abrogate their capacity for actual existence and actual multiplicity. If the unitary chair—or a single atom—were exploded into its ultimate material constituents, the elementary particles would assume the mode of actual existence which isolated particles have in a cyclotron; their virtual multiplicity would be transformed into an actual multitude.

The critical point here is that the mode of existence in which the particles are discrete units and have actual multiplicity cannot be the same as the mode of existence that they have when they are material constituents of the individual chair in actual existence.

If we assign the same mode of existence to the particles in a cyclotron and to the particles that enter into the constitution of an actual chair, the conflict between nuclear physics and the philosophical doctrine that affirms the reality of the material objects of common experience ceases to be merely an apparent conflict. It is a real conflict, and an irresolvable one, because the conflicting theories are irreconcilable. But if they are assigned different modes of existence, the theories that appear to be in conflict can be reconciled.

Not only is the conflict between the

view of the physical world advanced by physical science and the view held by common sense reconciled. We also reach the conclusion that the perceptible individual things of common experience have a higher degree of actual reality. This applies also to the sensible qualities—the so-called "secondary qualities"—that we experience these things as having. They are not merely figments of our consciousness with no status at all in the real world that is independent of our senses and our minds.

With this conclusion reached, the challenge to the reality of human existence and to the identifiable identity of the individual person is removed. There can be no question about the moral responsibility that each of us bears for his or her actions.

---

1. *Philosophic Problems of Nuclear Science* (New York: Pantheon Books, Inc., 1952), pp. 55–56.
2. Ibid., p. 103.

3. *Physics and Philosophy* (New York: Harper & Brothers Publishers, 1958), p. 186.

"Still Life: The Table." Painting by Georges Braque (1882–1963).

# The Invincible Ignorance of Science

## A. Brian Pippard

### Editor's Introduction

Where Eddington, his distinguished forerunner in physics at Cambridge, was interested chiefly in stars, Brian Pippard has made a reputation in the study of metals, working for many years in the Cavendish Laboratory at Cambridge University, where following the Second World War he began as a research assistant studying microwave impedance of superconductors and normal metals at low temperatures. In 1950 he was awarded a Ph.D.

For over thirty years he held various posts at Cambridge, being successively University demonstrator, lecturer, reader, J. H. Plummer Professor of Physics (1960), and Cavendish Professor of Physics as well as the head of the department (1971), until he retired in 1982. From 1966 to 1973 he was, in addition, the founding president of Clare Hall, a new graduate college at Cambridge.

Professor Pippard has written a text on classical thermodynamics, five books on the characteristics and behavior of metals, and about ninety papers, including seventy on the electrical properties of normal metals and superconductors. He has more recently been a frequent reviewer of scientific books in the *Times Literary Supplement* and the *London Review of Books*. Among honors and prizes that he has won over his career are fellowship in the Royal Society (1956) and its Hughes Medal (1959), and the Guthrie Prize (1970) from the Institute of Physics, of which he was president from 1974 to 1976. In 1975, in consideration of his scientific eminence, he was created a knight bachelor. This does not mean, however, that he is unmarried; in fact, he has a wife, Charlotte Dyer, and three daughters.

Apart from minor editorial changes, this essay was given as the Eddington memorial lecture delivered to a general audience at Cambridge in January of 1988 and was first published in *Contemporary Physics* in the same year.

On the occasion of the centenary of Eddington's birth, Professor Chandrasekhar [cf. *GIT* 1979, pp. 90–138] delivered two lectures in Trinity [Trinity College, Cambridge], of which the first was sub-titled "The most distinguished astrophysicist of his time"; and was roundly taken to task by Professor McCrea, who had no use for such niggardly praise. [1] It is indeed hard to find words that do justice to Eddington's great achievements, and I am glad not to be called upon to undertake such an impertinence. It is bad enough to stand in the shadow of an expositor whose popular books and public lectures show wide and humane learning allied to a felicity of style that few scientists have equalled. Still worse, I am expected to give you my thoughts on philosophical matters related to religion and ethics, a notorious danger area for anybody, but especially for scientists, who are inclined to believe that their expertise absolves them from the duty of studying other branches of knowledge before contributing their own penn'orth of wisdom. I therefore ask your indulgence for ignorantly repeating things that must have been said many times before; if excuse is needed, it is that they have also been challenged many times. In philosophy, no idea is secure enough to need no champion, however timid he may be—and in comparison with Eddington's robust audacity in philosophical matters, I am very timid indeed.

Not so, however, when it comes to the achievements of science on its own ground. We need not hesitate to acclaim the power of scientific method when it leads to a model by means of which observations in physics, chemistry, and biology may be related. It is no small thing to feel confidence in writing, as does Richard Feynman,

Everything is made of atoms. *That is the key hypothesis. The most important hypothesis in all of biology, for example, is that* everything that animals do, atoms do. *In other words,* there is nothing that living things do that cannot be understood from the point of view that they are made of atoms acting according to the laws of physics. *This was not known from the beginning; it took some experimenting and theorizing to suggest this hypothesis, but now it is accepted, and it is the most useful theory for producing new ideas in the field of biology.* [2]

(Feynman's emphasis is in the roman type, as quoted.) If he somewhat overstates the case, it is nevertheless one to which many scientists would assent without hesitation— that is the trouble, if they hesitated they might feel doubts.

For the moment, however, let us forget our doubts and note what Feynman claims. He does not claim that one can write down the equations governing the behaviour of a large number of elementary particles, and proceed to find a solution that describes a living cell. As a matter of fact even a single helium atom cannot be predicted purely mathematically from the starting point of two protons, two neutrons, and two electrons. But if one knows helium atoms exist it is possible to verify that their properties agree with the rules of quantum mechanics. Similarly with the other elements, and with chemical compounds. The chemist must tell the physicist that two hydrogens and an oxygen combine to form a V-shaped water molecule; the physicist then persuades himself, and hopes to persuade the chemist, that this also accords perfectly with quantum laws. At about this point the chemist ceases to be interested in *a priori* physical calculations, and develops his understanding of more complex molecules with the aid of rules appropriate to this higher level of complexity—ideas of valency and charge transfer that, as a physicist, I hardly understand; yet am satisfied that they would follow inexorably from the quantum mechanics of elementary particles, if only I had a big enough computer. So, too, if the chemist or biochemist assures me that the ability of a DNA molecule to replicate itself is compatible with his chemical rules, I am happy to agree with Feynman.

Now the hierarchy that I have outlined is something more than an arbitrary classification designed to divide a vast range of complexity into manageable units. It reflects, if only rather sketchily, the fact that the development of higher complexity from lower is not a continuous evolution, but is marked by discontinuities at which new properties suddenly appear. Thus an isolated atom of sodium is spherically symmetrical, with nothing to show that a number of sodium atoms will condense into a body-centred cubic array with an entirely different symmetry. If one wished to calculate from first principles how the atoms would pack, there is no mathematical routine that will guarantee reaching the right answer; one would have to work out the energy of every possible packing to find the lowest, stable arrangement. Similar discontinuities of symmetry are commonplace events when a minute change of temperature gives rise to a change of phase— the boiling or freezing of a liquid, or the changes of crystal structure that many solids undergo. Not infrequently a totally unexpected property makes its appearance at one of these points of discontinuity, as when a metal on cooling suddenly loses all

electrical resistance and acquires other attributes of the superconducting state. This is one of the critical phenomena for which an unusually complete theory has been given, so that one is satisfied that it is consistent with the known laws of physics, demanding only their correct application, not their extension. To use a term that has been employed by philosophers for something like a century, but is not normally used by physicists, superconductivity is an emergent property, and may serve as a well-understood exemplar of the concept of emergence as applied to more complicated situations, such as the evolution of life from nonliving matter, or sexual reproduction from asexual. [3]

There is no harm in stressing that the emergence of a new property is almost always—Feynman would probably say always—in accordance with physical laws, not demanding some additional postulate. Until about 1930 there were many physicists and chemists who doubted whether the known forces between particles could account for chemical bonds, and many more, well after that time, who believed a vital principle was essential for the appearance of life. One would have to search now to find a vitalist who commanded respect from his colleagues, so probable does it seem that the emergence of life can be interpreted as an extension of established principles to a system of high complexity.

It is not surprising then to find physicists claiming virtually unlimited power for their methods, either explicitly as Feynman does or implicitly, as do many lesser men, when they subject reported phenomena to the critical test of compatibility with the laws of physics. Some years ago a well-known theoretical physicist, stimulated, I think, by Uri Geller's performances, undertook critical examination of a variety of paranormal phenomena. His judgement, which probably surprised few, was that no known physical process would explain psychokinesis, spoon-bending, poltergeists, dowsing, telepathy, clairvoyance, or faith-healing. And the paper ended with the words "We can only conclude that the existence of any of the psychic phenomena we have considered is very doubtful."

Now I make no claim in support of any of these reported phenomena, but I have no doubt at all that the argument is invalid and represents not scientific method but scientism. If the existence of these phenomena is doubtful it is because the evidence is scanty and often of dubious provenance, it is not because they cannot be explained in physical terms. They involve, after all, a class of system beyond the scope of physical theory—that is to say, conscious human beings; and thinking is something that, *pace* Richard Feynman, living things do that cannot be understood from the laws of physics. Note, please, that I do not say consciousness is not at this time understood from the laws of physics—I say it *cannot* be so understood. I am sorry if I seem to stress, as I shall continue to stress for a few minutes longer, something which is perfectly obvious to you, as it is to me. But I have found many mathematicians and physicists reluctant to agree with the contention that the phenomenon of consciousness is intrinsically beyond the range of scientific method. I am not referring, of course, to the physical processes that occur in the brain and which can be studied and observed as public events like other phenomena. By consciousness I mean that private self-awareness which, far from being a somewhat irrelevant concomitant of neural activity, is for me a uniquely important fact of observation. You cannot share my self-awareness, as I cannot share yours. So far, indeed, am I from sharing yours that it is only an assumption on my part that you even possess this faculty—I have no means of proving it. However, there is a certain congruence between your behaviour and mine, and you quite often say things that I realize I might have said myself and wish I had (or sometimes am glad that I did not); and this encourages me to believe that I am not addressing an audience of automata (if I thought that, I should not be here).

It is conceivable that one thinking person might be able to conduct a dialogue which would enable him to decide logically whether he was talking to another thinking person or to an automaton. This has not yet been done, and may be impossible. What is surely impossible is that a theoretical physicist, given unlimited computing power, should deduce from the laws of physics that a certain complex structure is aware of its own existence. The laws of physics relate to observations in the public domain, what Eddington called pointer-readings, common to all who choose to share the information. No amount of mathematical juggling can generate from an input of public facts an output that is not equally public; any variable that appears in the theory is either an unobservable mathematical concept introduced as a computational aid, such as the wave-function in quantum mechanics, or it refers to an observable quantity that is accessible to all. The physicist who believes in nothing that is incompatible with the laws of physics is faced with a simple choice—either to deny the primary evidence of his senses concerning his own inner life, or to adopt an extreme dualistic stance and assert that mind has no influence on material behaviour. If he chooses the latter, as he must do if he is not an automaton, he must regard consciousness as an emergent phenomenon of physical matter, but one that is irrelevant to the physicist in his professional life.

Apparently this is a very widespread view. In an article which is something of a curiosity for so penetrating a scientist, Eugene Wigner writes,

*Does the human body deviate from the laws of physics, as gleaned from the study of inanimate nature? The traditional answer to this question is "No: the body influences the mind but the mind does not influence the body."* [4]

And he adds that "he never found an affirmative answer—not even after having perused the relevant articles in the earlier (more thorough) editions of the *Encyclopædia Britannica.*" I have probably not perused the earlier (more thorough) editions quite so assiduously, but I have found neither an affirmative nor a negative answer—the question is not discussed in these terms; and I cannot help suspecting that until quite recently the mutual influence of mind and body was so obvious as to be taken for granted. The physicist's claim to embrace the whole of creation, and the furious desire of the logical positivist and his behaviouristic camp-followers to excise from their vocabulary everything that cannot be defined according to their rules—these are both rather recent innovations which may be applauded as experiments in philosophy without believing for a moment that they address basic problems such as the possible influence of mind on matter.

I must not leave you with the impression that Wigner is a dogmatic adherer to what he calls the traditional view, that there is no influence. But the arguments that lead him to question it, which I need not repeat here, seem to me unnecessarily sophisticated as well as unconvincing. Something much simpler is sufficient to make the point. If, for example, as occasionally happens, I realize I have committed an embarrassing *faux pas,* I have no doubt that it is the conscious realization that precipitates the blush, not the other way round. One may choose to exclude this class of observation on the grounds that the evidence is only available to the subject, and is outside the range of scientific analysis, but this amounts to a critique of scientific method. There still remains an observation which most of us, remembering our own embarrassing experiences, would be disposed to confirm. And it is no part of scientific method to deny awkward evidence on the grounds that science knows only how to handle data that belong in the public domain; one can only admit that there are real problems beyond the scope of science.

In considering the mutual influences of mind and body we are, of course, dealing with a very special case of mind–matter interaction. It is quite possible that the physical seat of interaction is strictly within the brain, or even a small part of the brain (though probably not Descartes' choice of the pineal gland), and that the menagerie of reported paranormal phenomena is the product of error and wishful thinking. This is the creed of many physicists, and certainly counter-examples are so rare that they may be disregarded in the development of normal science. I think some scientists, and not only physicists, fear lest well-attested events may shake the foundations of their science, and are consequently vehement in their denial of the very possibility. Where should we be, they seem to ask, if even a single instance were reliably reported in which a signal was transmitted faster than light, or a body moved when no known force could have been responsible? The answer is: exactly where we were before this terrible thing happened. All that has changed is that we are forced to recognize that where human consciousness is involved we do not possess a scientific technique to handle its effects—something we should have known already. Only when regular paranormal events are reported in which no thinking creature is involved might we seriously wonder whether our normal science is as complete as we had hoped. But there is no cause so far for apprehension.

All the same, to have set our minds at rest about the security of the general structure of science does not stop us wondering how the phenomenon of consciousness comes about. Are we to be Cartesian dualists and regard mind and matter as entirely different things, with the brain as the mechanism by which they are coupled? Or is mind, as I suggested before, to be seen as an emergent property of matter? My strong inclination, in which I believe most scientists nowadays would follow me, is to the latter solution, certainly until we are forced to abandon it. After the triumphant annexation of at least the most primitive life-forms into the general body of physical science, it would be feeble to give up the notion that consciousness may be an automatic consequence of an appropriate degree of complexity. Let us not, however, embark on this conquest without counting the cost. Since we cannot recognize the occurrence of consciousness within the framework of science, we shall have to remove the blinkers which at present restrict us to the analysis of public information. If we were able to do this, and I confess I have no idea how it could be done, we might discover that instead of annexing the fact of consciousness into the body of science, the science of the material world might have been itself annexed into the wider science which has its sources in our own consciousness. This, after all, is our primary information about what we are pleased to call the material world.

Physicists have no appetite for any such revolution. We are confident that our models have progressed toward close correspondence with the real world. We subscribe to Sir Thomas Browne's assertion:

*The severe Schools shall never laugh me out of the Philosophy of Hermes, that this visible World is but a Picture of the invisible, wherein, as in a Pourtraict, things are not truely, but in equivocal shapes, and as they counterfeit some more real substance in that invisible fabrick.* [5]

But every time we are tempted to congratulate ourselves on our skill in penetrating the counterfeit, we should remember the structural weaknesses of our model. To indicate some of these I must concentrate for a while on physics. Let me assure you, however, that no technical expertise is required.

The history of physics can be likened superficially to the history of a city-state such as Rome, which progressively conquered its surroundings until it had enfolded within its empire almost the whole of the known world. In doing so it necessarily changed many of its methods and ideas while retaining at the heart an essential Romishness by which it judged its distant colonies, however different their native culture might be. Physics also from modest and tentative beginnings extended its spheres of conquest toward the very large and the very small, and found rules of conduct to prevail that were considerably different from those appropriate to the simple mechanisms at home. But amid all the changes of procedure that have brought the alien tribes under control, certain central ideas have kept their place. Our intuitive conceptions of time and space may have been refined and modified in the mathematical formulations of relativity theory. Our notions of continuity, as exemplified by the continuous trajectory of a ball, may have been rudely shaken by quantum mechanics. Nevertheless, like Nature in the proverb, however firmly one expels them with a pitchfork they find their way back. Misconceived inventions of the conscious mind, like phlogiston and caloric and the aether, may struggle against our attempts to weed them out, but they can in the end be eradicated; if it should seem desirable to abandon the idea of atoms and fundamental particles, they will struggle much harder, but once dismissed and replaced by a stronger growth they will be forgotten. Time and Space and Continuity, however, are not the intellectual artefacts of scientists; they are intrinsic to our thought, as is obvious from a superficial reading of the most ancient writings. Homer and Xenophon, though perhaps only in translation, soon convince us that, for all the differences in social context, their everyday perceptions were ours.

If the sensations of Time and Space are so deeply embedded in our being that we cannot define them in terms of anything more primitive, is there any reason to worry that they pervade physical theory, even theories of phenomena so large or so small as to lie well beyond personal experience? In fact for at least 300 years they have been the source of a nagging worry, especially to philosophers and to scientists with enough of a smattering of philosophy to be persuaded by Kant that we could never get behind these basic intuitions to know the thing-in-itself of which they are the shadow. How then can we hope to describe things as they really are, and not merely as they seem? If we had found, and continued to find that, on probing deeper, every new layer we uncovered was but a microcosm of the everyday world, we might conclude with relief that our native conceptions happened to be true images of reality. In the years following Newton's *Principia* [*GBWW*, Vol 34, pp. 1–372] there must have been many who, in view of the universal conformity of small objects as well as celestial bodies to a single rational system, were satisfied that what they saw was very much the same as what God saw, though presumably He saw it rather better. Newton himself was not so deceived, and it is worth looking a little closer at this turning-point in the history of science.

A highly characteristic feature of the *Principia* is that the fundamental assumptions are clearly stated at the outset, and their consequences then developed mathematically. The three famous laws of motion need not concern us, it is his inverse square law of gravitational attraction that caused the trouble, for he postulated that two bodies exert forces on one another across immense distances of empty space. Nowadays we tell our students of this postulate and, for the most part, they perceive no difficulty of principle—so effectively does conditioning shackle the imagination. In Newton's time a wild hypothesis like this could not be let pass, especially as the whole idea of subjecting natural phenomena to mathematical analysis was distinctly novel. Besides, Newton was openly contemptuous of Descartes' aetherial vortex theories, which underlay the generally

accepted cosmology of the time, and provided a space-filling continuum by which influences could be transmitted. No success attended various attempts to devise modified vortex theories which would explain in intelligible mechanical terms the origin of the inverse square law, so that the choice seemed to lie between a fluid aether that did not work, and unmediated action-at-a-distance which was patent nonsense. Newton, in the famous words "*hypotheses non fingo*," [6] seems to have taken a typically firm and idiosyncratic line by rejecting both explanations and getting on with the mathematical analysis.

A hundred years later the problem had become more acute, when the wave theory of light seemed to demand a rigid aether in which the light waves could propagate. And not only light, but electric and magnetic forces were added to gravitation, presenting a complex set of conditions to be simultaneously satisfied by aether theories. When eventually FitzGerald and Lorentz assigned to the aether such attributes as would ensure that its presence could not be detected by any experiment, the time was ripe (as we appreciate with the advantage of hindsight) for Einstein to sweep it all away and restore to space its primitive Newtonian vacuity.

It is only too easy to poke fun at the mechanical models devised by such as Kelvin and Maxwell, with fluid vortices geared together by chains of idler wheels, as if these great men really believed that space was filled with something like this. Of course they did not, but they found the models useful both to encourage and to restrain their imagination. Kelvin was quite explicit in declaring his doubts about any invented set of differential equations unless he could see that they described behaviour which could be simulated by a mechanical model; that was his guarantee that they did not imply a logical inconsistency. It is possible that here lies the seed of his cautious reluctance to follow Maxwell, who transcended the limitations of his own mechanical models when he wrote down his electromagnetic equations, as Einstein was to show, forty years later, in his special theory of relativity.

Maxwell's equations, Newton's gravitational theory, and Einstein's relativity theory are all model-free mathematical formulations, and they exemplify the purer form of physical theory that was enthusiastically propounded as an ideal by d'Alembert, Mach, and many others, who deplored the construction of elaborate systems on the basis of hypothetical and unobservable entities. Thus Mach would have happily swept molecular models into the dustbin, while admitting that they might serve a transitory purpose, like aether models, in channelling the imagination into profitable directions. I think history shows that the imagination needs these props. Few can build without scaffolding; in Maxwell's equations and Einstein's relativity what we see is the final result of a long process, after the scaffolding has been removed. Even Einstein in his quantum theory developments was unashamedly guided by private models of an as-yet-unobserved atomism; and in modern times perhaps only Heisenberg has succeeded in making a fundamental advance by deliberately concentrating on observables, and devising in matrix mechanics a model-free calculus for handling them. It is generally admitted, however, that matrix mechanics presents great difficulties in working anything out, and that Schrödinger's form of quantum mechanics, which certainly runs counter to Mach's ideals, is a much more convenient way of getting the same answers.

There is a striking parallel between Schrödinger's and Kelvin's achievements. Both tackled boldly the mathematical development of promising models, and both soon found themselves unable to shed the preconceptions which initially attracted them to their models, so that they grew to become reactionary opponents of further advances. With Schrödinger the disillusion was uncomfortably rapid—within a

year he was lamenting the interpretation that was developed by the circle around Bohr in Copenhagen, and which remains, sixty years later, the accepted orthodoxy. The trouble started with de Broglie's suggestion, in 1923, that one might associate waves with material particles, in analogy with light. Over the centuries, wave theories of light had alternated with particle theories until by 1923 it became clear that both were necessary. Soon after, experiments on electron diffraction showed that the same applies to material particles.

Seizing on de Broglie's suggestion, Schrödinger developed the differential equation that the wave must obey and, in doing so, released from its bottle a genie he was powerless to control. He seems to have hoped at first that the electron would turn out to be a small packet of waves, which would hold together and behave like a particle if not examined too closely. But the wave-packets described by his equation do not remain compact, but quickly spread out, and in any case can only too readily be sliced in two when they meet a knife-edge. The electron is never sliced in two—it goes to one side or the other. In a moment I shall have to look in a little more detail, but at present it is enough to recognize that what upset Schrödinger was that the electron is neither a particle nor a wave. He could have accepted either, but not the idea that when observed it seems to be a particle, while in between observations it behaves more like a wave. Moreover, wave mechanics in the Copenhagen interpretation has jettisoned the classical concept of determinacy; no longer can one say what will happen—the best available description involves making a list of possible outcomes and assigning to each the probability that it will happen in any single trial. I do not propose to enlarge on this outrageous denial of deeply-held beliefs, except to remark that indeterminacy was one of the strongest reasons why not only Schrödinger but de Broglie and Einstein also were convinced that the

331

new quantum mechanics was only a staging post on the way to a deeper and more satisfying theory. They did not deny its power, for they recognized its overwhelming success in reducing to order a host of atomic and molecular processes which had previously been intractable. But they belong in the company of many distinguished physicists from Newton onward, who have discovered their prescriptions for solving problems to be incompatible with their strongest convictions about the nature of material things. They would all have been happy Machian positivists but that they could not leave ill alone, and continued to assault the fortresses of incomprehension.

At this point physicists may expect me to illustrate the conflict between formalism and intuition by discussing some of the famous paradoxes, particularly that of Einstein, Podolsky, and Rosen (as sharpened by Bell's theorem and recent exquisite experiments by Aspect and others) and the paradoxes known as Schrödinger's cat and Wigner's friend. These have generated a vast literature, itself enough to reveal the continuing anxiety which arises because their resolution in quantum-mechanical terms obviously violates common sense. They all, however, demand leisurely exposition for which I have not the time, and I shall therefore expose the problem by means of more elementary examples. For this purpose I must show you how to set up the solution of a very simple quantum-mechanical problem. I shall not actually solve it since the technical manipulations involve no point of principle—a computer could do it considerably better.

A ball is rolling along an undulating path. Its total energy stays constant but its potential energy varies with the height of the path, so that the kinetic energy also varies. In classical physics this is a trivial problem; the kinetic energy is $\frac{1}{2}mv^2$, and once it is known, so is $v$ the velocity. It is then a straightforward matter to compute where it will have got to any moment. The same problem is tackled in quantum mechanics by transforming the energy equation into a differential equation (Schrödinger's equation). There is nothing mysterious about this—it is the standard procedure for setting up the differential equation describing a wave when you know how its frequency and wavelength are related; in this case, following de Broglie, the momentum defines the wavelength and the total energy defines the frequency. What is mysterious is that we have introduced a new quantity, the wave-function $\psi$, to describe the local displacement of the medium, if any, whose vibrations are associated with the particle. Unlike the waves of normal experience this wave is not in itself observable—there is in fact no medium to undulate—but this need not disturb anyone who believes in the wave theory of light after Einstein has abolished the aether. We interpret $\psi$ by analogy with light. Just as the intensity of a light wave tells us how frequently we may expect photons to arrive, so here the value of $\psi^2$ at any point tells us how likely we are to find the particle if we look there. Indeterminacy is built into this interpretation; instead of knowing exactly where the particle is at all times we now know exactly only $\psi^2$, the probability of finding it if we look. We are not allowed to know how it got from A to B—if we discover by measurement where it is at some instant, and how fast it is moving, we write an expression for an appropriately positioned wave-packet and see how it develops with time in accordance with Schrödinger's equation. This gives us the probability of its being discovered at any point when looked for later, but only if we do not look for it in between. If we should do so we inevitably disturb its motion and alter the subsequent behaviour, though not necessarily very greatly if it is a large body, or a very energetic elementary particle. In principle, however, to get as reliable a prediction as indeterminacy allows we should start again, entering into Schrödinger's equation a wave-packet describing our new knowledge.

In this hasty sketch of the rules of quantum mechanics I have tried to avoid using any form of words that might imply that $\psi$ is anything other than an auxiliary quantity introduced as a mathematical aid—the sort of thing Mach accepted as an unfortunate necessity to be forgotten as soon as it has served its immediate purpose. Undoubtedly, however, through continued use and familiarity physicists tend in unguarded moments to think of it as something real, a sort of pervasive waviness that controls the movement of its associated particle. I think this tendency results from the virtual impossibility of shedding intuitive feelings for continuity. Compared with a particle whose motion is indeterminate and unimaginable, the wave-function is cosily continuous—cosy, that is, until we people our universe with more than one particle.

Not long after the first experiments on electron diffraction verified de Broglie's relation between momentum and wavelength for an electron, Estermann and Stern [7] performed a similar but much harder experiment with helium atoms, and showed that the wavelength was that appropriate to a particle having the total mass of the atom, which is made up of two protons, two neutrons, and two electrons. Now we know enough about the energy of the particles in the nucleus to be certain that each individually should be assigned a wavelength hundreds of times smaller than that observed. If we were ever tempted to imagine that each particle carried its own private wave around with it, our enthusiasm is dashed by this simple result. I do not contend that a theory could not be derived on this basis, but no one has managed to do so, and I suspect no one has tried, since the Schrödinger prescription yields the required answer without any fuss. We write down the classical expression for the total energy of the six particles, including their mutual interaction energies. This gives an expression involving three position coordinates $(x, y,$ and $z)$ for each particle and three momentum components for each—a rather long expression involving eighteen position and eighteen momentum coordinates. Then we follow the rules and replace every momentum component by a differential coefficient, and let it operate on $\psi$. The resulting Schrödinger equation is a differential equation in eighteen position coordinates, and there is only one $\psi$, not a different one for each particle. There is no hope of solving this equation completely, but one result can be extracted with very little trouble—no matter how strongly the particles interact, the equation separates into two independent equations. One is still impossibly complicated and derives from the motions of the particles relative to one another, that is, the internal economy of the atom. The other is extremely simple and describes the motion of the centre of mass of the atom—and it is Schrödinger's equation for a free structureless particle having the total mass.

The observations are thus beautifully accounted for, but the implication is that the wave-function for the system of six particles is not the superposition of six waves, but a single function $\psi$ whose value at any instant is determined by the position of every particle. And the frequency of oscillation of this wave is determined by the total energy of all six, irrespective of how it may be divided between them. Of course, what goes for six goes for any number—the wave-function for a litre of gas is a single function $\psi$ of more than $10^{23}$ coordinates.

You must not suppose that the argument for preferring Schrödinger's prescription, above any that might assign a separate wave to each particle, rests on the one experimental fact concerning the diffraction of helium atoms; the whole theory of nuclei, of multi-electron atoms, of chemical molecules, indeed virtually the whole edifice of modern physics hangs crucially on the general applicability of this prescription. Without it, for example, there would be no Pauli exclusion principle.

Suppose now we set out to analyse a

problem involving two particles in close interaction; we must start by writing the initial state as a conjoint wave-function in a single Schrödinger equation. If the particles subsequently fly apart, out of range of their mutual interactions, we cannot at this later stage decide to describe each by its own equation. Until we make the next observation and modify the available information, the two particles retain their linkage, in the sense that what we observe of one influences the probabilities of what we may observe of the other. And this remains true however far apart the particles have flown. This was one of the consequences of quantum mechanics that Einstein could not accept. He took it as axiomatic that when two particles are so far apart that they exert no forces on one another, no observation made on one can influence what is observed with the other. And it is this issue which is addressed by Bell's theorem [8] and Aspect's experiments, [9] with an outcome decisively in favour of quantum mechanics. These recent developments also reinforce an important theorem of von Neumann, dating from 1930 but refined by Bell, to the effect that the description of phenomena provided by quantum mechanics cannot arise as an artefact of incomplete observation. Everyone is agreed that available instruments will not tell us precisely where a particle is and at the same time precisely how fast it is moving—this is Heisenberg's uncertainty principle. But it is tempting, when one first meets the idea, to take refuge in a hidden-variable theory, that is to imagine that the particle may really be behaving in a quite sensible way, but that we impose uncertainty through the grossness of our measuring procedures. It is this hope that the series of investigations from von Neumann to Aspect has destroyed. No hidden-variables model with remotely credible properties can act as a substructure underlying Schrödinger's equation. When we imagine elementary particles as small billiard balls

we imagine a vain thing, and no amount of furious raging together by the heathen is going to alter the fact.

Accepting then that what we call elementary particles cannot be in reality anything we can visualize by analogy with everyday experience, we must still try to come to terms with Einstein's problem, that particles which have once been in close interaction remain mutually dependent as regards the next observations made on them, however far apart they may be; and this is not the simple consequence of their pursuing deterministic trajectories. Many vain attempts have been made to sweep this difficulty under the carpet, often by recourse to the assumption that although quantum mechanics applies to atomic processes, it is irrelevant or even incorrect as applied to observations on a human scale. In other words, peculiar goings-on in the sub-world of atoms are acceptable provided they do not disturb the even tenor of normal life. The weakness of this compromise becomes clear when we recognize that the very processes by which we observe the world are compatible with quantum mechanics only in the strict form that caused Einstein his difficulties. The interdependence of two distant particles applies also to two distant human observers. We may reconcile ourselves to the old problem of action-at-a-distance through empty space, by the operation of long-range forces like gravitation; we must now try to accept action-at-a-distance in the absence of any long-range forces.

A simple example should suffice as illustration. Ever since Planck and Einstein, at the beginning of the century, we have lived with the idea of the photon as the quantum of light. To physicists and anyone concerned with photochemical processes the photon is as real a particle as the electron, and nobody questions the propriety of the concept of quantum efficiency applied to optical detectors. The quantum efficiency of a single rod in the retina is close to unity—only one photon is needed to initiate a chemical process whose ultimate outcome can in principle be a nerve impulse to the brain. To be sure, there are complex nerve linkages which may inhibit the observation of each photon individually, but they do not invalidate my argument which is concerned only with the primary triggering action of this photon. Let us suppose, as is now technically possible, that a single atom is held isolated in a vacuum, and stimulated so that from time to time it emits a single photon, and that we sit watching for these photons as they emerge. According to standard theory, at every emission process the atom is to be imagined radiating an electromagnetic wave which spreads in all directions; the intensity of the wave that is focused on to a rod receptor in one of my eyes determines the probability that the photon will turn up there rather than outside the eye. But what about my other eye, or for that matter one of your eyes if you are also sitting there waiting for an event? The wave reaches rods in every eye, yet there is only one photon available to stimulate a response. If I see a photon, how does your eye know that there is no photon for it, even though the wave is just as strong as it was for me? If we could believe that the atom emitted a real photon in one particular direction, and that the wave simply served to make some directions more likely than others, we should accept the uniqueness of the response without question. But it is precisely this escape route which is firmly blocked by von Neumann's hidden-variables theorem. Thus the only intuitively reasonable explanation is disallowed, while the unreasonable explanation provided by quantum mechanics yields the required answer without difficulty. We have to lump together into one grand Schrödinger equation the radiating atom and all the receptors that might be excited, and it then emerges that for every atomic process at most one receptor will record a stimulus.

Here, then, is the crux; if the very senses by which we learn to interpret the world around us are themselves subject to laws which make a mockery of the intuitions of space that they beget, is it not a waste of time to pretend that we might be able to make intelligible models of physical reality? I think so, and am content, once the rules have been established and adequately verified, to fall back to what I have labelled the Machian position and regard them as instruments for correlating and predicting observations in the public domain. It is no small thing that this limited enterprise has succeeded so well. Nevertheless there are many who feel that physics has failed if it cannot provide a picture of events that conforms with their private conception of reality. They resemble those "framers of hypotheses" that Newton repudiated, who could not accept a mathematical formulation, however successful, unless they could envisage the mechanism involved. I do not expect advances on this front. On the contrary, I prefer to see the pioneering spirits striving toward an entirely abstract theory, in which ideas like space and time do not appear explicitly, but emerge as inevitable consequences of the theoretical structure, rather like the spin of the electron did from Dirac's theory. And it would, of course, have to generate solutions that could be interpreted as equivalent to the successful achievements of existing theory.

I have no idea whether this ideal theory is possible, or whether one would be able to recognize the emergence of space and time in the solutions generated from the theory. But let us speculate on the consequences of success. Would it, for example, be so fundamental as to mark the end of the search? This is a question worth posing since at least one distinguished theorist not long ago proclaimed his belief that the end was in sight, and he did not, I think, have in mind anything so radical as my proposal. Yet for several reasons it seems to me that my suggestion must be regarded as no more than another step toward a very distant, even unattainable, goal.

In the first place, however deeply we dig to find the truly fundamental principles, we are still obeying the conventions of science and are therefore precluded from learning how consciousness emerges. Can we discover any way of combining public and private knowledge into a complete description? Only by joining to our outward-looking skills those employed by expert cultivators of the inner landscape, and preferably by combining both kinds of expertise in the same individuals. The languages are entirely different, however. For the scientist, words and the logic that is grounded in words are the means by which information is made public. The knowledge of the private world is the knowledge gained by mystics and musicians and lovers, knowledge which stands outside words and logic. I may communicate the fact that I have such knowledge, as I may communicate my feeling of well-being by smiling and singing a jolly song, but the knowledge itself—what the Eroica symphony really means to me—that I cannot express in words or gesture. Among the great physicists Planck, Einstein, and Heisenberg were all highly talented musicians, but neither activity gave support to the other except indirectly, by enhancing their lives in a general way. As for the lovers, and the mystics who are sometimes supposed to share kinship with the most abstract theoretical physicists (mainly on the grounds that neither sort can explain themselves in popular language without recourse to the same limited vocabulary of analogies), of them one can only say what the statue said to Don Giovanni, "Those who taste of the food of the Angels, eat no more the corrupt food of mortals."

If science cannot rise to the realm of mind, and mind will not, or cannot, stoop to interpret the reality governing the realm of science, even the most convinced monist must compromise for practical purposes by espousing a pragmatic dualism. The consequence for the scientist is that he must remain agnostic about phenomena that accompany the manifestation of mind. He need not waste his office hours discussing whether free will is wholly incompatible with what he refers to as the laws of nature; that is a metaphysical question appropriate to his leisure moments. My private view is that almost all the time I behave as an automaton, responding to my conditioning and exercising little, if any, free will. But my conditioning is as much self-imposed as imposed from outside—in other words what I desire, that I do; but purposeful contemplation in the intervals of automatism modifies the pattern of my desires. This is where free will operates and plays a central role in making me responsible for my actions, and it is precisely here, in the contemplative role of the conscious mind, that science has nothing to say.

To revert to my hypothetical fundamental theory, a second reason for doubting that it can represent a satisfactory end to the search lies at the opposite end to the question of consciousness. If less fundamental theoretical structures are any guide, the theory would, like Schrödinger's equation, admit of very general solutions, and in any specific case would require the imposition of boundary conditions. One might find, then, that it was capable of generating a wide variety of possible universes. Who or what determines the subsidiary conditions that ensure it is our own universe that emerges as the preferred solution? We know from various branches of physics and cosmology that the constants defining the strength of forces and the masses of particles are very finely balanced to allow the formation of a universe in which creatures like us could have evolved to the complexity required for thought. To some this seems an argument that the universe was designed with us in mind—in the language of coarse theology, God chose the subsidiary conditions to meet this requirement of His. If such lack of humility offends, one might prefer to imagine that all possible universes coexist independently in the spaceless, timeless primal structure, and that we are in the right sort of universe for us because we could not be anywhere else. But however we look at it, the question belongs to the farthest reaches of the hypothetical, and cannot be answered without knowledge of the cause of all things.

And that we shall never know, and will not even begin to know without calling to our aid every means by which we may attain knowledge. It is tempting for the scientist, with the assurance he commands in his own realm, to dismiss religious experience as a delusion. To be sure, he has a right to parade the evidence that makes him sceptical of antiquated cosmologies such as

religions are apt to carry in their train; and he is right to despise dogmas that imply a God whose grandeur does not match up to the grandeur of the universe he knows. But when we have chased out the mountebanks there remain the saints and others of transparent integrity whose confident belief is not to be dismissed simply because it is inconvenient and unshared. We may lack the gift of belief ourselves, just as we may be tone-deaf; but it is becoming in us to envy those whose lives are radiant with a truth which is no less true for being incommunicable. As scientists we have a craftsman's part to play in the City of God; we cannot receive the freedom of that city until we have learnt to respect the freedom of every citizen.

1. Subrahmanyan Chandrasekhar, *Eddington* (Cambridge University Press, 1983).

2. Richard P. Feynman, R. B. Leighton, and Matthew Sands, *The Feynman Lectures* (Reading, Mass.: Addison-Wesley, 1963), chap. 1, p. 8.

3. Emergence is the term introduced by G. H. Lewes to describe the evolution of properties distinct from those possessed by the forerunners. As used by Lloyd Morgan, *Emergent Evolution* (London: Williams and Norgate, 1927), the concept may be seen as a speculative generalization of the physicist's critical points and broken symmetry.

4. Eugene P. Wigner, in *The Scientist Speculates,* edited by I. J. Good (London: Heinemann, 1961).

5. Sir Thomas Browne, 1642, *Religio Medici;* in the Everyman edition of Browne's Works, "The Religio Medici and Other Writings" (London: Dent, 1906), p. 14.

6. Isaac Newton, 1686, *Principia;* Florian Cajori's revision of Andrew Motte's translation (University of California Press, 1947), p. 547.

7. Immanuel Estermann and Otto Stern, *Z. Physik,* 61, 95, 1930.

8. John S. Bell, *Physics,* 1, 195, 1965.

9. Alain Aspect, Philippe Grangier, and Gérard Roger, *Phys. Rev. Lett.,* 47, 460, 1981.

# The Stones of Venice
# (selections)

John Ruskin

## Editor's Introduction

It has been noted of John Ruskin (1819–1900) that he was both the writer on art by whom the Victorians set greatest store and also an impassioned critic, whom they did not credit, of the society, particularly the economic order in which they lived. These contradictory roles, which overlapped somewhat, though the art critic was for the most part superseded by the social one, are usually traced to Ruskin's upbringing. Certainly his father, a successful London wine merchant who was fond of travel and liked beautiful landscapes and fine art, introduced him to those things, while his mother, a profoundly pious woman, exposed him to daily readings of Scripture. And as he presumably derived the aesthetic appreciation, which is evident even in his theoretical discussions of art, from the first source, so he got the prophetic temper and moral mission that are found in his social essays from the second. But in fact the two strains were always mixed in him, with the result that the art critic was at the same time concerned with the good life and how it might be achieved, while the critic of society was never more severe than in drawing attention to the sheer ugliness by which the Victorians allowed themselves to be surrounded.

Travel, writing, and lecturing were the activities in which Ruskin spent his life, and spent it freely, for his literary output was enormous. Three phases can be discerned in this. The first was marked by a preoccupation with problems of art, and it began when he was twenty-three and had graduated from Oxford. His chief interest was in the English landscape painter J. M. W. Turner (1775–1851), whose expressionistic work, with its emphasis on light and color at the expense of detail, he undertook to defend in what eventually became a five-volume work known as *Modern Painters* (1843–1860). In this he praised Turner, with many forays into aesthetic questions and the importance of the imagination generally, as the great painter of the time.

The second phase began in the 1850s, when Ruskin became interested in architecture. Of the writings he devoted to this subject the most popular was *The Seven Lamps of Architecture* (1849), and the longest, *The Stones of Venice* (1851–53). In both of these Ruskin celebrated medieval design, that is to say, the Gothic, in which he saw the fulfillment of the artisan as distinct from the worker of his own, industrial, dehumanizing age. *The Stones of Venice,* a book of over 400,000 words which has never been printed in its entirety, contains his fullest argument to this effect, and indeed a volume can be made, as here, of selections containing only that, without substantial reference to Venice itself, in which Ruskin saw endless applications of his guiding principle. He was far from wholly pleased, however, by the Gothic revival in building which he did so much to cause, since most of it was done without the craftsmanship and the integrity by which it could in his view be justified.

His interest in architecture was from the beginning not only aesthetic but social, and he sought to determine the kind of society it had taken and would always take to produce great buildings. As this was his concern, it is not surprising that he found himself thinking and writing about economics. His ideas about wealth and the responsibilities it ought to have for workingmen and the general quality of human life were originally set forth in a series of articles for *The Cornhill Magazine,* but they caused such a stir that the editor, William Makepeace Thackeray, discontinued them, and Ruskin published them separately in *Unto This Last* (1862).

In 1869, notwithstanding his failure as a social critic, he was made a professor of fine art at Oxford, a position he held for ten years. But signs of mania, which had been coming over him for some time, now became too strong to ignore, and finding himself unable to work in any sustained way, he eventually resigned. His condition was in part a consequence of his unhappy experience with women, his wife having left him after an unconsummated marriage, and a young girl with whom he later fell hopelessly in love having died.

After half a dozen attacks of madness, and with an autobiography, *Praeterita,* unfinished, Ruskin gave up all attempts at intellectual work and spent the last ten years of his life incapable of effective communication with anyone. Despite this, he was at his death a celebrated man, the keeper of his country's artistic conscience, so far as it had one, and a social prophet whose thought had influence on both George Bernard Shaw and D. H. Lawrence after his death and contributed in important ways to the eventual formation of the Welfare State.

# The Stones of Venice
## (selections)

## Book One

### Chapter I

### The Quarry

Since first the dominion of men was asserted over the ocean, three thrones, of mark beyond all others, have been set upon its sands: the thrones of Tyre, Venice, and England. Of the first of these great powers only the memory remains; of the second, the ruin; the third, which inherits their greatness, if it forget their example, may be led through prouder eminence to less pitied destruction.

The exaltation, the sin, and the punishment of Tyre have been recorded for us, in perhaps the most touching words ever uttered by the Prophets of Israel against the cities of the stranger. But we read them as a lovely song; and close our ears to the sternness of their warning: for the very depth of the Fall of Tyre has blinded us to its reality, and we forget, as we watch the bleaching of the rocks between the sunshine and the sea, that they were once "as in Eden, the garden of God."

Her successor, like her in perfection of beauty, though less in endurance of dominion, is still left for our beholding in the final period of her decline: a ghost upon the sands of the sea, so weak—so quiet— so bereft of all but her loveliness, that we might well doubt, as we watched her faint reflection in the mirage of the lagoon, which was the City, and which the Shadow.

I would endeavor to trace the lines of this image before it be forever lost, and to record, as far as I may, the warning which seems to me to be uttered by every one of the fast-gaining waves, that beat like passing bells, against the Stones of Venice.

The state of Venice existed thirteen hundred and seventy-six years, from the first establishment of a consular government on the island of the Rialto, to the moment when the general-in-chief of the French army of Italy pronounced the Venetian republic a thing of the past. Of this period, two hundred and seventy-six years were passed in a nominal subjection to the cities of old Venetia, especially to Padua, and in an agitated form of democracy of which the executive appears to have been entrusted to tribunes, chosen, one by the inhabitants of each of the principal islands. For six hundred years, during which the power of Venice was continually on the increase, her government was an elective monarchy, her king or doge possessing, in early times at least, as much independent authority as any other European sovereign, but an authority gradually subjected to limitation, and shortened almost daily of its prerogatives, while it increased in a spectral and incapable magnificence. The final government of the nobles under the image of a king lasted for five hundred years, during which Venice reaped the fruits of her former energies, consumed them— and expired.

Let the reader therefore conceive the existence of the Venetian state as broadly divided into two periods: the first of nine hundred, the second of five hundred years, the separation being marked by what was called the "Serrar del Consiglio"; that is to say, the final and absolute distinction of the nobles from the commonalty, and the establishment of the government in their hands to the exclusion alike of the influence of the people on the one side, and the authority of the doge on the other.

Then the first period, of nine hundred years, presents us with the most interesting spectacle of a people struggling out of anarchy into order and power; and then governed, for the most part, by the worthiest and noblest man whom they could find among them, called their doge or leader, with an aristocracy gradually and resolutely forming itself around him, out of which, and at last by which, he was chosen; an aristocracy owing its origin to the accidental numbers, influence, and wealth of some among the families of the fugitives from the older Venetia, and gradually organizing itself, by its unity and heroism, into a separate body.

This first period includes the rise of Venice, her noblest achievements, and the circumstances which determined her character and position among European powers; and within its range, as might have been anticipated, we find the names of all her hero princes—of Pietro Urseolo, Ordalafo Falier, Domenico Michieli, Sebastiano Ziani, and Enrico Dandolo.

The second period opens with a hundred and twenty years, the most eventful in the career of Venice—the central struggle of her life—stained with her darkest crime, the murder of Carrara—disturbed by her most dangerous internal sedition, the conspiracy of Falier—oppressed by her most fatal war, the war of Chiozza—and distinguished by the glory of her two noblest citizens (for in this period the heroism of her citizens replaces that of her monarchs), Vittor Pisani and Carlo Zeno.

I date the commencement of the Fall of Venice from the death of Carlo Zeno, 8th May, 1418; the *visible* commencement from that of another of her noblest and wis-

est children, the Doge Tomaso Mocenigo, who expired five years later. The reign of Foscari followed, gloomy with pestilence and war; a war in which large acquisitions of territory were made by subtle or fortunate policy in Lombardy, and disgrace, significant as irreparable, sustained in the battles on the Po at Cremona, and in the marshes of Caravaggio. In 1454, Venice, the first of the states of Christendom, humiliated herself to the Turk: in the same year was established the Inquisition of State, and from this period her government takes the perfidious and mysterious form under which it is usually conceived. In 1477 the great Turkish invasion spread terror to the shores of the lagoons; and in 1508 the league of Cambrai marks the period usually assigned as the commencement of the decline of the Venetian power; the commercial prosperity of Venice in the close of the fifteenth century blinding her historians to the previous evidence of the diminution of her internal strength.

It is now necessary that the reader should have some general idea of the connection of the architecture of Venice with that of the rest of Europe, from its origin forward.

All European architecture, bad and good, old and new, is derived from Greece through Rome, and colored and perfected from the East. The history of architecture is nothing but the tracing of the various modes and directions of this derivation. Understand this, once for all: if you hold fast this great connecting clue, you may string all the types of successive architectural invention upon it like so many beads. The Doric and the Corinthian orders are the roots, the one of all Romanesque, massy-capitaled buildings—Norman, Lombard, Byzantine, and what else you can name of the kind; and the Corinthian of all Gothic, Early English, French, German, and Tuscan. Now observe: those old Greeks gave the shaft; Rome gave the arch; the Arabs pointed and foliated the arch.

There is high probability that the Greek

received his shaft system from Egypt; but I do not care to keep this earlier derivation in the mind of the reader. It is only necessary that he should be able to refer to a fixed point of origin, when the form of the shaft was first perfected. But it may be incidentally observed, that if the Greeks did indeed receive their Doric from Egypt, then the three families of the earth have each contributed their part to its noblest architecture.

I have said that the two orders, Doric and Corinthian, are the roots of all European architecture. You have, perhaps, heard of five orders: but there are only two real orders; and there never can be any more until doomsday. On one of these orders the ornament is convex: those are Doric, Norman, and what else you recollect of the kind. On the other the ornament is concave: those are Corinthian, Early English, Decorated, and what else you recollect of that kind. The transitional form, in which the ornamental line is straight, is the center or root of both. All other orders are varieties of these, or phantasms and grotesques, altogether indefinite in number and species.

This Greek architecture, then, with its two orders, was clumsily copied and varied by the Romans with no particular result, until they began to bring the arch into extensive practical service; except only that the Doric capital was spoiled in endeavors to mend it, and the Corinthian much varied and enriched with fanciful, and often very beautiful imagery. And in this state of things came Christianity: seized upon the arch as her own: decorated it, and delighted in it: invented a new Doric capital to replace the spoiled Roman one: and all over the Roman empire set to work, with such materials as were nearest at hand, to express and adorn herself as best she could. This Roman Christian architecture is the exact expression of the Christianity of the time, very fervid and beautiful—but very imperfect; in many respects ignorant, and yet radiant with a strong, child-ish light of imagination, which flames up under Constantine, illumines all the shores of the Bosphorus and the Aegean and the Adriatic Sea, and then gradually, as the people give themselves up to idolatry, becomes corpse-light. The architecture, like the religion it expressed, sinks into a settled form—a strange, gilded, and embalmed repose; and so would have remained forever—so *does* remain, where its languor has been undisturbed. But rough wakening was ordained for it.

This Christian art of the declining empire is divided into two great branches, western and eastern; one centered at Rome, the other at Byzantium, of which the one is the early Christian Romanesque, properly so called, and the other, carried to higher imaginative perfection by Greek workmen, is distinguished from it as Byzantine. But I wish the reader, for the present, to class these two branches of art together in his mind, they being, in points of main importance, the same; that is to say, both of them a true continuance and sequence of the art of old Rome itself, flowing uninterruptedly down from the fountainhead, and entrusted always to the best workmen who could be found—Latins in Italy and Greeks in Greece; and thus both branches may be ranged under the general term of Christian Romanesque, an architecture which had lost the refinement of pagan art in the degradation of the Empire, but which was elevated by Christianity to higher aims, and by the fancy of the Greek workmen endowed with brighter forms. And this art the reader may conceive as extending in its various branches over all the central provinces of the empire, taking aspects more or less refined, according to its proximity to the seats of government; dependent for all its power on the vigor and freshness of the religion which animated it; and as that vigor and purity departed, losing its own vitality, and sinking into nerveless rest, not deprived of its beauty, but benumbed, and incapable of advance or change.

Meantime there had been preparation for its renewal. While in Rome and Constantinople, and in the districts under their immediate influence, this Roman art of pure descent was practiced in all its refinement, an impure form of it—a patois of Romanesque—was carried by inferior workmen into distant provinces; and still ruder imitations of this patois were executed by the barbarous nations on the skirts of the Empire. But these barbarous nations were in the strength of their youth; and while, in the center of Europe, a refined and purely descended art was sinking into graceful formalism, on its confines a barbarous and borrowed art was organizing itself into strength and consistency. The reader must therefore consider the history of the work of the period as broadly divided into two great heads; the one embracing the elaborately languid succession of the Christian art of Rome; and the other, the imitations of it executed by nations in every conceivable phase of early organization, on the edges of the Empire, or included in its now merely nominal extent.

Some of the barbaric nations were, of course, not susceptible of this influence; and, when they burst over the Alps, appear like the Huns, as scourges only, or mix, as the Ostrogoths, with the enervated Italians, and give physical strength to the mass with which they mingle, without materially affecting its intellectual character. But others, both south and north of the Empire, had felt its influence, back to the beach of the Indian Ocean on the one hand, and to the ice creeks of the North Sea on the other. On the north and west the influence was of the Latins; on the south and east, of the Greeks. Two nations, preeminent above all the rest, represent to us the force of derived mind on either side. As the central power is eclipsed, the orbs of reflected light gather into their fullness; and when sensuality and idolatry had done their work, and the religion of the Empire was laid asleep in a glittering sepulcher, the living light rose upon both horizons,

and the fierce swords of the Lombard and Arab were shaken over its golden paralysis.

The work of the Lombard was to give hardihood and system to the enervated body and enfeebled mind of Christendom; that of the Arab was to punish idolatry, and to proclaim the spirituality of worship. The Lombard covered every church which he built with the sculptured representations of bodily exercises—hunting and war. The Arab banished all imagination of creature form from his temples, and proclaimed from their minarets, "There is no god but God." Opposite in their character and mission, alike in their magnificence of energy, they came from the North and from the South, the glacier torrent and the lava stream: they met and contended over the wreck of the Roman empire; and the very center of the struggle, the point of pause of both, the dead water of the opposite eddies, charged with embayed fragments of the Roman wreck, is Venice.

The Ducal Palace of Venice contains the three elements in exactly equal proportions—the Roman, Lombard, and Arab. It is the central building of the world.

The reader will now begin to understand something of the importance of the study of the edifices of a city which concludes, within the circuit of some seven or eight miles, the field of contest between the three preeminent architectures of the world—each architecture expressing a condition of religion; each an erroneous condition, yet necessary to the correction of the others, and corrected by them.

It will be part of my endeavor in the following work, to mark the various modes in which the northern and southern architectures were developed from the Roman: here I must pause only to name the distinguishing characteristics of the great families. The Christian Roman and Byzantine work is round-arched, with single and well-proportioned shafts; capitals imitated from classical Roman; moldings more or less so; and large surfaces of walls entirely covered with imagery, mosaic, and paintings, whether of scripture history or of sacred symbols.

The Arab school is at first the same in its principal features, the Byzantine workmen being employed by the caliphs; but the Arab rapidly introduces characters half Persepolitan, half Egyptian, into the shafts and capitals: in his intense love of excitement he points the arch and writhes it into extravagant foliations; he banishes the animal imagery, and invents an ornamentation of his own (called Arabesque) to replace it: this not being adapted for covering large surfaces, he concentrates it on features of interest, and bars his surfaces with horizontal lines of color, the expression of the level of the desert. He retains the dome and adds the minaret. All is done with exquisite refinement.

The changes effected by the Lombard are more curious still, for they are in the anatomy of the building, more than its decoration. The Lombard architecture represents, as I said, the whole of that of the northern barbaric nations. And this I believe was, at first, an imitation in wood of the Christian Roman churches or basilicas. Without staying to examine the whole structure of a basilica, the reader will easily understand thus much of it: that it had a nave and two aisles, the nave much higher than the aisles; that the nave was separated from the aisles by rows of shafts, which supported, above, large spaces of flat or dead wall, rising above the aisles, and forming the upper part of the nave, now called the clerestory, which had a gabled wooden roof.

These high dead walls were, in Roman work, built of stone; but in the wooden work of the North, they must necessarily have been made of horizontal boards or timbers attached to uprights on the top of the nave pillars, which were themselves also of wood. Now, these uprights were necessarily thicker than the rest of the timbers, and formed vertical square pilasters above the nave piers. As Christianity extended and civilization increased, these wooden

structures were changed into stone; but they were literally petrified, retaining the form which had been made necessary by their being of wood. The upright pilaster above the nave pier remains in the stone edifice, and is the first form of the great distinctive feature of Northern architecture—the vaulting shaft. In that form the Lombards brought it into Italy in the seventh century, and it remains to this day in Saint Ambrogio of Milan, and Saint Michele of Pavia.

When the vaulting shaft was introduced in the clerestory walls, additional members were added for its support to the nave piers. Perhaps two or three pine trunks, used for a single pillar, gave the first idea of the grouped shaft. Be that as it may, the arrangement of the nave pier in the form of a cross accompanies the superimposition of the vaulting shaft; together with correspondent grouping of minor shafts in doorways and apertures of windows. Thus, the whole body of the Northern architecture, represented by that of the Lombards, may be described as rough but majestic work, round arched, with grouped shafts, added vaulting shafts, and endless imagery of active life and fantastic superstitions.

The glacier stream of the Lombards, and the following one of the Normans, left their erratic blocks wherever they had flowed; but without influencing, I think, the Southern nations beyond the sphere of their own presence. But the lava stream of the Arab, even after it ceased to flow, warmed the whole of the Northern air; and the history of Gothic architecture is the history of the refinement and spiritualization of Northern work under its influence. The noblest buildings of the world, the Pisan-Romanesque, Tuscan (Giottesque) Gothic, and Veronese Gothic, are those of the Lombard schools themselves, under its close and direct influence; the various Gothics of the north are the original forms of the architecture which the Lombards brought into Italy, changing under the less direct influence of the Arab.

Understanding thus much of the formation of the great European styles, we shall have no difficulty in tracing the succession of architectures in Venice herself. From what I said of the central character of Venetian art, the reader is not, of course, to conclude that the Roman, Northern, and Arabian elements met together and contended for the mastery at the same period. The earliest element was the pure Christian Roman; but few, if any, remains of this art exist at Venice; for the present city was in the earliest times only one of many settlements formed on the chain of marshy islands which extend from the mouths of the Isonzo to those of the Adige, and it was not until the beginning of the ninth century that it became the seat of government; while the cathedral of Torcello, though Christian Roman in general form, was rebuilt in the eleventh century, and shows evidence of Byzantine workmanship in many of its details. This cathedral, however, with the church of Santa Fosca at Torcello, San Giacomo di Rialto at Venice, and the crypt of Saint Mark's, form a distinct group of buildings, in which the Byzantine influence is exceedingly slight; and which is probably very sufficiently representative of the earliest architecture on the islands.

The Ducal residence was removed to Venice in 809, and the body of Saint Mark was brought from Alexandria twenty years later. The first church of Saint Mark's was, doubtless, built in imitation of that destroyed at Alexandria, and from which the relics of the saint had been obtained. During the ninth, tenth, and eleventh centuries, the architecture of Venice seems to have been formed on the same model, and is almost identical with that of Cairo under the caliphs, it being quite immaterial whether the reader chooses to call both Byzantine or both Arabic; the workmen being certainly Byzantine, but forced to the invention of new forms by their Arabian masters, and bringing these forms into use in whatever other parts of the world they were employed.

To this style succeeds a transitional one of a character much more distinctly Arabian: the shafts become more slender, and the arches consistently pointed, instead of round; certain other changes, not to be enumerated in a sentence, taking place in the capitals and moldings. This style is almost exclusively secular. It was natural for the Venetians to imitate the beautiful details of the Arabian dwelling house, while they would with reluctance adopt those of the mosque for Christian churches.

I have not succeeded in fixing limiting dates for this style. It appears in part contemporary with the Byzantine manner, but outlives it. Its position is, however, fixed by the central date, 1180, that of the elevation of the granite shafts of the Piazzetta, whose capitals are the two most important pieces of detail in this transitional style in Venice. Examples of its application to domestic buildings exist in almost every street of the city.

The Venetians were always ready to receive lessons in art from their enemies (else had there been no Arab work in Venice). But their especial dread and hatred of the Lombards appear to have long prevented them from receiving the influence of the art which that people had introduced on the mainland of Italy. Nevertheless, during the practice of the two styles above distinguished, a peculiar and very primitive condition of pointed Gothic had arisen in ecclesiastical architecture. It appears to be a feeble reflection of the Lombard-Arab forms, which were attaining perfection upon the continent, and would probably, if left to itself, have been soon merged in the Venetian-Arab school, with which it had from the first so close a fellowship, that it will be found difficult to distinguish the Arabian ogives from those which seem to have been built under this early Gothic influence. The churches of San Giacopo dell' Orio, San Giovanni in Bragora, the

Carmine, and one or two more, furnish the only important examples of it. But, in the thirteenth century, the Franciscans and Dominicans introduced from the continent their morality and their architecture, already a distinct Gothic, curiously developed from Lombardic and Northern (German?) forms; and the influence of the principles exhibited in the vast churches of Saint Paul and the Frari began rapidly to affect the Venetian-Arab school. Still the two systems never became united; the Venetian policy repressed the power of the church, and the Venetian artists resisted its example; and thenceforward the architecture of the city becomes divided into ecclesiastical and civil: the one an ungraceful yet powerful form of the Western Gothic, common to the whole peninsula, and only showing Venetian sympathies in the adoption of certain characteristic moldings; the other a rich, luxuriant, and entirely original Gothic, formed from the Venetian-Arab by the influence of the Dominican and Franciscan architecture, and especially by the engrafting upon the Arab forms of the most novel feature of the Franciscan work, its traceries. These various forms of Gothic, the *distinctive* architecture of Venice are chiefly represented by the churches of Saint John and Paul, the Frari, and San Stefano, on the ecclesiastical side, and by the Ducal Palace, and the other principal Gothic palaces, on the secular side.

Now observe. The transitional (or especially Arabic) style of the Venetian work is centralized by the date 1180, and is transformed gradually into the Gothic, which extends in its purity from the middle of the thirteenth to the beginning of the fifteenth century; that is to say, over the precise period which I have described as the central epoch of the life of Venice. I dated her decline from the year 1418; Foscari became doge five years later, and in his reign the first marked signs appear in architecture of that mighty change to which London owes

Saint Paul's, Rome Saint Peter's, Venice and Vicenza the edifices commonly supposed to be their noblest, and Europe in general the degradation of every art she has since practiced.

This change appears first in a loss of truth and vitality in existing architecture all over the world. All the Gothics in existence, southern or northern, were corrupted at once: the German and French lost themselves in every species of extravagance; the English Gothic was confined, in its insanity, by a straitjacket of perpendicular lines; the Italian effloresced on the mainland into the meaningless ornamentation of the Certosa of Pavia and the Cathedral of Como (a style sometimes ignorantly called Italian Gothic), and at Venice into the insipid confusion of the Porta della Carta and wild crockets of Saint Mark's. This corruption of all architecture, especially ecclesiastical, corresponded with, and marked the state of religion over all Europe.

Now Venice, as she was once the most religious, was in her fall the most corrupt, of European states; and as she was in her strength the center of the pure currents of Christian architecture, so she is in her decline the source of the Renaissance. It was the originality and splendor of the palaces of Vicenza and Venice which gave this school its eminence in the eyes of Europe; and the dying city, magnificent in her dissipation, and graceful in her follies, obtained wider worship in her decrepitude than in her youth, and sank from the midst of her admirers into the grave.

It is in Venice, therefore, and in Venice only, that effectual blows can be struck at this pestilent art of the Renaissance. Destroy its claims to admiration there, and it can assert them nowhere else. This, therefore, will be the final purpose of the following essay. I shall, in my account of the earlier architecture, compare the forms of all its leading features with those into which they were corrupted by the Classicalists; and pause, in the close, on the edge of the precipice of decline, so soon as I have made its depth discernible. In doing this I shall depend upon two distinct kinds of evidence: the first, the testimony borne by particular incidents and facts to a want of thought or of feeling in the builders; from which we may conclude that their architecture must be bad: the second, the sense, which I doubt not I shall be able to excite in the reader, of a systematic ugliness in the architecture itself.

There is much evidence on which I shall depend for the proof of the inferiority of character in the Renaissance workmen. But the proof of the inferiority of the work itself is not so easy, for in this I have to appeal to judgments which the Renaissance work has itself distorted. I felt this difficulty very forcibly as I read a slight review of my former work, "The Seven Lamps," in *The Architect:* the writer noticed my constant praise of Saint Mark's: "Mr. Ruskin thinks it a very beautiful building! We," said *The Architect,* "think it a very ugly building." I was not surprised at the difference of opinion, but at the thing being considered so completely a subject of opinion. My opponents in matters of painting always assume that there *is* such a thing as a law of right, and that I do not understand it: but my architectural adversaries appeal to no law, they simply set their opinion against mine; and indeed there is no law at present to which either they or I can appeal. No man can speak with rational decision of the merits or demerits of buildings: he may with obstinacy; he may with resolved adherence to previous prejudices; but never as if the matter could be otherwise decided than by majority of votes, or pertinacity of partisanship. I had always, however, a clear conviction that there *was* a law in this matter: that good architecture might be indisputably discerned and divided from the bad; that the opposition in their very nature and essence was clearly visible; and that we were all of us just as unwise in disputing about the matter without reference to

principle, as we should be for debating about the genuineness of a coin without ringing it. I felt also assured that this law must be universal if it were conclusive: that it must enable us to reject all foolish and base work, and to accept all noble and wise work, without reference to style or national feeling; that it must sanction the design of all truly great nations and times, Gothic or Greek or Arab; that it must cast off and reprobate the design of all foolish nations and times, Chinese or Mexican or modern European; and that it must be easily applicable to all possible architectural inventions of human mind. I set myself, therefore, to establish such a law, in full belief that men are intended, without excessive difficulty, and by use of their general common sense, to know good things from bad; and that it is only because they will not be at the pains required for the discernment, that the world is so widely encumbered with forgeries and basenesses. I found the work simpler than I had hoped; the reasonable things ranged themselves in the order I required, and the foolish things fell aside, and took themselves away so soon as they were looked in the face. I had then, with respect to Venetian architecture, the choice, either to establish each division of law in a separate form, as I came to the features with which it was concerned, or else to ask the reader's patience, while I followed out the general inquiry first, and determined with him a code of right and wrong, to which we might together make retrospective appeal. I thought this the best, though perhaps the dullest way; and in these first following pages I have therefore endeavored to arrange those foundations of criticism, on which I shall rest in my account of Venetian architecture, in a form clear and simple enough to be intelligible even to those who never thought of architecture before. To those who have, much of what is stated in them will be well-known or self-evident; but they must not be indignant at a simplicity on which the whole argument depends for its usefulness. From that which appears a mere truism when first stated, they will find very singular consequences sometimes following—consequences altogether unexpected, and of considerable importance; I will not pause here to dwell on their importance, nor on that of the thing itself to be done; for I believe most readers will at once admit the value of a criterion of right and wrong in so practical and costly an art as architecture, and will be apt rather to doubt the possibility of its attainment than dispute its usefulness if attained. I invite them, therefore, to a fair trial, being certain that even if I should fail in my main purpose, and be unable to induce in my reader the confidence of judgment I desire, I shall at least receive his thanks for the suggestion of consistent reasons, which may determine hesitating choice, or justify involuntary preference. And if I should succeed, as I hope, in making the Stones of Venice touchstones, and detecting, by the moldering of her marble, poison more subtle than ever was betrayed by the rending of her crystal; and if thus I am enabled to show the baseness of the schools of architecture and nearly every other art, which have for three centuries been predominant in Europe, I believe the result of the inquiry may be serviceable for proof of a more vital truth than any at which I have hitherto hinted.

## Chapter II

### The Virtues of Architecture

We address ourselves, then, first to the task of determining some law of right, which we may apply to the architecture of all the world and of all time; and by help of which, and judgment according to which, we may as easily pronounce whether a building is good or noble, as, by applying a plumb line, whether it be perpendicular.

The first question will of course be, What are the possible virtues of architecture?

In the main, we require from buildings, as from men, two kinds of goodness: first, the doing their practical duty well: then that they be graceful and pleasing in doing it; which last is itself another form of duty.

Then the practical duty divides itself into two branches—acting and talking—acting, as to defend us from weather or violence; talking, as the duty of monuments or tombs, to record facts and express feelings; or of churches, temples, public edifices, treated as books of history, to tell such history clearly and forcibly.

We have thus, altogether, three great branches of architectural virtue, and we require of any building:

1. That it act well, and do the things it was intended to do in the best way.

2. That it speak well, and say the things it was intended to say in the best words.

3. That it look well, and please us by its presence, whatever it has to do or say.

Now, as regards the second of these virtues, it is evident that we can establish no general laws. First, because it is not a virtue required in all buildings; there are some which are only for covert or defense, and from which we ask no conversation. Second, because there are countless methods of expression, some conventional, some natural: each conventional mode has its own alphabet, which evidently can be no subject of general laws. Every natural mode is instinctively employed and instinctively understood, wherever there is true feeling; and this instinct is above law. The choice of conventional methods depends on circumstances out of calculation, and that of natural methods on sensations out of control; so that we can only say that the choice is right, when we feel that the means are effective; and we cannot always say that it is wrong when they are not so.

A building which recorded the Bible history by means of a series of sculptural pictures, would be perfectly useless to a person unacquainted with the Bible beforehand; on the other hand, the text of the

Old and New Testaments might be written on its walls, and yet the building be a very inconvenient kind of book, not so useful as if it had been adorned with intelligible and vivid sculpture. So, again, the power of exciting emotion must vary or vanish, as the spectator becomes thoughtless or cold; and the building may be often blamed for what is the fault of its critic, or endowed with a charm which is of its spectator's creation. It is not therefore possible to make expressional character any fair criterion of excellence in buildings, until we can fully place ourselves in the position of those to whom their expression was originally addressed, and until we are certain that we understand every symbol, and are capable of being touched by every association which its builders employed as letters of their language. I shall continually endeavor to put the reader into such sympathetic temper, when I ask for his judgment of a building; and in every work I may bring before him I shall point out, as far as I am able, whatever is peculiar in its expression: nay, I must even depend on such peculiarities for much of my best evidence respecting the character of the builders. But I cannot legalize the judgment for which I plead, nor insist upon it if it be refused. I can neither force the reader to feel this architectural rhetoric, nor compel him to confess that the rhetoric is powerful, if it have produced no impression on his own mind.

I leave therefore, the expression of buildings for incidental notice only. But their other two virtues are proper subjects of law—their performance of their common and necessary work, and their conformity with universal and divine canons of loveliness; respecting these there can be no doubt, no ambiguity. I would have the reader discern them so quickly that, as he passes along a street, he may by a glance of the eye, distinguish the noble from the ignoble work. He can do this, if he permit free play to his natural instincts; and all

that I have to do for him is to remove from those instincts the artificial restraints which prevent their action, and to encourage them to an unaffected and unbiased choice between right and wrong.

We have, then, two qualities of buildings for subjects of separate inquiry: their action, and aspect, and the sources of virtue in both; that is to say, strength and beauty, both of these being less admired in themselves, than as testifying the intelligence or imagination of the builder.

For we have a worthier way of looking at human than at divine architecture; much of the value both of construction and decoration, in the edifices of men, depends upon our being led by the thing produced or adorned, to some contemplation of the powers of mind concerned in its creation or adornment. We are not so led by divine work, but are content to rest in the contemplation of the thing created. I wish the reader to note this especially; we take pleasure, or *should* take pleasure, in architectural construction altogether as the manifestation of an admirable human intelligence; it is not the strength, not the size, not the finish of the work which we are to venerate: rocks are always stronger, mountains always larger, all natural objects more finished; but it is the intelligence and resolution of man in overcoming physical difficulty which are to be the source of our pleasure and subject of our praise. And again, in decoration or beauty, it is less the actual loveliness of the thing produced than the choice and invention concerned in the production, which are to delight us; the love and the thoughts of the workman more than his work; his work must always be imperfect, but his thoughts and affections may be true and deep.

The origin of our pleasure in architecture I must insist upon at somewhat greater length, for I would fain do away with some of the ungrateful coldness which we show toward the good builders of old time. In no art is there closer connection between our delight in the work, and our admiration of the workman's mind, than in architecture, and yet we rarely ask for a builder's name. The patron at whose cost, the monk through whose dreaming, the foundation was laid, we remember occasionally; never the man who verily did the work. Did the reader ever hear of William of Sens as having had anything to do with Canterbury Cathedral? or of Pietro Basegio as in anywise connected with the Ducal Palace of Venice? There is much ingratitude and injustice in this; and therefore I desire my reader to observe carefully how much of his pleasure in building is derived, or should be derived, from admiration of the intellect of men whose names he knows not.

The two virtues of architecture which we can justly weigh, are, we said, its strength or good construction, and its beauty or good decoration. Consider first, therefore, what you mean when you say a building is well constructed or well built; you do not merely mean that it answers its purpose— this is much, and many modern buildings fail of this much; but if it be verily well built; it must answer this purpose in the simplest way, and with no over-expenditure of means. We require of a lighthouse, for instance, that it shall stand firm and carry a light; if it do not this, assuredly it has been ill built; but it may do it to the end of time, and yet not be well built. It may have hundreds of tons of stone in it more than were needed, and have cost thousands of pounds more than it ought. To pronounce it well or ill built, we must know the utmost forces it can have to resist, and the best arrangements of stone for encountering them, and the quickest ways of effecting such arrangements: then only, so far as such arrangements have been chosen, and such methods used, is it well built. Then the knowledge of all difficulties to be met, and of all means of meeting them, and the quick and true fancy or invention of the modes of applying the means to the

end, are what we have to admire in the builder, even as he is seen through this first or inferior part of his work. Mental power, observe: not muscular, nor mechanical, not technical, nor empirical—pure, precious, majestic, massy intellect; not to be had at vulgar price, nor received without thanks, and without asking from whom.

Suppose, for instance, we are present at the building of a bridge: the bricklayers or masons have had their centering erected for them, and that centering was put together by a carpenter, who had the line of its curve traced for him by the architect: the masons are dexterously handling and fitting their bricks, or, by the help of machinery, carefully adjusting stones which are numbered for their places. There is probably in their quickness of eye and readiness of hand something admirable: but this is not what I ask the reader to admire: not the carpentering, nor the bricklaying, nor anything that he can presently see and understand, but the choice of the curve, and the shaping of the numbered stones, and the appointment of that number; there were many things to be known and thought upon before these were decided. The man who chose the curve and numbered the stones, had to know the times and tides of the river, and the strength of its floods, and the height and flow of them, and the soil of the banks, and the endurance of it, and the weight of the stones he had to build with, and the kind of traffic that day by day would be carried on over his bridge, all this especially, and all the great general laws of force and weight, and their working; and in the choice of the curve and numbering of stones are expressed not only his knowledge of these, but such ingenuity and firmness as he had, in applying special means to overcome the special difficulties about his bridge. There is no saying how much wit, how much depth of thought, how much fancy, presence of mind, courage, and fixed resolution there may have gone to the placing of a single stone of it. This is what we have to admire—this grand power and heart of man in the thing; not his technical or empirical way of holding the trowel and laying mortar.

Now, there is in everything properly called art this concernment of the intellect, even in the province of the art which seems merely practical. For observe: in this bridge building I suppose no reference to architectural principles; all that I suppose we want is to get safely over the river; the man who has taken us over is still a mere bridge builder—a *builder,* not an architect; he may be a rough, artless, feelingless man, incapable of doing any one truly fine thing all his days. I shall call upon you to despise him presently in a sort, but not as if he were a mere smoother of mortar; perhaps a great man, infinite in memory, indefatigable in labor, exhaustless in expedient, unsurpassable in quickness of thought. Take good heed you understand him before you despise him.

But why is he to be in anywise despised? By no means despise him, unless he happen to be without a soul, or at least to show no signs of it; which possibly he may not in merely carrying you across the river. He may be merely what Thomas Carlyle rightly calls a human beaver after all; and there may be nothing in all that ingenuity of his greater than a complication of animal faculties, an intricate bestiality—nest or hive building in its highest development. You need something more than this, or the man is despicable; you need that virtue of building through which he may show his affections and delights; you need its beauty or decoration.

Not that, in reality, one division of the man is more human than another; all the divisions of humanity are noble or brutal, immortal or mortal, according to the degree of their sanctification, and there is no part of the man which is not immortal and divine when it is once given to God, and no part of him which is not mortal by the second death, and brutal before the

first, when it is withdrawn from God. For to what shall we trust for our distinction from the beasts that perish? To our higher intellect? Yet are we not bidden to be wise as the serpent, and to consider the ways of the ant? Or to our affections? Nay, these are more shared by the lower animals than our intelligence: Hamlet leaps into the grave of his beloved, and leaves it; a dog would have stayed. Humanity and immortality consist neither in reason, nor in love; not in the body, nor in the animation of the heart of it, nor in the thoughts and stirrings of the brain of it, but in the dedication of them all to Him who will raise them up at the last day.

It is not, therefore, that the signs of his affections, which man leaves upon his work, are indeed more ennobling than the signs of his intelligence; but it is the balance of both whose expression we need, and the signs of the government of them all by conscience; and discretion, the daughter of conscience. So, then, the intelligent part of man being eminently, if not chiefly, displayed in the structure of his work, his affectionate part is to be shown in its decoration; and, that decoration may be indeed lovely, two things are needed: first, that the affections be vivid, and honestly shown; second, that they be fixed on the right things.

You think, perhaps, I have put the requirements in wrong order. Logically I have; practically I have not: for it is necessary first to teach men to speak out, and say what they like, truly; and in the second place, to teach them which of their likings are ill set, and which justly. If a man is cold in his likings and dislikings, or if he will not tell you what he likes, you can make nothing of him. Only get him to feel quickly and to speak plainly, and you may set him right. And the fact is, that the great evil of all recent architectural effort has not been that men liked wrong things; but that they either cared nothing about any, or pretended to like what they did not. Do you suppose that any modern architect likes what he builds, or enjoys it? Not in the least. He builds it because he had been told that such and such things are fine, and that he *should* like them. He pretends to like them, and gives them a false relish of vanity. Do you seriously imagine, reader, that any living soul in London likes triglyphs,* or gets any hearty enjoyment out of pediments?† You are much mistaken. Greeks did; English people never did—never will. Do you fancy that the architect of old Burlington Mews, in Regent Street, had any particular satisfaction in putting the blank triangle over the archway, instead of a useful garret window? By no manner of means. He had been told it was right to do so, and thought he should be admired for doing it. Very few faults of architecture are mistakes of honest choice: they are almost always hypocrisies.

So, then, the first thing we have to ask of the decoration is that it should indicate strong liking, and that honestly. It matters not so much what the thing is, as that the builder should really love it and enjoy it, and say so plainly. The architect of Bourges Cathedral liked hawthorns; so he has covered his porch with hawthorn— it is a perfect Niobe of May. Never was such hawthorn; you would try to gather it forthwith, but for fear of being pricked. The old Lombard architects liked hunting; so they covered their work with horses and hounds, and men blowing trumpets two yards long. The base Renaissance architects of Venice liked masquing and fiddling; so they covered their work with comic masks and musical instruments. Even that was better than our English way of liking nothing, and professing to like triglyphs.

But the second requirement in decoration, is that it should show we like the right thing. And the right thing to be liked is God's work, which He made for our delight and contentment in this world. And all noble ornamentation is the expression of man's delight in God's work.

So, then, these are the two virtues of building: first, the signs of man's own good work; second, the expression of man's delight in better work than his own. And these are the two virtues of which I desire my reader to be able quickly to judge, at least in some measure; to have a definite opinion up to a certain point. Beyond a certain point he cannot form one. When the science of the building is great, great science is of course required to comprehend it; and, therefore, of difficult bridges, and lighthouses, and harbor walls, and river dikes, and railway tunnels, no judgment may be rapidly formed. But of common buildings, built in common circumstances, it is very possible for every man, or woman, or child, to form judgment both rational and rapid. Their necessary, or even possible, features are but few; the laws of their construction are as simple as they are interesting. The labor of a few hours is enough to render the reader master of their main points; and from that moment he will find in himself a power of judgment which can neither be escaped nor deceived, and discover subjects of interest where everything before had appeared barren. For though the laws are few and simple, the modes of obedience to them are not so. Every building presents its own requirements and difficulties; and every good building has peculiar appliances or contrivances to meet them. Understand the laws of structure, and you will feel the special difficulty in every new building which you approach; and you will know also, or feel instinctively, whether it has been wisely met or otherwise. And an enormous number of buildings, and of styles of building, you will be able to cast aside at once, as at variance with these constant laws of structure, and therefore unnatural and monstrous.

Then, as regards decoration, I want you

---

*Triglyph. Literally, "Three Cut." The awkward upright ornament with two notches in it, and cut at each side, to be seen everywhere at the tops of Doric colonnades, ancient and modern.

†Pediment. The triangular space above Greek porticoes, as on the Mansion House or Royal Exchange, London.

only to consult your own natural choice and liking. There is a right and wrong in it; but you will assuredly like the right if you suffer your natural instinct to lead you. Half the evil in this world comes from people not knowing what they do like—not deliberately setting themselves to find out what they really enjoy. All people enjoy giving away money, for instance; they don't know *that*—they rather think they like keeping it, and they *do* keep it, under this false impression, often to their great discomfort. Everybody likes to do good; but not one in a hundred finds *this* out. Multitudes think they like to do evil; yet no man ever really enjoyed doing evil since God made the world.

So in this lesser matter of ornament. It needs some little care to try experiments upon yourself; it needs deliberate question and upright answer. But there is no difficulty to be overcome, no abstruse reasoning to be gone into; only a little watchfulness needed, and thoughtfulness, and so much honesty as will enable you to confess to yourself, and to all men, that you enjoy things, though great authorities say you should not.

This looks somewhat like pride; but it is true humility, a trust that you have been so created as to enjoy what is fitting for you, and a willingness to be pleased, as it was intended you should be. It is the child's spirit, which we are most happy when we most recover; remaining wiser than children in our gratitude that we can still be pleased with a fair color, or a dancing light. And, above all, do not try to make all these pleasures reasonable, nor to connect the delight which you take in ornament with that which you take in construction of usefulness. They have no connection; and every effort that you make to reason from one to the other will blunt your sense of beauty, or confuse it with sensations altogether inferior to it. You were made for enjoyment, and the world was filled with things which you will enjoy, unless you are too proud to be pleased by them, or too grasping to care for what you cannot turn to other account than mere delight. Remember that the most beautiful things in the world are the most useless; peacocks and lilies for instance; at least I suppose this quill I hold in my hand writes better than a peacock's would, and the peasants of Vevey, whose fields in springtime are as white with lilies as the Dent du Midi is with its snow, told me the hay was none the better for them.

Our task therefore divides itself into two branches, and these I shall follow in succession. I shall first consider the construction of buildings, dividing them into their really necessary members or features; and I shall endeavor so to lead the reader forward from the foundation upward, as that he may find out for himself the best way of doing everything, and having so discovered it, never forget it. I shall give him stones, and bricks, and straw, chisels and trowels, and the ground, and then ask him to build; only helping him, as I can, if I find him puzzled. And when he has built his house or church, I shall ask him to ornament it, and leave it to him to choose the ornaments as I did to find out the construction: I shall use no influence with him whatever, except to counteract previous prejudices, and leave him, as far as may be, free. And when he has thus found out how to build, and chosen his forms of decoration, I shall do what I can to confirm his confidence in what he has done. I shall assure him that no one in the world could, so far, have done better, and require him to condemn, as futile or fallacious, whatever has no resemblance to his own performances.

## Chapter III

### The Six Divisions of Architecture

The practical duties of buildings are twofold. They have either (1) to hold and protect something; or (2) to place and carry something.

1. *Architecture of Protection.* This is architecture intended to protect men or their possessions from violence of any kind, whether of men or of the elements. It will include all churches, houses, and treasuries; fortresses, fences, and ramparts; the architecture of the hut and sheepfold; of the palace and citadel; of the dike, breakwater, and seawall. And the protection, when of living creatures, is to be understood as including commodiousness and comfort of habitation, wherever these are possible under the given circumstances.

2. *Architecture of Position.* This is architecture intended to carry men or things to some certain places, or to hold them there. This will include all bridges, aqueducts, and road architecture; lighthouses, which have to hold light in appointed places; chimneys, to carry smoke or direct currents of air; staircases; towers, which are to be watched from or cried from, as in mosque, or to hold bells, or to place men in positions of offense, as ancient movable attacking towers, and most fortress towers.

Protective architecture has to do one or all of three things: to wall a space, to roof it, and to give access to it, of persons, light, and air; and it is therefore to be considered under the three divisions of walls, roofs, and apertures.

1. *Walls*—A wall is an even and united fence, whether of wood, earth, stone, or metal. When meant for purposes of mere partition or enclosure, it remains a wall proper; but it has generally also to sustain a certain vertical or lateral pressure, for which its strength is at first increased by some general addition to its thickness; but if the pressure becomes very great, it is gathered up into *piers* to resist vertical pressure, and supported by *buttresses* to resist lateral pressure.

If its functions of partition or enclosure are continued, together with that of resisting vertical pressure, it remains as a wall veil between the piers into which it has been partly gathered; but if it is required only to resist the vertical or roof pressure, it is gathered up into piers altogether, loses its wall character, and becomes a group or line of piers.

On the other hand, if the lateral pressure be slight, it may retain its character of a wall, being supported against the pressure by buttresses at intervals; but if the lateral pressure be very great, it is supported against such pressure by a continuous buttress, loses its wall character, and becomes a dike or rampart.

We shall have therefore (A) first to get a general idea of a wall, and of right construction of walls; then (B) to see how this wall is gathered into piers, and to get a general idea of piers and the right construction of piers; then (C) to see how a wall is supported by buttresses, and to get a general idea of buttresses and the right construction of buttresses. This is surely very simple, and it is all we shall have to do with walls and their divisions.

2. *Roofs*—A roof is the covering of a space, narrow or wide. It will be most conveniently studied by first considering the forms in which it may be carried over a narrow space, and then expanding these on a wide plan; only there is some difficulty here in the nomenclature, for an arched roof over a narrow space is called an arch; but a flat roof over a narrow space has (I believe) no name, except that which belongs properly to the piece of stone or wood composing such a roof, namely, lintel. But the reader will have no difficulty in understanding that he is first to consider roofs on the section only, thinking how best to construct a narrow bar or slice of them, of whatever form; as, for instance, $x$, $y$, or $z$, over the plan or area $a$, figure 1. Having done this, let him imagine these several divisions, first moved along (or set side by side) over a rectangle, $b$, figure 1, and then revolved round a point (or crossed at it) over a polygon, $c$, or circle, $d$, and he will have every form of simple roof; the arched section giving successively the vaulted roof and dome, and the

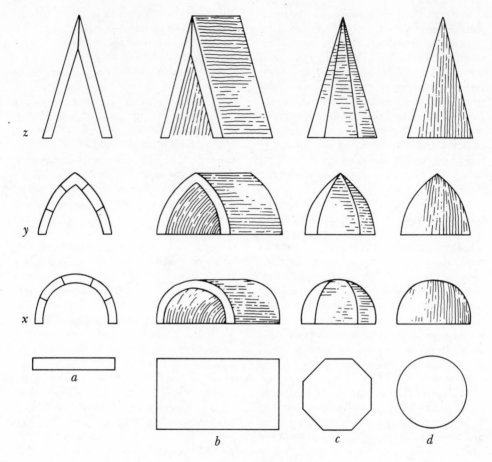

*Figure 1*

gabled section giving the gabled roof and spire.

Now, it also happens, from its place in buildings, that the sectional roof over a narrow space will need to be considered before we come to the expanded roof over a broad one. For when a wall has been gathered, as above explained, into piers, that it may better bear vertical pressure, it is generally necessary that it should be expanded again at the top into a continuous wall before it carries the true roof. Arches or lintels are, therefore, thrown from pier to pier, and a level preparation for carrying the real roof is made above them. After we have examined the structure of

piers, therefore, we shall have to see how lintels or arches are thrown from pier to pier, and the whole prepared for the superincumbent roof; this arrangement being universal in all good architecture prepared for vertical pressures: and we shall then examine the condition of the great roof itself. And because the structure of the roof very often introduces certain lateral pressures which have much to do with the placing of buttresses, it will be well to do all this before we examine the nature of buttresses, and, therefore, between parts (B) and (C) of the above plan. So now we shall have to study: (A) the construction of walls; (B) that of piers; (C) that of lintels

356

or arches prepared for roofing; (D) that of roofs proper; and (E) that of buttresses.

3. *Apertures*—There must either be intervals between the piers, of which intervals the character will be determined by that of the piers themselves, or else doors or windows in the walls proper. And, respecting doors or windows, we have to determine three things: first, the proper shape of the entire aperture; second, the way in which it is to be filled with valves or glass; and, third, the modes of protecting it on the outside, and fitting appliances of convenience to it, as porches or balconies. And this will be our division F; and if the reader will have the patience to go through these six heads, which include every possible feature of protective architecture, and to consider the simple necessities and fitnesses of each, I will answer for it, he shall never confound good architecture with bad any more. For, as to architecture of position, a great part of it involves necessities of construction with which the spectator cannot become generally acquainted, and of the compliance with which he is therefore never expected to judge—as in chimneys, lighthouses, etc.: and the other forms of it are so closely connected with those of protective architecture, that a few words in chapter X respecting staircases and towers, will contain all with which the reader need be troubled on the subject.

## Chapter IV

### The Wall Base

Our first business, then, is with Wall, and to find out wherein lies the true excellence of the "Wittiest Partition." For it is rather strange that, often as we speak of a "dead" wall, and that with considerable disgust, we have not often, since Snout's time,* heard of a living one. But the common epithet of opprobrium is justly bestowed, and marks a right feeling. A wall has no business to be dead. It ought to have members in its make, and purposes in its existence, like

an organized creature, and to answer its ends in a living and energetic way; and it is only when we do not choose to put any strength nor organization into it, that it offends us by its deadness. Every wall ought to be a "sweet and lovely wall." I do not care about its having ears; but, for instruction and exhortation, I would often have it to "hold up its fingers." What its necessary members and excellences are, it is our present business to discover.

A wall has been defined to be an even and united fence of wood, earth, stone, or metal. Metal fences, however, seldom, if ever, take the form of walls, but of railings; and, like all other metal constructions, must be left out of our present investigation; as may be also walls composed merely of light planks or laths for purposes of partition or enclosure. Substantial walls, whether of wood or earth (I use the word *earth* as including clay, baked or unbaked, and stone), have, in their perfect form, three distinct members—the foundation, body or veil, and cornice.

The foundation is to the wall what the paw is to an animal. It is a long foot, wider than the wall, on which the wall is to stand, and which keeps it from settling into the ground. It is most necessary that this great element of security should be visible to the eye, and therefore made a part of the structure above ground. Sometimes, indeed, it becomes incorporated with the entire foundation of the building, a vast table on which walls or piers are alike set: but even then, the eye, taught by the reason, requires some additional preparation or foot for the wall, and the building is felt to be imperfect without it. This foundation we shall call the base of the wall.

The body of the wall is of course the principal mass of it, formed of mud or clay, of bricks or stones, of logs or hewn timber; the condition of structure being, that it is of equal thickness everywhere below

---

*Cf. Shakespeare, *A Midsummer Night's Dream*, Act V (*GBWW*, Vol. 26, pp. 370–75) [Ed.].

and above. It may be half a foot thick, or six feet thick, or fifty feet thick; but if of equal thickness everywhere, it is still a wall proper: if to its fifty feet of proper thickness there be added so much as an inch of thickness in particular parts, that added thickness is to be considered as some form of buttress or pier, or other appliance.

In perfect architecture, however, walls are generally kept of moderate thickness, and strengthened by piers or buttresses; and the part of the wall between these, being generally intended only to secure privacy, or keep out the slighter forces of weather, may be properly called a wall veil. I shall always use this word *veil* to signify the even portion of a wall, it being more expressive than the term *body*.

When the materials with which this veil is built are very loose, or of shapes which do not fit well together, it sometimes becomes necessary, or at least adds to security, to introduce courses of more solid material. Thus, bricks alternate with rolled pebbles in the old walls of Verona, and hewn stones with brick in its Lombard churches. A banded structure, almost a stratification of the wall, is thus produced; and the courses of more solid material are sometimes decorated with carving. Even when the wall is not thus banded through its whole height, it frequently becomes expedient to lay a course of stone, or at least of more carefully chosen materials, at regular heights; and such belts or bands we may call string courses. These are a kind of epochs in the wall's existence; something like periods of rest and reflection in human life, before entering on a new career. Or else, in the building, they correspond to the divisions of its stories within, express its internal structure, and mark off some portion of the ends of its existence already attained.

Finally, on the top of the wall some protection from the weather is necessary, or some preparation for the reception of superincumbent weight, called a coping, or cornice. I shall use the word *cornice* for

both; for, in fact, a coping is a roof to the wall itself, and is carried by a small cornice as the roof of the building by a large one. In either case, the cornice, small or large, is the termination of the wall's existence, the accomplishment of its work. When it is meant to carry some superincumbent weight, the cornice may be considered as its hand, opened to carry something above its head; as the base was considered its foot; and the three parts should grow out of each other and form one whole, like the root, stalk, and bell of a flower.

These three parts we shall examine in succession; and, first, the base.

It may be sometimes in our power, and it is always expedient, to prepare for the whole building some settled foundation, level and firm, out of sight. But this has not been done in some of the noblest buildings in existence. It cannot always be done perfectly, except at enormous expense; and, in reasoning upon the superstructure, we shall never suppose it to be done. The mind of the spectator does not conceive it; and he estimates the merits of the edifice on the supposition of its being built upon the ground. Even if there be a vast tableland of foundation elevated for the whole of it, accessible by steps all round, as at Pisa, the surface of this table is always conceived as capable of yielding somewhat to superincumbent weight, and generally is so; and we shall base all our arguments on the widest possible supposition, that is to say, that the building stands on a surface either of earth, or, at all events, capable of yielding in some degree to its weight.

Now let the reader simply ask himself how, on such a surface, he would set about building a substantial wall, that should be able to bear weight and to stand for ages. He would assuredly look about for the largest stones he had at his disposal, and, rudely leveling the ground, he would lay these well together over a considerably larger width than he required the wall to be (suppose as at *a*, fig. 2), in order to

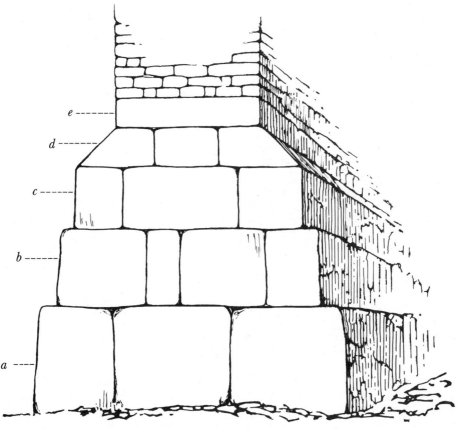

*Figure 2*

equalize the pressure of the wall over a large surface, and form its foot. On the top of these he would perhaps lay a second tier of large stones, *b,* or even a third, *c,* making the breadth somewhat less each time, so as to prepare for the pressure of the wall on the center, and, naturally or necessarily, using somewhat smaller stones above than below (since we supposed him to look about for the largest first), and cutting them more neatly. His third tier, if not his second, will probably appear a sufficiently secure foundation for finer work; for if the earth yield at all, it will probably yield pretty equally under the great mass of masonry now knit together over it. So he will prepare for the wall itself at once

by sloping off the next tier of stones to the right diameter, as at *d.* If there be any joints in this tier within the wall, he may perhaps, for further security, lay a binding stone across them, *e,* and then begin the work of the wall veil itself, whether in bricks or stones.

I have supposed the preparation here to be for a large wall, because such a preparation will give us the best general type. But it is evident that the essential features of the arrangement are only two, that is to say, one tier of massy work for foundation, suppose *c,* missing the first two; and the receding tier or real foot of the wall, *d.* The reader will find these members, though only of brick, in most of the considerable and independent walls in the suburbs of London.

It is evident, however, that the general type, figure 2, will be subject to many different modifications in different circumstances. Sometimes the ledges of the tiers *a* and *b* may be of greater width; and when the building is in a secure place, and of finished masonry, these may be sloped off also like the main foot *d*. In Venetian buildings these lower ledges are exposed to the sea, and therefore left rough hewn; but in fine work and in important positions the lower ledges may be leveled and decorated like the upper, or another added above *d;* and all these parts may be in different proportions, according to the disposition of the building above them. But we have nothing to do with any of these variations at present, they being all more or less dependent upon decorative considerations, except only one of very great importance, that is to say, the widening of the lower ledge into a stone seat, which may be often done in buildings of great size with most beautiful effect: it looks kind and hospitable, and preserves the work above from violence. In Saint Mark's at Venice, which is a small and low church, and needing no great foundation for the wall veils of it, we find only the three members, *b, c,* and *d*. Of these the first rises about a foot above the pavement of Saint Mark's Place, and forms an elevated dais in some of the recesses of the porches, checkered red and white; *c* forms a seat which follows the line of the walls, while its basic character is marked by its also carrying certain shafts with which we have here no concern; *d* is of white marble; and all are enriched and decorated in the simplest and most perfect manner possible. And thus much may serve to fix the type of wall bases, a type oftener followed in real practice than any other we shall hereafter be enabled to determine: for wall bases of necessity must be solidly built, and the architect is therefore driven into the adoption of the right form; or if he deviate from it, it is generally in meeting some necessity of peculiar circumstances, as in obtaining cellars and underground room, or in preparing for some grand features or particular parts of the wall, or in some mistaken idea of decoration—into which errors we had better not pursue him until we understand something more of the rest of the building: let us therefore proceed to consider the wall veil.

## Chapter V

## The Wall Veil

A fragment of building among the Alps is singularly illustrative of the chief feature which I have at present to develop as necessary to the perfection of the wall veil. It is a fragment of some size; a group of broken walls, one of them overhanging; crowned with a cornice, nodding some hundred and fifty feet over its massive flank, three thousand above its glacier base, and fourteen thousand above the sea—a wall truly of some majesty, at once the most precipitous and the strongest mass in the whole chain of the Alps, the Mont Cervin (or Matterhorn). Its northern spur is one of the few points from which its mass is in anywise approachable. It is a continuation of the masonry of the mountain itself, and affords us the means of examining the character of its materials.

Few architects would like to build with them. The slope of the rocks to the northwest is covered two feet deep with their ruins, a mass of loose and slaty shale, of a dull brick-red color, which yields beneath the foot like ashes, so that, in running down, you step one yard, and slide three. The rock is indeed hard beneath, but still disposed in thin courses of these cloven shales, so finely laid that they look in places more like a heap of crushed autumn leaves than a rock; and the first sensation is one of unmitigated surprise, as if the mountain were upheld by miracle; but surprise becomes more intelligent reverence for the great Builder, when we find, in the middle of the mass of these dead leaves, a course of living rock, of quartz as white as the snow that encircles it, and harder than a bed of steel.

It is one only of a thousand iron bands that knit the strength of the mighty mountain. Through the buttress and the wall alike, the courses of its varied masonry are seen in their successive order, smooth and true as if laid by line and plummet,* but of thickness and strength continually varying, and with silver cornices glittering along the edge of each, laid by the snowy winds and carved by the sunshine.

I do not, however, bring this forward as an instance of any universal law of natural building; there are solid as well as coursed masses of precipice, but it is somewhat curious that the most noble cliff in Europe, which this eastern front of the Cervin is, I believe, without dispute, should be to us an example of the utmost possible stability of precipitousness attained with materials of imperfect and variable character; and, what is more, there are very few cliffs which do not display alternations between compact and friable conditions of their material, marked in their contours by beveled slopes when the bricks are soft, and vertical steps when they are harder. And, although we are not hence to conclude that it is well to introduce courses of bad materials when we can get perfect material, I believe we may conclude with great certainty that it is better and easier to strengthen a wall necessarily of imperfect substance, as of brick, by introducing carefully laid courses of stone, than by adding to its thickness; and the first impression we receive from the unbroken aspect of a wall veil, unless it be of hewn stone throughout, is that it must be both thicker and weaker than it would have been, had it been properly coursed. The decorative reasons for adopting the coursed arrangement are so weighty, that they would alone be almost sufficient to

enforce it: and the constructive ones will apply universally, except in the rare cases in which the choice of perfect or imperfect material is entirely open to us, or where the general system of the decoration of the building requires absolute unity in its surface.

As regards the arrangement of the intermediate parts themselves, it is regulated by certain conditions of bonding and fitting the stones or bricks, which the reader need hardly be troubled to consider, and which I wish that bricklayers themselves were always honest enough to observe. But I hardly know whether to note under the head of aesthetic or constructive law, this important principle, that masonry is always bad which appears to have arrested the attention of the architect more than absolute conditions of strength require. Nothing is more contemptible in any work than an appearance of the slightest desire on the part of the builder to *direct attention* to the way its stones are put together, or of any trouble taken either to show or to conceal it more than was rigidly necessary: it may sometimes, on the one hand, be necessary to conceal it as far as may be, by delicate and close fitting, when the joints would interfere with lines of sculpture or of moldings; and it may often, on the other hand, be delightful to show it, as it is delightful in places to show the anatomy even of the most delicate human frame: but *studiously* to conceal it is the error of vulgar painters, who are afraid to show that their figures have bones; and studiously to display it is the error of the base pupils of Michelangelo, who turned heroes' limbs into surgeons' diagrams—but with less excuse than theirs, for there is less interest in the anatomy displayed.

There is, however, no excuse for errors in disposition of masonry, for there is but one law upon the subject, and that easily

---

*On the eastern side: violently contorted on the northern and western.

complied with, to avoid all affectation and all unnecessary expense, either in showing or concealing. Everyone knows a building is built of separate stones; nobody will ever object to seeing that it is so, but nobody wants to count them. The divisions of a church are much like the divisions of a sermon; they are always right, so long as they are necessary to edification, and always wrong when they are thrust upon the attention as divisions only. There may be neatness in carving when there is richness in feasting; but I have heard many a discourse, and seen many a church wall, in which it was all carving and no meat.

## Chapter VI

### The Wall Cornice

We have lastly to consider the close of the wall's existence or its cornice. It was above stated, that a cornice has one of two offices: if the walls have nothing to carry, the cornice is its roof, and defends it from the weather; if there is weight to be carried above the wall, the cornice is its hand, and is expanded to carry the said weight.

There are several ways of roofing or protecting independent walls, according to the means nearest at hand: sometimes the wall has a true roof all to itself; sometimes it terminates in a small gabled ridge, made of bricks set slanting, as constantly in the suburbs of London; or of hewn stone, in stronger work; or in a single sloping face, inclined to the outside. We need not trouble ourselves at present about these small roofings, which are merely the diminutions of large ones; but we must examine the important and constant member of the wall structure, which prepares it either for these small roofs or for weight above, and is its true cornice.

The reader will, perhaps, as heretofore, be kind enough to think for himself, how, having carried up his wall veil as high as it may be needed, he will set about pro-

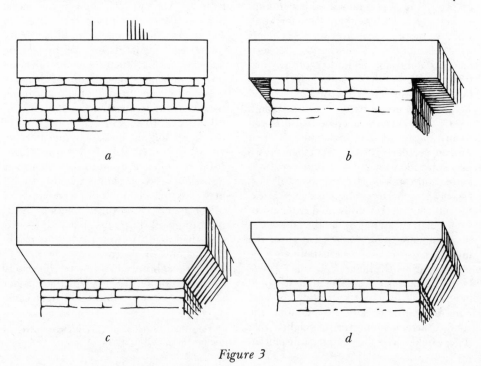

*a*

*b*

*c*

*d*

*Figure 3*

tecting it from weather, or preparing it for weight. Let him imagine the top of the unfinished wall, as it would be seen from above, with all the joints, perhaps uncemented, or imperfectly filled up with cement, open to the sky; and small broken materials filling gaps between large ones, and leaving cavities ready for the rain to soak into, and loosen and dissolve the cement, and split, as it froze, the whole to pieces. I am much mistaken if his first impulse would not be to take a great flat stone and lay it on the top; or rather a series of such, side by side, projecting well over the edge of the wall veil. If, also, he proposed to lay a weight (as, for instance, the end of a beam) on the wall, he would feel at once that the pressure of this beam on, or rather among, the small stones of the wall veil, might very possibly dislodge or disarrange some of them; and his first impulse would be, in this case, also to lay a large flat stone on the top of all to receive the beam, or any other weight, and distribute it equally among the small stones below, as at *a,* figure 3.

We must therefore have our flat stone in either case; and let *b,* figure 3, be the section or side of it, as it is set across the wall. Now, evidently, if by any chance this weight happen to be thrown more on the edges of this stone than the center, there will be a chance of these edges breaking off. Had we not better, therefore, put another stone, sloped off to the wall, beneath the projecting one, as at *c?* But now our cornice looks somewhat too heavy for the wall; and as the upper stone is evidently of needless thickness, we will thin it somewhat, and we have the form *d.* Now observe: the lower or beveled stone here at *d* corresponds to *d* in the base (fig. 2). That was the foot of the wall; this is its hand. And the top stone here, which is a constant member of cornices, corresponds to the under stone *c* in figure 2, which is a constant member of bases. The reader has no idea at present of the enormous importance of these members; but as we shall

have to refer to them perpetually, I must ask him to compare them, and fix their relations well in his mind: and, for convenience, I shall call the beveled or sloping stone, X, and the upright-edged stone, Y. The reader may remember easily which is which; for X is an intersection of two slopes, and may therefore properly mean either of the two sloping stones; and Y is a figure with a perpendicular line and two slopes, and may therefore fitly stand for the upright stone in relation to each of the sloping ones.

Now the form at *d,* figure 3, is the great root and primal type of all cornices whatsoever. In order to see what forms may be developed from it, let us take its profile a little larger—*a,* figure 4, with X and Y duly marked. Now this form, being the root of all cornices, may either have to finish the wall, and so keep off rain; or, as so often stated, to carry weight. If the former, it is evident that, in its present profile, the rain will run back down the slope of X; and if the latter, that the sharp angle or edge of X, at *k,* may be a little too weak for its work, and run a chance of giving way. To avoid the evil in the first case, suppose we hollow the slope of X inward, as at *b;* and to avoid it in the second case, suppose we strengthen X by letting it bulge outward, as at *c.*

These (*b* and *c*) are the profiles of two vast families of cornices, springing from the same root, which, with a third arising from their combination (owing its origin to aesthetic considerations, and inclining sometimes to the one, sometimes to the other), have been employed, each on its third part of the architecture of the whole world throughout all ages, and must continue to be so employed through such time as is yet to come. We do not at present speak of the third or combined group; but the relation of the two main branches to each other, and to the line of origin, is given at *e,* figure 4; where the dotted lines are the representatives of the two families, and the straight line of the root. The slope

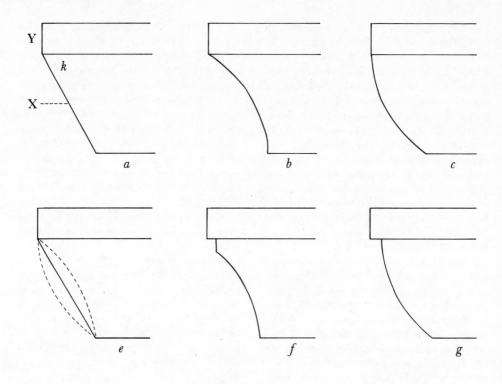

*Figure 4*

of this right line, as well as the nature of the curves, here drawn as segments of circles, we leave undetermined: the slope, as well as the proportion of the depths of X and Y to each other, vary according to the weight to be carried, the strength of the stone, the size of the cornice, and a thousand other accidents; and the nature of the curves according to aesthetic laws. It is in these infinite fields that the invention of the architect is permitted to expatiate, but not in the alteration of primitive forms.

But to proceed. It will doubtless appear to the reader, that, even allowing for some of these permissible variations in the curve or slope of X, neither the form at *b*, nor any approximation to that form, would be sufficiently undercut to keep the rain from running back upon it. This is true; but we have to consider that the cornice, as the close of the wall's life, is of all its features

that which is best fitted for honor and ornament. But it is evident that, as it is high above the eye, the fittest place to receive the decoration is the slope of X, which is inclined toward the spectator; and if we cut away or hollow out this slope more than we have done at *b*, all decoration will be hid in the shadow. If, therefore, the climate be fine, and rain of long continuance not to be dreaded, we shall not hollow the stone X further, adopting the curve at *b*, merely as the most protective in our power. But if the climate be one in which rain is frequent and dangerous, as in alternations with frost, we may be compelled to consider the cornice in a character distinctly protective, and to hollow out X farther, so as to enable it thoroughly to accomplish its purpose. A cornice thus treated loses its character as the crown or honor of the wall, takes the office of its protector, and is called a dripstone. The dripstone is naturally the attribute of Northern buildings, and therefore especially of Gothic architecture; the true cornice is the attribute of Southern buildings, and therefore of Greek and Italian architecture: and it is one of their peculiar beauties, and eminent features of superiority.

Before passing to the dripstone, however, let us examine a little farther into the nature of the true cornice. We cannot, indeed, render either of the forms, *b* or *c* (fig. 4), perfectly protective from rain, but we can help them a little in their duty by a slight advance of their upper ledge. This, with the form *b*, we can best manage by cutting off the sharp upper point of its curve, which is evidently weak and useless; and we shall have the form *f*. By a slight advance of the upper stone in *c*, we shall have the parallel form *g*.

These two cornices, *f* and *g*, are characteristic of early Byzantine work, and are found on all the most lovely examples of it in Venice. The type *a* is rarer, but occurs pure in the most exquisite piece of composition in Venice—the northern portico of Saint Mark's.

Now the reader has doubtless noticed that these forms of cornice result, from considerations of fitness and necessity, far more neatly and decisively than the forms of the base, which we left only very generally determined. The reason is, that there are many ways of building foundations, and many *good* ways, dependent upon the peculiar accidents of the ground and nature of accessible materials. There is also room to spare in width, and a chance of a part of the arrangement being concealed by the ground, so as to modify height. But we have no room to spare in width on the top of a wall, and all that we do must be thoroughly visible; and we can but have to deal with bricks or stones of a certain degree of fineness, and not with mere gravel or sand, or clay—so that as the conditions are limited, the forms become determined; and our steps will be more clear and certain the farther we advance. The sources of a river are usually half lost among moss and pebbles, and its first movements doubtful in direction; but, as the current gathers force, its banks are determined, and its branches are numbered.

So far of the true cornice: we have still to determine the form of the dripstone.

We go back to our primal type or root of cornice, *a* of figure 4. We take this at *a* in figure 5, and we are to consider it entirely as a protection against rain. Now the only way in which the rain can be kept from running back on the slope of X is by a bold hollowing out of it upward, *b*. But clearly, by thus doing, we shall so weaken the projecting part of it that the least shock would break it at the neck, *c;* we must therefore cut the whole out of one stone which will give us the form *d*. That the water may not lodge on the upper ledge of this, we had better round it off; and it will better protect the joint at the bottom of the slope if we let the stone project over it in a roll, cutting the recess deeper above.

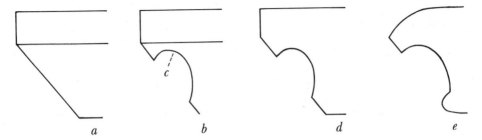

*a*        *b*        *d*        *e*

*Figure 5*

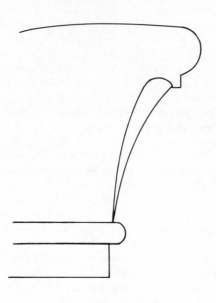

*Figure 6*

These two changes are made in *e; e* is the type of dripstones; the projecting part being, however, more or less rounded into an approximation to the shape of a falcon's beak, and often reaching it completely. But the essential part of the arrangement is the up and under cutting of the curve. Wherever we find this, we are sure that the climate is wet, or that the builders have been *bred* in a wet country, and that the rest of the building will be prepared for rough weather. The up cutting of the curve is sometimes all the distinction between the moldings of far-distant countries and utterly strange nations. Figure 6 represents a molding with an outer and inner curve, the latter undercut. Take the outer line, and this molding is one constant in Venice, in architecture traceable to Arabian types, and chiefly to the early mosques of Cairo. But take the inner line; it is a dripstone at Salisbury. In that narrow interval between the curves there is, when we read it rightly, an expression of another and a mightier curve—the orbed sweep of the earth and sea, between the desert of the

Pyramids, and the green and level fields through which the clear streams of Sarum wind so slowly.

And so delicate is the test, that though pure cornices are often found in the North—borrowed from classical models—so surely as we find a true dripstone molding in the South, the influence of Northern builders has been at work: for the true Byzantine and Arab moldings are all open to the sky and light, but the Lombards brought with them from the North the fear of rain, and in all the Lombardic Gothic we instantly recognize the shadowy dripstone: *a,* figure 7, is from a noble fragment at Milan, in the Piazza dei Mercanti; *b,* from the Broletto of Como. Compare them with *c* and *d,* both from Salisbury; *e* and *f,* from Lisieux, Normandy; *g* and *h,* from Wenlock Abbey, Shropshire.

The reader is now master of all that he need know about the construction of the general wall cornice, fitted either to become a crown of the wall, or to carry weight above. If, however, the weight above become considerable, it may be necessary to support the cornice at intervals with brackets; especially if it be required to project far, as well as to carry weight; as, for instance, if there be a gallery on the top of the wall. This kind of bracket-cornice, deep or shallow, forms a separate family, essentially connected with roofs and galleries; for if there be no superincumbent weight, it is evidently absurd to put brackets to a plain cornice or dripstone (though this is sometimes done in carrying out a style); so that, as soon as we see a bracket put to a cornice, it implies, or should imply, that there is a roof or gallery above it. Hence this family of cornices I shall consider in connection with roofing, calling them "roof cornices," while what we have hitherto examined are proper "wall cornices."

We are not, however, as yet nearly ready for our roof. We have only obtained that which was to be the object of our first division (A); we have got, that is to say,

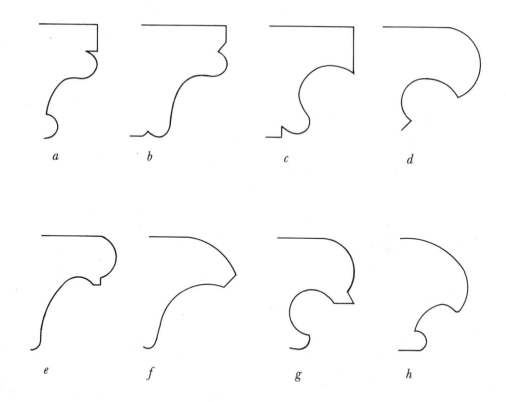

| | | | |
|---|---|---|---|
| *a* | *b* | *c* | *d* |

| | | | |
|---|---|---|---|
| *e* | *f* | *g* | *h* |

*Figure 7*

a general idea of a wall and of the three essential parts of a wall; and we have next, it will be remembered, to get an idea of a pier and the essential parts of a pier, which were to be the subjects of our second division (B).

It has been stated that when a wall had to sustain an addition of vertical pressure, it was first fitted to sustain it by some addition to its own thickness; but if the pressure became very great, by being gathered up into piers.

I must first make the reader understand what I mean by a wall's being gathered up. Take a piece of tolerably thick drawing paper, or thin bristol board, five or six inches square. Set it on its edge on the table, and put a small octavo book on the edge or top of it, and it will bend instantly. Tear it into four strips all across, and roll

up each strip tightly. Set these rolls on end on the table, and they will carry the small octavo perfectly well. Now the thickness or substance of the paper employed to carry the weight is exactly the same as it was before, only it is differently arranged, that is to say, "gathered up." If, therefore, a wall be gathered up like the bristol board, it will bear greater weight than it would if it remained a wall veil. The sticks into which you gather it are called *piers*. A pier is a coagulated wall.

Now you cannot quite treat the wall as you did the bristol board, and twist it up at once; but let us see how you *can* treat it. Let A, figure 8, be the plan of a wall which you have made inconveniently and expensively thick, and which still appears to be slightly too weak for what it must carry; divide it, as at B, into equal spaces,

367

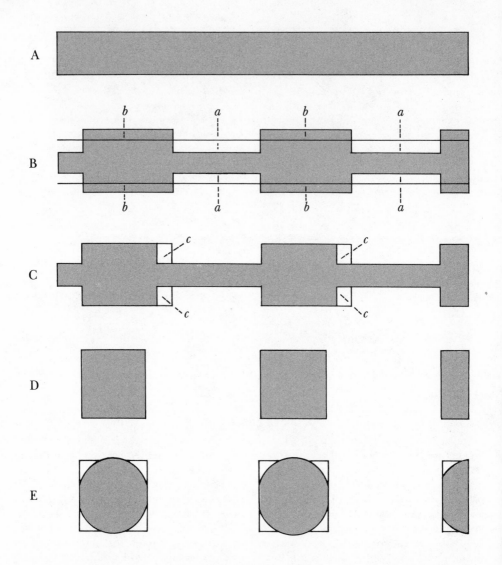

*Figure 8*

a, b, a, b, etc. Cut out a thin slice of it at every *a* on each side, and put the slices you cut out on at every *b* on each side, and you will have the plan at B, with exactly the same quantity of bricks. But your wall is now so much concentrated, that, if it was only slightly too weak before it will be stronger now than it need be; so you may spare some of your space as well as

your bricks by cutting off the corners of the thicker parts, as suppose *c, c, c, c,* at C: and you have now a series of square piers connected by a wall veil, which, on less space and with less materials, will do the work of the wall at A perfectly well.

I do not say *how much* may be cut away in the corners *c, c*—that is a mathematical question with which we need not trouble ourselves: all that we need know is, that out of every slice we take from the "*a's*" and put on at the "*b's*," we may keep a certain percentage of room and bricks, until, supposing that we do not want the wall veil for its own sake, this latter is thinned entirely away, like the girdle of the Lady of Avenel,* and finally breaks, and we have nothing but a row of square piers, D.

But have we yet arrived at the form which will spare most room, and use fewest materials? No; and to get farther we must apply the general principle to our wall, which is equally true in morals and mathematics, that the strength of materials or of men, or of minds, is always most available when it is applied as closely as possible to a single point.

Let the point to which we wish the strength of our square piers to be applied, be chosen. Then we shall of course put them directly under it, and the point will be in their center. But now some of their materials are not so near or close to this point as others. Those at the corners are farther off than the rest.

Now, if every particle of the pier be brought as near as possible to the center of it, the form it assumes is the circle.

The circle must be, therefore, the best possible form of plan for a pier, from the beginning of time to the end of it. A circular pier is called a pillar or column, and all good architecture adapted to vertical support is made up of pillars, has always been so, and must ever be so, as long as the laws of the universe hold.

The final condition is represented at E, in its relation to that at D. It will be observed that though each circle projects a little beyond the side of the square out of which it is formed, the space cut off at the angles is greater than that added at the sides; for, having our materials in a more concentrated arrangement, we can afford to part with some of them in this last transformation, as in all the rest.

And now, what have the base and the cornice of the wall been doing while we

have been cutting the veil to pieces and gathering it together?

The base is also cut to pieces, gathered together, and becomes the base of the column.

The cornice is cut to pieces, gathered together, and becomes the capital of the column. Do not be alarmed at the new word; it does not mean a new thing; a capital is only the cornice of a column, and you may, if you like, call a cornice the capital of a wall.

## Chapter VII

## The Arch

We have seen how our means of vertical support may, for the sake of economy both of space and material, be gathered into piers or shafts, and directed to the sustaining of particular points. The next question is how to connect these points or tops of shafts with each other, so as to be able to lay on them a continuous roof. This the reader, as before, is to favor me by finding out for himself under these following conditions.

Let *s, s,* figure 9, be two shafts, with their capitals ready prepared for their work; and *a, b, b,* and *c, c, c,* be six stones of different sizes, one very long and large, and two smaller, and three smaller still, of which the reader is to choose which he likes best, in order to connect the tops of the shafts.

I suppose he will first try if he can lift the great stone *a,* and if he can, he will put it very simply on the tops of the two pillars, as at A.

Very well indeed: he has done already what a number of Greek architects have been thought very clever for having done. But suppose he *cannot* lift the great stone *a,* or suppose I will not give it to him, but only the two smaller stones at *b, b;* he will doubtless try to put them up, tilted against

*Cf. Sir Walter Scott, "The Monastery" and "The Abbot" [Ed.].

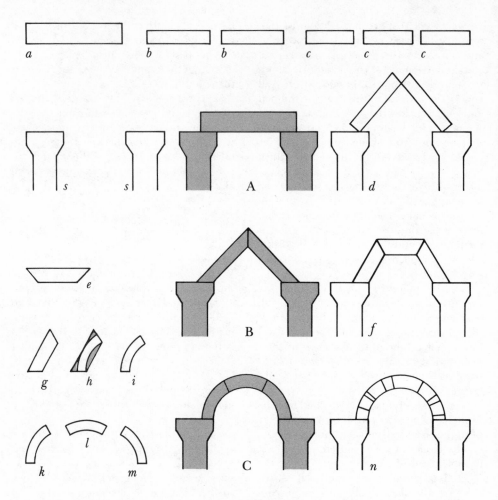

*Figure 9*

each other, as at *d*. Very awkward this; worse than cardhouse building. But if he cuts off the corners of the stones, so as to make each of them of the form *e,* they will stand up very securely as at B.

But suppose he cannot lift even these less stones, but can raise those at *c, c, c.* Then, cutting each of them into the form at *e,* he will doubtless set them up as at *f.*

This last arrangement looks a little dangerous. Is there not a chance of the stone in the middle pushing the others out, or tilting them up and aside, and slipping down itself between them? There is such

a chance: and if, by somewhat altering the form of the stones, we can diminish this chance, all the better. I must say "we" now, for perhaps I may have to help the reader a little.

The danger is, observe, that the midmost stone at *f* pushes out the side ones: then if we can give the side ones such a shape as that, left to themselves, they would fall heavily forward, they will resist this push *out* by their weight, exactly in proportion to their own particular inclination or desire to tumble *in.* Take one of them separately, standing up as at *g;* it is

370

just possible it may stand up as it is, like the Tower of Pisa; but we want it to fall forward. Suppose we cut away the parts that are shaded at *h* and leave it as at *i*, it is very certain it cannot stand alone now, but will fall forward to our entire satisfaction.

Farther: the midmost stone at *f* is likely to be troublesome chiefly by its weight, pushing down between the others: the more we lighten it the better; so we will cut it into exactly the same shape as the side ones, chiseling away the shaded parts, as at *h*. We shall then have all the three stones, *k*, *l*, *m*, of the same shape; and now putting them together, we have, at C, what the reader, I doubt not, will perceive at once to be a much more satisfactory arrangement than at *f*.

We have now got three arrangements; in one using only one piece of stone, in the second two, and in the third three. The first arrangement has no particular name, except the "horizontal": but the single stone (or beam, it may be), is called a lintel; the second arrangement is called a "gable"; the third an "arch."

We might have used pieces of wood instead of stone in all these arrangements, with no difference in plan, so long as the beams were kept loose, like the stones; but as beams can be securely nailed together at the ends, we need not trouble ourselves so much about their shape or balance, and therefore the plan at *f* is a peculiarly wooden construction (the reader will doubtless recognize in it the profile of many a farmhouse roof); and again, because beams are tough, and light, and long, as compared with stones, they are admirably adapted for the constructions at A and B, the plain lintel and gable, while that at C is, for the most part, left to brick and stone.

But farther. The constructions, A, B, and C, though very conveniently to be first considered as composed of one, two, and three pieces, are by no means necessarily so. When we have once cut the stones of the arch into a shape like that of *k*, *l*, and

*m*, they will hold together, whatever their number, place, or size, as at *n*; and the great value of the arch is, that it permits small stones to be used with safety instead of large ones, which are not always to be had. Stones cut into the shape of *k*, *l*, and *m*, whether they be short or long (I have drawn them all sizes at *n* on purpose), are called *voussoirs*; this is a hard, ugly French name; but the reader will perhaps be kind enough to recollect it; it will save us both some trouble: and to make amends for this infliction, I will relieve him of the term *keystone*. One voussoir is as much a keystone as another; only people usually call the stone which is last put in the keystone; and that one happens generally to be at the top or middle of the arch.

Not only the arch, but even the lintel, may be built of many stones or bricks. The reader may see lintels built in this way over most of the windows of our brick London houses, and so also the gable: there are, therefore, two distinct questions respecting each arrangement—first, what is the line, or direction of it, which gives it its strength? and, second, what is the manner of masonry of it, which gives it its consistence?

Now the arch line is the ghost or skeleton of the arch; or rather it is the spinal marrow of the arch, and the voussoirs are the vertebrae, which keep it safe and sound, and clothe it. This arch line the architect has first to conceive and shape in his mind, as opposed to, or having to bear, certain forces which will try to distort it this way and that; and against which he is first to direct and bend the line itself into as strong resistance as he may, and then, with his voussoirs and what else he can, to guard it, and help it, and keep it to its duty and in its shape. So the arch line is the moral character of the arch, and the adverse forces are its temptations; and the voussoirs, and what else we may help it with, are its armor and its motives to good conduct.

This moral character of the arch is called

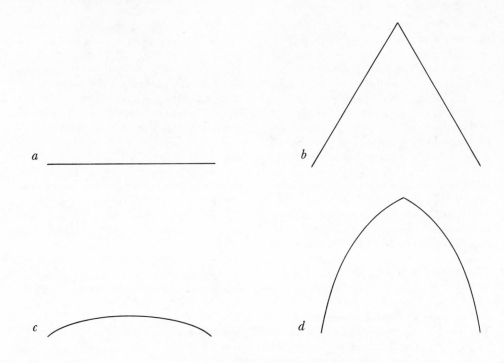

*Figure 10*

by architects its "line of resistance." There is a great deal of nicety in calculating it with precision, just as there is sometimes in finding out very precisely what is a man's true line of moral conduct: but this, in arch morality and in man morality, is a very simple and easily to be understood principle—that if either arch or man expose themselves to their special temptations or adverse forces, *outside* of their voussoirs or proper and appointed armor, both will fall. An arch whose line of resistance is in the middle of its voussoirs is perfectly safe: in proportion as the said line runs near the edge of its voussoirs, the arch is in danger, as the man is who nears temptation; and the moment the line of resistance emerges out of the voussoirs the arch falls.

There are, therefore, properly speaking, two arch lines. One is the visible direction or curve of the arch, which may generally be considered as the under edge of its voussoirs, and which has often no more to do with the real stability of the arch, than a man's apparent conduct has with his heart. The other line, which is the line of resistance, or line of good behavior, may or may not be consistent with the outward and apparent curves of the arch; but if not, then the security of the arch depends simply upon this, whether the voussoirs which assume or pretend to the one line are wide enough to include the other.

Now when the reader is told that the line of resistance varies with every change either in place or quantity of the weight above the arch, he will see at once that we have no chance of arranging arches by their moral characters: we can only take the apparent arch line, or visible direction, as a ground of arrangement.

Look back to figure 9. Evidently the abstract or ghost line of the arrangement at A is a plain horizontal line, as at *a,* figure 10.

The abstract line of the arrangement at B, figure 9, is composed of two straight lines set against each other, as at *b*. The abstract line of C, figure 9, is a curve of some kind, not at present determined, suppose *c*, figure 10. Then, as *b* is two of the straight lines at *a*, set up against each other, we may conceive an arrangement, *d*, made up of two of the curved lines at *c*, set against each other. This is called a pointed arch, which is a contradiction in terms; it ought to be called a curved gable; but it must keep the name it has got.

Now *a*, *b*, *c*, *d*, figure 10, are the ghosts of the lintel, the gable, the arch, and the pointed arch. With the poor lintel ghost we need trouble ourselves no farther; there are no changes in him; but there is much variety in the other three, and the method

of their variety will be best discerned by studying *b* and *d*, as subordinate to and connected with the simple arch at *c*.

Many architects, especially the worst, have been very curious in designing out-of-the-way arches—elliptical arches, and four-centered arches, so-called, and other singularities. The good architects have generally been content, and we for the present will be so, with God's arch, the arch of the rainbow and of the apparent heaven, and which the sun shapes for us as it sets and rises. Let us watch the sun for a moment as it climbs; when it is a quarter up, it will give us the arch *a*, figure 11; when it is half up, *b*; and when three-quarters up, *c*. There will be an infinite number of arches between these, but we will take these as sufficient representatives of all. Then *a* is

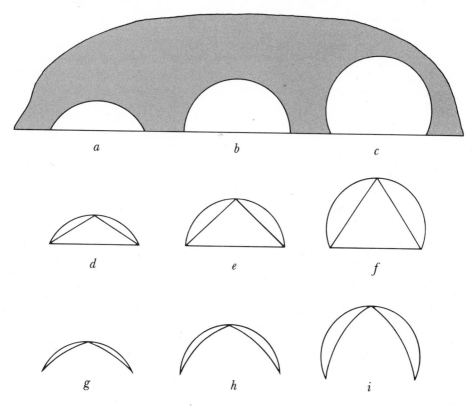

*Figure 11*

the low arch, *b* the central or pure arch, *c* the high arch, and the rays of the sun would have drawn for us their voussoirs.

We will take these several arches successively, and fixing the top of each accurately, draw two right lines thence to its base, *d, e, f,* figure 11. Then these lines give us the relative gables of each of the arches; *d* is the Italian or southern gable, *e* the central gable, *f* the Gothic gable.

We will again take the three arches with their gables in succession, and on each of the sides of the gable, between it and the arch, we will describe another arch, as at *g, h, i.* Then the curves so described give the pointed arches belonging to each of the round arches; *g,* the flat pointed arch, *h,* the central pointed arch, and *i,* the lancet pointed arch.

If the radius with which these intermediate curves are drawn be the base of *f,* the last is the equilateral pointed arch, one of great importance in Gothic work. But between the gable and circle, in all the three figures, there are an infinite number of pointed arches, describable with different radii; and the three round arches, be it remembered, are themselves representatives of an infinite number, passing from the flattest conceivable curve, through the semicircle and horseshoe, up to the full circle.

The central and the last group are the most important. The central round, or semicircle, is the Roman, the Byzantine, and Norman arch; and its relative pointed includes one wide branch of Gothic. The horseshoe round is the Arabic and Moorish arch, and its relative pointed includes the whole range of Arabic and lancet, or Early English and French Gothics. I mean of course by the relative pointed the entire group of which the equilateral arch is the representative. Between it and the outer horseshoe, as this latter rises higher, the reader will find, on experiment, the great families of what may be called the horseshoe pointed—curves of the highest importance, but which are all included, with

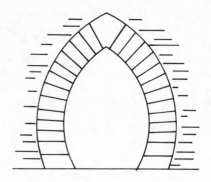

*Figure 12*

English lancet, under the term, relative pointed of the horseshoe arch (*see* fig. 12).

The groups above described are all formed of circular arcs, and include all truly useful and beautiful arches for ordinary work. I believe that singular and complicated curves are made use of in modern engineering, but with these the general reader can have no concern: the Ponte della Trinita at Florence is the most graceful instance I know of such structure; the arch made use of being very subtle, and approximating to the low ellipse; for which, in common work a barbarous pointed arch, called four-centered, and composed of bits of circles, is substituted by the English builders. The high ellipse, I believe, exists in eastern architecture. I have never myself met with it on a large scale; but it occurs in the niches of the later portions of the Ducal Palace at Venice.

We are, however, concerned to notice the absurdity of another form of arch, which, with the four-centered, belongs to the English perpendicular Gothic.

Taking the gable of any of the groups in figure 11 (suppose the equilateral), here at *b,* in figure 13, the dotted line representing the relative pointed arch, we may evidently conceive an arch formed by reversed curves on the inside of the gable, as here shown by the inner curved lines.

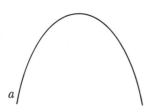  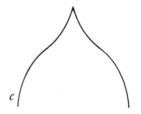

*Figure 13*

I imagine the reader by this time knows enough of the nature of arches to understand that, whatever strength or stability was gained by the curve on the *outside* of the gable, exactly so much is lost by curves on the *inside*. The natural tendency of such an arch to dissolution by its own mere weight renders it a feature of detestable ugliness wherever it occurs on a large scale. It is eminently characteristic of Tudor work, and it is the profile of the Chinese roof (I say on a large scale, because this, as well as all other capricious arches, may be made secure by their masonry when small, but not otherwise). Some allowable modifications of it will be noticed in the chapter on roofs.

There is only one more form of arch which we have to notice. When the last described arch is used, not as the principal arrangement, but as a mere heading to a common pointed arch, we have the form *c,* figure 13. Now this is better than the entirely reversed arch for two reasons: first, less of the line is weakened by reversing; second, the double curve has a very high aesthetic value, not existing in the mere segments of circles. For these reasons arches of this kind are not only admissible, but even of great desirableness, when their scale and masonry render them secure, but above a certain scale they are altogether barbarous: and, with the reversed Tudor arch wantonly employed, are the characteristics of the worst and meanest schools of architecture, past or present.

This double curve is called the ogee;

it is the profile of many German leaden roofs, of many Turkish domes (there more excusable, because associated and in sympathy with exquisitely managed arches of the same line in the walls below), of Tudor turrets, as in Henry the Seventh's Chapel,* and it is at the bottom or top of sundry other blunders all over the world.

On the subject of the stability of arches, volumes have been written, and volumes more are required. The reader will not, therefore, expect from me any very complete explanation of its conditions within the limits of a single chapter. But that which is necessary for him to know is very simple and very easy; and yet, I believe, some part of it is very little known, or noticed.

We must first have a clear idea of what is meant by an arch. It is curved *shell* of firm materials, on whose back a burden is to be laid of *loose* materials. So far as the materials above it are *not loose,* but themselves hold together, the opening below is not an arch, but an *excavation.* Note this difference very carefully. If the King of Sardinia tunnels through the Mont Cenis, as he proposes,† he will not require to build a brick arch under his tunnel to carry the weight of the Mont Cenis: that would need scientific masonry indeed. The Mont

---

*Located in Westminster Abbey, London [Ed.].

†The Mont Cenis Tunnel (actually under Mont Fréjus), 1870, was the first Alpine tunnel connecting France and Italy [Ed.].

Cenis will carry itself, by its own cohesion, and a succession of invisible granite arches, rather larger than the tunnel. But when Mr. Brunel tunneled the Thames bottom,* he needed to build a brick arch to carry the six or seven feet of mud and the weight of water above. That is a type of all arches proper.

Now arches, in practice, partake of the nature of the two. So far as their masonry above is Mont-Cenisian, that is to say, colossal in comparison of them, and granitic, so that the arch is a mere hole in the rock substance of it, the form of the arch is of no consequence whatever: it may be rounded, or lozenged, or ogee'd, or anything else; and in the noblest architecture there is always *some* character of this kind given to the masonry. It is independent enough not to care about the holes cut in it, and does not subside into them like sand. But the theory of arches does not presume on any such condition of things: it allows itself only the shell of the arch proper; the vertebrae, carrying their marrow of resistance; and, above this shell, it assumes the wall to be in a state of flux, bearing down on the arch, like water or sand, with its whole weight. And farther, the problem which is to be solved by the arch builder is not merely to carry this weight, but to carry it with the least thickness of shell. It is easy to carry it by continually thickening your voussoirs: if you have six feet depth of sand or gravel to carry, and you choose to employ granite voussoirs six feet thick, no question but your arch is safe enough. But it is perhaps somewhat too costly: the thing to be done is to carry the sand or gravel with brick voussoirs, six inches thick, or, at any rate, with the least thickness of voussoir which will be safe; and to do this requires peculiar arrangement of the lines of the arch. There are many arrangements, useful all in their way, but we have only to do, in the best architecture, with the simplest and most easily understood.

What we have to say will apply to all arches, but the central pointed arch is the best for general illustration. Let *a*, figure 14, be the shell of a pointed arch with loose loading above; and suppose you find that shell not quite thick enough, and that the weight bears too heavily on the top of the arch, and is likely to break it in, you proceed to thicken your shell, but need you thicken it all equally? Not so; you would only waste your good voussoirs. If you have any common sense you will thicken it at the top, where a Mylodon's skull is thickened for the same purpose (and some human skulls, I fancy), as at *b*. The pebbles and gravel above will now shoot off it right and left, as the bullets do off a cuirassier's breastplate, and will have no chance of beating it in.

If still it be not strong enough, a farther addition may be made, as at *c*, now thickening the voussoirs a little at the base also. But as this may perhaps throw the arch inconveniently high, or occasion a waste of voussoirs at the top, we may employ another expedient.

I imagine the reader's common sense, if not his previous knowledge, will enable him to understand that if the arch at *a*, figure 14, burst *in* at the top, it must burst *out* at the sides. Set up two pieces of pasteboard, edge to edge, and press them down with your hand, and you will see them bend out at the sides. Therefore, if you can keep the arch from starting out at the points *p, p,* it *cannot* curve in at the top, put what weight on it you will, unless by sheer crushing of the stones to fragments.

Now you may keep the arch from starting out at *p* by loading it at *p,* putting more weight upon it and against it at that point; and this, in practice, is the way it is usually done. But we assume at present that the weight above is sand or water, quite unmanageable, not to be directed to the points we choose; and in practice, it

---

*The Thames Tunnel, from Wapping to Rotherhithe, in England, was completed in 1843 [Ed.].

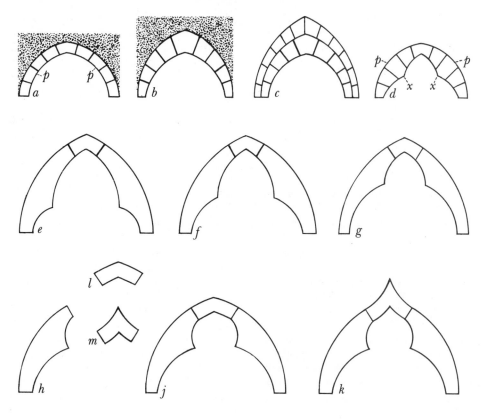

*Figure 14*

may sometimes happen that we cannot put weight upon the arch at *p*. We may perhaps want an opening above it, or it may be at the side of the building, and many other circumstances may occur to hinder us.

But if we are not sure that we can put weight above it, we are perfectly sure that we can hang weight under it. You may always thicken your shell inside, and put the weight upon it as at *x, x,* in *d*, figure 14. Not much chance of its bursting out at *p* now, is there?

Whenever, therefore, an arch has to bear vertical pressure, it will bear it better when its shell is shaped as at *b* or *d*, than as at *a: b* and *d* are, therefore, the types of arches built to resist vertical pressure, all over the world, and from the beginning of architecture to its end. None others can

be compared with them: all are imperfect except these.

The added projections at *x, x,* in *d,* are called cusps, and they are the very soul and life of the best northern Gothic; yet never thoroughly understood nor found in perfection, except in Italy, the northern builders working often, even in the best times, with the vulgar form at *a*.

The form at *b* is rarely found in the north; its perfection is in the Lombardic Gothic: and branches of it, good and bad according to their use, occur in Saracenic work.

The true and perfect cusp is single only. But it was probably invented (by the Arabs?) not as a constructive, but a decorative feature, in pure fantasy; and in early northern work it is only the application to the arch of the foliation, so called, of penetrated spaces in stone surfaces. It is degraded in dignity, and loses in usefulness, exactly in proportion to its multiplication on the arch. In later architecture, especially English Tudor, it is sunk into dotage, and becomes a simple excrescence, a bit of stone pinched up out of the arch, as a cook pinches the paste at the edge of a pie.

Now, in the arches *e, f, g,* a slight modification has been made in the form of the central piece, in order that it may continue the curve of the cusp. This modification is not to be given to it in practice without considerable nicety of workmanship; and some curious results took place in Venice from this difficulty.

At *h* (fig. 14) is the shape of the Venetian side stone, with its cusp; detached from the arch. Nothing can possibly be better or more graceful, or have the weight better disposed in order to cause it to nod forward against the keystone, as above explained, where I developed the whole system of the arch from three pieces, in order that the reader might now clearly see the use of the weight of the cusp.

Now a Venetian Gothic palace has usually at least three stories; with perhaps ten or twelve windows in each story, and this, on two or three of its sides, requiring altogether some hundred to a hundred and fifty side pieces.

I have no doubt, from observation of the way the windows are set together, that the side pieces were carved in pairs, like hooks, of which the keystones were to be the eyes; that these side pieces were ordered by the architect in the gross, and were used by him sometimes for wider, sometimes for narrower windows; beveling the two ends as required, fitting in keystones as he best could, and now and then varying the arrangement by turning the side pieces *upside down.*

There are various conveniences in this way of working, one of the principal being that the side pieces with their cusps were always cut to their complete form, and that no part of the cusp was carried out into the keystone, which followed the curve of the outer arch itself. The ornaments of the cusp might thus be worked without any troublesome reference to the rest of the arch.

Now let us take a pair of side pieces, made to order, like that at *h,* and see what we can make of them. We will try to fit them first with a keystone which continues the curve of the outer arch as at *j.* This the reader surely thinks an ugly arch. There are a great many of them in Venice, the ugliest things there, and the Venetian builders quickly began to feel them so. What could they do to better them? The arch at *j* has a central piece of the form *l.* Substitute for it a piece of the form *m* and we have the arch at *k.*

This arch at *k* is not as strong as that at *j;* but, built of good marble, and with its pieces of proper thickness, it is quite strong enough for all practical purposes on a small scale. I have examined at least two thousand windows of this kind and of the other Venetian ogees, and I never found *one,* even in the most ruinous palaces (in which they had had to sustain the distorted weight of falling walls) in which the central piece was fissured; and this is the only danger to which the window is exposed; in other respects it is as strong an arch as can be built.

## Chapter VIII

## The Roof

Hitherto our inquiry has been unembarrassed by any considerations relating exclusively either to the exterior or interior of buildings. But it can remain so no longer. As far as the architect is concerned, one side of a wall is generally the same as another; but in the roof there are usually two distinct divisions of the structure; one, a shell, vault, or flat ceiling internally visible, the other, an upper structure, built of timber, to protect the lower; or of some different form, to support it. Sometimes, indeed, the internally visible structure is the real roof, and sometimes there are more than two divisions, as in Saint Paul's, where we have a central shell with a masque below and above. Still it will be convenient to remember the distinction between the part of the roof which is usually visible from within, and whose only business is to stand strongly, and not fall in, which I shall call the roof proper; and, second, the upper roof, which, being often partly supported by the lower, is not so much concerned with its own stability as with the weather, and is appointed to throw off snow, and get rid of rain, as fast as possible, which I shall call the roof mask.

It is, however, needless for me to engage the reader in the discussion of the various methods of construction of roofs proper, for this simple reason, that no person without long experience can tell whether a roof be wisely constructed or not; nor tell at all, even with help of any amount of experience, without examination of the several parts and bearings of it, very different from any observation possible to the general critic: and more than this, the inquiry would be useless to us in our Venetian studies, where the roofs are either not contemporary with the buildings, or flat, or else vaults of the simplest possible constructions.

The forms resulting from the other curves of the arch developed in the last chapter; that is to say, the various eastern domes and cupolas arising out of the revolution of the horseshoe and ogee curves, together with the well-known Chinese concave roof are of course purely decorative, the bulging outline, or concave surface being of no more use, or rather of less, in throwing off snow or rain, than the ordinary spire and gable; and it is rather curious, therefore, that all of them, on a small scale, should have obtained so extensive use in Germany and Switzerland, their native climate being that of the east, where their purpose seems rather to concentrate light upon their orbed surfaces. I much doubt their applicability, on a large scale, to architecture of any admirable dignity: their chief charm is, to the European eye, that of strangeness; and it seems to me possible that in the east the bulging form may be also delightful, from the idea of its enclosing a volume of cool air. I enjoy them in Saint Mark's chiefly because they increase the fantastic and unreal character of Saint Mark's Place; and because they appear to sympathize with an expression, common, I think, to all the buildings of that group, of a natural buoyancy, as if they floated in the air or on the surface of the sea. But assuredly, they are not features to be recommended for imitation.

Circumstances and sentiment aiding each other, the steep roof becomes generally adopted, and delighted in, throughout the north; and then, with the gradual exaggeration with which every pleasant idea is pursued by the human mind, it is raised into all manner of peaks, and points, and ridges; and pinnacle after pinnacle is added on its flanks, and the walls increased in height in proportion, until we get indeed a very sublime mass.

As the height of the walls increased, in sympathy with the rise of the roof, while their thickness remained the same, it became more and more necessary to support them by buttresses; but it is not the steep roof which requires the buttress, but the vaulting beneath it; the roof mask being a mere wooden frame tied together by cross timbers, and in small buildings often put together on the ground, raised afterward, and set on the walls like a hat, bearing vertically upon them; and farther, I believe in most cases the northern vaulting requires its great array of external buttress, not so much from any peculiar boldness in its own forms, as from the greater comparative thinness and height of the walls, and more determined throwing of the whole weight of the roof on particular points.

## Chapter IX

### The Buttress

Buttresses are of many kinds, according to the character and direction of the lateral forces they are intended to resist. But their first broad division is into buttresses which meet and break the force before it arrives at the wall, and buttresses which stand on the lee side of the wall and prop it against the force.

The lateral forces which walls have to sustain are of three distinct kinds: dead weight, as of masonry or still water; moving weight, as of wind or running water; and sudden concussion, as of earthquakes, explosions, etc.

1. Clearly, dead weight can only be resisted by the buttress acting as a prop; for a buttress on the side of, or toward the weight, would only add to its effect. This, then, forms the first great class of buttressed architecture; lateral thrusts of roofing or arches being met by props of masonry outside—the thrust from within, the prop without; or the crushing force of water on a ship's side met by its cross timbers—the thrust here from without the wall, the prop within.

2. Moving weight may, of course, be resisted by the prop on the lee side of the wall, but is often more effectually met, on the side which is attacked, by buttresses of peculiar forms, cunning buttresses, which do not attempt to sustain the weight, but *parry* it, and throw it off in directions clear of the wall.

3. Concussions and vibratory motion, though in reality only supported by the prop buttress, must be provided for by buttresses on both sides of the wall, as their direction cannot be foreseen, and is continually changing.

We shall briefly glance at these three systems of buttressing; but the two latter, being of small importance to our present purpose, may as well be dismissed first.

*Buttresses for guard against moving weight, set, therefore, toward the weight they resist—* The most familiar instance of this kind of buttress we have in the sharp piers of a bridge in the center of a powerful stream, which divide the current on their edges, and throw it to each side under the arches. A ship's bow is a buttress of the same kind, and so also the ridge of a breastplate, both adding to the strength of it in resisting a cross blow, and giving a better chance of a bullet glancing aside. In Switzerland, projecting buttresses of this kind are often built round churches, heading uphill, to divide and throw off the avalanches. The various forms given to piers and harbor quays, and to the bases of lighthouses, in order to meet the force of the waves, are all conditions of this kind of buttress. But in works of ornamental architecture such buttresses are of rare occurrence; and I merely name them in order to mark their place in our architectural system, since in the investigation of our present subject we shall not meet with a single example of them, unless sometimes the angle of the foundation of a palace against the sweep of the tide, or the wooden piers of some canal bridge quivering in its current.

*Buttresses for guard against vibratory motion—* The whole formation of this kind of buttress resolves itself into mere expansion of the base of the wall, so as to make it stand steadier, as a man stands with his feet apart when he is likely to lose his balance. The approach to a pyramidal form is also of great use as a guard against the action of artillery; that if a stone or tier of stones be battered out of the lower portions of the wall, the whole upper part may not topple over or crumble down at once. Various forms of this buttress, sometimes applied to particular points of the wall, sometimes forming a great sloping rampart along its base, are frequent in buildings of countries exposed to earthquake. They give a peculiarly heavy outline to much of the architecture of the kingdom of Naples, and they are of the form in which strength and solidity are first naturally sought, in the slope of the Egyptian wall. The base of Guy's tower at Warwick is a singularly bold example of their military use; and so, in general, bastion and rampart profiles, where, however, the object of stability against a shock is complicated with that of sustaining weight of earth in the rampart behind.

*Prop buttresses against dead weight*—This is the group with which we have principally to do; and a buttress of the kind acts in two ways, partly by its weight and partly by its strength. It acts by its weight when its mass is so great that the weight it sustains cannot stir it, but is lost upon it, buried in it, and annihilated: neither the shape of such a buttress nor the cohesion of its materials is of much consequence: a heap of stones or sandbags laid up against the wall will answer as well as a built and cemented mass.

But a buttress acting by its strength is not of mass sufficient to resist the weight by mere inertia; but it conveys the weight through its body to something else which is so capable; as, for instance, a man leaning against a door with his hands, and propping himself against the ground, conveys the force which would open or close the door against him through his body to the ground. A buttress acting in this way must be of perfectly coherent materials, and so strong that though the weight to be borne could easily move it, it cannot break it: this kind of buttress may be called a conducting buttress. Practically, however, the two modes of action are always in some sort united. Again, the weight to be borne may either act generally on the whole wall surface, or with excessive energy on particular points: when it acts on the whole wall surface, the whole wall is generally supported; and the arrangement becomes a continuous rampart, as a dike, or bank of reservoir.

It is, however, very seldom that lateral force in architecture is equally distributed.

In most cases the weight of the roof, or the force of any lateral thrust, is more or less confined to certain points and directions. In an early state of architectural science this definiteness of direction is not yet clear, and it is met by uncertain application of mass or strength in the buttress, sometimes by mere thickening of the wall into square piers, which are partly piers, partly buttresses, as in Norman keeps and towers. But as science advances, the weight to be borne is designedly and decisively thrown upon certain points; the direction and degree of the forces which are then received are exactly calculated, and met by conducting buttresses of the smallest possible dimensions; themselves, in their turn, supported by vertical buttresses acting by weight, and these, perhaps, in their turn, by another set of conducting buttresses: so that, in the best examples of such arrangements, the weight to be borne may be considered as the shock of an electric fluid, which, by a hundred different rods and channels, is divided and carried away into the ground.

In order to give greater weight to the vertical buttress piers which sustain the conducting buttresses, they are loaded with pinnacles, which, however, are, I believe, in all the buildings in which they become very prominent, merely decorative: they are of some use, indeed, by their weight; but if this were all for which they were put there, a few cubic feet of lead would much more securely answer the purpose, without any danger from exposure to wind. If the reader likes to ask any Gothic architect with whom he may happen to be acquainted, to substitute a lump of lead for his pinnacles, he will see by the expression of the face how far he considers the pinnacles decorative members. In the work which seems to me the great type of simple and masculine buttress structure, the apse of Beauvais, the pinnacles are altogether insignificant, and are evidently added just as exclusively to entertain the eye and lighten the aspect

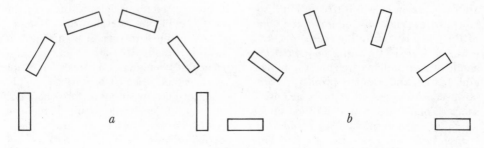

*a*　　　　　　　　　　　　*b*

*Figure 15*

of the buttress, as the slight shafts which are set on its angles; while in other very noble Gothic buildings the pinnacles are introduced as niches for statues, without any reference to construction at all; and sometimes even, as in the tomb of Can Signorio at Verona, on small piers detached from the main building.

I believe, therefore, that the development of the pinnacle is merely a part of the general erectness and picturesqueness of northern work above alluded to; and that, if there had been no other place for the pinnacles, the Gothic builders would have put them on the tops of their arches (they often *did* on the tops of gables and pediments), rather than not have had them; but the natural position of the pinnacle is, of course, where it adds to, rather than diminishes, the stability of the building; that is to say, on its main wall piers and the vertical piers of the buttresses. And thus the edifice is surrounded at last by a complete company of detached piers and pinnacles, each sustaining the inclined prop against the central wall, and looking something like a band of giants holding it up with the butts of their lances. This arrangement would imply the loss of an enormous space of ground, but the intervals of the buttresses are usually walled in below, and form minor chapels.

The science of this arrangement has made it the subject of much enthusiastic declamation among the Gothic architects, almost as unreasonable, in some respects,

as the declamation of the Renaissance architects respecting Greek structure. The fact is, that the whole northern buttress-system is based on the grand requirement of tall windows and vast masses of light at the end of the apse. In order to gain this quantity of light, the piers between the windows are diminished in thickness until they are far too weak to bear the roof, and then sustained by external buttresses. In the Italian method the light is rather dreaded than desired, and the wall is made wide enough between the windows to bear the roof, and so left. In fact, the simplest expression of the difference in the systems is, that a northern apse is a southern one with its interfenestral piers set edgeways. Thus, *a,* figure 15, is the general idea of the southern apse; take it to pieces, and set all its piers edgeways, as at *b,* and you have the northern one. You gain much light for the interior, but you cut the exterior to pieces, and instead of a bold rounded or polygonal surface, ready for any kind of decoration, you have a series of dark and damp cells, which no device that I have yet seen has succeeded in decorating in a perfectly satisfactory manner. If the system be farther carried, and a second or third order of buttresses be added, the real fact is that we have a building standing on two or three rows of concentric piers, with the *roof off* the whole of it except the central circle, and only ribs left, to carry the weight of the bit of remaining roof in the middle;

and after the eye has been accustomed to the bold and simple rounding of the Italian apse, the skeleton character of the disposition is painfully felt. After spending some months in Venice, I thought Bourges Cathedral looked exactly like a half-built ship on its shores. It is useless, however, to dispute respecting the merits of the two systems; both are noble in their place; the northern decidedly the most scientific, or at least involving the greatest display of science, the Italian the calmest and purest; this having in it the sublimity of a calm heaven or a windless noon, the other that of a mountain flank tormented by the north wind, and withering into grisly furrows of alternate chasm and crag.

If I have succeeded in making the reader understand the veritable action of the buttress, he will have no difficulty in determining its fittest form. He has to deal with two distinct kinds; one, a narrow vertical pier, acting principally by its weight, and crowned by a pinnacle; the other, commonly called a flying buttress, a cross bar set from such a pier (when detached from the building) against the main wall. This latter, then, is to be considered as a mere prop or shore, and its use by the Gothic architects might be illustrated by the supposition that we were to build all our houses with walls too thin to stand without wooden props outside, and then to substitute stone props for wooden ones. I have some doubts of the real dignity of such a proceeding, but at all events the merit of the form of the flying buttress depends on its faithfully and visibly performing this somewhat humble office; it is, therefore, in its purity, a mere sloping bar of stone, with an arch beneath it to carry its weight, that is to say, to prevent the action of gravity from in any wise deflecting it, or causing it to break downward under the lateral thrust; it is thus found quite simple in Notre Dame of Paris, and in the Cathedral of Beauvais, while at Cologne the sloping bars are pierced with quatrefoils, and at Amiens with traceried arches. Both seem to me effeminate and false in principle; not, of course, that there is any occasion to make the flying buttress heavy, if a light one will answer the purpose; but it seems as if some security were sacrificed to ornament. At Amiens the arrangement is now seen to great disadvantage, or the early traceries have been replaced by base flamboyant ones, utterly weak and despicable.

The form of the common buttress must be familiar to the eye of every reader, sloping if low, and thrown into successive steps if they are to be carried to any considerable height. There is much dignity in them when they are of essential service; but, even in their best examples, their awkward angles are among the least manageable features of the Northern Gothic, and the whole organization of its system was destroyed by their unnecessary and lavish application on a diminished scale; until the buttress became actually confused with the shaft, and we find strangely crystallized masses of diminutive buttresses applied, for merely vertical support, in the northern tabernacle-work; while in some recent copies of it the principle has been so far distorted that the tiny buttressings look as if they carried the superstructure on the points of their pinnacles, as in the Cranmer memorial at Oxford. Indeed, in most modern Gothic, the architects evidently consider buttresses as convenient breaks of blank surface, and general apologies for deadness of wall. They stand in the place of ideas, and I think are supposed also to have something of the odor of sanctity about them; otherwise one hardly sees why a warehouse seventy feet high should have nothing of the kind, and a chapel, which one can just get into with one's hat off, should have a bunch of them at every corner; and worse than this, they are even thought ornamental when they can be of no possible use; and these stupid penthouse outlines are forced upon the eye in every species of decoration: in some of our modern chapels I have actually seen a couple of buttresses at the end of every pew.

It is almost impossible, in consequence of these unwise repetitions of it, to contemplate the buttress without some degree of prejudice; and I look upon it as one of the most justifiable causes of the unfortunate aversion with which many of our best architects regard the whole Gothic school. It may, however, always be regarded with respect, when its form is simple and its service clear; but no treason to Gothic can be greater than the use of it in indolence or vanity, to enhance the intricacies of structure, or occupy the vacuities of design.

## Chapter X

### Superimposition

The reader has now some knowledge of every feature of all possible architecture. Whatever the nature of the building which may be submitted to his criticism, if it be an edifice at all, if it be anything else than a mere heap of stones, like a pyramid or breakwater, or than a large stone hewn into shape, like an obelisk, it will be instantly and easily resolvable into some of the parts which we have been hitherto considering: its pinnacles will separate themselves into their small shafts and roofs; its supporting members into shafts and arches, or walls penetrated by apertures of various shape, and supported by various kinds of buttresses. Respecting each of these several features I am certain that the reader feels himself prepared, by understanding their plain function, to form something like a reasonable and definite judgment whether they be good or bad; and this right judgment of parts will, in most cases, lead him to just reverence or condemnation of the whole.

The various modes in which these parts are capable of combination, and the merits of buildings of different form and expression, are evidently not reducible into lists, nor to be estimated by general laws. The nobility of each building depends on its special fitness for its own purposes; and these purposes vary with every climate, every soil, and every national custom: nay, there were never, probably, two edifices erected in which some accidental difference of condition did not require some difference of plan or of structure; so that, respecting plan and distribution of parts, I do not hope to collect any universal law of right; but there are a few points necessary to be noticed respecting the means by which height is attained in buildings of various plans, and the expediency and methods of superimposition of one story or tier of architecture above another.

For, in the preceding inquiry, I have always supposed either that a single shaft would reach to the top of the building, or that the farther height required might be added in plain wall above the heads of the arches; whereas it may often be rather expedient to complete the entire lower series of arches, or finish the lower wall, with a bold stringcourse or cornice, and build another series of shafts, or another wall, on the top of it.

This superimposition is seen in its simplest form in the interior shafts of a Greek temple; and it has been largely used in nearly all countries where buildings have been meant for real service. Outcry has often been raised against it, but the thing is so sternly necessary that it has always forced itself into acceptance; and it would, therefore, be merely losing time to refute the arguments of those who have attempted its disparagement. Thus far, however, they have reason on their side, that if a building can be kept in one grand mass, without sacrificing either its visible or real adaptation to its objects, it is not well to divide it into stories until it has reached proportions too large to be justly measured by the eye. It ought then to be divided in order to mark its bulk; and decorative divisions are often possible, which rather increase than destroy the expression of general unity.

Superimposition, wisely practiced, is of two kinds, directly contrary to each other, of weight on lightness, and of lightness on weight; while the superimposition of weight on weight, or lightness on lightness, is nearly always wrong.

First, weight on lightness: I do not say weight on *weakness*. The superimposition of the human body on its limbs I call weight on lightness; the superimposition of the branches on a tree trunk I call lightness on weight: in both cases the support is fully adequate to the work, the form of support being regulated by the differences of requirement. Nothing in architecture is half so painful as the apparent want of sufficient support when the weight above is visibly passive; for all buildings are not passive; some seem to rise by their own strength, or float by their own buoyancy; a dome requires no visibility of support, one fancies it supported by the air. But passive architecture without help for its passiveness in unendurable. In a lately built house, No. 86, in Oxford Street, three huge stone pillars in the second story are carried apparently by the edges of three sheets of plate glass in the first. I hardly know anything to match the painfulness of this and some other of our shop structures, in which the ironwork is concealed; nor even when it is apparent, can the eye ever feel satisfied of their security, when built, as at present, with fifty or sixty feet of wall above a rod of iron not the width of this page.

The proper forms of this superimposition of weight on lightness have arisen, for the most part, from the necessity or desirableness, in many situations, of elevating the inhabited portions of buildings considerably above the ground level, especially those exposed to damp or inundation, and the consequent abandonment of the ground story as unserviceable, or else the surrender of it to public purposes.

Thus, in many market and town houses, the ground story is left open as a general place of sheltered resort, and the enclosed apartments raised on pillars. In almost all warm countries the luxury, almost the necessity, of arcades to protect the passengers from the sun, and the desirableness of large space in the rooms above, lead to the same construction. Throughout the Venetian islet group, the houses seem to have been thus, in the first instance, universally built; all the older palaces appearing to have had the *rez-de-chaussée* perfectly open, the upper parts of the palace being sustained on magnificent arches, and the smaller houses sustained in the same manner on wooden piers, still retained in many of the cortili, and exhibited characteristically throughout the main street of Murano. As ground became more valuable and houseroom more scarce, these ground floors were enclosed with wall veils between the original shafts, and so remain; but the type of the structure of the entire city is given in the Ducal Palace.

To this kind of superimposition we owe the most picturesque street effects throughout the world, and the most graceful, as well as the most grotesque, buildings, from the many-shafted fantasy of the Alhambra (a building as beautiful in disposition as it is base in ornamentation) to the four-legged stolidity of the Swiss chalet:* nor these only, but great part of the effect of our cathedrals, in which, necessarily, the close triforium and clerestory walls are superimposed on the nave piers; perhaps with most majesty where with greatest simplicity, as

---

*I have spent much of my life among the Alps; but I never pass, without some feeling of new surprise, the chalet, standing on its four pegs (each topped with a flat stone), balanced in the fury of the Alpine winds. It is not, perhaps, generally known that the chief use of the arrangement is not so much to raise the building above the snow, as to get a draught of wind beneath it, which may prevent the drift from rising against its sides.

in the old basilican types, and the noble cathedral of Pisa.

For the sake of the delightfulness and security of all such arrangements, this law must be observed: that in proportion to the height of wall above them, the shafts are to be short. You may take your given height of wall, and turn any quantity of that wall into shaft that you like; but you must not turn it all into tall shafts, and then put more wall above. Thus, having a house five stories high, you may turn the lower story into shafts, and leave the four stories in wall; or the two lower stories into shafts, and leave three in wall; but, whatever you add to the shaft, you must take from the wall. Then also, of course, the shorter the shaft the thicker will be its *proportionate*, if not its actual, diameter. In the Ducal Palace of Venice the shortest shafts are always the thickest.

The second kind of superimposition, lightness on weight, is, in its most necessary uses, of stories of houses one upon another, where, of course, wall veil is required in the lower ones, and has to support wall veil above, aided by as much of shaft structure as is attainable within the given limits. The greatest, if not the only, merit of the Roman and Renaissance Venetian architects is their graceful management of this kind of superimposition; sometimes of complete courses of external arches and shafts one above the other; sometimes of apertures with intermediate cornices at the levels of the floors, and large shafts from top to bottom of the building; always observing that the upper stories shall be at once lighter and richer than the lower ones. The entire value of such buildings depends upon the perfect and easy expression of the relative strength of the stories, and the unity obtained by the varieties of their proportions, while yet the fact of superimposition and separation by floors is frankly told.

But this superimposition of lightness on weight is still more distinctly the system of many buildings of the kind which I have above called Architecture of Position, that is to say, architecture of which the greater part is intended merely to keep something in a peculiar position; as in lighthouses, and many towers and belfries. The subject of spire and tower architecture, however, is so interesting and extensive, that I have thoughts of writing a detached essay upon it, and, at all events, cannot enter upon it here: but this much is enough for the reader to note for our present purpose, that, although many towers do in reality stand on piers or shafts, as the central towers of cathedrals, yet the expression of all of them, and the real structure of the best and strongest, are the elevation of gradually diminishing weight on massy or even solid foundation. Nevertheless, since the tower is in its origin a building for strength of defense, and faithfulness of watch, rather than splendor of aspect, its true expression is of just so much diminution of weight upward as may be necessary to its fully balanced strength, not a jot more. There must be no light-headedness in your noble tower: impregnable foundation, wrathful crest, with the visor down, and the dark vigilance seen through the clefts of it; not the filigree crown or embroidered cap. No towers are so grand as the square browed ones, with massy cornices and rent battlements; next to these come the fantastic towers, with their various forms of steep roof; the best, not the cone, but the plain gable thrown very high; last of all in my mind (of good towers), those with spires or crowns, though these, of course, are fittest for ecclesiastical purposes, and capable of the richest ornament. The paltry four or eight pinnacled things we call towers in England (as in York Minster), are mere confectioner's Gothic, and not worth classing.

But, in all of them, this I believe to be a point of chief necessity—that they shall seem to stand, and shall verily stand, in their own strength; not by help of buttresses nor artful balancings on this side and on that. Your noble tower must need no help, must be sustained by no crutches, must give place to no suspicion of decrepitude. Its office may be to withstand war, look forth for tidings, or to point to heaven: but it must have in its own walls the strength to do this; it is to be itself a bulwark, not to be sustained by other bulwarks; to rise and look forth, "the tower of Lebanon that looketh toward Damascus,"* like a stern sentinel, not like a child held up in its nurse's arms. A tower may, indeed, have a kind of buttress, a projection, or subordinate tower at each of its angles; but these are to its main body like the satellites to a shaft, joined with its strength, and associated in its uprightness, part of the tower itself: exactly in the proportion in which they lose their massive unity with its body, and assume the form of true buttress walls set on its angles, the tower loses its dignity.

These two characters, then, are common to all noble towers, however otherwise different in purpose or feature—the first, that they rise from massive foundation to lighter summits, frowning with battlements perhaps, but yet evidently more pierced and thinner in wall than beneath, and, in most ecclesiastical examples, divided into rich open work: the second, that whatever the form of the tower, it shall not appear to stand by help of buttresses. It follows from the first condition, as indeed it would have followed from ordinary aesthetic requirements, that we shall have continual variation in the arrangements of the stories, and the larger number of apertures toward the top—a condition exquisitely carried out in the old Lombardic towers, in which, however small they may be, the number of apertures is always regularly increased toward the summit; generally one window in the lowest stories, two in the second, then three, five, and six; often, also, one, two, four, and six, with beautiful symmetries of placing, not at present to our purpose. We may sufficiently exemplify the general laws of tower building by placing side by side, drawn to the same scale, a medieval tower, in which most of them are simply

and unaffectedly observed, and one of our own modern towers, in which every one of them is violated in small space, convenient for comparison.

The old tower is that of Saint Mark's at Venice,† not a very perfect example, for its top is Renaissance, but as good Renaissance as there is in Venice; and it is fit for our present purpose, because it owes none of its effect to ornament. It is built as simply as it well can be to answer its purpose: no buttresses; no external features whatever, except some huts at the base, and the loggia, afterward built, which, on purpose, I have not drawn; one bold square mass of brickwork; double walls, with an ascending inclined plane between them, with apertures as small as possible, and these only in necessary places, giving just the light required for ascending the stair or slope, not a ray more; and the weight of the whole relieved only by the double pilasters on the sides, sustaining small arches at the top of the mass, each decorated with the scallop or cockleshell, frequent in Renaissance ornament, and here, for once, thoroughly well applied. Then, when the necessary height is reached, the belfry is left open, as in the ordinary Romanesque campanile, only the shafts more slender, but severe and simple, and the whole crowned by as much spire as the tower would carry, to render it more serviceable as a landmark. The arrangement is repeated in numberless campaniles throughout Italy.

The one beside it is one of those of the lately built college at Edinburgh.‡ I have not taken it as worse than many others (just as I have not taken the Saint Mark's tower as better than many others); but it happens to compress our British system of tower building into small space. The Vene-

---

*Cf. Song of Solomon, 7:4 [Ed.].

†Known as the Campanile, it stood for 1,000 years, then collapsed in 1902 and was replaced by the present copy [Ed.].

‡The United Free Church College of Scotland [Ed.].

Plate I. Types of towers: British (left) and Venetian (right). This was
Plate II in the original publication.

tian tower rises 350 feet, and has no buttresses, though built of brick; the British tower rises 121 feet, and is built of stone, but is supposed to be incapable of standing without two huge buttresses on each angle. The Saint Mark's tower has a high sloping roof, but carries it simply, requiring no pinnacles at its angles; the British tower has no visible roof, but has four pinnacles for mere ornament. The Venetian tower has its lightest part at the top, and is massy at the base; the British tower has its lightest part at the base, and shuts up its windows into a mere arrow-slit at the top. What the tower was built for at all must therefore, it seems to me, remain a mystery to every beholder; for surely no studious inhabitant of its upper chambers will be conceived to be pursuing his employments by the light of the single chink on each side; and had it been intended for a belfry, the sound of its bells would have been as effectually prevented from getting out, as the light from getting in.

We may, here, close our inquiries into the subject of construction; nor must the reader be dissatisfied with the simplicity or apparent barrenness of their present results. He will find, when he begins to apply them, that they are of more value than they now seem; but I have studiously avoided letting myself be drawn into any intricate question because I wished to ask from the reader only so much attention as it seemed that even the most indifferent would not be unwilling to pay to a subject which is hourly becoming of greater practical interest. Evidently it would have been altogether beside the purpose of this essay to have entered deeply into the abstract science, or closely into the mechanical detail, of construction: both have been illustrated by writers far more capable of doing so than I, and may be studied at the reader's discretion; all that has been here endeavored was the leading him to appeal to something like definite principle, and refer to the easily intelligible laws of convenience and necessity, whenever he found his judgment likely to be overborne by authority on the one hand, or dazzled by novelty on the other. If he has time to do more, and to follow out in all their brilliancy the mechanical inventions of the great engineers and architects of the day, I, in some sort, envy him, but must part company with him; for my way lies not along the viaduct, but down the quiet valley which its arches cross, not through the tunnel, but up the hillside which its cavern darkens, to see what gifts Nature will give us, and with what imagery she will fill our thoughts, that the stones we have ranged in rude order may now be touched with life; nor lose forever, in their hewn nakedness, the voices they had of old, when the valley streamlet eddied round them in palpitating light, and the winds of the hillside shook over them the shadows of the fern.

## Chapter XI

## The Material of Ornament

We enter now on the second division of our subject. We have no more to do with heavy stones and hard lines; we are going to be happy: to look round in the world and discover (in a serious manner always however, and under a sense of responsibility) what we like best in it, and to enjoy the same at our leisure: to gather it, examine it, fasten all we can of it into imperishable forms, and put it where we may see it forever.

This it is to decorate architecture.

There are, therefore, three steps in the process; first, to find out in a grave manner what we like best; second, to put as much of this as we can (which is little enough) into form; third, to put this formed abstraction into a proper place.

I said in chapter II, that all noble ornamentation was the expression of man's delight in God's work. This implied that there was an *ig*noble ornamentation, which was the expression of man's delight in his *own*. There is such a school, chiefly degraded classic and Renaissance, in which the ornament is composed of imitations of things made by man. I think, before inquiring what we like best of God's work, we had better get rid of all this imitation of man's, and be quite sure we do not like *that*.

We shall rapidly glance, then, at the material of decoration hence derived. And now I cannot, as I before have done respecting construction, *convince* the reader of one thing being wrong, and another right. I have confessed as much again and again; I am now only to make appeal to him, and cross-question him, whether he really does like things or not. If he likes the ornament on the base of the column of the Place Vendôme [Paris], composed of Wellington boots and laced frock coats, I cannot help it; I can only say I differ from him, and don't like it. And if, therefore, I speak dictatorially, and say this is base or degraded or ugly, I mean only that I believe men of the longest experience in the matter would either think it so, or would be prevented from thinking it so only by some morbid condition of their minds; and I believe that the reader, if he examine himself candidly, will usually agree in my statements.

I conclude, then, with the reader's leave, that all ornament is base which takes for its subject human work, that it is utterly base—painful to every rightly-toned mind, without perhaps immediate sense of the reason, but for a reason palpable enough when we *do* think of it. For to carve our own work, and set it up for admiration, is a miserable self-complacency, a contentment in our own wretched doings, when we might have been looking at God's doings. And all noble ornament is the exact reverse of this. It is the expression of man's delight in God's work.

For observe, the function of ornament is to make you happy. Now in what are you rightly happy? Not in thinking of what you have done yourself; not in your own pride; not your own birth; not in your own being, or your own will, but in looking at God; watching what He does; what He is; and obeying His law, and yielding yourself to His will.

You are to be made happy by ornaments; therefore they must be the expression of all this. Not copies of your own handiwork; not boastings of your own grandeur; not heraldries; not king's arms, nor any creature's arms, but God's arm, seen in His work. Not manifestation of your delight in your own laws, or your own liberties, or your own inventions; but in divine laws, constant, daily, common laws—not Composite laws, nor Doric laws, nor laws of the five orders, but of the Ten Commandments.

Then the proper material of ornament will be whatever God has created; and its proper treatment, that which seems in accordance with or symbolic of His laws. And, for material, we shall therefore have, first, the abstract lines which are most frequent in nature; and then, from lower to higher, the whole range of systematized inorganic and organic forms. We shall rapidly glance in order at their kinds; and, however absurd the elemental division of inorganic matter by the ancients may seem to the modern chemist, it is one so grand and simple for arrangements of external appearances, that I shall here follow it; noticing first, after abstract lines, the imitable forms of the four elements of Earth, Water, Fire, and Air, and then those of animal organisms. It may be convenient to the reader to have the order stated in a clear succession at first, thus:

1. Abstract lines.
2. Forms of Earth (Crystals).
3. Forms of Water (Waves).
4. Forms of Fire (Flames and Rays).
5. Forms of Air (Clouds).
6. (Organic forms). Shells.
7. Fish.
8. Reptiles and insects.
9. Vegetation (A). Stems and Trunks.

10. Vegetation (B). Foliage.
11. Birds.
12. Mammalian animals and Man.

1. *Abstract lines*—I have not with lines named also shades and colors, for this evident reason, that there are no such things as abstract shadows, irrespective of the forms which exhibit them, and distinguished in their own nature from each other; and that the arrangement of shadows, in greater or less quantity, or in certain harmonic successions, is an affair of treatment, not of selection. And when we use abstract colors, we are in fact using a part of nature herself, using a quality of her light, correspondent with that of the air, to carry sound; and the arrangement of color in harmonious masses is again a matter of treatment, not selection. Yet even in this separate art of coloring, as referred to architecture, it is very notable that the best tints are always those of natural stones. These can hardly be wrong; I think I never yet saw an offensive introduction of the natural colors of marble and precious stones, unless in small mosaics, and in one or two glaring instances of the resolute determination to produce something ugly at any cost. On the other hand, I have most assuredly never yet seen a painted building, ancient or modern, which seemed to me quite right.

Our first constituents of ornament will therefore be abstract lines, that is to say, the most frequent contours of natural objects, transferred to architectural forms when it is not right or possible to render such forms distinctly imitative. For instance, the line or curve of the edge of a leaf may be accurately given to the edge of a stone, without rendering the stone in the least *like* a leaf, or suggestive of a leaf; and this the more fully, because the lines of Nature are alike in all her works; simpler or richer in combination, but the same in character; and when they are taken out of their combinations it is impossible to say from which of her works they have been borrowed, their universal property being that of ever-varying curvature in the most subtle and subdued transitions, with peculiar expressions of motion, elasticity, or dependence. But, that the reader may here be able to compare them for himself as deduced from different sources, I have drawn, as

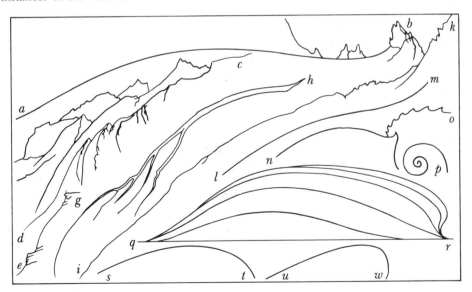

*Figure 16*

accurately as I can, some ten or eleven lines from natural forms of very different substances and scale: the first, *ab*, is, in the original, I think, the most beautiful simple curve I have ever seen in my life; it is a curve about three-quarters of a mile long, formed by the surface of a small glacier of the second order, on a spur of the Aiguille de Blaitère (Chamouni [France]). I have merely outlined the crags on the right of it, to show their sympathy and united action with the curve of the glacier, which is of course entirely dependent on their opposition to its descent; softened, however, into unity by the snow, which rarely melts on this high glacier surface.

The line *dc* is some mile and a half or two miles long; it is part of the flank of the chain of the Dent d'Oche above the lake of Geneva, one or two of the lines of the higher and more distant ranges being given in combination with it.

*h* is a line about four feet long, a branch of spruce fir. I have taken this tree because it is commonly supposed to be stiff and ungraceful: its outer sprays are, however, more noble in their sweep than almost any that I know; but this fragment is seen at great disadvantage, because placed upside down in order that the reader may compare its curvatures with *cd, eg,* and *ik,* which are all mountain lines: *eg,* about five hundred feet of the southern edge of the Matterhorn; *ik,* the entire slope of the Aiguille Bouchard, from its summit into the valley of Chamouni, a line some three miles long; *lm* is the line of the side of a willow leaf traced by laying the leaf on the paper; *no,* one of the innumerable groups of curves at the lip of a paper Nautilus; *p,* a spiral, traced on the paper round a Serpula (worm); *qr,* the leaf of the Alisma Plantago with its interior ribs, half size; *st,* the side of a bay leaf; *uw,* of a salvia leaf: and it is to be carefully noted that these last curves, being never intended by nature to be seen singly, are more heavy and less agreeable than any of the others which would be seen as independent lines. But

all agree in their character and changeful curvature, the mountain and glacier lines only excelling the rest in delicacy and richness of transition.

Why lines of this kind are beautiful, I endeavored to show in the "Modern Painters";* but one point, there omitted, may be mentioned here—that almost all these lines are expressive of action or *force* of some kind, while the circle is a line of limitation or support. In leafage they mark the forces of its growth and expansion, but some among the most beautiful of them are described by bodies variously in motion, or subjected to force; as by projectiles in the air, by the particles of water in a gentle current, by planets in motion in an orbit, by their satellites, if the actual path of the satellite in space be considered instead of its relation to the planet; by boats, or birds, turning in the water or air, by clouds in various action upon the wind, by sails in the curvatures they assume under its force, and by thousands of other objects moving or bearing force. In the Alisma leaf, *qr,* the lines through its body, which are of peculiar beauty, mark the different expansions of its fibers, and are, I think, exactly the same as those which would be traced by the currents of a river entering a lake of the shape of the leaf, at the end where the stalk is, and passing out at its point. Circular curves, on the contrary, are always, I think, curves of limitation or support; that is to say, curves of perfect rest. The cylindrical curve round the stem of a plant binds its fibers together; while the *ascent* of the stem is in lines of various curvature: so the curve of the horizon and of the apparent heaven, of the rainbow, etc.: and though the reader might imagine that the circular orbit of any moving body, or the curve described by a sling, was a curve of motion, he should observe that the circular character is given to the curve not by the

---

*Ruskin's *Modern Painters* (5 vols.) was published 1843–60, after this later revision of *The Stones of Venice* [Ed.].

motion, but by the confinement: the circle is the consequence not of the energy of the body, but of its being forbidden to leave the center; and whenever the whirling or circular motion can be fully impressed on it we obtain instant balance and rest with respect to the center of the circle.

Hence the peculiar fitness of the circular curve as a sign of rest, and security of support, in arches; while the other curves, belonging especially to action, are to be used in the more active architectural features—the hand and foot (the capital and base), and in all minor ornaments; more freely in proportion to their independence of structural conditions.

2. *Forms of Earth (Crystals)*—It may be asked why I do not say rocks or mountains? Simply, because the nobility of these depends, first, on their scale, and, second, on accident. Their scale cannot be represented, nor their accident systematized. No sculptor can in the least imitate the peculiar character of accidental fracture: he can obey or exhibit the laws of nature, but he cannot copy the felicity of her fancies, nor follow the steps of her fury.

But against crystalline form, which is the completely systematized natural structure of the earth, none of these objections hold good, and, accordingly, it is an endless element of decoration, where higher conditions of structure cannot be represented. The four-sided pyramid, perhaps the most frequent of all natural crystals, is called in architecture a dogtooth; its use is quite limitless, and always beautiful: the cube and rhomb are almost equally frequent in checkers and dentils; and all moldings of the middle Gothic are little more than representations of the canaliculated crystals of the beryl, and such other minerals.

3. *Forms of Water (Waves)*—The reasons which prevent rocks from being used for ornament repress still more forcibly the portraiture of the sea. Yet the constant necessity of introducing some representation of water in order to explain the

scene of events, or as a sacred symbol, has forced the sculptors of all ages to the invention of some type or letter for it, if not an actual imitation. We find every degree of conventionalism or of naturalism in these types, the earlier being, for the most part, thoughtful symbols; the later, awkward attempts at portraiture. The most conventional of all types is the Egyptian zigzag, preserved in the astronomical sign of Aquarius; but every nation with any capacities of thought, has given, in some of its work, the same great definition of open water, as "an undulatory thing with fish in it."

4. *Forms of Fire (Flames and Rays)*—If neither the sea nor the rock can be imaged, still less the devouring fire. It has been symbolized by radiation both in painting and sculpture, for the most part in the latter very unsuccessfully. It was suggested to me, not long ago, that the zigzag decorations of Norman architects were typical of light springing from the half-set orb of the sun; the resemblance to the ordinary sun type is indeed remarkable, but I believe accidental. The imitations of fire in the torches of Cupids and genii, and burning in tops of urns, which attest and represent the mephitic inspirations of the seventeenth century in most London churches, and in monuments all over civilized Europe, together with the gilded rays of Romanist altars, may be left to such mercy as the reader is inclined to show them.

5. *Forms of Air (Clouds)*—Hardly more manageable than flames, and of no ornamental use, their majesty being in scale and color, and inimitable in marble.

6. *Shells*—I place these lowest in the scale (after inorganic forms) as being molds or coats of organism; not themselves organic. The sense of this, and of their being mere emptiness and deserted houses, must always prevent them, however beautiful in their lines, from being largely used in ornamentation. It is better to take the line and leave the shell. One form indeed, that of the cockle, has been in all ages used as

the decoration of half-domes, which were named conchae from their shell form; and I believe the wrinkled lip of the cockle, so used, to have been the origin, in some parts of Europe at least, of the exuberant foliation of the round arch. The scallop also is a pretty radiant form, and mingles well with other symbols when it is needed. The crab is always as delightful as a grotesque, for here we suppose the beast inside the shell; and he sustains his part in a lively manner among the other signs of the zodiac, with the scorpion; or scattered upon sculptured shores, as beside the Bronze Boar of Florence. We shall find him in a basket at Venice, at the base of one of the Piazzetta shafts.

7. *Fish*—These, as beautiful in their forms as they are familiar to our sight, while their interest is increased by their symbolic meaning, are of great value as material of ornament. Love of the picturesque has generally induced a choice of some supple form with scaly body and lashing tail, but the simplest fish form is largely employed in medieval work. We shall find the plain oval body and sharp head of the Thunny constantly at Venice; and the fish used in the expression of seawater, or water generally, are always plain-bodied creatures in the best medieval sculpture. The Greek type of the dolphin, however, sometimes but slightly exaggerated from the real outline of the *Delphinus delphis,* is one of the most picturesque of animal forms; and the action of its slow revolving plunge is admirably caught upon the surface sea represented in Greek vases.

8. *Reptiles and Insects*—The forms of the serpent and lizard exhibit almost every element of beauty and horror in strange combination; the horror, which in an imitation is felt only as a pleasurable excitement, has rendered them favorite subjects in all periods of art; and the unity of both lizard and serpent in the ideal dragon, the most picturesque and powerful of all animal forms, and of peculiar symbolic interest to the Christian mind, is perhaps the principal of

all the materials of medieval picturesque sculpture. By the best sculptors it is always used with this symbolic meaning, by the cinquecento sculptors as an ornament merely. The best and most natural representations of mere viper or snake are to be found interlaced among their confused groups of meaningless objects. The real power and horror of the snake head has, however, been rarely reached.

Other less powerful reptile forms are not unfrequent. Small frogs, lizards, and snails almost always enliven the foregrounds and leafage of good sculpture. The tortoise is less usually employed in groups. Beetles are chiefly mystic and colossal. Various insects, like everything else in the world, occur in cinquecento work; grasshoppers most frequently.

9. *Branches and Stems of Trees*—I arrange these under a separate head: because, while the forms of leafage belong to all architecture, and ought to be employed in it always, those of the branch and stem belong to a peculiarly imitative and luxuriant architecture, and are only applicable at times. Pagan sculptors seem to have perceived little beauty in the stems of trees; they were little else than timber to them; and they preferred the rigid and monstrous triglyph, or the fluted column, to a broken bough or gnarled trunk. But with Christian knowledge came a peculiar regard for the forms of vegetation, from the root upward. The actual representation of entire trees required in many Scripture subjects, familiarized the sculptors of bas-relief to the beauty of forms before unknown; for some time, nevertheless, the sculpture of trees was confined to bas-relief, but it at last affected even the treatment of the main shafts in Lombard Gothic buildings. It was then discovered to be more easy to carve branches than leaves; and, much helped by the frequent employment in later Gothic of the "Tree of Jesse" for traceries and other purposes, the system reached full development in a perfect thicket of twigs, which form the

richest portion of the decoration of the porches of Beauvais [Cathedral]. It had now been carried to its richest extreme; men wearied of it and abandoned it, and, like all other natural and beautiful things, it was ostracized by the mob of Renaissance architects. But it is interesting to observe how the human mind, in its acceptance of this feature of ornament, proceeded from the ground, and followed as it were, the natural growth of the tree. It began with the rude and solid trunk, as at Genoa; then the branches shot out, and became loaded with leaves; autumn came, the leaves were shed, and the eye was directed to the extremities of the delicate branches—the Renaissance frosts came, and all perished.

10. *Foliage, Flowers, and Fruit*—It is necessary to consider these as separated from the stems; not only, as above noted, because their separate use marks another school of architecture, but because they are the only organic structures which are capable of being so treated, and intended to be so, without strong effort of imagination. To pull animals to pieces, and use their paws for feet of furniture, or their heads for terminations of rods and shafts, is *usually* the characteristic of feelingless schools; the greatest men like their animals whole: you cannot cut an animal to pieces as you can gather a flower or a leaf. These were intended for our gathering, and for our constant delight: wherever men exist in a perfectly civilized and healthy state, they have vegetation around them; wherever their state approaches that of innocence or perfectness, it approaches that of Paradise—it is a dressing of garden. And, therefore, where nothing else can be used for ornament, vegetation may; vegetation in any form, however fragmentary, however abstracted. A single leaf laid upon the angle of a stone, or the mere form or framework of the leaf drawn upon it, or the mere shadow and ghost of the leaf— the hollow "foil" cut out of it—possesses a charm which nothing else can replace; a charm not exciting, nor demanding laborious thought or sympathy, but perfectly simple, peaceful, and satisfying.

Fruit is, for the most part, more valuable in color than form; nothing is more beautiful as a subject of sculpture on a tree; but, gathered and put in baskets, it is quite possible to have too much of it.

11. *Birds*—The perfect and simple grace of bird form, in general, has rendered it a favorite subject with early sculptors, and with those schools which loved form more than action; but the difficulty of expressing action, where the muscular markings are concealed, has limited the use of it in later art. The heads of birds of prey are always beautiful, and used as the richest ornaments in all ages.

12. *Quadrupeds and Men*—Of quadrupeds the horse has received an elevation into the primal rank of sculptural subject, owing to his association with men. The full value of other quadruped forms has hardly been perceived, or worked for, in late sculpture; and the want of science is more felt in these subjects than in any other branches of early work. The greatest richness of quadruped ornament is found in the hunting sculpture of the Lombards; but rudely treated (the most noble examples of treatment being the lions of Egypt, the Ninevite bulls, and the medieval griffins). Quadrupeds of course form the noblest subjects of ornament next to the human form; this latter, the chief subject of sculpture, being sometimes the end of architecture rather than its decoration.

We have thus completed the list of the materials of architectural decoration, and the reader may be assured that no effort has ever been successful to draw elements of beauty from any other sources than these.

## Chapter XII

## Treatment of Ornament

We now know where we are to look for subjects of decoration. The next question is, as the reader must remember, how to treat or express these subjects.

There are evidently two branches of treatment: the first being the expression, or rendering to the eye and mind, of the thing itself; and the second, the arrangement of the things so expressed: both of these being quite distinct from the placing of the ornament in proper parts of the building. For instance, suppose we take a vine leaf for our subject. The first question is, how to cut the vine leaf? Shall we cut its ribs and notches on the edge, or only its general outline? and so on. Then, how to arrange the vine leaves when we have them; whether symmetrically, or at random; or unsymmetrically, yet within certain limits? All these I call questions of treatment. Then, whether the vine leaves so arranged are to be set on the capital of a pillar or on its shaft, I call a question of place.

So, then, the questions of mere treatment are twofold: how to express, and how to arrange.

If, to produce a good or beautiful ornament, it were only necessary to produce a perfect piece of sculpture, and if a well-cut group of flowers or animals were indeed an ornament wherever it might be placed, the work of the architect would be comparatively easy. Sculpture and architecture would become separate arts: and the architect would order so many pieces of such subject and size as he needed, without troubling himself with any questions but those of disposition and proportion. But this is not so. *No perfect piece either of painting or sculpture is an architectural ornament at all,* except in that vague sense in which any beautiful thing is said to ornament the place it is in. Thus we say that pictures ornament a room; but we should not thank an architect who told us that his design, to be complete, required a Titian to be put in one corner of it, and a Velasquez in the other; and it is just as unreasonable to call perfect sculpture, niched in, or encrusted on a building, a portion of the ornament of that building, as it would be to hang pictures by way of ornament on the outside of it. It is very possible that the sculptured work may be harmoniously associated with the building, or the building executed with reference to it; but in this latter case the architecture is subordinate to the sculpture, as in the Medici Chapel, and I believe also in the Parthenon. And so far from the perfection of the work conducing to its ornamental purpose, we may say, with entire security, that its perfection, in some degree, unfits it for its purpose, and that no absolutely complete sculpture can be decoratively right. We have a familiar instance in the flower work of Saint Paul's, which is probably, in the abstract, as perfect flower sculpture as could be produced at the time; and which is just as rational an ornament of the building as so many valuable van Huysums, framed and glazed, and hung up over each window.

The especial condition of true ornament is, that it be beautiful in its place, and nowhere else, and that it aid the effect of every portion of the building over which it has influence; that it does not, by its richness, make other parts bald, or by its delicacy, make other parts coarse. Every one of its qualities has reference to its place and use: *and it is fitted for its service by what would be faults and deficiencies if it had no special duty.*

Next we have to consider that which is required when incompleteness or simplicity of execution necessary in architectural ornament is referred to the sight, and the various modifications of treatment which are rendered necessary by the variation of its distance from the eye. I say necessary: not merely expedient or economical. It is foolish to carve what is to be seen forty feet off with the delicacy which the eye demands within two yards; not merely because such delicacy is lost in the distance, but because it is a great deal worse than lost—the delicate work has actually worse effect in the distance than rough work. This is a fact well known to painters, and, for the most part, acknowledged by the critics of painting, namely, that there is a certain distance for which a picture is painted; and that the finish, which is delightful if that distance be small, is actually injurious if the distance be great: and, moreover, that there is a particular method of handling which none but consummate artists reach, which has its effect at the intended distance, and is altogether hieroglyphic and unintelligible at any other. This, I say, is acknowledged in painting, but it is not practically acknowledged in architecture; nor until my attention was specially directed to it, had I myself any idea of the care with which this great question was studied by the medieval architects. On my first careful examination of the capitals of the upper arcade of the Ducal Palace at Venice, I was induced, by their singular inferiority of workmanship, to suppose them posterior to those of the lower arcade. It was not till I discovered that some of those which I thought the worst above, were the best when seen from below, that I obtained the key to this marvelous system of adaptation; a system which I afterward found carried out in every building of the great times which I had opportunity of examining.

There are two distinct modes in which this adaptation is effected. In the first, the same designs which are delicately worked when near the eye, are rudely cut, and have far fewer details when they are removed from it. In this method it is not always easy to distinguish economy from skill, or slovenliness from science. But, in the second method, a different kind of design is adopted, composed of fewer parts and of simpler lines, and this is cut with exquisite precision. This is of course the higher method, and the more satisfactory proof of purpose; but an equal degree of imperfection is found in both kinds when they are seen close: in the first, a bald execution of a perfect design; in the second, a baldness of design with perfect execution. And in these very imperfections lies the admirableness of the ornament.

Such are the main principles to be observed in the adaptation of ornament to the sight. We have lastly to inquire by what method, and in what quantities, the ornament, thus adapted to mental contemplation, and prepared for its physical position, may most wisely be arranged. The system of creation is one in which "God's creatures leap not, but express a feast, where all the guests sit close, and nothing wants."* It is also a feast where there is nothing redundant. So, then, in distributing our ornament, there must never be any sense of gap or blank, neither any sense of there being a single member, or fragment of a member, which could be spared. Whatever has nothing to do, whatever could go without being missed, is not ornament; it is deformity and encumbrance. Away with it. And, on the other hand, care must be taken either to diffuse the ornament which we permit, in due relation over the whole building, or so to concentrate it, as never to leave a sense of its having got into knots, and curdled upon some points, and left the rest of the building whey. It is very difficult to give the rules, or analyze the feelings, which should direct us in this matter: for some shafts may be carved and others left unfinished, and that with advantage; some windows may be jeweled like Aladdin's, and one left plain, and still with advantage; the door or doors, or a single turret, or the whole western facade of a church, or the apse or transept, may be made special subjects of decoration, and the rest left plain, and still sometimes with advantage. But in all such cases there is either sign of the desire of rather doing some portion of the building as we would have it, and leaving the rest plain, than doing the whole imperfectly; or else there is choice made of some important feature, to which, as more honorable than the rest, the decoration is confined. The evil is when, without system, and without preference of the nobler members, the ornament alter-

―――――――

*From *The Temple* by George Herbert [Ed.].

nates between sickly luxuriance and sudden blandness. In many of our Scotch and English abbeys, especially Melrose, this is painfully felt; but the worst instance I have ever seen is the window in the side of the arch under the Wellington statue, next Saint George's Hospital. In the first place, a window has no business there at all; in the second, the bars of the window are not the proper place for decoration, especially *wavy* decoration, which one instantly fancies of cast iron; in the third, the richness of the ornament is a mere patch and eruption upon the wall, and one hardly knows whether to be most irritated at the affectation of severity in the rest, or at the vain luxuriance of the dissolute parallelogram.

Finally, as regards quantity of ornament, I have already said, again and again, you cannot have too much if it be good; that is, if it be thoroughly united and harmonized by the laws hitherto insisted upon. But you may easily have too much, if you have more than you have sense to manage. For with every added order of ornament increases the difficulty of discipline. It is exactly the same as in war; you cannot, as an abstract law, have too many soldiers, but you may easily have more than the country is able to sustain, or than your generalship is competent to command. And every regiment which you cannot manage will, on the day of battle, be in your way, and encumber the movements it is not in disposition to sustain.

As an architect, therefore, you are modestly to measure your capacity of governing ornament. Remember, its essence, its being ornament at all, consists in its being governed. Lose your authority over it, let it command you, or lead you, or dictate to you in any wise, and it is an offense, an encumbrance, and a dishonor. And it is always ready to do this; wild to get the bit in its teeth, and rush forth on its own devices. Measure, therefore, your strength; and as long as there is no chance of mutiny, add soldier to soldier, battalion to battalion; but be assured that all are heartily in the cause, and that there is not one of whose position you are ignorant, or whose service you could spare.

# Book Two

## Chapter IV

## The Nature of Gothic

We are now about to enter upon the examination of that school of Venetian architecture which forms an intermediate step between the Byzantine and Gothic forms, but which I find may be conveniently considered in its connection with the latter style. In order that we may discern the tendency of each step of this change, it will be wise in the outset to endeavor to form some general idea of its final result. We know already what the Byzantine architecture is* from which the transition was made, but we ought to know something of the Gothic architecture into which it led. I shall endeavor therefore to give the reader in this chapter an idea, at once broad and definite, of the true nature of *Gothic* architecture, properly so called; not of that of Venice only, but of universal Gothic.

The principal difficulty in doing this arises from the fact that every building of the Gothic period differs in some important respect from every other; and many include features which, if they occurred in other buildings, would not be considered Gothic at all; so that all we have to reason upon is merely, if I may be allowed so to express it, a greater or less degree of *Gothicness* in each building we examine. And it is this Gothicness—the character which, according as it is found more or less in a building, makes it more or less Gothic—of which I want to define the nature; and I feel the same kind of difficulty in doing so which would be encountered by anyone who undertook to explain, for instance, the Nature of Redness, without any actually red thing to point to, but only orange and purple things. Suppose he had only a piece of heather and a dead oak leaf to do it with. He might say, the color which is mixed with the yellow in this oak leaf, and with the blue in this heather, would be red, if you had it separate; but it would be difficult, nevertheless, to make the abstraction perfectly intelligible; and it is so in a far greater degree to make the abstraction of the Gothic character intelligible, because that character itself is made up of many mingled ideas, and can consist only in their union. That is to say, pointed arches do not constitute Gothic, nor vaulted roofs, nor flying buttresses, nor grotesque sculptures; but all or some of these things, and many other things with them, when they come together so as to have life.

Observe also, that, in the definition proposed, I shall only endeavor to analyze the idea which I suppose already to exist in the reader's mind. We all have some notion, most of us a very determined one, of the meaning of the term Gothic; but I know that many persons have this idea in their minds without being able to define it: that is to say, understanding generally that Westminster Abbey is Gothic, and Saint Paul's is not, that Strasburg Cathedral is Gothic, and Saint Peter's is not, they have, nevertheless, no clear notion of what it is that they recognize in the one or miss in the other, such as would enable them to say how far the work at Westminster or Strasburg is good and pure of its kind; still less to say of any nondescript building, like Saint James's Palace or Windsor Castle, how much right Gothic element there is in it, and how much wanting. And I believe this inquiry to be a pleasant and profitable one; and that there will be found something more than usually interesting in tracing out this gray, shadowy, many-pinnacled image

---

*From previous chapters, here omitted [Ed.].

of the Gothic spirit within us; and discerning what fellowship there is between it and our Northern hearts. And if, at any point of the inquiry, I should interfere with any of the reader's previously formed conceptions, and use the term Gothic in any sense which he would not willingly attach to it, I do not ask him to accept, but only to examine and understand, my interpretation, as necessary to the intelligibility of what follows in the rest of the work.

We have, then, the Gothic character submitted to our analysis, just as the rough mineral is submitted to that of the chemist, entangled with many other foreign substances, itself perhaps in no place pure, or ever to be obtained or seen in purity for more than an instant; but nevertheless a thing of definite and separate nature; however inextricable or confused in appearance. Now observe: the chemist defines his mineral by two separate kinds of character; one external, its crystalline form, hardness, luster, etc.; the other internal, the proportions and nature of its constituent atoms. Exactly in the same manner, we shall find that Gothic architecture has external forms and internal elements. Its elements are certain mental tendencies of the builders, legibly expressed in it; as fancifulness, love of variety, love of richness, and such others. Its external forms are pointed arches, vaulted roofs, etc. And unless both the elements and the forms are there, we have no right to call the style Gothic. It is not enough that it has the form, if it have not also the power and life. It is not enough that it has the power, if it have not the form. We must therefore inquire into each of these characters successively; and determine first, what is the mental expression, and second, what the material form of Gothic architecture, properly so called.

First, Mental Power or Expression. What characters, we have to discover, did the Gothic builders love, or instinctively express in their work, as distinguished from all other builders?

Let us go back for a moment to our chemistry, and note that, in defining a mineral by its constituent parts, it is not one nor another of them, that can make up the mineral, but the union of all: for instance, it is neither in charcoal, nor in oxygen, nor in lime, that there is the making of chalk, but in the combination of all three in certain measures; they are all found in very different things from chalk, and there is nothing like chalk either in charcoal or in oxygen, but they are nevertheless necessary to its existence.

So in the various mental characters which make up the soul of Gothic. It is not one nor another that produces it; but their union in certain measures. Each one of them is found in many other architectures beside Gothic; but Gothic cannot exist where they are not found, or, at least, where their place is not in some way supplied. Only there is this great difference between the composition of the mineral and of the architectural style, that if we withdraw one of its elements from the stone, its form is utterly changed, and its existence as such and such a mineral is destroyed; but if we withdraw one of its mental elements from the Gothic style, it is only a little less Gothic than it was before, and the union of two or three of its elements is enough already to bestow a certain Gothicness of character, which gains in intensity as we add the others, and loses as we again withdraw them.

I believe, then, that the characteristic or moral elements of Gothic are the following, placed in the order of their importance:

1. Savageness.
2. Changefulness.
3. Naturalism.
4. Grotesqueness.
5. Rigidity.
6. Redundance.

These characters are here expressed as belonging to the building; as belonging to the builder, they would be expressed thus: 1. Savageness or Rudeness. 2. Love of Change. 3. Love of Nature. 4. Disturbed Imagination. 5. Obstinacy. 6. Generosity.

And I repeat, that the withdrawal of any one, or any two, will not at once destroy the Gothic character of a building, but the removal of a majority of them will. I shall proceed to examine them in their order.

*Savageness*—I am not sure when the word *Gothic* was first generically applied to the architecture of the North; but I presume that, whatever the date of its original usage, it was intended to imply reproach, and express the barbaric character of the nations among whom that architecture arose. It never implied that they were literally of Gothic lineage, far less that their architecture had been originally invented by the Goths themselves; but it did imply that they and their buildings together exhibited a degree of sternness and rudeness, which, in contradistinction to the character of Southern and Eastern nations, appeared like a perpetual reflection of the contrast between the Goth and the Roman in their first encounter. And when that fallen Roman, in the utmost impotence of his luxury, and insolence of his guilt, became the model for the imitation of civilized Europe, at the close of the so-called Dark Ages, the word *Gothic* became a term of unmitigated contempt, not unmixed with aversion. From that contempt, by the exertion of the antiquaries and architects of this century, Gothic architecture has been sufficiently vindicated; and perhaps some among us, in our admiration of the magnificent science of its structure, and sacredness of its expression, might desire that the term of ancient reproach should be withdrawn, and some other, of more apparent honorableness, adopted in its place. There is no chance, as there is no need, of such a substitution. As far as the epithet was used scornfully, it was used falsely; but there is no reproach in the word, rightly understood; on the contrary, there is a profound truth, which the instinct of mankind almost unconsciously recognizes. It is true, greatly and deeply true, that the architecture of the North is rude and wild; but it is not true, that, for this reason, we are

to condemn it, or despise. Far otherwise: I believe it is in this very character that it deserves our profoundest reverence.

The charts of the world which have been drawn up by modern science have thrown into a narrow space the expression of a vast amount of knowledge, but I have never yet seen any one pictorial enough to enable the spectator to imagine the kind of contrast in physical character which exists between Northern and Southern countries. We know the differences in detail, but we have not the broad glance and grasp which would enable us to feel them in their fullness. We know that gentians grow on the Alps, and olives on the Apennines; but we do not enough conceive for ourselves that variegated mosaic of the world's surface which a bird sees in its migration, that difference between the district of the gentian and of the olive which the stork and the swallow see far off, as they lean upon the sirocco wind. Let us, for a moment, try to raise ourselves even above the level of their flight, and imagine the Mediterranean lying beneath us like an irregular lake, and all its ancient promontories sleeping in the sun: here and there an angry spot of thunder, a gray stain of storm, moving upon the burning field; and here and there a fixed wreath of white volcano smoke, surrounded by its circle of ashes; but for the most part a great peacefulness of light, Syria and Greece, Italy and Spain, laid like pieces of a golden pavement into the sea-blue, chased, as we stoop nearer to them, with bossy beaten work of mountain chains, and glowing softly with terraced gardens, and flowers heavy with frankincense, mixed among masses of laurel, and orange, and plumy palm, that abate with their gray-green shadows the burning of the marble rocks, and of the ledges of porphyry sloping under lucent sand. Then let us pass farther toward the north, until we see the orient colors change gradually into a vast belt of rainy green, where the pastures of Switzerland, and poplar valleys of France, and dark forests of the Danube and Carpathians stretch from the mouths of the Loire to those of the Volga, seen through clefts in gray swirls of rain cloud and flaky veils of the mist of the brooks, spreading low along the pasturelands: and then, farther north still, to see the earth heave into mighty masses of leaden rock and heathy moor, bordering with a broad waste of gloomy purple that belt of field and wood, and splintering into irregular and grisly islands amid the northern seas, beaten by storm, and chilled by ice drift, and tormented by furious pulses of contending tide, until the roots of the last forests fail from among the hill ravines, and the hunger of the north wind bites their peaks into barrenness; and, at last, the wall of ice, durable like iron, sets, deathlike, its white teeth against us out of the polar twilight. And, having once traversed in thought this gradation of the zoned iris of the earth in all its material vastness, let us go down nearer to it, and watch the parallel change in the belt of animal life; the multitudes of swift and brilliant creatures that glance in the air and sea, or tread the sands of the southern zone; striped zebras and spotted leopards, glistening serpents, and birds arrayed in purple and scarlet. Let us contrast their delicacy and brilliancy of color, and swiftness of motion, with the frost-cramped strength, and shaggy covering, and dusky plumage of the northern tribes; contrast the Arabian horse with the Shetland, the tiger and leopard with the wolf and bear, the antelope with the elk, the bird of paradise with the osprey: and then, submissively acknowledging the great laws by which the earth and all that it bears are ruled throughout their being, let us not condemn, but rejoice in the expression by man of his own rest in the statues of the lands that gave him birth. Let us watch him with reverence as he sets side by side the burning gems, and smooths with soft sculpture the jasper pillars, that are to reflect a ceaseless sunshine, and rise into a cloudless sky: but not with less reverence

let us stand by him, when, with rough strength and hurried stroke, he smites an uncouth animation out of the rocks which he has torn from among the moss of the moorland, and heaves into the darkened air of the pile of iron buttress and rugged wall, instinct with a work of an imagination as wild and wayward as the northern sea; creations of ungainly shape and rigid limb, but full of wolfish life; fierce as the winds that beat, and changeful as the clouds that shade them.

There is, I repeat, no degradation, no reproach in this, but all dignity and honorableness: and we should err grievously in refusing either to recognize as an essential character of the existing architecture of the North, or to admit as a desirable character in that which it yet may be, this wildness of thought, and roughness of work; this look of mountain brotherhood between the cathedral and the Alp; this magnificence of sturdy power, put forth only the more energetically because the fine finger touch was chilled away by the frosty wind, and the eye dimmed by the moor mist, or blinded by the hail; this outspeaking of the strong spirit of men who may not gather redundant fruitage from the earth, nor bask in dreamy benignity of sunshine, but must break the rock for bread, and cleave the forest for fire, and show, even in what they did for their delight, some of the hard habits of the arm and heart that grew on them as they swung the ax or pressed the plow.

The second mental element above named was *Changefulness*, or Variety.

I have already enforced the allowing independent operation to the inferior workman, simply as a duty *to him*, and as ennobling the architecture by rendering it more Christian. We have now to consider what reward we obtain for the performance of this duty, namely, the perpetual variety of every feature of the building.

Wherever the workman is utterly enslaved, the parts of the building must of course be absolutely like each other; for the perfection of his execution can only be reached by exercising him in doing one thing, and giving him nothing else to do. The degree in which the workman is degraded may be thus known at a glance, by observing whether the several parts of the building are similar or not; and if, as in Greek work, all the capitals are alike, and all the moldings unvaried, then the degradation is complete; if, as in Egyptian or Ninevite work, though the manner of executing certain figures is always the same, the order of design is perpetually varied, the degradation is less total; if, as in Gothic work, there is perpetual change both in design and execution, the workman must have been altogether set free.

How much the beholder gains from the liberty of the laborer may perhaps be questioned in England, where one of the strongest instincts in nearly every mind is that Love of Order which makes us desire that our house windows should pair like our carriage horses, and allows us to yield our faith unhesitatingly to architectural theories which fix a form for everything, and forbid variation from it. I would not impeach love of order: it is one of the most useful elements of the English mind; it helps us in our commerce and in all purely practical matters; and it is in many cases one of the foundation stones of morality. Only do not let us suppose that love of order is love of art. It is true that order, in its highest sense, is one of the necessities of art, just as time is a necessity of music; but love of order has no more to do with our right enjoyment of architecture or painting, than love of punctuality with the appreciation of an opera. Experience, I fear, teaches us that accurate and methodical habits in daily life are seldom characteristic of those who either quickly perceive, or richly possess, the creative powers of art; there is, however, nothing inconsistent between the two instincts, and nothing to hinder us from retaining our business habits, and yet fully allowing and enjoying the noblest gifts of invention. We

already do so, in every other branch of art except architecture, and we only do *not* so there because we have been taught that it would be wrong. Our architects gravely inform us that, as there are four rules of arithmetic, there are five orders of architecture; we, in our simplicity, think that this sounds consistent, and believe them. They inform us also that there is one proper form for Corinthian capitals, another for Doric, and another for Ionic. We, considering that there is also a proper form for the letters A, B, and C, think that this also sounds consistent, and accept the proposition. Understanding, therefore, that one form of the said capitals is proper, and no other, and having a conscientious horror of all impropriety, we allow the architect to provide us with the said capitals, of the proper form, in such and such a quantity, and in all other points to take care that the legal forms are observed; which having done, we rest in forced confidence that we are well housed.

But our higher instincts are not deceived. We take no pleasure in the building provided for us, resembling that which we take in a new book or a new picture. We may be proud of its size, complacent in its correctness, and happy in its convenience. We may take the same pleasure in its symmetry and workmanship as in a well-ordered room, or a skillful piece of manufacture. And this we suppose to be all the pleasure that architecture was ever intended to give us. The idea of reading a building as we would read Milton or Dante, and getting the same kind of delight out of the stones as out of the stanzas, never enters our mind for a moment. And for good reason; there is indeed rhythm in the verses, quite as strict as the symmetries or rhythm of the architecture, and a thousand times more beautiful, but there is something else than rhythm. The verses were neither made to order, nor to match, as the capitals were; and we have therefore a kind of pleasure in them other than a sense of propriety. But it requires a strong effort of common sense to shake ourselves quit of all that we have been taught for the last two centuries, and wake to the perception of a truth just as simple and certain as it is new: that great art, whether expressing itself in words, colors, or stones, does *not* say the same thing over and over again; that the merit of architectural, as of every other art, consists in its saying new and different things; that to repeat itself is no more a characteristic of genius in marble than it is of genius in print; and that we may, without offending any laws of good taste, require of an architect, as we do of a novelist, that he should be not only correct, but entertaining.

Yet all this is true, and self-evident; only hidden from us, as many other self-evident things are, by false teaching. Nothing is a great work of art, for the production of which either rules or models can be given. Exactly so far as architecture works on known rules, and from given models, it is not an art, but a manufacture; and it is, of the two procedures, rather less rational (because more easy) to copy capitals or moldings from Phidias, and call ourselves architects, than to copy heads and hands from Titian and call ourselves painters.

Let us then understand at once that change or variety is as much a necessity to the human heart and brain in buildings as in books; that there is no merit, though there is some occasional use, in monotony; and that we must no more expect to derive either pleasure or profit from an architecture whose ornaments are of one pattern, and whose pillars are of one proportion, than we should out of a universe in which the clouds were all of one shape, and the trees all of one size.

And this we confess in deeds, though not in words. All the pleasure which the people of the nineteenth century take in art, is in pictures, sculpture, minor objects of virtu or medieval architecture, which we enjoy under the term *picturesque:* no pleasure is taken anywhere in modern buildings, and we find all men of true feeling delighting

to escape out of modern cities into natural scenery: hence that peculiar love of landscape which is characteristic of the age. It would be well, if, in all other matters, we were as ready to put up with what we dislike, for the sake of compliance with established law, as we are in architecture.

How so debased a law ever came to be established, we shall see when we come to describe the Renaissance schools; here we have only to note, as a second most essential element of the Gothic spirit, that it broke through that law wherever it found it in existence; it not only dared, but delighted in, the infringement of every servile principle; and invented a series of forms of which the merit was, not merely that they were new, but that they were *capable of perpetual novelty.* The pointed arch was not merely a bold variation from the round, but it admitted of millions of variations in itself; for the proportions of a pointed arch are changeable to infinity, while a circular arch is always the same. The grouped shaft was not merely a bold variation from the single one, but it admitted of millions of variations in its grouping, and in the proportions resultant from its grouping. The introduction of tracery was not only a startling change in the treatment of window lights, but admitted endless changes in the interlacement of the tracery bars themselves. So that, while in all living Christian architecture the love of variety exists, the Gothic schools exhibited that love in culminating energy; and their influence, wherever it extended itself, may be sooner and farther traced by this character than by any other; the tendency to the adoption of Gothic types being always first shown by greater irregularity and richer variation in the forms of the architecture it is about to supersede, long before the appearance of the pointed arch or of any other recognizable *outward* sign of the Gothic mind.

The variety of the Gothic schools is the more healthy and beautiful, because in many cases it is entirely unstudied, and results, not from mere love of change, but from practical necessities. For in one point of view Gothic is not only the best, but the *only rational* architecture, as being that which can fit itself most easily to all services, vulgar or noble. Undefined in its slope of roof, height of shaft, breadth of arch, or disposition of ground plan, it can shrink into a turret, expand into a hall, coil into a staircase, or spring into a spire, with undegraded grace and unexhausted energy; and whenever it finds occasion for change in its form or purpose, it submits to it without the slightest sense of loss either to its unity or majesty—subtle and flexible like a fiery serpent, but ever attentive to the voice of the charmer. And it is one of the chief virtues of the Gothic builders, that they never suffered ideas of outside symmetries and consistencies to interfere with the real use and value of what they did. If they wanted a window, they opened one; a room, they added one; a buttress, they built one; utterly regardless of any established conventionalities of external appearance, knowing (as indeed it always happened) that such daring interruptions of the formal plan would rather give additional interest to its symmetry than injure it. So that, in the best times of Gothic, a useless window would rather have been opened in a unexpected place for the sake of the surprise, than a useful one forbidden for the sake of symmetry. Every successive architect, employed upon a great work, built the pieces he added in his own way, utterly regardless of the style adopted by his predecessors; and if two towers were raised in nominal correspondence at the sides of a cathedral front, one was nearly sure to be different from the other, and in each the style at the top to be different from the style at the bottom.

The third constituent element of the Gothic mind was stated to be *Naturalism;* that is to say, the love of natural objects for their own sake, and the effort to represent them frankly, unconstrained by artistic laws.

This characteristic of the style partly follows in necessary connection with those named above. For, so soon as the workman is left free to represent what subjects he chooses, he must look to the nature that is round him for material, and will endeavor to represent it as he sees it, with more or less accuracy according to the skill he possesses, and with much play of fancy, but with small respect for law. There is, however, a marked distinction between the imaginations of the Western and Eastern races, even when both are left free; the Western, or Gothic, delighting most in the representation of facts, and the Eastern (Arabian, Persian, and Chinese) in the harmony of colors and forms.

The Gothic builders were of that central class which unites fact with design; but the part of the work which was more especially their own was the truthfulness. Their power of artistic invention or arrangement was not greater than that of Romanesque and Byzantine workmen: by those workmen they were taught the principles, and from them received their models, of design; but to the ornamental feeling and rich fancy of the Byzantine the Gothic builder added a love of *fact* which is never found in the South. Both Greek and Roman used conventional foliage in their ornament, passing into something that was not foliage at all, knotting itself into strange cuplike buds or clusters, and growing out of lifeless rods instead of stems; the Gothic sculptor received these types, at first, as things that ought to be, just as we have a second time received them; but he could not rest in them. He saw there was no veracity in them, no knowledge, no vitality. Do what he would, he could not help liking the true leaves better; and cautiously, a little at a time, he put more of nature into his work, until at last it was all true, retaining, nevertheless, every valuable character of the original well-disciplined and designed arrangement.

Nor is it only in external and visible subject that the Gothic workman wrought for truth: he is as firm in his rendering of imaginative as of actual truth; that is to say, when an idea would have been by a Roman, or Byzantine, symbolically represented, the Gothic mind realizes it to the utmost. For instance, the purgatorial fire is represented in the mosaic of Torcello (Romanesque) as a red stream, longitudinally striped like a riband, descending out of the throne of Christ, and gradually extending itself to envelop the wicked. When we are once informed what this means, it is enough for its purpose; but the Gothic inventor does not leave the sign in need of interpretation. He makes the fire as like real fire as he can; and in the porch of Saint Maclou at Rouen the sculptured flames burst out of the Hades gate, and flicker up, in writhing tongues of stone, through the interstices of the niches, as if the church itself were on fire. This is an extreme instance, but it is all the more illustrative of the entire difference in temper and thought between the two schools of art, and of the intense love of veracity which influenced the Gothic design.

In the second place, Gothic work, when referred to the arrangement of all art, as purist, naturalist, or sensualist, is naturalist. This character follows necessarily on its extreme love of truth, prevailing over the sense of beauty, and causing it to take delight in portraiture of every kind, and to express the various characters of the human countenance and form, as it did the varieties of leaves and the ruggedness of branches. And this tendency is both increased and ennobled by the same Christian humility which we saw expressed in the first character of Gothic work, its rudeness. For as that resulted from a humility which confessed the imperfection of the workman, so this naturalist portraiture is rendered more faithful by the humility which confesses the imperfection of the subject. The Greek sculptor could neither bear to confess his own feebleness, nor to tell the faults of the forms that he portrayed. But the Christian workman, believing that all is finally to work together for good, freely confesses

both, and neither seeks to disguise his own roughness of work, nor his subject's roughness of make. Yet this frankness being joined, for the most part, with depth of religious feeling in other directions, and especially with charity, there is sometimes a tendency to Purism in the best Gothic sculpture; so that it frequently reaches great dignity of form and tenderness of expression, yet never so as to lose the veracity of portraiture wherever portraiture is possible; not exalting its kings into demigods, nor its saints into archangels, but giving what kingliness and sanctity was in them, to the full, mixed with due record of their faults; and this in the most part with a great indifference like that of Scripture history, which sets down, with unmoved and unexcusing resoluteness, the virtues and errors of all men of whom it speaks, often leaving the reader to form his own estimate of them, without an indication of the judgment of the historian. And this veracity is carried out by the Gothic sculptors in the minuteness and generality, as well as the equity, of their delineation: for they do not limit their art to the portraiture of saints and kings, but introduce the most familiar scenes and most simple subjects: filling up the backgrounds of Scripture histories with vivid and curious representations of the commonest incidents of daily life, and availing themselves of every occasion in which, either as a symbol, or an explanation of a scene or time, the things familiar to the eye of the workman could be introduced and made of account. Hence Gothic sculpture and painting are not only full of valuable portraiture of the greatest men, but copious records of all the domestic customs and inferior arts of the ages in which it flourishes.

There is, however, one direction in which the naturalism of the Gothic workmen is peculiarly manifested; and this direction is even more characteristic of the school than the naturalism itself; I mean their peculiar fondness for the forms of vegetation. To the Gothic workman the living foliage became a subject of intense affection, and he struggled to render all its characters with as much accuracy as was compatible with the laws of his design and the nature of his material, not unfrequently tempted in his enthusiasm to transgress the one and disguise the other.

There is a peculiar significance in this, indicative both of higher civilization and gentler temperament, than had before been manifested in architecture. Rudeness, and the love of change, which we have insisted upon as the first elements of Gothic, are also elements common to all healthy schools. But here is a softer element mingled with them, peculiar to the Gothic itself. The rudeness of ignorance which would have been painfully exposed in the treatment of the human form, is still not so great as to prevent the successful rendering of the wayside herbage; and the love of change, which becomes morbid and feverish in following the haste of the hunter and the rage of the combatant, is at once soothed and satisfied as it watches the wandering of the tendril, and the budding of the flower. Nor is this all: the new direction of mental interest marks an infinite change in the means and the habits of life. The nations whose chief support was in the chase, whose chief interest was in the battle, whose chief pleasure was in the banquet, would take small care respecting the shapes of leaves and flowers; and notice little in the forms of the forest trees which sheltered them, except the signs indicative of the wood which would make the toughest lance, the closest roof, or the clearest fire. The affectionate observation of the grace and outward character of vegetation is the sure sign of a more tranquil and gentle existence, sustained by the gifts, and gladdened by the splendor, of the earth. In that careful distinction of species, and richness of delicate and undisturbed organization, which characterize the Gothic design, there is the history of rural and thoughtful life, influenced by habitual tenderness, and devoted to subtle inquiry; and every

discriminating and delicate touch of the chisel, as it rounds the petal or guides the branch, is a prophecy of the development of the entire body of the natural sciences, beginning with that of medicine, of the recovery of literature, and the establishment of the most necessary principles of domestic wisdom and national peace.

The fourth essential element of the Gothic mind was above stated to be the sense of the *Grotesque;* but I shall defer the endeavor to define this most curious and subtle character until we have occasion to examine one of the divisions of the Renaissance schools, which was morbidly influenced by it. It is the less necessary to insist upon it here, because every reader familiar with Gothic architecture must understand what I mean, and will, I believe, have no hesitation in admitting that the tendency to delight in fantastic and ludicrous, as well as in sublime, images, is a universal instinct of the Gothic imagination.

The fifth element above named was *Rigidity;* and this character I must endeavor carefully to define, for neither the word I have used, not any other that I can think of, will express it accurately. For I mean, not merely stable, but *active* rigidity; the peculiar energy which gives tension to movement, and stiffness to resistance, which makes the fiercest lightning forked rather than curved, and the stoutest oak branch angular rather than bending, and is as much seen in the quivering of the lance as in the glittering of the icicle.

I have before had occasion to note some manifestations of this energy of fixedness; but it must be still more attentively considered here, as it shows itself throughout the whole structure and decoration of Gothic work. Egyptian and Greek buildings stand, for the most part, by their own weight and mass, one stone passively incumbent on another; but in the Gothic vaults and traceries there is a stiffness analogous to that of the bones of a limb, or fibers of a tree; an elastic tension and communication of force from part to part, and also a studious expression of this throughout every visible line of the building. And, in like manner, the Greek and Egyptian ornament is either mere surface engraving, as if the face of the wall had been stamped with a seal, or its lines are flowing, lithe, and luxuriant; in either case, there is no expression of energy in the framework of the ornament itself. But the Gothic ornament stands out in prickly independence, and frosty fortitude, jutting into crockets, and freezing into pinnacles; here starting up into a monster, there germinating into a blossom, anon knitting itself into a branch, alternately thorny, bossy, and bristly, or writhed into every form of nervous entanglement; but, even when most graceful, never for an instant languid, always quickset: erring, if at all, ever on the side of brusquerie.

The feelings or habits in the workman which give rise to this character in the work, are more complicated and various than those indicated by any other sculptural expression hitherto named. There is, first, the habit of hard and rapid working; the industry of the tribes of the North, quickened by the coldness of the climate, and giving an expression of sharp energy to all they do as opposed to the languor of the Southern tribes, however much of fire there may be in the heart of that languor, for lava itself may flow languidly. There is also the habit of finding enjoyment in the signs of cold, which is never found, I believe, in the inhabitants of countries south of the Alps. Cold is to them an unredeemed evil, to be suffered and forgotten as soon as may be; but the long winter of the North forces the Goth (I mean the Englishman, Frenchman, Dane, or German), if he would lead a happy life at all, to find sources of happiness in foul weather as well as fair, and to rejoice in the leafless as well as in the shady forest. And this we do with all our hearts; finding perhaps nearly as much contentment by the Christmas fire as in the summer sunshine, and gaining health and strength on the ice fields of winter, as well as among the meadows of spring. So that there is nothing adverse or painful to our feelings in the cramped and stiffened structure of vegetation checked by cold; and instead of seeking, like the Southern sculptor, to express only the softness of leafage nourished in all tenderness, and tempted into all luxuriance by warm winds and glowing rays, we find pleasure in dwelling upon the crabbed, perverse, and morose animation of plants that have known little kindness from earth or heaven, but, season after season, have had their best efforts palsied by frost, their brightest buds buried under snow, and their goodliest limbs lopped by tempest.

There are many subtle sympathies and affections which join to confirm the Gothic mind in this peculiar choice of subject; and when we add to the influence of these, the necessities consequent upon the employment of a rougher material, compelling the workman to seek for vigor of effect, rather than refinement of texture or accuracy of form, we have direct and manifest causes for much of the difference between the northern and southern cast of conception: but there are indirect causes holding a far more important place in the Gothic heart, though less immediate in their influence on design. Strength of will, independence of character, resoluteness of purpose, impatience of undue control, and that general tendency to set the individual reason against authority, and the individual deed against destiny, which, in the Northern tribes, has opposed itself throughout all ages to the languid submission, in the Southern, of thought to tradition, and purpose to fatality, are all more or less traceable in the rigid lines, vigorous and various masses, and daringly projecting and independent structure of the Northern Gothic ornament: while the opposite feelings are in like manner legible in the graceful and softly guided waves and wreathed bands, in which Southern decoration is constantly disposed; in its tendency to lose its independence, and fuse itself into the surface of the masses upon which it is traced; and in the expression seen so often, in the arrangement of those masses themselves, of an abandonment of their strength to an inevitable necessity, or a listless repose.

Last, because the least essential, of the constituent elements of this noble school, was placed that of *Redundance;* the uncalculating bestowal of the wealth of its labor. There is, indeed, much Gothic, and that of the best period, in which this element is hardly traceable, and which depends for its effect almost exclusively on loveliness of simple design and grace of uninvolved proportion: still, in the most characteristic buildings, a certain portion of their effect depends upon accumulation of ornament; and many of those which have most influence on the minds of men, have attained it by means of this attribute alone. And although, by careful study of the school, it is possible to arrive at a condition of taste which shall be better contented by a few perfect lines than by a whole facade covered with fretwork, the building which only satisfies such a taste is not to be considered the best. For the very first requirement of Gothic architecture being, as we saw above, that it shall both admit the aid, and appeal to the admiration, of the rudest as well as the most refined minds, the richness of the work is, paradoxical as the statement may appear, a part of its humility. No architecture is so haughty as that which is simple; which refuses to address the eye, except in a few clear and forceful lines; which implies, in offering so little to our regards, that all it has offered is perfect; and disdains, either by the complexity or the attractiveness of its features, to embarrass our investigation, or betray us into delight. That humility, which is the very life of the Gothic school, is shown not only in the imperfection, but in the accumulation, of ornament. The inferior rank of the workman is often shown as much in the richness, as the roughness, of his work; and if the cooperation of every hand, and the sympathy of every heart, are to be received, we must be content to allow the redundance which disguises the failure of the feeble, and wins the regard of the inattentive. There are, however, far nobler interests mingling, in the Gothic heart, with the rude love of decorative accumulation: a magnificent enthusiasm, which feels as if it never could do enough to reach the fullness of its ideal; an unselfishness of sacrifice, which would rather cast fruitless labor before the altar than stand idle in the market; and, finally, a profound sympathy with the fullness and wealth of the material universe, rising out of that Naturalism whose operation we have already endeavored to define. The sculptor who sought for his models among the forest leaves, could not but quickly and deeply feel that complexity need not involve the loss of grace, nor richness that of repose; and every hour which he spent in the study of the minute and various work of Nature, made him feel more forcibly the barrenness of what was best in that of man: nor is it to be wondered at, that, seeing her perfect and exquisite creations poured forth in a profusion which conception could not grasp nor calculation sum, he should think that it ill became him to be niggardly of his own rude craftsmanship; and where he saw throughout the universe a faultless beauty lavished on measureless spaces of broidered field and blooming mountain, to grudge his poor and imperfect labor to the few stones that he had raised one upon another, for habitation or memorial. The years of his life passed away before his task was accomplished; but generation succeeded generation with unwearied enthusiasm, and the cathedral front was at last lost in the tapestry of its traceries, like a rock among the thickets and herbage of spring.

We have now, I believe, obtained a view approaching to completeness of the various moral or imaginative elements which composed the inner spirit of Gothic architecture. We have, in the second place, to define its outward form.

Now, as the Gothic spirit is made up of several elements, some of which may, in particular examples, be wanting, so the Gothic form is made up of minor conditions of form, some of which may, in particular examples, be imperfectly developed.

We cannot say, therefore, that a building is either Gothic or not Gothic in form, any more than we can in spirit. We can only say that it is more or less Gothic, in proportion to the number of Gothic forms which it unites.

There have been made lately many subtle and ingenious endeavors to base the definition of Gothic form entirely upon the roof vaulting; endeavors which are both forced and futile: for many of the best Gothic buildings in the world have roofs of timber, which have no more connection with the main structure of the walls of the edifice than a hat has with that of the head it protects; and other Gothic buildings are merely enclosures of spaces, as ramparts and walls, or enclosures of gardens or cloisters, and have no roofs at all, in the sense in which the word *roof* is commonly accepted. But every reader who has ever taken the slightest interest in architecture must know that there is a great popular impression on this matter, which maintains itself stiffly in its old form, in spite of all ratiocination and definition; namely, that a flat lintel from pillar to pillar is Grecian, a round arch Norman or Romanesque, and a pointed arch Gothic.

And the old popular notion, as far as it goes, is perfectly right, and can never be bettered. The most striking outward feature in all Gothic architecture is, that it is composed of pointed arches, as in Romanesque that it is in like manner composed of round; and this distinction would be quite as clear, though the roofs were taken off every cathedral in Europe. And yet if we examine carefully into the real force and meaning of the term *roof,* we shall perhaps be able to retain the old pop-

ular idea in a definition of Gothic architecture which shall also express whatever dependence that architecture has upon true forms of roofing.

The reader will remember that roofs were considered as generally divided into two parts: the roof proper, that is to say, the shell, vault, or ceiling, internally visible; and the roof mask, which protects this lower roof from the weather. In some buildings these parts are united in one framework; but, in most, they are more or less independent of each other, and in nearly all Gothic buildings there is a considerable interval between them.

Now it will often happen, as above noticed, that owing to the nature of the apartments required, or the materials at hand, the roof proper may be flat, coved, or domed, in buildings which in their walls employ pointed arches, and are, in the straitest sense of the word, Gothic in all other respects. Yet so far forth as the roofing alone is concerned, they are not Gothic unless the pointed arch be the principal form adopted either in the stone vaulting or the timbers of the roof proper.

I shall say then, in the first place, that "Gothic architecture is that which uses, if possible, the pointed arch in the roof proper." This is the first step in our definition.

Second, although there may be many advisable or necessary forms for the lower roof or ceiling, there is, in cold countries exposed to rain and snow, only one advisable form of the roof mask, and that is the gable, for this alone will throw off both rain and snow from all parts of its surface as speedily as possible. Snow can lodge on the top of a dome, not on the ridge of a gable. And thus, as far as roofing is concerned, the gable is a far more essential feature of Northern architecture than the pointed vault, for the one is a thorough necessity, the other often a graceful conventionality; the gable occurs in the timber roof of every dwelling house and every cottage, but not the vault; and the gable built on a polygonal or circular plan, is the origin of the turret and spire; and all the so-called aspiration of Gothic architecture is nothing more than its development. So that we must add to our definition another clause, which will be, at present, by far the most important, and it will stand thus: "Gothic architecture is that which uses the pointed arch for the roof proper, and the gable for the roof mask."

The reader will also remember that I carefully extended my definition of a roof so as to include more than is usually understood by the term. It was there said to be the covering of a space, *narrow or wide.* It does not in the least signify, with respect to the real nature of the covering, whether the space protected be two feet wide, or ten; though in the one case we call the protection an arch, in the other a vault or roof. But the real point to be considered is, the manner in which this protection stands, and not whether it is narrow or broad. We call the vaulting of a bridge "an arch," because it is narrow with respect to the river it crosses; but if it were built above us on the ground, we should call it a wagon vault, because then we should feel the breadth of it. The real question is the nature of the curve, not the extent of space over which it is carried: and this is more the case with respect to Gothic than to any other architecture; for, in the greater number of instances, the form of the roof is entirely dependent on the ribs; the domical shells being constructed in all kinds of inclinations, quite indeterminable by the eye, and all that is definite in their character being fixed by the curves of the ribs.

Let us then consider our definition as including the narrowest arch or tracery bar, as well as the broadest roof, and it will be nearly a perfect one. For the fact is, that all good Gothic is nothing more than the development, in various ways, and on every conceivable scale, of the group formed by the *pointed arch for the bearing line* below, and *the gable for the protecting line* above; and from the huge, gray, shaley slope of

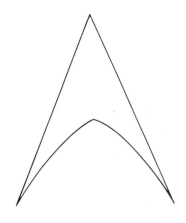

*Figure 17*

the cathedral and with its elastic pointed vaults beneath, to the slight crown-line points that enrich the smallest niche of its doorway, one law and one expression will be found in all. The modes of support and of decoration are infinitely various, but the real character of the building, in all good Gothic, depends upon the single lines of the gable over the pointed arch, figure 17, endlessly rearranged or repeated.

Let us try whether we cannot get the forms of the other great architectures of the world broadly expressed by relations of the same lines into which we have compressed the Gothic. We may easily do this if the reader will first allow me to remind him of the true nature of the pointed arch. It was said that it ought to be called a "curved gable," for, strictly speaking, an "arch" cannot be "pointed." The so-called pointed arch ought always to be considered as a gable, with its sides curved in order to enable them to bear pressure from without. Thus considering it, there are but three ways in which an interval between piers can be bridged—the three ways represented by A, B, and C, figure 18—A, the lintel; B, the round arch; C, the gable. All the architects in the world will never discover any other ways of bridging a space than these three; they may vary the curve of the arch, or curve the sides of

411

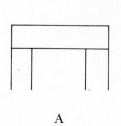 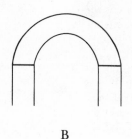 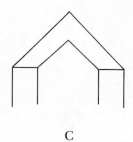

A                              B                              C

*Figure 18*

the gable or break them; but in doing this they are merely modifying or subdividing not adding to the generic forms.

Now there are three good architectures in the world, and there never can be more, correspondent to each of these three simple ways of covering in a space, which is the original function of all architectures. And those three architectures are *pure* exactly in proportion to the simplicity and directness with which they express the condition of roofing on which they are founded. They have many interesting varieties, according to their scale, manner of decoration, and character of the nations by whom they are practiced, but all their varieties are finally referable to the three great heads—

A. Greek: Architecture of the Lintel.

B. Romanesque: Architecture of the Round Arch.

C. Gothic: Architecture of the Gable.

The three names, Greek, Romanesque, and Gothic, are indeed inaccurate when used in this vast sense, because they imply national limitations; but the three architectures may nevertheless not unfitly receive their names from those nations by whom they were carried to the highest perfection. We may thus briefly state their existing varieties.

A. *Greek:* Lintel Architecture. The worst of the three; and, considered with reference to stone construction, always in some measure barbarous. Its simplest type is Stonehenge; its most refined, the Parthenon; its noblest, the Temple of Karnak.

In the hands of the Egyptian, it is sublime; in those of the Greek, pure; in those of the Roman, rich; and in those of the Renaissance builder, effeminate.

B. *Romanesque:* Round-arch Architecture. Never thoroughly developed until Christian times. It falls into two great branches, Eastern and Western, or Byzantine and Lombardic; changing respectively in process of time, with certain helps from each other, into Arabian Gothic, and Teutonic Gothic. Its most perfect Lombardic type is the Duomo of Pisa; its most perfect Byzantine type (I believe), Saint Mark's at Venice. Its highest glory is, that it has no corruption. It perishes in giving birth to another architecture as noble as itself.

C. *Gothic:* Architecture of the Gable. The daughter of the Romanesque; and, like the Romanesque, divided into two great branches, Western and Eastern, or Pure Gothic and Arabian Gothic; of which the latter is called Gothic, only because it has many Gothic forms, pointed arches, vaults, etc., but its spirit remains Byzantine, more especially in the form of the roof mask, of which, with respect to these three great families, we have next to determine the typical form.

For, observe, the distinctions we have hitherto been stating depend on the form of the stones first laid from pier to pier; that is to say, of the simplest condition of roofs proper. Adding the relations of the roof mask to these lines, we shall have the perfect type of form for each school.

In the Greek, the Western Romanesque, and Western Gothic, the roof mask is the gable; in the Eastern Romanesque, and Eastern Gothic, it is the dome: but I have not studied the roofing of either of these last two groups, and shall not venture to generalize them in a diagram. But the three groups, in the hands of the Western builders, may be thus simply represented: *a*, figure 19, Greek; *b*, Western Romanesque; *c*, Western, or true, Gothic.

Now, observe, first, that the relation of the roof mask to the roof proper, in the Greek type, forms that pediment which gives its most striking character to the temple, and is the principal recipient of its sculptural decoration. The relation of these lines, therefore, is just as important in the Greek as in the Gothic schools.

Second, the reader must observe the difference of steepness in the Romanesque and Gothic gables. This is not an unimportant distinction, nor an undecided one. The Romanesque gable does not pass gradually into the more elevated form; there is a great gulf between the two; the whole effect of all Southern architecture being dependent upon the use of the flat gable, and of all Northern upon that of the acute.

I need not here dwell upon the difference between the lines of an Italian village, or the flat tops of most Italian towers, and the peaked gables and spires of the North, attaining their most fantastic development, I believe, in Belgium: but it may be well to state the law of separation, namely, that a Gothic gable *must* have all its angles acute, and a Romanesque one *must* have the upper one obtuse; or, to give the reader a simple practical rule, take any gable, *a* or *b*, figure 20 [following page], and strike a semicircle on its base; if its top rises above the semicircle, as at *b*, it is a Gothic gable; if it falls beneath it, a Romanesque one, but the best forms in each group are those which are distinctly steep, or distinctly low. In the figure, *f* is, perhaps, the average of Romanesque slope, and *g* of Gothic.

We have thus determined the relation of Gothic to the other architectures of the world, as far as regards the main lines of its construction; but there is still one word which needs to be added to our definition of its form, with respect to a part of its decoration, which rises out of that construction. We have seen that the first condition of its form is, that it shall have pointed arches. When Gothic is perfect, therefore,

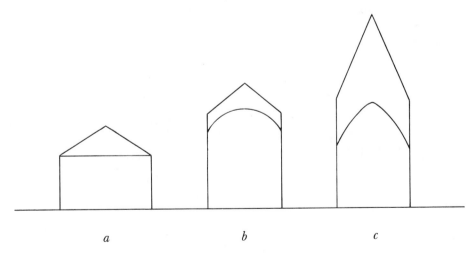

*a*        *b*        *c*

*Figure 19*

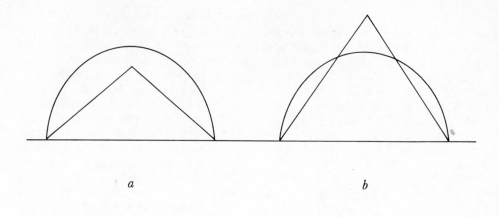

a                                    b

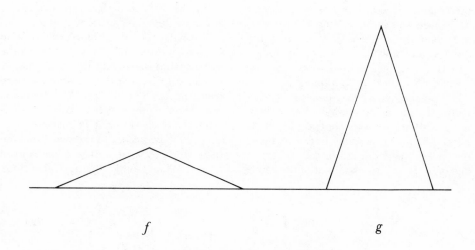

f                                    g

*Figure 20*

it will follow that the pointed arches must be built in the strongest possible manner.

The subject of the masonry of the pointed arch has already been discussed at length, and the conclusion deduced, that of all possible forms of the pointed arch (a certain weight of material being given), that generically represented at *e,* figure 21, is the strongest. In fact, the reader can see in a moment that the weakness of the pointed arch is in its flanks, and that by merely thickening them gradually at this point all chance of fracture is removed. Or, perhaps, more simply still: Suppose a gable built of stone, as at *a,* and pressed upon from without by a weight in the direction of the arrow, clearly it would be liable to fall in, as at *b*. To prevent this, we make a pointed arch of it, as at *c;* and now it cannot fall inward, but if pressed upon from above may give way outward, as at *d*. But at last we build it as at *e,* and now it can neither fall out nor in.

The forms of arch thus obtained, with

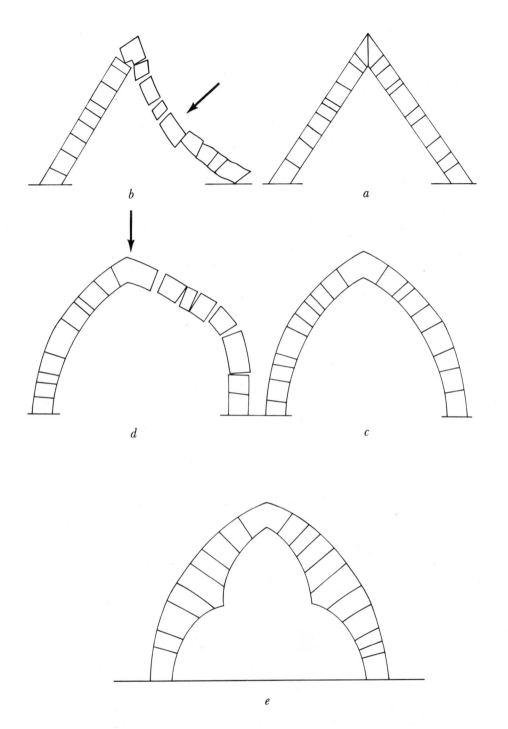

*Figure 21*

a pointed projection called a cusp on each side, must forever be delightful to the human mind, as being expressive of the utmost strength and permanency obtainable with a given mass of material. But it was not by any such process of reasoning, nor with any reference to laws of construction, that the cusp was originally invented. It is merely the special application to the arch of the great ornamental system of foliation; or the adaptation of the forms of leafage which has been above insisted upon as the principal characteristic of Gothic Naturalism. This love of foliage was exactly proportioned, in its intensity, to the increase of strength in the Gothic spirit: in the Southern Gothic it is *soft* leafage that is most loved; in the Northern, *thorny* leafage. And if we take up any Northern illuminated manuscript of the great Gothic time, we shall find every one of its leaf ornaments surrounded by a thorny structure laid round it in gold or in color.

The system, then, of what is called foliation, whether simple, as in the cusped arch, or complicated, as in tracery, rose out of this love of leafage; not that the form of the arch is intended to *imitate* a leaf, but *to be invested with the same characters of beauty which the designer had discovered in the leaf.* Observe, there is a wide difference between these two intentions. The idea that large Gothic structure, in arches and roofs, was intended to imitate vegetation, is untenable for an instant in the front of facts. But the Gothic builder perceived that, in the leaves which he copied for his minor decorations, there was a peculiar beauty, arising from certain characters of curvature in outline, and certain methods of subdivision and of radiation in structure. On a small scale, in his sculptures and his missal painting, he copied the leaf or thorn itself; on a large scale he adopted from it its abstract sources of beauty, and gave the same kind of curvatures and the same species of subdivision to the outline of his arches, so far as was consistent with their strength, never, in any single instance, suggesting the resem-

blance to leafage by irregularity of outline, but keeping the structure perfectly simple, and, as we have seen, so consistent with the best principles of masonry, that in the finest Gothic designs of arches, which are always single-cusped (the cinquefoiled arch being licentious, though in early work often very lovely), it is literally impossible, without consulting the context of the building, to say whether the cusps have been added for the sake of beauty or of strength; nor, though in medieval architecture they were, I believe, assuredly first employed in mere love of their picturesque form, am I absolutely certain that their earliest invention was not a structural effort.

It is evident, however, that the structural advantage of the cusp is available only in the case of arches on a comparatively small scale. If the arch becomes very large, the projections under the flanks must become too ponderous to be secure; the suspended weight of stone would be liable to break off, and such arches are therefore never constructed with heavy cusps, but rendered secure by general mass of masonry; and what additional appearance of support may be thought necessary (sometimes a considerable degree of *actual* support) is given by means of tracery.

Tracery began in the use of penetrations through the stonework of windows or walls, cut into forms which looked like stars when seen from within, and like leaves when seen from without; the name foil or feuille being universally applied to the separate lobes of their extremities, and the pleasure received from them being the same as that which we feel in the triple, quadruple, or other radiated leaves of vegetation, joined with the perception of a severely geometric order and symmetry. A few of the most common forms are represented, unconfused by exterior moldings, in figure 22, and the best traceries are nothing more than close clusters of such forms, with moldings following their outlines.

The term *foliated,* therefore, is equally descriptive of the most perfect conditions

*Figure 22*

both of the simple arch and of the traceries by which in later Gothic it is filled: and this foliation is an essential character of the style. No Gothic is either good or characteristic, which is not foliated either in its arches or apertures. Sometimes the bearing arches are foliated, and the ornamentation above composed of figure sculpture; sometimes the bearing arches are plain, and the ornamentation above them is composed of foliated apertures. But the element of foliation *must* enter somewhere, or the style is imperfect. And our final definition of Gothic will, therefore, stand thus: "*Foliated* Architecture, which uses the pointed arch for the roof proper, and the gable for the roof mask."

We have now, I believe, obtained a sufficiently accurate knowledge both of the spirit and form of Gothic architecture; but it may, perhaps, be useful to the general reader, if, in conclusion, I set down a few plain and practical rules for determining, in every instance, whether a given building be good Gothic or not, and, if not Gothic,

whether its architecture is of a kind which will probably reward the pains of careful examination.

First, look if the roof rises in a steep gable, high above the walls. If it does not do this, there is something wrong: the building is not quite pure Gothic, or has been altered.

Second, look if the principal windows and doors have pointed arches with gables over them. If not pointed arches, the building is not Gothic; if they have not any gables over them, it is either not pure, or not first-rate.

If, however, it has the steep roof, the pointed arch, and gable all united, it is nearly certain to be a Gothic building of a very fine time.

Third, look if the arches are cusped, or apertures foliated. If the building has met the first two conditions, it is sure to be foliated somewhere; but, if not everywhere, the parts which are unfoliated are imperfect, unless they are large bearing arches, or small and sharp arches in groups, forming a kind of foliation by their own multiplicity, and relieved by sculpture and rich moldings. The upper windows, for instance, in the east end of Westminster Abbey are imperfect for want of foliation. If there be no foliation anywhere, the building is assuredly imperfect Gothic.

Fourth, if the building meets all the first three conditions, look if its arches in general, whether of windows and doors, or of minor ornamentation, are carried on *true shafts with bases and capitals.* If they are, then the building is assuredly of the finest Gothic style. It may still, perhaps, be an imitation, a feeble copy, or a bad example, of a noble style; but the manner of it, having met all these four conditions, is assuredly first-rate.

If its apertures have not shafts and capitals, look if they are plain openings in the walls, studiously simple, and unmolded at the sides. If so, the buildings may still be of the finest Gothic adapted to some domestic or military service. But if the sides of the window be molded, and yet there are no capitals at the spring of the arch, it is assuredly of an inferior school.

This is all that is necessary to determine whether the building be of fine Gothic style. The next tests to be applied are in order to discover whether it be good architecture or not; for it may be very impure Gothic, and yet very noble architecture; or it may be very pure Gothic, and yet if a copy, or originally raised by an ungifted builder, very bad architecture.

If it belong to any of the great schools of color, its criticism becomes as complicated, and needs as much care, as that of a piece of music, and no general rules for it can be given; but if not—

First, see if it looks as if it had been built by strong men; if it has the sort of roughness, and largeness, and nonchalance, mixed in places with the exquisite tenderness which seems always to be the sign manual of the broad vision, and massy power of men who can see *past* the work they are doing, and betray here and there something like disdain for it. If the building has this character, it is much already in its favor; it will go hard but it proves a noble one. If it has not this, but is altogether accurate, minute, and scrupulous in its workmanship, it must belong to either the very best or the very worst of schools: the very best, in which exquisite design if wrought out with untiring and conscientious care, as in the Giottesque Gothic; or the very worst, in which mechanism has taken the place of design. It is more likely, in general, that it should belong to the worst than the best: so that, on the whole, very accurate workmanship is to be esteemed a bad sign; and if there is nothing remarkable about the building but its precision, it may be passed at once with contempt.

Second, observe if it be irregular, its different parts fitting themselves to different purposes, no one caring what becomes of them, so that they do their work. If one part always answers accurately to another part, it is sure to be a bad building; and the greater and more conspicuous the irregularities, the greater the chances are that it is a good one. For instance, in the Ducal Palace, of which a rough drawing is given on Plate II, the general idea is sternly symmetrical; but two windows are lower than the rest of the six; and if the reader will count the arches of the small arcade as far as to the great balcony, he will find it is not in the center, but set to the right-hand side by the whole width of one of those arches. We may be pretty sure that the building is a good one; none but a master of his craft would have ventured to do this.

Third, observe if all the traceries, capitals, and other ornaments are of perpetually varied design. If not, the work is assuredly bad.

Lastly, *Read* the sculpture. Preparatory to reading it, you will have to discover whether it is legible (and, if legible, it is nearly certain to be worth reading). On a good building, the sculpture is *always* so set, and on such a scale, that at the ordinary distance from which the edifice is seen, the sculpture shall be thoroughly intelligible and interesting. In order to accomplish this, the uppermost statues will be ten or twelve feet high, and the upper ornamentation will be colossal, increasing in fineness as it descends, till on the foundation it will often be wrought as if for a precious cabinet in a king's chamber; but the spectator will not notice that the upper sculptures are colossal. He will merely feel that he can see them plainly, and make them all out at his ease.

And having ascertained this, let him set himself to read them. Thenceforward the criticism of the building is to be conducted precisely on the same principles as that of a book; and it must depend on the knowledge, feeling, and not a little on the industry and perseverance of the reader, whether, even in the case of the best works, he either perceive them to be great, or feel them to be entertaining.

Plate II. The Ducal Palace, ground plan (top) and general view (bottom). This was
Plate IV in the original publication.

## Chapter IX

## Conclusion

The grotesques of the seventeenth and eighteenth centuries close the career of the architecture of Europe. They were the last evidences of any feeling consistent with itself, and capable of directing the efforts of the builder to the formation of anything worthy the name of a style or school. From that time to this, no resuscitation of energy has taken place, nor does any for the present appear possible.

If, though, any of my readers should determine, according to their means, to set themselves to the revival of a healthy school of architecture in England, and wish to know in few words how this may be done, the answer is clear and simple. First, let us cast out utterly whatever is connected with the Greek, Roman, or Renaissance architecture, in principle or in form. The whole mass of the architecture, founded on Greek and Roman models, which we have been in the habit of building for the last three centuries is utterly devoid of all life, virtue, honorableness, or power of doing good. It is base, unnatural, unfruitful, unenjoyable, and impious. Pagan in its origin, proud and unholy in its revival, paralyzed in its old age, yet making prey in its dotage of all the good and living things that were springing around it in their youth, as the dying and desperate king, who had long fenced himself so strongly with the towers of it, is said to have filled his failing veins with the blood of children;* an architecture invented, as it seems, to make plagiarists of its architects, slaves of its workmen, and sybarites of its inhabitants; an architecture in which intellect is idle, invention impossible, but in which all luxury is gratified, and all insolence fortified—the first thing we have to do is to cast it out, and shake the dust of it from our feet forever. Whatever has any connection with the five orders, or with any one of the orders—whatever is Doric, or Ionic, or Tuscan, or Corinthian, or Composite, or in any wise Grecized or Romanized; whatever betrays the smallest respect for Vitruvian laws, or conformity with Palladian work—that we are to endure no more. To cleanse ourselves of these "cast clouts and rotten rags" is the first thing to be done in the court of our prison.

Then, to turn our prison into a palace is an easy thing. Exactly in the degree in which Greek and Roman architecture is lifeless, unprofitable, and unchristian, in that same degree our own ancient Gothic is animated, serviceable, and faithful. It is flexible to all duty, enduring to all time, instructive to all hearts, honorable and holy in all offices. It is capable alike of all lowliness and all dignity, fit alike for cottage porch or castle gateway; in domestic service familiar, in religious, sublime; simple, and playful, so that childhood may read it, yet clothed with a power that can awe the mightiest, and exalt the loftiest of human spirits: an architecture that kindles every faculty in its workman, and addresses every emotion in its beholder; which, with every stone that is laid on its solemn walls, raises some human heart a step nearer heaven, and which from its birth has been incorporated with the existence, and in all its form is symbolic of the faith, of Christianity. In this architecture let us henceforward build alike the church, the palace, and the cottage; but chiefly let us use it for our civil and domestic buildings. These once ennobled, our ecclesiastical work will be exalted together with them; but churches are not

---

*Louis the Eleventh. "In the month of March, 1481, Louis was seized with a fit of apoplexy at *St. Benoit-du-lac-mort,* near Chinon. He remained speechless and bereft of reason three days; and then, but very imperfectly restored, he languished in a miserable state. . . . To cure him," says a contemporary historian, "wonderful and terrible medicines were compounded. It was reported among the people that his physicians opened the veins of little children, and made him drink their blood, to correct the poorness of his own."—*Bussey's History of France,* London, 1850.

the proper scenes for experiments in untried architecture, nor for exhibitions of unaccustomed beauty. It is certain that we must often fail before we can again build a natural and noble Gothic: let not our temples be the scenes of our failures. It is certain that we must offend many deep-rooted prejudices, before ancient Christian architecture can be again received by all of us: let not religion be the first source of such offense. We shall meet with difficulties in applying Gothic architecture to churches, which would in nowise affect the designs of civil buildings, for the most beautiful forms of Gothic chapels are not those which are best fitted for Protestant worship. I am quite sure, for instance, that if such noble architecture as has been employed for the interior of the church just built in Margaret Street* had been seen in a civil building, it would have decided the question with many men at once; whereas, at present, it will be looked upon with fear and suspicion, as the expression of the ecclesiastical principles of a particular party. But, whether thus regarded or not, this church assuredly decides one question conclusively, that of our present capability of Gothic design. It is the first piece of architecture I have seen, built in modern days, which is free from all signs of timidity or incapacity. In general proportion of parts, in refinement and piquancy of moldings, above all, in force, vitality, and grace of floral ornament, worked in a broad and masculine manner, it challenges fearless comparison with the noblest work of any time. Having done this, we may do anything; there need be no limits to our hope or our confidence; and I believe it to be possible for us, not only to equal, but far to surpass, in some respects, any Gothic yet seen in Northern countries. In the introduction of figure sculpture, we must, indeed, for the present, remain utterly inferior, for we have no figures to study from. No architectural sculpture was ever good for anything which did not represent the dress and persons of the people living

at the time; and our modern dress will *not* form decorations for spandrels and niches. But in floral sculpture we may go far beyond what has yet been done, as well as in refinement of inlaid work and general execution. For, although the glory of Gothic architecture is to receive the rudest work, it refuses not the best; and, when once we have been content to admit the handling of the simplest workman, we shall soon be rewarded by finding many of our simple workmen become cunning ones: and, with the help of modern wealth and science, we may do things like Giotto's campanile [Florence], instead of like our own rude cathedrals; but better than Giotto's campanile, insomuch as we may adopt the pure and perfect forms of the Northern Gothic, and work them out with the Italian refinement. It is hardly possible at present to imagine what may be the splendor of buildings designed in the forms of English and French thirteenth-century *surface* Gothic, and wrought out with the refinement of Italian art in the details, and with a deliberate resolution, since we cannot have figure sculpture, to display in them the beauty of every flower and herb of the English fields, each by each; doing as much for every tree that roots itself in our rocks, and every blossom that drinks our summer rains, as our ancestors did for the oak, the ivy, and the rose. Let this be the object of our ambition, and let us begin to approach it, not ambitiously, but in all humility, accepting help from the feeblest hands; and the London of the nineteenth century may yet become as Venice without her despotism, and as Florence without her dispeace.

---

*Mr. Hope's church, in Margaret Street, Portland Place [London]. I do not altogether like the arrangements of color in the brickwork; but these will hardly attract the eye, where so much has been already done with precious and beautiful marble, and is yet to be done in fresco. Much will depend, however, upon the coloring of this latter portion. I wish that either Holman Hunt or Millais [nineteenth-century British painters] could be prevailed upon to do at least some of these smaller frescoes.

# A Simple Heart

Gustave Flaubert

## Editor's Introduction

Gustave Flaubert was born in 1821 in Rouen, the son of a surgeon, and had his first piece published when he was sixteen, in a review. When he was twenty, he was enrolled in law school in Paris but developed a nervous condition soon after, which made him give up law and devote himself to literature. His father and his sister died in 1846, and Flaubert retired with his mother and infant niece to their country estate at Croisset, near Rouen, where he spent most of the rest of his life.

He was known for his great kindnesses to his friends and especially to his niece, but also for harshness and cruelty when provoked. He was also known, in his writing, for his laborious efforts to make prose into something like poetry, and with the possible exception of Tolstoy he devoted more care than any novelist ever has to the actual labor of sentences. Although his writings reflect a contempt for bourgeois life, Flaubert himself was in many ways part of that world, and he was certainly dominated by his bourgeois mother for most of his years. After her death he spent more time in Paris, where he cultivated friendships with George Sand, Ivan Turgenev, Émile Zola, and Guy de Maupassant, among others, but he always remained a provincial man who preferred country life.

His major works were the result of constant preoccupation with the same themes. His first full-length work to be published was *The Temptation of Saint Anthony* (1874), of which four distinct versions exist, and which he began to write in 1839. The version which was published included a catalog of errors in the field of the Unknown. When his friends Maxime du Camp, a writer, and the poet Louis Bouilhet read this work, they condemned it, suggesting that Flaubert write in a less flamboyant, exuberant style and develop a stronger sense of objectivity. Bouilhet even suggested a topic, the story of Eugène Delamare, a country doctor in Normandy who died of grief after being deceived and ruined by his wife. This became *Madame Bovary*.

*Madame Bovary* is the story of an adulterous woman, told with detachment by an objective narrator. More than that, it is a pitiless look at the bourgeoisie in its character study of Emma Bovary. Of his character, Flaubert wrote: "My poor Bovary suffers and cries in more than a score of villages in France at this very moment." *Madame Bovary* was the culmination of five years of work and eventually appeared in installments in *Revue de Paris* in the fall and winter of 1856. In response, the French government took Flaubert to trial for committing "an outrage to public morals and religion," but he escaped conviction. The same court within the year found the poet Charles Baudelaire guilty on the same charge.

Soon after, Flaubert began work on *Salammbô* (1862), which combined a fictitious character with the historical background of the revolt of the mercenaries against Carthage in 240–237 BC. Following this he published *A Sentimental Education* (1870), on which he had been working since 1842. He also published three plays, which were for the most part unsuccessful. In 1875 he abandoned work on a long, satirical novel, *Bouvard and Pécuchet* (which was to go unfinished at his death), to write *Three Tales*.

This was the last of his works to be published (in 1877) before his death, of an apoplectic stroke, in 1880. About the same time Flaubert began writing this work, he was forced to sell most of his property to help his niece's husband, who was bankrupt, and this episode was at the end of a string of deaths among his friends as well as the death of his mother. *Three Tales* reflects this sadness. The tales are "A Simple Heart," "The Legend of St. Julien Hospitaler," and "Herodias."

The middle one of these was the first to be written and was in fact the product of thoughts some thirty years earlier on the subject of a murderer who is taken to Heaven and sanctity. "Herodias" was a result of Flaubert's trip early in life to the Middle East as well. For this tale, he did much historical research but was quoted as saying that the story "has nothing to do with religion. . . . The racial question dominated everything."

"A Simple Heart" has the closest associations with Flaubert's own life; all the people and places in the story correspond to incidents in the author's past. In many ways he identified himself with his main character, Félicité; for example, he suffered his first attack of nervous disease at the spot where Félicité herself is struck down on the Honfleur road. He wrote this tale in response to a comment by one of his dearest friends, the author George Sand, who had reproached him for "spreading unhappiness" in his books, and who had challenged him to write a tender story in a detached, unemotional style. Flaubert himself said about the end of the story that ". . . it is not at all ironical as you may suppose, but on the contrary very serious and very sad. I want to move tender hearts to pity and tears, for I am tender-hearted myself." He added: "Now, surely, no one will accuse me of being inhuman any more. . . ."

# A Simple Heart

Madame Aubain's servant Félicité was the envy of the ladies of Pont-l'Évêque for half a century.

She received four pounds a year. For that she was cook and general servant and did the sewing, washing, and ironing; she could bridle a horse, fatten poultry, and churn butter—and she remained faithful to her mistress, unamiable as the latter was.

Mme Aubain had married a gay bachelor without money who died at the beginning of 1809, leaving her with two small children and a quantity of debts. She then sold all her property except the farms of Toucques and Geffosses, which brought in two hundred pounds a year at most, and left her house in Saint-Melaine for a less expensive one that had belonged to her family and was situated behind the market.

This house had a slate roof and stood between an alley and a lane that went down to the river. There was an unevenness in the levels of the rooms which made you stumble. A narrow hall divided the kitchen from the "parlor" where Mme Aubain spent her day, sitting in a wicker easy chair by the window. Against the panels, which were painted white, was a row of eight mahogany chairs. On an old piano under the barometer a heap of wooden and cardboard boxes rose like a pyramid. A stuffed armchair stood on either side of the Louis-Quinze chimneypiece, which was in yellow marble with a clock in the middle of it modeled like a temple of Vesta. The whole room was a little musty, as the floor was lower than the garden.

The first floor began with "Madame's" room: very large, with a pale-flowered wallpaper and a portrait of "Monsieur" as a dandy of the period. It led to a smaller room, where there were two children's cots without mattresses. Next came the drawing room, which was always shut up and full of furniture covered with sheets. Then there was a corridor leading to a study. The shelves of a large bookcase were respectably lined with books and papers, and its three wings surrounded a broad writing table in darkwood. The two panels at the end of the room were covered with pendrawings, watercolor landscapes, and engravings by Audran, all relics of better days and vanished splendor. Félicité's room on the top floor got its light from a dormer window, which looked over the meadows.

She rose at daybreak to be in time for Mass and worked till evening without stopping. Then, when dinner was over, the plates and dishes in order, and the door shut fast, she thrust the log under the ashes and went to sleep in front of the hearth with her rosary in her hand. Félicité was the stubbornest of all bargainers; and as for cleanness, the polish on her saucepans was the despair of other servants. Thrifty in all things, she ate slowly, gathering off the table in her fingers the crumbs of her loaf—a twelve-pound loaf expressly baked for her, which lasted for three weeks.

At all times of year she wore a print handkerchief fastened with a pin behind, a bonnet that covered her hair, gray stockings, a red skirt, and a bibbed apron—such as hospital nurses wear—over her jacket.

Her face was thin and her voice sharp. At twenty-five she looked like forty. From

fifty onward she seemed of no particular age; and with her silence, straight figure, and precise movements she was like a woman made of wood and going by clockwork.

II

She had had her love story like another. Her father, a mason, had been killed by falling off some scaffolding. Then her mother died, her sisters scattered, and a farmer took her in and employed her, while she was still quite little, to herd the cows at pasture. She shivered in rags and would lie flat on the ground to drink water from the ponds; she was beaten for nothing and finally turned out for the theft of a shilling which she did not steal. She went to another farm, where she became dairymaid; and as she was liked by her employers her companions were jealous of her.

One evening in August (she was then eighteen) they took her to the assembly at Colleville. She was dazed and stupefied in an instant by the noise of the fiddlers, the lights in the trees, the gay medley of dresses, the lace, the gold crosses, and the throng of people jigging all together.

While she kept shyly apart a young man with a well-to-do air, who was leaning on the shaft of a cart and smoking his pipe, came up to ask her to dance. He treated her to cider, coffee, and cake, and bought her a silk handkerchief; and then, imagining she had guessed his meaning, offered to see her home. At the edge of a field of oats he pushed her roughly down. She was frightened and began to cry out; and he went off.

One evening later she was on the Beaumont road. A big hay wagon was moving slowly along; she wanted to get in front of it, and as she brushed past the wheels she recognized Theodore. He greeted her quite calmly, saying she must excuse it all because it was "the fault of the drink." She could not think of any answer and wanted to run away.

He began at once to talk about the harvest and the worthies of the commune, for his father had left Colleville for the farm at Les Écots, so that now he and she were neighbors. "Ah!" she said. He added that they thought of settling him in life. Well, he was in no hurry; he was waiting for a wife to his fancy. She dropped her head; and then he asked her if she thought of marrying. She answered with a smile that it was mean to make fun of her.

"But I am not, I swear!"—and he passed his left hand round her waist. She walked in the support of his embrace; their steps grew slower. The wind was soft, the stars glittered, the huge wagonload of hay swayed in front of them, and dust rose from the dragging steps of the four horses. Then, without a word of command, they turned to the right. He clasped her once more in his arms, and she disappeared into the shadow.

The week after Theodore secured some assignations with her.

They met at the end of farmyards, behind a wall, or under a solitary tree. She was not innocent as young ladies are— she had learned knowledge from the animals—but her reason and the instinct of her honor would not let her fall. Her resistance exasperated Theodore's passion; so much so that to satisfy it—or perhaps quite artlessly—he made her an offer of marriage. She was in doubt whether to trust him, but he swore great oaths of fidelity.

Soon he confessed to something troublesome; the year before his parents had bought him a substitute for the army, but any day he might be taken again, and the idea of serving was a terror to him. Félicité took this cowardice of his as a sign of affection, and it redoubled hers. She stole away at night to see him, and when she reached their meeting place Theodore racked her with his anxieties and urgings.

At last he declared that he would go himself to the prefecture for information and would tell her the result on the following Sunday, between eleven and midnight.

When the moment came she sped toward her lover. Instead of him she found one of his friends.

He told her that she would not see Theodore anymore. To ensure himself against conscription he had married an old woman, Madame Lehoussais, of Toucques, who was very rich.

There was an uncontrollable burst of grief. She threw herself on the ground, screamed, called to the God of mercy, and moaned by herself in the fields till daylight came. Then she came back to the farm and announced that she was going to leave; and at the end of the month she received her wages, tied all her small belongings with a handkerchief, and went to Pont-l'Évêque.

In front of the inn there she made inquiries of a woman in a widow's cap, who, as it happened, was just looking for a cook. The girl did not know much, but her willingness seemed so great and her demands so small that Mme Aubain ended by saying: "Very well, then, I will take you."

A quarter of an hour afterward Félicité was installed in her house.

She lived there at first in a tremble, as it were, at "the style of the house" and the memory of "Monsieur" floating over it all. Paul and Virginie, the first aged seven and the other hardly four, seemed to her beings of a precious substance; she carried them on her back like a horse; it was a sorrow to her that Mme Aubain would not let her kiss them every minute. And yet she was happy there. Her grief had melted in the pleasantness of things all round.

Every Thursday regular visitors came in for a game of boston, and Félicité got the cards and foot warmers ready beforehand. They arrived punctually at eight and left before the stroke of eleven.

On Monday mornings the dealer who lodged in the covered passage spread out all his old iron on the ground. Then a hum of voices began to fill the town, mingled with the neighing of horses, bleating of lambs, grunting of pigs, and the sharp rattle of carts along the street. About noon, when the market was at its height, you might see a tall, hook-nosed old countryman with his cap pushed back making his appearance at the door. It was Robelin, the farmer of Geffosses. A little later came Liébard, the farmer from Toucques—short, red, and corpulent—in a gray jacket and gaiters shod with spurs.

Both had poultry or cheese to offer their

landlord. Félicité was invariably a match for their cunning, and they went away filled with respect for her.

At vague intervals Mme Aubain had a visit from the Marquis de Gremanville, one of her uncles, who had ruined himself by debauchery and now lived at Falaise on his last remaining morsel of land. He invariably came at the luncheon hour, with a dreadful poodle whose paws left all the furniture in a mess. In spite of efforts to show his breeding, which he carried to the point of raising his hat every time he mentioned "my late father," habit was too strong for him; he poured himself out glass after glass and fired off improper remarks. Félicité edged him politely out of the house—"You have had enough, Monsieur de Gremanville! Another time!"—and she shut the door on him.

She opened it with pleasure to M. Bourais, who had been a lawyer. His baldness, his white stock, frilled shirt, and roomy brown coat, his way of rounding the arm as he took snuff—his whole person, in fact, created that disturbance of mind which overtakes us at the sight of extraordinary men.

As he looked after the property of "Madame" he remained shut up with her for hours in "Monsieur's" study, though all the time he was afraid of compromising himself. He respected the magistracy immensely and had some pretensions to Latin.

To combine instruction and amusement he gave the children a geography book made up of a series of prints. They represented scenes in different parts of the world: cannibals with feathers on their heads, a monkey carrying off a young lady, Bedouins in the desert, the harpooning of a whale, and so on. Paul explained these engravings to Félicité; and that, in fact, was the whole of her literary education. The children's education was undertaken by Guyot, a poor creature employed at the town hall, who was famous for his beautiful hand and sharpened his penknife on his boots.

When the weather was bright the household set off early for a day at Geffosses Farm.

Its courtyard is on a slope, with the farmhouse in the middle, and the sea looks like a gray streak in the distance.

Félicité brought slices of cold meat out of her basket, and they breakfasted in a room adjoining the dairy. It was the only surviving fragment of a country house which was now no more. The wallpaper hung in tatters, and quivered in the draughts. Mme Aubain sat with bowed head, overcome by her memories; the children became afraid to speak. "Why don't you play, then?" she would say, and off they went.

Paul climbed into the barn, caught birds, played at ducks and drakes over the pond, or hammered with his stick on the big casks, which boomed like drums. Virginie fed the rabbits or dashed off to pick cornflowers, her quick legs showing their embroidered little drawers.

One autumn evening they went home by the fields. The moon was in its first quarter, lighting part of the sky; and mist floated like a scarf over the windings of the Toucques. Cattle, lying out in the middle of the grass, looked quietly at the four people as they passed. In the third meadow some of them got up and made a half circle in front of the walkers. "There's nothing to be afraid of," said Félicité, as she stroked the nearest on the back with a kind of crooning song; he wheeled round and the others did the same. But when they crossed the next pasture there was a formidable bellow. It was a bull, hidden by the mist. Mme Aubain was about to run. "No! no! don't go so fast!" They mended their pace, however, and heard a loud breathing behind them which came nearer. His hoofs thudded on the meadow grass like hammers; why, he was galloping now! Félicité turned round and tore up clods of earth with both hands and threw them in his eyes. He lowered his muzzle, waved his horns, and quivered with fury, bellowing terribly. Mme Aubain, now at the end of the pasture with her two little ones, was looking wildly for a place to get over the high bank. Félicité was retreating, still with her face to the bull, keeping up a shower of clods which blinded him, and crying all the time, "Be quick! be quick!"

Mme Aubain went down into the ditch, pushed Virginie first and then Paul, fell several times as she tried to climb the bank, and managed it at last by dint of courage.

The bull had driven Félicité to bay against a rail fence; his slaver was streaming into her face; another second, and he would have gored her. She had just time to slip between two of the rails, and the big animal stopped short in amazement.

This adventure was talked of at Pont-l'Évêque for many a year. Félicité did not pride herself on it in the least, not having the barest suspicion that she had done anything heroic.

Virginie was the sole object of her thoughts, for the child developed a nervous complaint as a result of her fright, and M. Poupart, the doctor, advised sea bathing at Trouville. It was not a frequented place then. Mme Aubain collected information, consulted Bourais, and made preparations as though for a long journey.

Her luggage started a day in advance, in Liébard's cart. The next day he brought round two horses, one of which had a lady's saddle with a velvet back to it, while a cloak was rolled up to make a kind of seat on the crupper of the other. Mme Aubain rode on that, behind the farmer. Félicité took charge of Virginie, and Paul mounted M. Lechaptois' donkey, lent on condition that great care was taken of it.

The road was so bad that its five miles took two hours. The horses sank in the mud up to their pasterns, and their haunches jerked abruptly in the effort to get out; or else they stumbled in the ruts, and at other moments had to jump. In some places Liébard's mare came suddenly to a halt. He waited patiently until she went on again, talking about the people who had properties along the road and adding moral

reflections to their history. So it was that as they were in the middle of Toucques, and passed under some windows bowered with nasturtiums, he shrugged his shoulders and said: "There's a Mme Lehoussais lives there; instead of taking a young man she . . ." Félicité did not hear the rest; the horses were trotting and the donkey galloping. They all turned down a bypath; a gate swung open and two boys appeared; and the party dismounted in front of a manure heap at the very threshold of the farmhouse door.

When Mme Liébard saw her mistress she gave lavish signs of joy. She served her a luncheon with a sirloin of beef, tripe, black pudding, a fricassee of chicken, sparkling cider, a fruit tart, and brandied plums; seasoning it all with compliments to Madame, who seemed in better health; Mademoiselle, who was "splendid" now; and Monsieur Paul, who had "filled out" wonderfully. Nor did she forget their deceased grandparents, whom the Liébards had known, as they had been in the service of the family for several generations. The farm, like them, had the stamp of antiquity. The beams on the ceiling were worm-eaten, the walls blackened with smoke, and the windowpanes gray with dust. There was an oak dresser laden with every sort of useful article—jugs, plates, pewter bowls, wolf traps, and sheep shears; and a huge syringe made the children laugh. There was not a tree in the three courtyards without mushrooms growing at the bottom of it or a tuft of mistletoe on its boughs. Several of them had been thrown down by the wind. They had taken root again at the middle; and all were bending under their wealth of apples. The thatched roofs, like brown velvet and of varying thickness, withstood the heaviest squalls. The cart shed, however, was falling into ruin. Mme Aubain said she would see about it and ordered the animals to be saddled again.

It was another half hour before they reached Trouville. The little caravan dismounted to pass Écores—it was an overhanging cliff with boats below it—and three minutes later they were at the end of the quay and entered the courtyard of the Golden Lamb, kept by good Mme David.

From the first days of their stay Virginie began to feel less weak, thanks to the change of air and the effect of the sea baths. These, for want of a bathing dress, she took in her chemise; and her nurse dressed her afterward in a coast guard's cabin which was used by the bathers.

In the afternoons they took the donkey and went off beyond the Black Rocks, in the direction of Hennequeville. The path climbed at first through ground with dells in it like the greensward of a park and then reached a plateau where grass fields and arable lay side by side. Hollies rose stiffly out of the briary tangle at the edge of the road, and here and there a great withered tree made zigzags in the blue air with its branches.

They nearly always rested in a meadow, with Deauville on their left, Havre on their right, and the open sea in front. It glittered in the sunshine, smooth as a mirror and so quiet that its murmur was scarcely to be heard; sparrows chirped in hiding and the immense sky arched over it all. Mme Aubain sat doing her needlework; Virginie plaited rushes by her side; Félicité pulled up lavender; and Paul was bored and anxious to start home.

Other days they crossed the Toucques in a boat and looked for shells. When the tide went out sea urchins, starfish, and jellyfish were left exposed; and the children ran in pursuit of the foam flakes which scudded in the wind. The sleepy waves broke on the sand and unrolled all along the beach; it stretched away out of sight, bounded on the land side by the dunes which parted it from the Marsh, a wide meadow shaped like an arena. As they came home that way, Trouville, on the hillside in the background, grew bigger at every step, and its miscellaneous throng of houses seemed to break into a gay disorder.

On days when it was too hot they did not leave their room. From the dazzling brilliance outside light fell in streaks between the laths of the blinds. There were no sounds in the village, and on the pavement below not a soul. This silence round them deepened the quietness of things. In the distance, where men were caulking, there was a tap of hammers as they plugged the hulls, and a sluggish breeze wafted up the smell of tar.

The chief amusement was the return of the fishing boats. They began to tack as soon as they had passed the buoys. The sails came down on two of the three masts; and they drew on with the foresail swelling like a balloon, glided through the splash of the waves, and when they had reached the middle of the harbor suddenly dropped anchor. Then the boats drew up against the quay. The sailors threw quivering fish over the side; a row of carts was waiting, and women in cotton bonnets darted out to take the baskets and give their men a kiss.

One of them came up to Félicité one day, and she entered the lodgings a little later in a state of delight. She had found a sister again—and then Nastasie Barette, "wife of Leroux," appeared, holding an infant at her breast and another child with her right hand, while on her left was a little cabin boy with his hands on his hips and a cap over his ear.

After a quarter of an hour Mme Aubain sent them off; but they were always to be found hanging about the kitchen, or encountered in the course of a walk. The husband never appeared.

Félicité was seized with affection for them. She bought them a blanket, some shirts, and a stove; it was clear that they were making a good thing out of her. Mme Aubain was annoyed by this weakness of hers, and she did not like the liberties taken by the nephew, who said "thee" and "thou" to Paul. So as Virginie was coughing and the fine weather gone, she returned to Pont-l'Évêque.

There M. Bourais enlightened her on the choice of a boys' school. The one at Caen was reputed to be the best, and Paul was sent to it. He said his good-byes bravely, content enough at going to live in a house where he would have companions.

Mme Aubain resigned herself to her son's absence as a thing that had to be. Virginie thought about it less and less. Félicité missed the noise he made. But she found an occupation to distract her; from Christmas onward she took the little girl to catechism every day.

### III

After making a genuflection at the door she walked up between the double row of chairs under the lofty nave, opened Mme Aubain's pew, sat down, and began to look about her. The choir stalls were filled with the boys on the right and the girls on the left, and the curé stood by the lectern. On a painted window in the apse the Holy Ghost looked down upon the Virgin. Another window showed her on her knees before the child Jesus, and a group carved in wood behind the altar shrine represented Saint Michael overthrowing the dragon.

The priest began with a sketch of sacred history. The Garden, the Flood, the Tower of Babel, cities in flames, dying nations, and overturned idols passed like a dream before her eyes; and the dizzying vision left her with reverence for the Most High and fear of his wrath. Then she wept at the story of the Passion. Why had they crucified Him, when He loved the children, fed the multitudes, healed the blind, and had willed, in His meekness, to be born among the poor, on the dung heap of a stable? The sowings, harvests, winepresses, all the familiar things the Gospel speaks of, were a part of her life. They had been made holy by God's passing; and she loved the lambs more tenderly for her love of the Lamb, and the doves because of the Holy Ghost.

She found it hard to imagine Him in person, for He was not merely a bird, but a flame as well, and a breath at other times. It may be His light, she thought, which flits at night about the edge of the marshes, His breathing which drives on the clouds, His voice which gives harmony to the bells; and she would sit rapt in adoration, enjoying the cool walls and the quiet of the church.

Of doctrines she understood nothing—did not even try to understand. The curé discoursed, the children repeated their lesson, and finally she went to sleep, waking up with a start when their wooden shoes clattered on the flagstones as they went away.

It was thus that Félicité, whose religious education had been neglected in her youth, learned the catechism by dint of hearing it; and from that time she copied all Virginie's observances, fasting as she did and confessing with her. On Corpus Christi Day they made a festal altar together.

The first communion loomed distractingly ahead. She fussed over the shoes, the rosary, the book and gloves; and how she trembled as she helped Virginie's mother to dress her!

All through the Mass she was racked with anxiety. She could not see one side of the choir because of M. Bourais; but straight in front of her was the flock of maidens, with white crowns above their hanging veils, making the impression of a field of snow; and she knew her dear child at a distance by her dainty neck and thoughtful air. The bell tinkled. The heads bowed, and there was silence. As the organ pealed, singers and congregation took up the "Agnus Dei"; then the procession of the boys began, and after them the girls rose. Step by step, with their hands joined in prayer, they went toward the lighted altar, knelt on the first step, received the sacrament in turn, and came back in the same order to their places. When Virginie's turn came Félicité leaned forward to see her; and with the imaginativeness of deep and tender feeling it seemed to her that she actually was the child; Virginie's face became hers, she was dressed in her clothes, it was her heart beating in her breast. As

the moment came to open her mouth she closed her eyes and nearly fainted.

She appeared early in the sacristy next morning for Monsieur the curé to give her the communion. She took it with devotion, but it did not give her the same exquisite delight.

Mme Aubain wanted to make her daughter into an accomplished person; and as Guyot could not teach her music or English she decided to place her in the Ursuline Convent at Honfleur as a boarder. The child made no objection. Félicité sighed and thought that Madame lacked feeling. Then she reflected that her mistress might be right; matters of this kind were beyond her.

So one day an old spring-van drew up at the door, and out of it stepped a nun to fetch the young lady. Félicité hoisted the luggage on to the top, admonished the driver, and put six pots of preserves, a dozen pears, and a bunch of violets under the seat.

At the last moment Virginie broke into a fit of sobbing; she threw her arms round her mother, who kissed her on the forehead, saying over and over "Come, be brave! be brave!" The step was raised, and the carriage drove off.

Then Mme Aubain's strength gave way; and in the evening all her friends—the Lormeau family, Mme Lechaptois, the Rochefeuille ladies, M. de Houppeville, and Bourais—came in to console her.

To be without her daughter was very painful for her at first. But she heard from Virginie three times a week, wrote to her on the other days, walked in the garden, and so filled up the empty hours.

From sheer habit Félicité went into Virginie's room in the mornings and gazed at the walls. It was boredom to her not to have to comb the child's hair now, lace up her boots, tuck her into bed—and not to see her charming face perpetually and hold her hand when they went out together. In this idle condition she tried making lace. But her fingers were too heavy and broke the threads; she could not attend to anything, she had lost her sleep, and was, in her own words, "destroyed."

To "divert herself" she asked leave to have visits from her nephew Victor.

He arrived on Sundays after Mass, rosy-cheeked, bare-chested, with the scent of the country he had walked through still about him. She laid her table promptly and they had lunch, sitting opposite each other. She ate as little as possible herself to save expense but stuffed him with food so generously that at last he went to sleep. At the first stroke of vespers she woke him up, brushed his trousers, fastened his tie, and went to church, leaning on his arm with maternal pride.

Victor was always instructed by his parents to get something out of her—a packet of moist sugar, it might be, a cake of soap, spirits, or even money at times. He brought his things for her to mend and she took over the task, only too glad to have a reason for making him come back.

In August his father took him off on a coasting voyage. It was holiday time, and she was consoled by the arrival of the children. Paul, however, was getting selfish, and Virginie was too old to be called "thou" any longer; this put a constraint and barrier between them.

Victor went to Morlaix, Dunkirk, and Brighton in succession and made Félicité a present on his return from each voyage. It was a box made of shells the first time, a coffee cup the next, and on the third occasion a large gingerbread man. Victor was growing handsome. He was well made, had a hint of a mustache, good honest eyes, and a small leather hat pushed backward like a pilot's. He entertained her by telling stories embroidered with nautical terms.

On a Monday, July 14, 1819 (she never forgot the date), he told her that he had signed on for the big voyage and next night but one he would take the Honfleur boat and join his schooner, which was to weigh anchor from Havre before long. Perhaps he would be gone two years.

The prospect of this long absence threw Félicité into deep distress; one more good-bye she must have, and on the Wednesday evening, when Madame's dinner was finished, she put on her clogs and made short work of the twelve miles between Pont-l'Évêque and Honfleur.

When she arrived in front of the Calvary she took the turn to the right instead of the left, got lost in the timber-yards, and retraced her steps; some people to whom she spoke advised her to be quick. She went all round the harbor basin, full of ships, and knocked against hawsers; then the ground fell away, lights flashed across each other, and she thought her wits had left her, for she saw horses up in the sky.

Others were neighing by the quayside, frightened at the sea. They were lifted by a tackle and deposited in a boat, where passengers jostled each other among cider casks, cheese baskets, and sacks of grain; fowls could be heard clucking, the captain swore; and a cabin boy stood leaning over the bows, indifferent to it all. Félicité, who had not recognized him, called "Victor!" and he raised his head; all at once, as she was darting forward, the gangway was drawn back.

The Honfleur packet, women singing as they hauled it, passed out of harbor. Its framework creaked and the heavy waves whipped its bows. The canvas had swung round, no one could be seen on board now; and on the moon-silvered sea the boat made a black speck which paled gradually, dipped, and vanished.

As Félicité passed by the Calvary she had a wish to commend to God what she cherished most, and she stood there praying a long time with her face bathed in tears and her eyes toward the clouds. The town was asleep, coast guards were walking to and fro; and water poured without cessation through the holes in the sluice, with the noise of a torrent. The clocks struck two.

The convent parlor would not be open before day. If Félicité were late Madame would most certainly be annoyed; and in spite of her desire to kiss the other child she turned home. The maids at the inn were waking up as she came in to Pont-l'Évêque.

So the poor slip of a boy was going to toss for months and months at sea! She had not been frightened by his previous voyages. From England or Brittany you came back safe enough; but America, the colonies, the islands—these were lost in a dim region at the other end of the world.

Félicité's thoughts from that moment ran entirely on her nephew. On sunny days she was harassed by the idea of thirst; when there was a storm she was afraid of the lightning on his account. As she listened to the wind growling in the chimney or carrying off the slates she pictured him lashed by that same tempest, at the top of a shattered mast, with his body thrown backward under a sheet of foam; or else (with a reminiscence of the illustrated geography) he was being eaten by savages, captured in a wood by monkeys, or dying on a desert shore. And never did she mention her anxieties.

Mme Aubain had anxieties of her own, about her daughter. The good sisters found her an affectionate but delicate child. The slightest emotion unnerved her. She had to give up the piano.

Her mother stipulated for regular letters from the convent. She lost patience one morning when the postman did not come and walked to and fro in the parlor from her armchair to the window. It was really amazing; not a word for four days!

To console Mme Aubain by her own example Félicité remarked:

"As for me, Madame, it's six months since I heard. . . ."

"From whom, pray?"

"Why . . . from my nephew," the servant answered gently.

"Oh! your nephew!" And Mme Aubain resumed her walk with a shrug of the shoulders, as much as to say: "I was not thinking of him! And what is more, it's absurd! A scamp of a cabin boy—what does he matter? . . . whereas my daughter . . . why, just think!''

Félicité, though she had been brought up on harshness, felt indignant with Madame—and then forgot. It seemed the simplest thing in the world to her to lose one's head over the little girl. For her the two children were equally important; a bond in her heart made them one, and their destinies must be the same.

She heard from the chemist that Victor's ship had arrived at Havana. He had read this piece of news in a gazette.

Cigars—they made her imagine Havana as a place where no one does anything but smoke, and there was Victor moving among the Negroes in a cloud of tobacco. Could you, she wondered, "in case you needed," return by land? What was the distance from Pont-l'Évêque? She questioned M. Bourais to find out.

He reached for his atlas and began explaining the longitudes; Félicité's consternation provoked a fine pedantic smile. Finally he marked with his pencil a black, imperceptible point in the indentations of an oval spot and said as he did so, "Here it is." She bent over the map; the maze of colored lines wearied her eyes without conveying anything; and on an invitation from Bourais to tell him her difficulty she begged him to show her the house where Victor was living. Bourais threw up his arms, sneezed, and laughed immensely: a simplicity like hers was a positive joy. And Félicité did not understand the reason; how could she when she expected, very likely, to see the actual image of her nephew—so stunted was her mind!

A fortnight afterward Liébard came into the kitchen at market time as usual and handed her a letter from her brother-in-law. As neither of them could read she took it to her mistress.

Mme Aubain, who was counting the stitches in her knitting, put the work down by her side, broke the seal of the letter, started, and said in a low voice, with a look of meaning:

"It is bad news . . . that they have to tell you. Your nephew . . ."

He was dead. The letter said no more.

Félicité fell on to a chair, leaning her head against the wainscot; and she closed her eyelids, which suddenly flushed pink. Then with bent forehead, hands hanging, and fixed eyes, she said at intervals:

"Poor little lad! poor little lad!"

Liébard watched her and heaved sighs. Mme Aubain trembled a little.

She suggested that Félicité should go to see her sister at Trouville. Félicité answered by a gesture that she had no need.

There was a silence. The worthy Liébard thought it was time for them to withdraw.

Then Félicité said:

"They don't care, not they!"

Her head dropped again; and she took up mechanically, from time to time, the long needles on her worktable.

Women passed in the yard with a barrow of dripping linen.

As she saw them through the windowpanes she remembered her washing; she had put it to soak the day before, today she must wring it out; and she left the room.

Her plank and tub were at the edge of the Toucques. She threw a pile of linen on the bank, rolled up her sleeves, and taking her wooden beater dealt lusty blows whose sound carried to the neighboring gardens. The meadows were empty, the river stirred in the wind; and down below long grasses wavered, like the hair of corpses floating in the water. She kept her grief down and was very brave until the evening; but once in her room she surrendered to it utterly, lying stretched on the mattress with her face in the pillow and her hands clenched against her temples.

Much later she heard, from the captain himself, the circumstances of Victor's end. They had bled him too much at the hospital for yellow fever. Four doctors held him at once. He had died instantly, and the chief had said:

"Bah! there goes another!"

His parents had always been brutal to him. She preferred not to see them again; and they made no advances, either because they forgot her or from the callousness of the wretchedly poor.

Virginie began to grow weaker.

Tightness in her chest, coughing, continual fever, and veinings on her cheekbones betrayed some deep-seated complaint. M. Poupart had advised a stay in Provence. Mme Aubain determined on it and would have brought her daughter home at once but for the climate of Pont-l'Évêque.

She made an arrangement with a jobmaster, and he drove her to the convent every Tuesday. There is a terrace in the garden, with a view over the Seine. Virginie took walks there over the fallen vine-leaves, on her mother's arm. A shaft of sunlight through the clouds made her blink sometimes, as she gazed at the sails in the distance and the whole horizon from the castle of Tancarville to the lighthouses at Havre. Afterward they rested in the arbor. Her mother had secured a little cask of excellent Malaga; and Virginie, laughing at the idea of getting tipsy, drank a thimbleful of it, no more.

Her strength came back visibly. The autumn glided gently away. Félicité reassured Mme Aubain. But one evening, when she had been out on a commission in the neighborhood, she found M. Poupart's gig at the door. He was in the hall, and Mme Aubain was tying her bonnet.

Give me my foot warmer, purse, gloves! Quicker, come!"

Virginie had inflammation of the lungs; perhaps it was hopeless.

"Not yet!" said the doctor, and they both got into the carriage under whirling flakes of snow. Night was coming on and it was very cold.

Félicité rushed into the church to light a taper. Then she ran after the gig, came up with it in an hour, and jumped lightly in behind. As she hung on by the fringes a thought came into her mind: "The courtyard has not been shut up; supposing burglars got in!" And she jumped down.

At dawn next day she presented herself at the doctor's. He had come in and started for the country again. Then she waited in the inn, thinking that a letter would come by some hand or other. Finally, when it was twilight, she took the Lisieux coach.

The convent was at the end of a steep lane. When she was about halfway up it she heard strange sounds—a death bell tolling. "It is for someone else," thought Félicité, and she pulled the knocker violently.

After some minutes there was a sound of trailing slippers, the door opened ajar, and a nun appeared.

The good sister, with an air of compunction, said that "she had just passed away." On the instant the bell of Saint Leonard's tolled twice as fast.

Félicité went up to the second floor.

From the doorway she saw Virginie stretched on her back, with her hands joined, her mouth open, and head thrown back under a black crucifix that leaned toward her, between curtains that hung stiffly, less pale than was her face. Mme Aubain, at the foot of the bed, which she clasped with her arms, was choking with sobs of agony. The mother superior stood on the right. Three candlesticks on the chest of drawers made spots of red, and the mist came whitely through the windows. Nuns came and took Mme Aubain away.

For two nights Félicité never left the dead child. She repeated the same prayers, sprinkled holy water over the sheets, came and sat down again, and watched her. At the end of the first vigil she noticed that the face had grown yellow, the lips turned blue, the nose was sharper, and the eyes sunk in. She kissed them several times and would not have been immensely surprised if Virginie had opened them again; to minds like hers the supernatural is quite simple. She made the girl's toilette, wrapped her in her shroud, lifted her down into her bier, put a garland on her head, and spread out her hair. It was fair, and extraordinarily

long for her age. Félicité cut off a big lock and slipped half of it into her bosom, determined that she should never part with it.

The body was brought back to Pont-l'Évêque, as Mme Aubain intended; she followed the hearse in a closed carriage.

It took another three-quarters of an hour after the Mass to reach the cemetery. Paul walked in front, sobbing. M. Bourais was behind, and then came the chief residents, the women shrouded in black mantles, and Félicité. She thought of her nephew; and because she had not been able to pay these honors to him her grief was doubled, as though the one were being buried with the other.

Mme Aubain's despair was boundless. It was against God that she first rebelled, thinking it unjust of Him to have taken her daughter from her—she had never done evil and her conscience was so clear! Ah, no!—she ought to have taken Virginie off to the south. Other doctors would have saved her. She accused herself now, wanted to join her child, and broke into cries of distress in the middle of her dreams. One dream haunted her above all. Her husband, dressed as a sailor, was returning from a long voyage, and shedding tears he told her that he had been ordered to take Virginie away. Then they consulted how to hide her somewhere.

She came in once from the garden quite upset. A moment ago—and she pointed out the place—the father and daughter had appeared to her, standing side by side, and they did nothing, but they looked at her.

For several months after this she stayed inertly in her room. Félicité lectured her gently; she must live for her son's sake, and for the other, in remembrance of "her."

"Her?" answered Mme Aubain, as though she were just waking up. "Ah, yes! . . . yes! . . . You do not forget her!" This was an allusion to the cemetery, where she was strictly forbidden to go.

Félicité went there every day.

Precisely at four she skirted the houses, climbed the hill, opened the gate, and came to Virginie's grave. It was a little column of pink marble with a stone underneath and a garden plot enclosed by chains. The beds were hidden under a coverlet of flowers. She watered their leaves, freshened the gravel, and knelt down to break up the earth better. When Mme Aubain was able to come there she felt a relief and a sort of consolation.

Then years slipped away, one like another, and their only episodes were the great festivals as they recurred—Easter, the Assumption, All Saints' Day. Household occurrences marked dates that were referred to afterward. In 1825, for instance, two glaziers whitewashed the hall; in 1827 a piece of the roof fell into the courtyard and nearly killed a man. In the summer of 1828 it was Madame's turn to offer the consecrated bread; Bourais, about this time, mysteriously absented himself; and one by one the old acquaintances passed away: Guyot, Liébard, Mme Lechaptois, Robelin, and Uncle Gremanville, who had been paralyzed for a long time.

One night the driver of the mail coach announced the Revolution of July in Pont-l'Évêque. A new subprefect was appointed a few days later—Baron de Larsonnière, who had been consul in America, and brought with him, besides his wife, a sister-in-law and three young ladies, already growing up. They were to be seen about on their lawn, in loose blouses, and they had a Negro and a parrot. They paid a call on Mme Aubain which she did not fail to return. The moment they were seen in the distance Félicité ran to let her mistress know. But only one thing could really move her feelings—the letters from her son.

He was swallowed up in a tavern life and could follow no career. She paid his debts, he made new ones; and the sighs that Mme Aubain uttered as she sat knitting by the window reached Félicité at her spinning wheel in the kitchen.

They took walks together along the espaliered wall, always talking of Virginie and wondering if such and such a thing would have pleased her and what, on some occasion, she would have been likely to say.

All her small belongings filled a cupboard in the two-bedded room. Mme Aubain inspected them as seldom as she could. One summer day she made up her mind to it—and some moths flew out of the wardrobe.

Virginie's dresses were in a row underneath a shelf, on which there were three dolls, some hoops, a set of toy pots and pans, and the basin that she used. They took out her petticoats as well, and the stockings and handkerchiefs, and laid them out on the two beds before folding them up again. The sunshine lit up these poor things, bringing out their stains and the creases made by the body's movements. The air was warm and blue, a blackbird warbled, life seemed bathed in a deep sweetness. They found a little plush hat with thick, chestnut-colored pile; but it was eaten all over by moth. Félicité begged it for her own. Their eyes met fixedly and filled with tears; at last the mistress opened her arms, the servant threw herself into them, and they embraced each other, satisfying their grief in a kiss that made them equal.

It was the first time in their lives, Mme Aubain's nature not being expansive. Félicité was as grateful as though she had received a favor and cherished her mistress from that moment with the devotion of an animal and a religious worship.

The kindness of her heart unfolded.

When she heard the drums of a marching regiment in the street she posted herself at the door with a pitcher of cider and asked the soldiers to drink. She nursed cholera patients and protected the Polish refugees; one of these even declared that he wished to marry her. They quarreled, however; for when she came back from the Angelus one morning she found that he had got into her kitchen and made himself a vinegar salad which he was quietly eating.

After the Poles came father Colmiche, an old man who was supposed to have committed atrocities in '93. He lived by the side of the river in the ruins of a pigsty. The little boys watched him through the cracks in the wall and threw pebbles at him, which fell on the pallet where he lay constantly shaken by a catarrh; his hair was very long, his eyes inflamed, and there was a tumor on his arm bigger than his head. She got him some linen and tried to clean up his miserable hole; her dream was to establish him in the bakehouse, without letting him annoy Madame. When the tumor burst she dressed it every day; sometimes she brought him cake and would put him in the sunshine on a truss of straw. The poor old man, slobbering and trembling, thanked her in his worn-out voice, was terrified that he might lose her, and stretched out his hands when he saw her go away. He died; and she had a Mass said for the repose of his soul.

That very day a great happiness befell her; just at dinnertime appeared Mme de Larsonnière's Negro, carrying the parrot in its cage, with perch, chain, and padlock. A note from the baroness informed Mme Aubain that her husband had been raised to a prefecture and they were starting that evening; she begged her to accept the bird as a memento and mark of her regard.

For a long time he had absorbed Félicité's imagination, because he came from America; and that name reminded her of Victor, so much so that she made inquiries of the Negro. She had once gone so far as to say "How Madame would enjoy having him!"

The Negro repeated the remark to his mistress; and as she could not take the bird away with her she chose this way of getting rid of him.

## IV

His name was Loulou. His body was green and the tips of his wings rose-pink; his forehead was blue and his throat golden.

But he had the tiresome habits of biting his perch, tearing out his feathers, sprinkling his dirt about, and spattering the water of his tub. He annoyed Mme Aubain, and she gave him to Félicité for good.

She endeavored to train him; soon he could repeat "Nice boy! Your servant, sir! Good morning, Marie!" He was placed by the side of the door and astonished several people by not answering to the name Jacquot, for all parrots are called Jacquot. People compared him to a turkey and a log of wood and stabbed Félicité to the heart each time. Strange obstinacy on Loulou's part!—directly you looked at him he refused to speak.

Nonetheless he was eager for society; for on Sundays, while the Rochefeuille ladies, M. de Houppeville, and new familiars— Onfroy the apothecary, Monsieur Varin, and Captain Mathieu—were playing their game of cards, he beat the windows with his wings and threw himself about so frantically that they could not hear each other speak.

Bourais' face, undoubtedly, struck him as extremely droll. Directly he saw it he began to laugh—and laugh with all his might. His peals rang through the courtyard and were repeated by the echo; the neighbors came to their windows and laughed too; while M. Bourais, gliding along under the wall to escape the parrot's eye, and hiding his profile with his hat, got to the river and then entered by the garden gate. There was a lack of tenderness in the looks which he darted at the bird.

Loulou had been slapped by the butcher boy for making so free as to plunge his head into his basket; and since then he was always trying to nip him through his shirt. Fabu threatened to wring his neck, although he was not cruel, for all his tattooed arms and large whiskers. Far from it; he really rather liked the parrot, and in a jovial humor even wanted to teach him to swear. Félicité, who was alarmed by such proceedings, put the bird in the kitchen. His little chain was taken off and he roamed about the house.

His way of going downstairs was to lean

on each step with the curve of his beak, raise the right foot, and then the left; and Félicité was afraid that these gymnastics brought on fits of giddiness. He fell ill and could not talk or eat any longer. There was a growth under his tongue, such as fowls have sometimes. She cured him by tearing the pellicle off with her fingernails. M. Paul was thoughtless enough one day to blow some cigar smoke into his nostrils, and another time when Mme Lormeau was teasing him with the end of her umbrella he snapped at the ferrule. Finally he got lost.

Félicité had put him on the grass to refresh him and gone away for a minute, and when she came back—no sign of the parrot! She began by looking for him in the shrubs, by the waterside, and over the roofs, without listening to her mistress's cries of "Take care, do! You are out of your wits!" Then she investigated all the gardens in Pont-l'Évêque and stopped the passersby. "You don't ever happen to have seen my parrot, by any chance, do you?" And she gave a description of the parrot to those who did not know him. Suddenly, behind the mills at the foot of the hill she thought she could make out something green that fluttered. But on the top of the hill there was nothing. A hawker assured her that he had come across the parrot just before, at Saint-Melaine, in Mère Simon's shop. She rushed there; they had no idea of what she meant. At last she came home exhausted, with her slippers in shreds and despair in her soul; and as she was sitting in the middle of the garden seat at Madame's side, telling the whole story of her efforts, a light weight dropped on to her shoulder—it was Loulou! What on earth had he been doing? Taking a walk in the neighborhood, perhaps!

She had some trouble in recovering from this, or rather never did recover. As the result of a chill she had an attack of quinsy, and soon afterward an earache. Three years later she was deaf; and she spoke very loud, even in church. Though

Félicité's sins might have been published in every corner of the diocese without dishonor to her or scandal to anybody, his Reverence the priest thought it right now to hear her confession in the sacristy only.

Imaginary noises in the head completed her upset. Her mistress often said to her, "Heavens! how stupid you are!" "Yes, Madame," she replied, and looked about for something.

Her little circle of ideas grew still narrower; the peal of church bells and the lowing of cattle ceased to exist for her. All living beings moved as silently as ghosts. One sound only reached her ears now— the parrot's voice.

Loulou, as though to amuse her, reproduced the click-clack of the turnspit, the shrill call of a man selling fish, and the noise of the saw in the joiner's house opposite; when the bell rang he imitated Mme Aubain's "Félicité! the door! the door!"

They carried on conversations, he endlessly reciting the three phrases in his repertory, to which she replied with words that were just as disconnected but uttered what was in her heart. Loulou was almost a son and a lover to her in her isolated state. He climbed up her fingers, nibbled at her lips, and clung to her kerchief; and when she bent her forehead and shook her head gently to and fro, as nurses do, the great wings of her bonnet and the bird's wings quivered together.

When the clouds massed and the thunder rumbled Loulou broke into cries, perhaps remembering the downpours in his native forests. The streaming rain made him absolutely mad; he fluttered wildly about, dashed up to the ceiling, upset everything, and went out through the window to dabble in the garden; but he was back quickly to perch on one of the firedogs and hopped about to dry himself, exhibiting his tail and his beak in turn.

One morning in the terrible winter of 1837 she had put him in front of the fireplace because of the cold. She found him dead, in the middle of his cage: head downward, with his claws in the wires. He had died from congestion, no doubt. But Félicité thought he had been poisoned with parsley, and though there was no proof of any kind her suspicions inclined to Fabu.

She wept so piteously that her mistress said to her, "Well, then, have him stuffed!"

She asked advice from the chemist, who had always been kind to the parrot. He wrote to Havre, and a person called Fellacher undertook the business. But as parcels sometimes got lost in the coach she decided to take the parrot as far as Honfleur herself.

Along the sides of the road were leafless apple trees, one after the other. Ice covered the ditches. Dogs barked about the farms; and Félicité, with her hands under her cloak, her little black sabots and her basket, walked briskly in the middle of the road.

She crossed the forest, passed High Oak, and reached Saint Gatien.

A cloud of dust rose behind her, and in it a mail coach, carried away by the steep hill, rushed down at full gallop like a hurricane. Seeing this woman who would not get out of the way, the driver stood up in front and the postilion shouted too. He could not hold in his four horses, which increased their pace, and the two leaders were grazing her when he threw them to one side with a jerk of the reins. But he was wild with rage, and lifting his arm as he passed at full speed, gave her such a lash from waist to neck with his big whip that she fell on her back.

Her first act, when she recovered consciousness, was to open her basket. Loulou was happily none the worse. She felt a burn in her right cheek, and when she put her hands against it they were red; the blood was flowing.

She sat down on a heap of stones and bound up her face with her handkerchief. Then she ate a crust of bread which she had put in the basket as a precaution and found a consolation for her wound in gazing at the bird.

When she reached the crest of Ecquemauville she saw the Honfleur lights sparkling in the night sky like a company of stars; beyond, the sea stretched dimly. Then a faintness overtook her and she stopped; her wretched childhood, the disillusion of her first love, her nephew's going away, and Virginie's death all came back to her at once like the waves of an oncoming tide, rose to her throat, and choked her.

Afterward, at the boat, she made a point of speaking to the captain, begging him to take care of the parcel, though she did not tell him what was in it.

Fellacher kept the parrot a long time. He was always promising it for the following week. After six months he announced that a packing case had started, and then nothing more was heard of it. It really seemed as though Loulou was never coming back. "Ah, they have stolen him!" she thought.

He arrived at last, and looked superb. There he was, erect upon a branch which screwed into a mahogany socket, with a foot in the air and his head on one side, biting a nut which the bird stuffer—with a taste for impressiveness—had gilded.

Félicité shut him up in her room. It was a place to which few people were admitted and held so many religious objects and miscellaneous things that it looked like a chapel and bazaar in one.

A big cupboard impeded you as you opened the door. Opposite the window commanding the garden a little round one looked into the court; there was a table by the folding bed with a water jug, two combs, and a cube of blue soap in a chipped plate. On the walls hung rosaries, medals, several benign Virgins, and a holy water vessel made out of coconut; on the chest of drawers, which was covered with a cloth like an altar, was the shell box that Victor had given her, and after that a watering can, a toy balloon, exercise books, the illustrated geography, and a pair of young lady's boots; and, fastened by its ribbons to the nail of the looking glass,

hung the little plush hat! Félicité carried observances of this kind so far as to keep one of Monsieur's frock coats. All the old rubbish which Mme Aubain did not want any longer she laid hands on for her room. That was why there were artificial flowers along the edge of the chest of drawers and a portrait of the Comte d'Artois in the little window recess.

With the aid of a bracket Loulou was established over the chimney, which jutted into the room. Every morning when she woke up she saw him there in the dawning light and recalled old days and the smallest details of insignificant acts in a deep quietness which knew no pain.

Holding, as she did, no communication with anyone, Félicité lived as insensibly as if she were walking in her sleep. The Corpus Christi processions roused her to life again. Then she went round begging mats and candlesticks from the neighbors to decorate the altar they put up in the street.

In church she was always gazing at the Holy Ghost in the window and observed that there was something of the parrot in him. The likeness was still clearer, she thought, on a crude color print representing the baptism of Our Lord. With his purple wings and emerald body he was the very image of Loulou.

She bought him, and hung him up instead of the Comte d'Artois, so that she could see them both together in one glance. They were linked in her thoughts; and the parrot was consecrated by his association with the Holy Ghost, which became more vivid to her eye and more intelligible. The Father could not have chosen to express Himself through a dove, for such creatures cannot speak; it must have been one of Loulou's ancestors, surely. And though Félicité looked at the picture while she said her prayers she swerved a little from time to time toward the parrot.

She wanted to join the Ladies of the Virgin, but Mme Aubain dissuaded her.

And then a great event loomed up before them—Paul's marriage.

He had been a solicitor's clerk to begin with, and then tried business, the Customs, the Inland Revenue, and made efforts, even, to get into the Rivers and Forests. By an inspiration from heaven he had suddenly, at thirty-six, discovered his real line—the Registrar's Office. And there he showed such marked capacity that an inspector had offered him his daughter's hand and promised him his influence.

So Paul, grown serious, brought the lady to see his mother.

She sniffed at the ways of Pont-l'Évêque, gave herself great airs, and wounded Félicité's feelings. Mme Aubain was relieved at her departure.

The week after came news of M. Bourais' death in an inn in Lower Brittany. The rumor of suicide was confirmed, and doubts arose as to his honesty. Mme Aubain studied his accounts and soon found out the whole tale of his misdoings—embezzled arrears, secret sales of wood, forged receipts, etc. Besides that he had an illegitimate child and "relations with a person at Dozulé."

These shameful facts distressed her greatly. In March 1853 she was seized with a pain in the chest; her tongue seemed to be covered with film, and leeches did not ease the difficult breathing. On the ninth evening of her illness she died, just at seventy-two.

She passed as being younger, owing to the bands of brown hair which framed her pale, pockmarked face. There were few friends to regret her, for she had a stiffness of manner which kept people at a distance.

But Félicité mourned for her as one seldom mourns for a master. It upset her ideas and seemed contrary to the order of things, impossible and monstrous, that Madame should die before her.

Ten days afterward, which was the time it took to hurry there from Besançon, the heirs arrived. The daughter-in-law ransacked the drawers, chose some furniture, and sold the rest; and then they went back to their registering.

Madame's armchair, her small round table, her foot warmer, and the eight chairs were gone! Yellow patches in the middle of the panels showed where the engravings had hung. They had carried off the two little beds and the mattresses, and all Virginie's belongings had disappeared from the cupboard. Félicité went from floor to floor dazed with sorrow.

The next day there was a notice on the door, and the apothecary shouted in her ear that the house was for sale.

She tottered and was obliged to sit down. What distressed her most of all was to give up her room, so suitable as it was for poor Loulou. She enveloped him with a look of anguish when she was imploring the Holy Ghost and formed the idolatrous habit of kneeling in front of the parrot to say her prayers. Sometimes the sun shone in at the attic window and caught his glass eye, and a great luminous ray shot out of it and put her in an ecstasy.

She had a pension of fifteen pounds a year which her mistress had left her. The garden gave her a supply of vegetables. As for clothes, she had enough to last her to the end of her days, and she economized in candles by going to bed at dusk.

She hardly ever went out, as she did not like passing the dealer's shop, where some of the old furniture was exposed for sale. Since her fit of giddiness she dragged one leg; and as her strength was failing Mère Simon, whose grocery business had collapsed, came every morning to split the wood and pump water for her.

Her eyes grew feeble. The shutters ceased to be thrown open. Years and years passed, and the house was neither let nor sold.

Félicité never asked for repairs because she was afraid of being sent away. The boards on the roof rotted; her bolster was wet for a whole winter. After Easter she spat blood.

Then Mère Simon called in a doctor. Félicité wanted to know what was the matter with her. But she was too deaf to hear, and the only word which reached her was "pneumonia." It was a word she knew, and she answered softly "Ah! like Madame," thinking it natural that she should follow her mistress.

The time for the festal shrines was coming near. The first one was always at the bottom of the hill, the second in front of the post office, and the third toward the middle of the street. There was some rivalry in the matter of this one, and the women of the parish ended by choosing Mme Aubain's courtyard.

The hard breathing and fever increased. Félicité was vexed at doing nothing for the altar. If only she could at least have put something there! Then she thought of the parrot. The neighbors objected that it would not be decent. But the priest gave her permission, which so intensely delighted her that she begged him to accept Loulou, her sole possession, when she died.

From Tuesday to Saturday, the eve of the festival, she coughed more often. By the evening her face had shriveled, her lips stuck to her gums, and she had vomitings; and at twilight next morning, feeling herself very low, she sent for a priest.

Three kindly women were round her during the extreme unction. Then she announced that she must speak to Fabu. He arrived in his Sunday clothes, by no means at his ease in the funereal atmosphere.

"Forgive me," she said, with an effort to stretch out her arm; "I thought it was you who had killed him."

What did she mean by such stories? She suspected him of murder—a man like him! He waxed indignant and was on the point of making a row.

"There," said the women, "she is no longer in her senses, you can see it well enough!"

Félicité spoke to shadows of her own from time to time. The women went away, and Mère Simon had breakfast. A little later she took Loulou and brought him close to Félicité with the words:

"Come, now, say good-bye to him!"

Loulou was not a corpse, but the worms devoured him; one of his wings was broken, and the tow was coming out of his stomach. But she was blind now; she kissed him on the forehead and kept him close against her cheek. Mère Simon took him back from her to put him on the altar.

## V

Summer scents came up from the meadows; flies buzzed; the sun made the river glitter and heated the slates. Mère Simon came back into the room and fell softly asleep.

She woke at the noise of bells; the people were coming out from vespers. Félicité's delirium subsided. She thought of the procession and saw it as if she had been there.

All the schoolchildren, the church singers, and the firemen walked on the pavement, while in the middle of the road the verger armed with his halberd and the beadle with a large cross advanced in front. Then came the schoolmaster, with an eye on the boys, and the sister, anxious about her little girls; three of the daintiest, with angelic curls, scattered rose petals in the air; the deacon controlled the band with outstretched arms; and two censer bearers turned back at every step toward the Holy Sacrament, which was borne by Monsieur the curé, wearing his beautiful chasuble, under a canopy of dark red velvet held up by four churchwardens. A crowd of people pressed behind, between the white cloths covering the house walls, and they reached the bottom of the hill.

A cold sweat moistened Félicité's temples. Mère Simon sponged her with a piece of linen, saying to herself that one day she would have to go that way.

The hum of the crowd increased, was very loud for an instant, and then went further away.

A fusillade shook the windowpanes. It was the postilions saluting the monstrance. Félicité rolled her eyes and said as audibly as she could: "Does he look well?" The parrot was weighing on her mind.

Her agony began. A death rattle that grew more and more convulsed made her sides heave. Bubbles of froth came at the corners of her mouth, and her whole body trembled.

Soon the booming of the ophicleides, the high voices of the children, and the deep voices of the men were distinguishable. At intervals all was silent, and the tread of feet, deadened by the flowers they walked on, sounded like a flock pattering on grass.

The clergy appeared in the courtyard. Mère Simon clambered on to a chair to reach the attic window and so looked down straight upon the shrine. Green garlands hung over the altar, which was decked with a flounce of English lace. In the middle was a small frame with relics in it; there were two orange trees at the corners, and all along stood silver candlesticks and china vases, with sunflowers, lilies, peonies, foxgloves, and tufts of hortensia. This heap of blazing color slanted from the level of the altar to the carpet, which went on over the pavement; and some rare objects caught the eye. There was a silver-gilt sugar basin with a crown of violets; pendants of Alençon stone glittered on the moss, and two Chinese screens displayed their landscapes. Loulou was hidden under roses and showed nothing but his blue forehead, like a plaque of lapis lazuli.

The churchwardens, singers, and children took their places round the three sides of the court. The priest went slowly up the steps, and placed his great, radiant golden sun upon the lace. Everyone knelt down. There was a deep silence, and the censers glided to and fro on the full swing of their chains.

An azure vapor rose up into Félicité's room. Her nostrils met it; she inhaled it sensuously, mystically, and then closed her eyes. Her lips smiled. The beats of her heart lessened one by one, vaguer each time and softer, as a fountain sinks, an echo disappears; and when she sighed her last breath she thought she saw an opening in the heavens, and a gigantic parrot hovering above her head.

# PICTURE CREDITS

# The Great Ideas Today 1961-1990

This is a thirty-year cumulative index of *The Great Ideas Today,* 1961–1990. It is arranged in sections: AUTHORS, SUBJECTS, and TITLES. The entries under SUBJECTS are in four categories: HISTORY, ECONOMICS, POLITICS, AND SOCIAL SCIENCE; LITERATURE AND THE ARTS; PHILOSOPHY AND RELIGION; and SCIENCE AND MATHEMATICS. Titles in capital letters are of works that appeared in "Additions to the Great Books Library" as reprinted works, distinct from original articles. The year listed after each work refers to the issue of *The Great Ideas Today* in which it appeared.

## AUTHORS

Stanley, Steven M. Evolution of Life: Evidence for a New Pattern. 1983: 2–54.

Stent, Gunther S. The New Biology: Decline of the Baconian Creed. 1976: 152–193.

Strachey, John. THE CHALLENGE OF DEMOCRACY. 1965: 520–589.

Straight, Michael. Public Funding of the Arts in America. 1977: 53–73.

Sullivan, John Edward. The Idea of Religion— Part One. 1977: 204–276.

——. The Idea of Religion—Part Two. 1978: 218–312.

Sullivan, Walter. The Year's Developments in the Physical Sciences and Technology. 1961: 188–243.

Swift, Jonathan. THE BATTLE OF THE BOOKS. 1971: 380–401.

Tawney, R. H. THE ACQUISITIVE SOCIETY. 1962: 403–483.

Theobald, Robert. Cybernation, Unemployment, and Freedom. 1964: 48–69.

Thompson, D'Arcy Wentworth. THE COMPARISON OF RELATED FORMS. 1977: 320–367.

Thoreau, Henry David. WALDEN (selections). 1965: 438–519.

Thurman, Robert A. F. *The Teaching of Vimalakīrti.* 1987: 253–259.

Thurow, Lester C. The American Economy. 1987: 2–51.

Tillich, Paul. Has Man's Conquest of Space Increased or Diminished His Stature? 1963: 48–59.

Tobin, James. Economic Stabilization Policies in the United States. 1976: 39–55.

Tocqueville, Alexis de. DEMOCRACY IN AMERICA (selections). 1964: 414–475.

Tolstoy, Leo. TWO OLD MEN. 1979: 456–471.

Toulmin, Stephen. The Emergence of Post-Modern Science. 1981: 68–114.

——. The Year's Developments in the Physical Sciences. 1967: 158–195.

Toynbee, Arnold J. Revolutionary Change. 1970: 4–27.

——. THREE ESSAYS. 1961: 529–562.

Trevor-Roper, Hugh. Edward Gibbon's *Decline and Fall of the Roman Empire.* 1981: 116–158.

Tugwell, Franklin. The Energy Crisis and Foreign Policy: The Diplomacy of Transition. 1980: 52–71.

Tugwell, Rexford G. *The Federalist.* 1975: 256–300.

Ubell, Earl. The Year's Developments in the Biological Sciences and Medicine. 1962: 272–313.

Van Doren, Charles. Braudel's *Mediterranean.* 1983: 266–288.

——. The Idea of Freedom—Part One. 1972: 300–392.

——. The Idea of Freedom—Part Two. 1973: 232–300.

——. Machine Thinking and Thinking Machines. 1982: 256–279.

——. Morris Kline: *Mathematics—The Loss of Certainty.* 1981: 204–218.

——. Why the Computer Is Only as Good as It Is. 1985: 230–257.

Van Doren, John. Ashley Montagu (ed.): *Sociobiology Examined.* 1981: 219–234.

——. The Idea of Civil Police. 1983: 182–202.

Van Doren, John, and Otto Bird. The Hero and the Heroic Ideal in *Great Books of the Western World.* 1973: 5–36.

Van Doren, Mark. *The Canterbury Tales.* 1973: 180–229.

——. DON QUIXOTE'S PROFESSION. 1976: 428–473.

——. Great Books of the Twentieth Century in Literature. 1969: 276–314.

——. The Year's Developments in Literature. 1961: 142–187.

Veatch, H. B., and M. S. Gram. Philosophy and Ethics. 1970: 228–270.

Voltaire. CANDIDE. 1981: 368–435.

Wallace, William A. Three Classics of Science. 1974: 212–272.

Watson, Burton. T'ang Poetry: A Return to Basics. 1987: 267–277.

Weismann, August. THE DURATION OF LIFE. 1972: 394–415.

Wells, H. G. THE TIME MACHINE. 1971: 446–505.

Wharton, Edith. ETHAN FROME. 1988: 406–467.

Whitman, Walt. DEMOCRATIC VISTAS. 1984: 428–469.

Wilson, Curtis. Newton's Path to the *Principia.* 1985: 178–229.

Wilson, Woodrow. THE PRESIDENT OF THE UNITED STATES. 1982: 450–469.

Wordsworth, William. SELECTED PROSE AND POETRY. 1968: 352–405.

Worsthorne, Peregrine. Is Democracy the Best Form of Government for the Newly Formed Nations? (The Case Against Democracy). 1961: 47–76.

Wyllie, Peter J. Revolution in the Earth Sciences. 1971: 168–237.

Xenophon. IN DEFENSE OF SOCRATES. 1973: 302–313.

## SUBJECTS

HISTORY, ECONOMICS, POLITICS, AND SOCIAL SCIENCE

THE ACQUISITIVE SOCIETY. R. H. Tawney. 1962: 403–483.

Adam Smith and the Spirit of Capitalism. Irving Kristol. 1976: 274–308.

America from Far and Near. Alexei Adzhubei. 1964: 4–29.

The American Economy. Lester C. Thurow. 1987: 2–51.

The Americanization of Europe. Milton Mayer. 1964: 118–161.

The Americanization of Europe. A Review in Pictures. 1964: 162–178.

Anarchism and Revolution. Paul Goodman. 1970: 44–65.

PHYSICS AND POLITICS. Walter Bagehot. 1968: 406–495.

The Planning of the Future. Bertrand de Jouvenel. 1974: 126–164.

Police That Serve Society. Ramsey Clark. 1972: 4–21.

Political Ideas in the United States. Richard H. Rovere. 1968: 36–47.

Political Philosophy in Our Time. Maurice Cranston. 1975: 102–145.

Politics and Dissent. Theodore C. Sorensen. 1968: 20–35.

PRELIMINARY DRAFT OF A WORLD CONSTITUTION. Robert M. Hutchins et al. 1971: 328–345.

THE PRESIDENT OF THE UNITED STATES. Woodrow Wilson. 1982: 450–469.

The Problem of Power. Casamayor. 1972: 72–89.

THE PROBLEM OF WORLD GOVERNMENT. Jacques Maritain. 1971: 346–363.

Progress Sharing: Key to a Private Property Economy. Arthur Larson. 1964: 70–89.

The Proper Role of the Criminal Law. Norval Morris. 1972: 22–39.

The Prospects for World Government. Joseph S. Clark. 1971: 72–88.

Reassessment. Eugene J. McCarthy. 1968: 4–19.

A REVIEW OF TOCQUEVILLE. John Stuart Mill. 1964: 476–491.

Revolutionary Change. Arnold J. Toynbee. 1970: 4–27.

THE RIGHTS OF MAN. Thomas Paine. 1987: 300–405.

Scott Buchanan's *So Reason Can Rule*. Ramsey Clark. 1983: 289–301.

THE SETTLEMENT HOUSE. Jane Addams. 1989: 406–431.

Seventeen New Nations—Colonialism Comes to an End. Milton Mayer. 1961: 79–101.

The Social Contracts of Jean-Jacques Rousseau. Maurice Cranston. 1985: 80–119.

Social Science and Practical Problems. William Letwin. 1970: 92–137.

Social Sciences, Law, and History, The Year's Developments in.

| | |
|---|---|
| 1961 — Edward A. Shils | 244–289. |
| 1962 — Irving Kristol | 220–271. |
| 1963 — Reuel Denney | 358–392. |
| 1964 — Daniel Bell | 314–364. |
| 1965 — Kenneth E. Boulding | 254–285. |
| 1966 — Asa Briggs | 194–239. |

The Social Sciences Since the Second World War—Part One. Daniel Bell. 1979: 139–181.

The Social Sciences Since the Second World War—Part Two. Daniel Bell. 1980: 184–232.

Some American Images of Democracy. John Plamenatz. 1968: 250–300.

The Sorry Condition of Counterrevolutionary Doctrine. William F. Buckley, Jr. 1970: 66–78.

STATE AND REVOLUTION. V. I. Lenin. 1970: 386–453.

THE SUBJECTION OF WOMAN. John Stuart Mill. 1966: 454–528.

Synchophantasy in Economics: A Review of George Gilder's *Wealth and Poverty*. Louis O. and Patricia Hetter Kelso. 1982: 280–292.

THREE ESSAYS. Arnold J. Toynbee. 1961: 529–562.

THUCYDIDES. J. B. Bury. 1979: 306–335.

Toward a Reading of *Capital*. Thomas K. Simpson. 1987: 74–125.

Toward a Sustainable Energy Future. David J. Rose. 1980: 9–26.

Trade in the World Economy. Herbert Giersch. 1976: 5–20.

Tradition in Law. Harry Kalven, Jr. 1974: 21–34.

THE TRUE HISTORY. Lucian. 1981: 236–255.

The U.S. and the U.S.S.R. William Benton. 1964: xii–xv.

Wealth and Happiness; Work and Leisure in *Great Books of the Western World*. Editors. 1965: 90–104.

The Welfare State in the World Economy. Martin Bronfenbrenner. 1976: 75–93.

We Must Have Heroes. S. L. A. Marshall. 1973: 37–44.

We the People: The Rulers and the Ruled. George Anastaplo. 1987: 52–72.

What Europeans Have to Say About Americans in *Great Books of the Western World*. Editors. 1964: 112–116.

Work, Wealth, and Leisure. A Symposium (Yale Brozen, Adolf A. Berle, Jr., Robert Theobald, Arthur Larson). 1965: 1–104.

The World Community. A Symposium (René Cassin, Henry J. Kellermann, Arthur Lall, E. J. Mishan, Joseph S. Clark). 1971: 1–120.

World Economy. A Symposium (Herbert Giersch, Grant L. Reuber, James Tobin, Jagdish Bhagwati, Martin Bronfenbrenner, Arnold C. Harberger). 1976: 1–106.

World Energy and the Challenge to Industrial Civilization. Willis Harman. 1980: 84–99.

Youth—The Young Go "Boom." Milton Mayer. 1961: 125–140.

LITERATURE AND THE ARTS

The Ambiguities of *Don Quixote*. Otto Bird. 1984: 94–122.

American Art Since Mid-Century. Donald B. Kuspit. 1986: 2–61.

ART AND UTILITY. Horatio Greenough. 1984: 292–357.

THE BATTLE OF THE BOOKS. Jonathan Swift. 1971: 380–401.

Beethoven 1770–1827. Robert Mann. 1970: 85–90.

BENITO CERENO. Herman Melville. 1972: 416–473.

Beyond Narrative: The Future of the Feature Film. Roger Ebert. 1978: 176–215.

THE BIRTH OF TRAGEDY. Friedrich Nietzsche. 1983: 396–469.

CANDIDE. Voltaire. 1981: 368–435.

*The Canterbury Tales*. Mark Van Doren. 1973: 180–229.

The Child as Reader. Clifton Fadiman. 1983: 236–264.

Contemporary Poetry. A Symposium (Louis Simpson, James Dickey, Stephen Spender). 1968: 78–119.

SIR GAWAIN AND THE GREEN KNIGHT. Anonymous. 1967: 426–536.
THE SONG OF ROLAND. Anonymous. 1973: 314–371.
SONGS OF INNOCENCE and SONGS OF EXPERIENCE. William Blake. 1989: 316–353.
Sources of Our Common Thought: Homer and Plato. I. A. Richards. 1971: 280–326.
The State of Fiction Today. Susan Fromberg Schaeffer. 1984: 11–42.
State Subsidy and Artistic Freedom. Arnold Goodman. 1977: 41–52.
THE STONES OF VENICE (selections). John Ruskin. 1990: 338–421.
*The Tale of Genji.* Edward Seidensticker. 1987: 286–291.
T'ang Poetry: A Return to Basics. Burton Watson. 1987: 267–277.
Technology and Beauty. Mario Salvadori. 1984: 178–232.
Television. Milton Mayer. 1962: 104–111.
Theatre in the Twentieth Century. Norris Houghton. 1981: 4–67.
Theories of Literature in the Twentieth Century. Harvey Goldstein. 1982: 158–210.
THE TIME MACHINE. H. G. Wells. 1971: 446–505.
TOKENS OF OURSELVES (poetry anthology). William Darkey. 1984: 378–427.
Tradition in the Arts. Frank Kermode. 1974: 35–50.
Tragedy and Comedy. Harvey D. Goldstein. 1990: 140–173.
ON TRANSLATING HOMER. Matthew Arnold. 1971: 402–445.
Twentieth-Century Music. Douglas Allanbrook. 1988: 78–129.
Two Approaches to the Authors of the Great Books. Mortimer J. Adler. 1986: 178–183.
TWO OLD MEN. Leo Tolstoy. 1979: 456–471.
Virgil and Hippocrates: A Reading of the *Georgics.* Otto Bird. 1989: 102–122.
The Vital Self and Secondary Means. Stephen Spender. 1968: 98–107, 117–119 (poems).
WALLENSTEIN—PART ONE: THE PICCOLOMINI. Friedrich Schiller. 1969: 418–537.
WALLENSTEIN—PART TWO: THE DEATH OF WALLENSTEIN. Friedrich Schiller. 1970: 454–530.
Woman in *Great Books of the Western World.* Editors. 1966: 72–82.
YOUNG GOODMAN BROWN. Nathaniel Hawthorne. 1979: 444–455.

PHILOSOPHY AND RELIGION

THE ABOLITION OF MAN. C. S. Lewis. 1968: 496–536.
THE ANALECTS. Confucius. 1984: 236–290.
Animals and Men. Anthony Quinton. 1986: 94–153.
BHAGAVAD GĪTĀ. Anonymous. 1985: 290–337.
A Catechism for Our Times. Mortimer J. Adler. 1969: 79–97.
The Changing Role of Woman: A Biosocial Interpretation. Lucius F. Cervantes. 1966: 28–43.

The Christian Skepticism of Montaigne. Otto Bird. 1985: 120–149.
The Church and Women. James A. Pike. 1966: 56–71.
A COMMENTARY ON ARISTOTLE'S *NICOMACHEAN ETHICS.* Mortimer J. Adler. 1988: 290–311.
The Confusion of the Animalists. Mortimer J. Adler. 1975: 72–89.
THE CONSOLATION OF PHILOSOPHY. Boethius. 1982: 296–379.
Dante the Thinker: Poetry and Philosophy. Otto Bird. 1983: 204–235.
On Death. Milton Mayer. 1965: 106–149.
On Death. A Review in Pictures. 1965: 150–164.
IN DEFENSE OF SOCRATES. Xenophon. 1973: 302–313.
Determinism and Reality. Stanley L. Jaki. 1990: 276–302.
"On the Development of Ideas" from ESSAY ON THE DEVELOPMENT OF CHRISTIAN DOCTRINE. John Henry Newman. 1966: 406–453.
The Difference of Woman and the Difference It Makes. A Symposium (Elisabeth Mann Borgese, Lucius F. Cervantes, Anna Rosenberg Hoffman, James A. Pike). 1966: 1–98.
Does Secular Theology Have a Future? Martin E. Marty. 1967: 38–53.
"The Dynamo and the Virgin" from THE EDUCATION OF HENRY ADAMS. Henry Adams. 1980: 452–460.
ECLIPSE OF GOD. Martin Buber. 1967: 310–371.
EDDINGTON'S TWO TABLES. A. Brian Pippard. 1990: 311–317.
Education and the State: Learning Community. Joseph J. Schwab. 1976: 234–272.
THE EPIC OF GILGAMESH. Anonymous. 1986: 318–347.
An Essay on Time: The Tempo of History (An Analysis). Milton Mayer. 1963: 83–131.
Ethics: Fourth Century B.C. and Twentieth Century A.D. Mortimer J. Adler. 1988: 274–287.
Ethics in a Permissive Society: The Controversy Regarding the Objectivity of Moral Values. Otto Bird. 1981: 160–186.
EXISTENTIALISM. Jean-Paul Sartre. 1963: 443–462.
EXPERIENCE AND EDUCATION. John Dewey. 1961: 379–419.
THE FREEDOM OF A CHRISTIAN. Martin Luther. 1962: 375–402.
The Function of the University in a Time of Crisis. Noam Chomsky. 1969: 40–61.
God of Abraham, Isaac, and Jacob. Joe Sachs. 1988: 224–251.
The Great Anti-School Campaign. Robert M. Hutchins. 1972: 154–227.
THE GREAT DIDACTIC (selections). John Amos Comenius. 1988: 312–381.
THE GREAT INSTAURATION. Francis Bacon. 1981: 436–452.
Hans Küng: *Does God Exist?* Mortimer J. Adler and Wayne F. Moquin. 1981: 188–203.
Has Man's Conquest of Space Increased or Diminished His Stature? A Symposium (Herbert J. Muller, Aldous Huxley, Hannah Arendt, Paul

## SCIENCE AND MATHEMATICS

## TITLES

N ow there's a way to identify all your fine books with flair and style. As part of our continuing service to you, Britannica Home Library Service, Inc. is proud to be able to offer you the fine quality item shown on the next page.

B ooklovers will love the heavy-duty personalized embosser. Now you can personalize all your fine books with the mark of distinction, just the way all the fine libraries of the world do.

T o order this item, please type or print your name, address and zip code on a plain sheet of paper. (Note special instructions for ordering the embosser). Please send a check or money order only (your money will be refunded in full if you are not delighted) for the full amount of purchase, including postage and handling, to:

**Britannica Home Library Service, Inc.**
**Attn: Yearbook Department**
**Post Office Box 6137**
**Chicago, Illinois 60680**

(Please make remittance payable to: Britannica Home Library Service, Inc.)

# IN THE BRITANNICA TRADITION OF QUALITY...

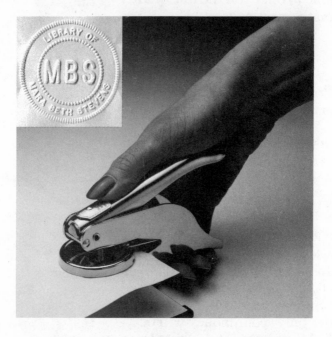

## PERSONAL EMBOSSER

A mark of distinction for your fine books. A book embosser just like the ones used in libraries. The 1½″ seal imprints "Library of _____" (with the name of your choice) and up to three centered initials. Please type or print clearly BOTH full name (up to 26 letters including spaces between names) and up to three initials.
Please allow six weeks for delivery.

Just **$20.00**

plus $2.00 shipping and handling

This offer available only in the United States.
Illinois residents please add sales tax

## Britannica Home Library Service, Inc.

# Authors

*in Great Books of the Western World*

Homer

Aeschylus

Sophocles

Herodotus

Euripides

Thucydides

Hippocrates

Aristophanes

Plato

Aristotle

Euclid

Archimedes

Apollonius

Lucretius

Virgil

Plutarch

Tacitus

Epictetus

Nicomachus

Ptolemy

Marcus Aurelius

Galen

Plotinus

Augustine

Thomas Aquinas

Dante

Chaucer

Machiavelli

Copernicus

Rabelais

Montaigne

Gilbert

Cervantes

Francis Bacon

Galileo

Shakespeare

Kepler